ANNALS OF THE NEW YORK ACADEMY OF SCIENCES
Volume 632

SUBSTANCE P AND RELATED PEPTIDES: CELLULAR AND MOLECULAR PHYSIOLOGY

Edited by Susan E. Leeman, James E. Krause, and Fred Lembeck

The New York Academy of Sciences
New York, New York
1991

Library of Congress Cataloging-in-Publication Data

Substance P and related peptides: cellular and molecular physiology/
  edited by Susan E. Leeman, James E. Krause, and Fred Lembeck.
    p. cm.—(Annals of the New York Academy of Sciences, ISSN
  0077-8923; v. 632).
    Contains the proceedings of the International Symposium on
  Substance P and Related Peptides, held in Worcester, Mass., on July
  18–21, 1990, sponsored by the New York Academy of Sciences and the
  University of Massachusetts Medical Center.
    Includes bibliographical references and index.
    ISBN 0-89766-663-1 (cloth: alk. paper).—ISBN 0-89766-664-X
  (paper: alk. paper).
    1. Substance P—Congresses. 2. Tachykinins—Congresses.
  I. Leeman, Susan E. II. Krause, James E. III. Lembeck, Fred.
  IV. New York Academy of Sciences. V. University of Massachusetts
  Medical Center/Worcester. VI. International Symposium on Substance
  P and Related Peptides (1990: Worcester, Mass.). VII. Series.
    [DNLM: 1. Peptides—physiology—congresses. 2. Substance P—
  physiology—congresses. W1 AN626YL v. 632/QU 68 S9408 1990]
  Q11.N5   vol. 632
  [QP552.S9]
  500 s—dc20
  [612.8′042]
  DNLM/DLC
  for Library of Congress   91-27322
                                                                  CIP

SP
Printed in the United States of America
ISBN 0-89766-663-1 (cloth)
ISBN 0-89766-664-X (paper)
ISSN 0077-8923

ANNALS OF THE NEW YORK ACADEMY OF SCIENCES

Volume 632
September 30, 1991

SUBSTANCE P AND RELATED PEPTIDES: CELLULAR AND MOLECULAR PHYSIOLOGY[a]

Editors and Conference Organizers
SUSAN E. LEEMAN, JAMES E. KRAUSE, and FRED LEMBECK

Scientific Advisory Committee
VIKTOR BAUER, ELIZABETH BURCHER, LORIS A. CHAHL, MARCELLO COSTA,
JACQUES GLOWINSKI, JAMES L. HENRY, TOMAS HÖKFELT, LESLIE L. IVERSEN,
SHIGETADA NAKANISHI, PETER OEHME, MASANORI OTSUKA, BENGT PERNOW,
DOMENICO C. REGOLI, and JOHN M. STEWART

CONTENTS

[a]This volume is the result of a conference entitled Substance P and Related Peptides:
Cellular and Molecular Physiology, which was sponsored by the New York Academy of
Sciences and the University of Massachusetts Medical Center and held on July 18–21, 1990, in
Worcester, Massachusetts.

Part VII. Summary

Financial assistance was received from:

Supporters

- EASTMAN KODAK COMPANY/STERLING
- NATIONAL INSTITUTE OF NEUROLOGICAL DISORDERS AND STROKE—NATIONAL INSTITUTES OF HEALTH
- NATIONAL SCIENCE FOUNDATION
- UNIVERSITY OF MASSACHUSETTS MEDICAL CENTER
- UNITED STATES ARMY MEDICAL RESEARCH AND DEVELOPMENT COMMAND

Contributors

- BRISTOL-MYERS COMPANY
- CIBA-GEIGY CORPORATION
- E. I. DUPONT DE NEMOURS & COMPANY
- ELI LILLY AND COMPANY
- ICI PHARMACEUTICALS GROUP
- MERCK SHARP & DOHME RESEARCH LABORATORIES
- MARION MERRELL DOW RESEARCH INSTITUTE
- MILES INC./BAYER AG
- PARKE-DAVIS PHARMACEUTICAL RESEARCH DIVISION
- PFIZER CENTRAL RESEARCH
- SCHERING CORPORATION
- SMITHKLINE BEECHAM PHARMACEUTICALS

Introduction

This volume contains the proceedings of the International Symposium on Substance P and Related Peptides held in Worcester, Massachusetts, on July 18–21, 1990. This was the first of these International Symposia to be held in the United States. In the time interval following the initial detection of substance P in 1931 by von Euler and Gaddum and the recognition of substance P as a sensory neurotransmitter by Lembeck in 1953, relatively little work with impact was done on this peptide until its isolation by Chang and Leeman in 1970. However, since 1971, research in the field of substance P and related peptides has flourished. This resulted largely from the preparation of the synthetic peptide, the generation of specific antisera, and the usefulness of a selective excitotoxin, capsaicin, for sensory neurons containing substance P. Also, in the early 1980s, two additional members of the mammalian tachykinin peptide family were discovered and it was soon appreciated that multiple tachykinin receptors exist that can be preferentially activated by these natural agonists. The major recent achievements of cloning the genes that code for the multiple mammalian tachykinins and the genes that code for their receptors have added immeasurably to the tools available for studying the structure, function, and regulation of these peptides and their receptors. The discovery of new antagonists, both peptide and nonpeptide, has also helped to increase the scope of possible investigations.

Many of these new tools and reagents were discussed at this meeting and some results gained from their use were presented. It is clear that structural knowledge of the peptides and their receptors has brought a new perspective to this field and that questions of physiologic function and regulation can now be addressed more specifically. Broad aspects of the roles of tachykinins in central, autonomic, and enteric neuronal systems, as well as sensory neurons, were addressed. Attention was also paid to other important physiological roles of the tachykinins in the regulation of gastrointestinal function, immune function, response to stress, reproduction, and behavior. The excellence of the work presented and the excitement generated at the meeting assure continued progress in this field.

Susan E. Leeman

Developmental and Hormonal Regulation of the Sex Difference in Preprotachykinin Gene Expression in Rat Anterior Pituitaries[a]

JULIE A. JONASSEN AND SUSAN E. LEEMAN

Department of Physiology
University of Massachusetts Medical Center
Worcester, Massachusetts 01655

INTRODUCTION

The tachykinin peptides, substance P (SP) and neurokinin A (NKA, also called substance K), are generated from a preprotachykinin (PPT) protein precursor, encoded by the PPT gene.[1-4] The primary PPT mRNA transcript is differentially processed into three mature PPT mRNAs: α, β, and γ.[1-4] In the rat, the β- and γ-PPT mRNAs, each encoding SP and NKA, are predominant.[4]

SP and NKA are present in rat anterior pituitary glands.[5-20] Our previous work,[11] recently confirmed by others,[16-18] demonstrated that the PPT gene is expressed in rat anterior pituitary, suggesting that this tissue is a site of tachykinin synthesis. After puberty, male rat anterior pituitaries have more SP and NKA than do anterior pituitaries of female rats.[7,8,13,14,17] A comparable difference in adenohypophyseal PPT mRNA[17] suggests that sex differences in tachykinin concentrations arise from sex differences in PPT gene expression.

The present studies analyzed more extensively the regulation of PPT gene expression in rat anterior pituitaries. In particular, effects of sexual maturation, gonadal steroids, sexual differentiation, and thyroid status on PPT mRNA abundance and tachykinin concentrations in anterior pituitaries were assessed.

MATERIALS AND METHODS

Rats were purchased from Charles River Laboratories (Kingston, New York) and were maintained on laboratory chow and water *ad libitum*. Animal care was performed according to the NIH Guide for the Care and Use of Laboratory Animals. To quantitate adenohypophyseal PPT mRNA and tachykinins during development, male and female rats were purchased on days 24, 38, 54, and 82 days of age and were killed two days later. To determine if the testes mediate the sex differences in adenohypophyseal tachykinins, male rats were bilaterally orchidectomized on day 38 of age; castrated rats and age-matched controls were killed eight weeks later. To determine if male rat adenohypophyseal tachykinins were responsive to estradiol, groups of adult male rats were injected with estradiol (2 μg/day, sc) or with oil for

[a]This work was supported by NIH Grant No. DK38627 to J. A. Jonassen and NIH Grant No. DK29876 to S. E. Leeman.

1

three days. To determine whether neonatal androgenization would generate an adult male pattern of adenohypophyseal tachykinins, female pups were injected with 150 µg of testosterone propionate in 50 µL of peanut oil, or with peanut oil alone, subcutaneously on day 2 of age; rats were killed eight weeks later. Effects of thyroid hormone status were examined in adult male rats that had been surgically thyroidectomized by the vendor. Thyroidectomized rats drank tap water supplemented with 1% calcium lactate and were killed three weeks after surgery.

Rats were decapitated, trunk blood was collected, and anterior pituitaries were rapidly removed. Total RNA was isolated from individual pituitaries,[11] dotted onto nitrocellulose, and hybridized to 50 ng of ^{32}P rat β-PPT cDNA insert, labeled by nick-translation, as previously described.[11] This clone (pSP 27-4, a gift from Jim Krause, George Washington University, St. Louis, Missouri) encodes the β-splicing variant of PPT mRNA.[4] Blots were stringently washed, exposed to X-ray film (Kodak XAR-5), washed in boiling water to remove PPT probe, and rehybridized to ^{32}P-labeled polythymidylic acid to estimate poly (A+) mRNA abundance, as previously described.[11] Developed autoradiograms were scanned with a video-based image analysis system. Hybridization of RNA to the PPT probe was normalized to its hybridization to the polythymidylic acid probe and is expressed as relative PPT mRNA abundance.

To identify the PPT mRNA species expressed in rat anterior pituitary, a nuclease-protection assay was performed.[4,17] Total pituitary RNA (10 µg) isolated from adult male euthyroid or hypothyroid rats was hybridized in solution to an antisense β-PPT [^{32}P]-labeled riboprobe prepared by T7 RNA polymerase–catalyzed transcription of the plasmid pG1 β-PPT. This PPT cDNA clone, a gift from Jim Krause,[4] contains exons 1–6 and 90 nucleotides of exon 7 of the β-PPT cDNA. Hybridization of this antisense RNA probe with pituitary RNA distinguishes among the α-, β-, and γ-PPT mRNA splicing variants that are derived from the primary PPT mRNA transcript.[4,17] Following S1 nuclease digestion of the PPT mRNA/antisense [^{32}P]-PPT RNA hybrids, the protected bands corresponding to different spliced forms of PPT mRNA were fractionated electrophoretically on a denaturing 6% polyacrylamide gel; protected bands were visualized by autoradiography.

To determine SP and NKA concentrations, individual anterior pituitaries were homogenized in 1 mL of 2 N acetic acid, lyophilized, and reconstituted with assay buffer; SP[22] and NKA[11] were determined by specific radioimmunoassays, as previously described. Unless otherwise stated, SP and NKA concentrations are expressed as fmol/mg pituitary protein.[21]

Estradiol concentrations in unextracted sera were determined by double antibody radioimmunoassay, using a commercial kit (Diagnostic Products Corporation, Los Angeles, California).

Statistical comparisons between two treatment groups were made using Student's unpaired t-test. Multiple comparisons among three or more groups were made after one-way analysis of variance using the Student-Newman-Keul's test.[23] A p value of <0.05 was considered significant.

Molecular biology reagents were purchased from Bethesda Research Laboratories (Gaithersburg, Maryland), New England Biolabs (Beverly, Massachusetts), or Promega Biotech (Madison, Wisconsin). Nitrocellulose was purchased from Schleicher and Schuell (Keene, New Hampshire). Radiolabeled deoxyribonucleotide triphosphates were obtained from Amersham (Arlington Heights, Illinois). Other reagents were purchased from Sigma (St. Louis, Missouri) or J. T. Baker Chemical Company (Phillipsburg, New Jersey).

RESULTS

We[19] and others[7,8,13,14,17] have shown previously that male rat anterior pituitaries contain more SP and NKA and have a greater abundance of PPT mRNA. A developmental study was performed here to determine when this sex difference emerged. PPT mRNA abundance and concentrations of SP and NKA were similar in anterior pituitaries of male and female rats on days 26 and 40,[20] as shown in FIGURE 1. In male rats at 56 and 84 days of age, pituitary tachykinins and PPT mRNA abundance were significantly elevated compared to age-matched females. PPT

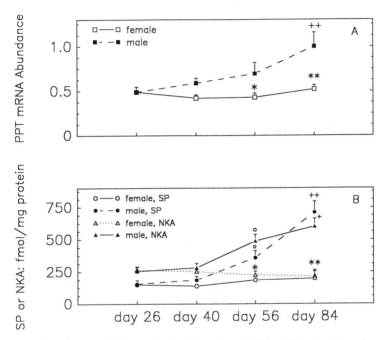

FIGURE 1. Developmental changes in adenohypophyseal PPT mRNA abundance (panel A) and SP and NKA concentrations (panel B) in male (filled symbols) and female (open symbols) rats. Each point represents the mean ± SEM for 5–8 rats. Symbols above points refer to statistical comparisons—+: $p < 0.05$ versus day 56 male; ++: $p < 0.01$ versus day 56 male; ○: $p < 0.05$ versus day 40 male; *: $p < 0.05$ versus age-matched male group; **: $p < 0.01$ versus age-matched male group.

mRNA abundance and SP and NKA concentrations increased in male anterior pituitaries on day 56 relative to day 40 and continued to rise between days 56 and 84 in male rats.

To determine whether the testes mediated this sex difference, juvenile male rats were castrated prior to puberty on day 38 of age and adenohypophyseal tachykinins and PPT mRNA abundance were determined eight weeks later. As shown in TABLE 1, males castrated prior to puberty had diminished adenohypophyseal PPT mRNA abundance and reduced SP and NKA in anterior pituitaries.

TABLE 1. Prepubertal Castration of Male Rats Blunts the Postpubertal Rise in Adenohypophyseal Tachykinins

	PPT mRNA	AP-SP	AP-NKA
Control male	100 ± 11^a	100 ± 17	100 ± 17
Castrated male[b]	$51 \pm 7^{***}$	$39 \pm 6^{***}$	$37 \pm 5^{***}$

[a]Data are plotted as mean ± SEM percentage of control values; 18–19 rats per group.
[b]Prepubertal male rats were castrated on day 38 of age and were killed eight weeks later, with age-matched (94-day-old) control males; ***: $p < 0.005$ versus control male.

Previous studies[15,17,18] demonstrated that adenohypophyseal PPT mRNA and tachykinin concentrations[7,8,10,13] in female rats were increased by removal of the ovaries and reduced by the ovarian steroid estradiol; whether estradiol exerted a similar effect on male rat anterior pituitaries was not known. To determine if pituitary tachykinins and PPT gene expression were similarly inhibited by estradiol in adult male rats, animals were treated with daily injections of either estradiol or oil for three days. As shown in FIGURE 2, estradiol rapidly decreased PPT mRNA abundance and reduced SP and NKA concentrations in adult male rat anterior pituitary glands.

Yoshikawa and Hong[14] suggested that the sex difference in pituitary tachykinins could be ascribed to neonatal sexual differentiation of the hypothalamus. To

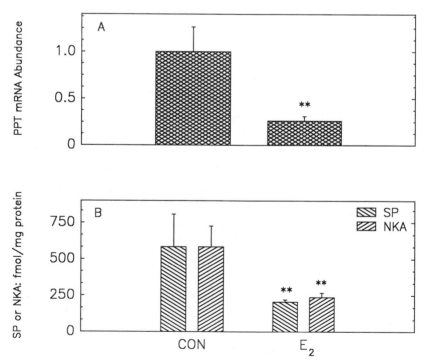

FIGURE 2. Estradiol reduces adenohypophyseal PPT mRNA abundance (panel A) and concentrations of SP and NKA (panel B) in rat anterior pituitaries. Adult male rats were injected daily with 2 μg of estradiol (E_2) or with oil (CON) for three days. Data are plotted as mean ± SEM for 5–6 rats per group; ** indicates $p < 0.01$ versus control.

determine whether neonatal androgenization also altered adenohypophyseal PPT gene expression, female pups were treated with testosterone propionate or oil on day 2 of age. This treatment led to androgen-sterilization, as evidenced by a lack of estrous cycles in adult animals. Two months after androgenization, pituitary weights as well as circulating estradiol concentrations were significantly increased in androgenized females (FIGURE 3). Furthermore, the pituitary content of tachykinin peptides was increased in androgenized females. In contrast, when tachykinins were normalized to pituitary protein concentrations, there were no significant differences between testosterone propionate– and oil-treated controls. Moreover, there was no difference in PPT mRNA abundance between testosterone- and oil-treated females.

We[11] and others[16] have demonstrated previously that thyroidectomy increases PPT mRNA abundance as well as SP and NKA concentrations.[8–12,15,16] To determine

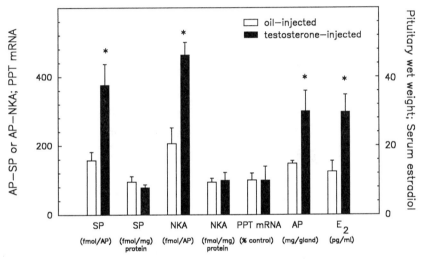

FIGURE 3. Effects of neonatal androgenization on pituitary tachykinins. Two-day-old female pups were injected with 150 μg of testosterone propionate (filled bars) or oil (open bars) and were killed eight weeks later. Adenohypophyseal (AP) content of SP and NKA, AP concentrations (per mg pituitary protein) of SP and NKA, pituitary weight, PPT mRNA abundance, and serum estradiol (E$_2$) concentrations are presented as mean ± SEM for 7–8 rats per group; * indicates $p < 0.05$ versus oil-treated control.

whether thyroidectomy altered the distribution of PPT mRNA splicing variants, a solution hybridization/nuclease protection assay was performed on RNA isolated from anterior pituitaries of adult male euthyroid and thyroidectomized rats. As shown in FIGURE 4, thyroidectomy increased the abundance of both β- and γ-PPT mRNAs approximately fivefold. As previously shown by Brown et al.,[17] levels of α-PPT mRNA in rat anterior pituitary were not detectable.

DISCUSSION

Our studies[11,15,19,20] and those from the laboratories of Krause[17] and Bloom[16,18] have demonstrated that expression of the PPT gene in rat anterior pituitary is developmentally and hormonally regulated. Several laboratories have reported a sex difference in adenohypophyseal tachykinin concentrations[7,8,13,14,17] and in PPT gene expression.[17] We demonstrate here that PPT mRNA abundance and tachykinin concentrations begin to increase at eight weeks of age in pituitaries of male rats, coinciding with sexual maturation. In contrast, SP, NKA, and PPT mRNA remain relatively constant in pituitaries of prepubertal and sexually mature female rats.

There is much evidence that the gonads control adenohypophyseal PPT gene expression and tachykinin concentrations and may be responsible, at least in part, for the observed sex differences. Ovariectomy increases, whereas estradiol decreases PPT mRNA abundance in female rat anterior pituitaries.[15,17,18] Similarly, male

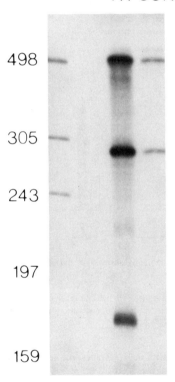

FIGURE 4. Thyroidectomy increases β- and γ-PPT mRNA species in rat anterior pituitaries. Adult male rats were thyroidectomized (TX) for three weeks. Ten μg of total adenohypophyseal RNA from TX or euthyroid control (CON) male rats was hybridized with [^{32}P]-labeled antisense PPT RNA, digested with S1 nuclease, and fractionated by electrophoresis on a 6% denaturing polyacrylamide gel. Positions of single-stranded RNA molecular weight markers are indicated on the left. β-PPT mRNA protects a 508-nucleotide fragment; γ-PPT mRNA protects two fragments, 295 and 168 nucleotides in length; α-PPT mRNA would protect two fragments, 364 and 90 bases in length, but is not expressed in the rat anterior pituitary.

anterior pituitaries are also responsive to estradiol, showing a rapid suppression of PPT mRNA and tachykinin concentrations within three days. The ability of male adenohypophyseal tachykinins to be inhibited by exogenous estradiol suggests that the absence of high circulating estradiol concentrations may be permissive to the male pattern of adenohypophyseal tachykinin expression. Nevertheless, whereas removal of endogenous estradiol by ovariectomy increases adenohypophyseal tachykinins in female rats,[7,13,15,17] SP and NKA concentrations do not reach the levels found in adult male pituitaries. Thus, other factors may also lead to the sex difference.

It is likely that the testes contribute to the sex difference in adenohypophyseal tachykinins. Removal of the testes prior to puberty blunts the rise in adenohypophyseal PPT mRNA and tachykinin peptides normally observed at puberty in male rats. This suggests that the testes may mediate, at least in part, the sex difference in adenohypophyseal tachykinins that emerges at the time of puberty. Effects of postpubertal castration are more variable, leading to smaller decreases in adenohypophyseal PPT mRNA abundance[17,20] and SP and NKA concentrations.[7,13,17,20] Nonetheless, exogenous testosterone propionate reversed the decrease in adenohypophyseal PPT mRNA abundance induced by short-term castration.[17] Furthermore, 5α-dihydrotestosterone, an androgen that cannot be metabolized to estradiol, increases adenohypophyseal SP concentrations in male[13] and female[7,13] rats. This suggests that androgens may stimulate pituitary PPT mRNA and tachykinin synthesis. Hence, the testes may continue to exert some influence on adenohypophyseal tachykinins after puberty, although they may be permissive to (rather than essential for) expression of PPT mRNA in adult male rats.

Yoshikawa and Hong[14] suggested that sexual differentiation of the nervous system may play a role in the development of sex differences in adult pituitary tachykinin concentrations. They observed that neonatal androgenization of female rats increased adenohypophyseal SP content in adulthood, suggesting that neonatal imprinting of the nervous system by testosterone might mediate the postpubertal sex difference in pituitary tachykinins. Whereas we also observed that the pituitary content of SP and NKA increased in androgenized females, tachykinin concentrations, expressed per mg protein, did not change after androgenization because there was a concomitant increase in pituitary protein in the enlarged pituitaries of androgenized females. Moreover, PPT mRNA abundance in androgen-sterilized females was also unchanged. Besides the fact that androgenized females do not have cyclic gonadotropin secretion, estrous cycles, or normal female sexual behavior, masculinization of the nervous system in neonatal female pups does not masculinize tachykinin synthesis in the anterior pituitary. As described earlier, it is likely that the sex difference in pituitary tachykinins is mediated by the gonads at the time of puberty rather than by neonatal sexual differentiation. Nevertheless, possible masculinizing effects of neonatal testosterone treatment on adenohypophyseal tachykinins might have been obscured in the face of the increased circulating estradiol concentrations found in androgenized females; the present and previous studies demonstrate that estradiol can decrease adenohypophyseal PPT mRNA abundance and tachykinin concentrations[7,8,14,17,18] in both sexes.

Thyroid hormone status also controls adenohypophyseal tachykinins. Thyroidectomy increases PPT mRNA abundance in both male and female rats[11,15,16] without altering the distribution of PPT mRNA splicing variants. Brown et al.[17] also found no difference in the distribution of PPT mRNA species in gonadectomized or steroid hormone–treated rats. This parallel regulation of the abundance of PPT mRNA splicing variants suggests that thyroid hormone regulation probably occurs at the level of PPT gene transcription rather than by posttranscriptional PPT RNA processing.

Receptors for SP have been identified and characterized in rat anterior pituitary,[24–26] suggesting that tachykinins synthesized within the anterior pituitary might have a local site of action. In particular, SP modulates secretion of LH[25–30] both in vivo and in vitro. Moreover, the ability of SP to modulate LH secretion appears to be dependent upon age and sex: whereas exogenous SP stimulates LH secretion from anterior pituitary cells from juvenile male and female rats, only pituitary cells from adult female and not from adult male rats can respond to SP by increasing their secretion of LH[26] (M. D. Shamgochian and S. E. Leeman, in preparation). Whether the sex difference in responsiveness to SP is a consequence of the sex difference in pituitary tachykinin concentrations or of other developmental or hormonal differences between male and female rats is still unknown. Nonetheless, these intriguing data suggest that intrapituitary tachykinins may be important autocrine or paracrine regulators of adenohypophyseal function.

ACKNOWLEDGMENTS

We would like to thank Stephen Benoit and Janet Hoogasian for expert technical assistance, Bryant Bullock for his assistance with the nuclease protection experiment, and George Drake (Department of Zoology, University of Massachusetts, Amherst, Massachusetts) for development of the software used for the video-based densitometry of autoradiograms.

REFERENCES

1. NAWA, H., T. HIROSE, H. TAKASHIMA, S. INAYAMA & S. NAKANISHI. 1983. Nucleotide sequences of cloned cDNAs for two types of bovine brain substance P precursor. Nature **306:** 32–36.
2. NAWA, H., H. KOTANI & S. NAKANISHI. 1984. Tissue-specific generation of two preprotachykinin mRNAs from one gene by alternative RNA splicing. Nature **312:** 729–734.
3. KOTANI, H., M. HOSHIMARU, H. NAWA & S. NAKANISHI. 1986. Structure and gene organization of bovine neuromedin K precursor. Proc. Natl. Acad. Sci. U.S.A. **83:** 7074–7078.
4. KRAUSE, J. E., J. M. CHIRGWIN, M. S. CARTER, Z. S. XU & A. D. HERSHEY. 1987. Three preprotachykinin mRNAs encode the neuropeptides substance P and neurokinin A. Proc. Natl. Acad. Sci. U.S.A. **84:** 881–885.
5. MOREL, G., J. A. CHAYVIALLE, B. KERDELHUÉ & P. M. DUBOIS. 1982. Ultrastructural evidence for endogenous substance P–like immunoreactivity in the rat pituitary gland. Neuroendocrinology **33:** 86–92.
6. DEPALATIS, L. R., O. KHORRAM, R. H. HO, A. NEGRO-VILAR & S. M. MCCANN. 1984. Partial characterization of immunoreactive substance P in the rat pituitary gland. Life Sci. **34:** 225–238.
7. COSLOVSKY, R., R. W. EVANS, S. E. LEEMAN, L. E. BRAVERMAN & N. ARONIN. 1984. The effects of gonadal steroids on the content of substance P in the rat anterior pituitary. Endocrinology **115:** 2285–2289.
8. COSLOVSKY, R., L. E. BRAVERMAN, S. E. LEEMAN & N. ARONIN. 1985. The differential effects of thyroid and gonadal hormones on substance P in the anterior pituitary of the prepubertal rat. Endocrinology **117:** 2198–2202.
9. ARONIN, N., K. MORENCY, S. E. LEEMAN, L. E. BRAVERMAN & R. COSLOVSKY. 1984. Regulation by thyroid hormone of the concentration of substance P in the rat anterior pituitary. Endocrinology **114:** 2138–2142.
10. ARONIN, N., R. COSLOVSKY & S. LEEMAN. 1986. Substance P and neurotensin: their roles in the regulation of anterior pituitary function. Annu. Rev. Physiol. **48:** 537–549.
11. JONASSEN, J. A., D. MULLIKIN-KILPATRICK, A. MCADAM & S. E. LEEMAN. 1987. Thyroid hormone status regulates preprotachykinin-A gene expression in male rat anterior pituitary. Endocrinology **121:** 1555–1561.
12. ARONIN, N., R. COSLOVSKY & K. CHASE. 1988. Hypothyroidism increases substance P concentration in the heterotopic anterior pituitary. Endocrinology **122:** 2911–2914.
13. DEPALATIS, L. R., O. KHORRAM & S. M. MCCANN. 1985. Age-, sex-, and gonadal steroid–related changes in immunoreactive substance P in the rat anterior pituitary gland. Endocrinology **117:** 1368–1373.
14. YOSHIKAWA, K. & J-S. HONG. 1983. Sex-related difference in substance P level in rat

anterior pituitary: a model of neonatal imprinting by testosterone. Brain Res. **273:** 362–365.

15. JONASSEN, J. A., D. MULLIKIN-KILPATRICK & S. E. LEEMAN. 1986. Thyroid hormone status and sex steroid hormones regulate preprotachykinin gene expression in female rat anterior pituitary gland (abstract). Program of the 16th Annual Meeting of the Society for Neuroscience (Washington, District of Columbia), p. 691.

16. JONES, P. M., M. A. GHATEI, J. STEEL, D. O'HALLORAN, G. GON, S. LEGON, J. M. BURRIN, U. LEONHARDT, J. M. POLAK & S. R. BLOOM. 1989. Evidence for neuropeptide Y synthesis in the rat anterior pituitary and the influence of thyroid hormone status: comparison with vasoactive intestinal peptide, substance P, and neurotensin. Endocrinology **125:** 334–341.

17. BROWN, E. R., R. E. HARLAN & J. E. KRAUSE. 1990. Gonadal steroid regulation of substance P (SP) and SP-encoding messenger ribonucleic acids in the rat anterior pituitary and hypothalamus. Endocrinology **126:** 330–340.

18. O'HALLORAN, D. J., P. M. JONES, M. A. GHATEI, J. DOMIN & S. R. BLOOM. 1990. The regulation of neuropeptide expression in rat anterior pituitary following chronic manipulation of estrogen status: a comparison between substance P, neuropeptide Y, neurotensin, and vasoactive intestinal peptide. Endocrinology **127:** 1463–1469.

19. JONASSEN, J. A., D. MULLIKIN-KILPATRICK, J. HOOGASIAN & S. LEEMAN. 1988. Sex differences in regulation of SP, NKA, and preprotachykinin gene expression in anterior pituitary. Regulat. Peptides **22:** 99.

20. JONASSEN, J. A. & S. E. LEEMAN. 1990. Adenohypophyseal preprotachykinin gene expression during development (abstract). Program of the 72d Annual Meeting of the Endocrine Society (Atlanta, Georgia), p. 337.

21. LOWRY, O., N. ROSEBROUGH, A. FARR & R. RANDALL. 1951. Protein measurement with the Folin reagent. J. Biol. Chem. **193:** 265–275.

22. MROZ, E. A. & S. E. LEEMAN. 1979. Substance P. *In* Methods of Hormone Radioimmunoassay (second edition). R. M. Jaffe & H. R. Behrman, Eds.: 121–137. Academic Press. New York.

23. STEEL, R. G. D. & J. H. TORRIE. 1960. Principles and Procedures of Statistics. McGraw–Hill. New York.

24. MIKKELSEN, J. D., P. J. LARSEN, M. MOLLER, H. VILHARD & T. SOEMARK. 1989. Substance P in the median eminence and pituitary of the rat: demonstration of immunoreactive fibers and specific binding sites. Neuroendocrinology **50:** 100–108.

25. KERDELHUÉ, B., A. TARTAR, V. LENOIR, A. EL ABED, P. HUBLAU & R. P. MILLAR. 1985. Binding studies of substance P anterior pituitary binding sites during the rat estrous cycle. Regulat. Peptides **10:** 133–143.

26. SHAMGOCHIAN, M. D. & S. E. LEEMAN. 1989. Sex difference in the stimulation of LH secretion by SP in adult rats (abstract). Proceedings of the 71st Annual Meeting of the Endocrine Society (Seattle, Washington), p. 74.

27. KERDELHUÉ, B., A. KHAR, D. DENAY, Y. LANGLOIS, TH. BENNARDO, J. LINSKA & M. JUTISZ. 1979. Inhibition *in vitro* par la substance P de l'excrétion des gonadotropines induites par le LHRH à partir de cellules adénohypophysaires de rat en culture. C. R. Acad. Sci. Paris (Ser. D) **287:** 879–882.

28. ARISAWA, M., L. DEPALATIS, R. HO, G. D. SNYDER, W. H. YU, G. PAN & S. M. MCCANN. 1990. Stimulatory role of substance P on gonadotropin release in ovariectomized rats. Neuroendocrinology **51:** 523–529.

29. DEBELJUK, L., M. LASAGA, J. HORVATH, B. H. DUVILANSKI, A. SEILICOVICH & M. DEL C. DIAZ. 1987. Effect of an anti–substance P serum on prolactin and gonadotropins in hyperprolactinemic rats. Regulat. Peptides **19:** 91–98.

30. VIJAYAN, E. & S. M. MCCANN. 1979. *In vivo* and *in vitro* effects of substance P and neurotensin on gonadotropin and prolactin release. Endocrinology **105:** 64–68.

Regulation of Substance P Expression in Sympathetic Neurons

JOHN A. KESSLER AND MONA FREIDIN

Departments of Neurology and Neuroscience
Albert Einstein College of Medicine
Yeshiva University
Bronx, New York 10461

The extraordinary diversity of neurotransmitters in the nervous system requires precise mechanisms to ensure expression of specific transmitters by appropriate neurons. The neuronal choice of transmitter does not depend solely on intrinsic cellular information, but is also influenced by the neuronal microenvironment.[1-5] Thus, it is well established in both developing and mature neurons that the neurotransmitters synthesized and secreted may be altered by changes in the cellular milieu. In addition, multiple transmitters coexpressed by the same cell may be regulated differently, so the quantitative balance among coexpressed transmitters may be altered by changes in the physiologic state or environment of the neuron.[6]

Study of peripheral autonomic ganglia has been particularly useful in defining mechanisms governing neurotransmitter expression because these structures provide readily accessible and easily manipulated systems allowing a variety of experimental perturbations. Furthermore, sympathetic neurons are readily cultured, facilitating study of molecular mechanisms underlying transmitter expression. In particular, study of autonomic neurons in the rat sympathetic superior cervical ganglion (SCG) has extended our knowledge in this area. Sympathetic neurons in the SCG *in vivo* express predominantly noradrenergic traits. However, these neurons also contain a number of peptide neurotransmitters including substance P and neuropeptide Y (NPY). NPY is coreleased with norepinephrine in sympathetic nerve terminals in target structures, and the actions on target function of the peptide and the catecholamine reinforce one another.[7,8] In contrast, substance P in SCG neurons *in vivo* does not appear to be transported to nerve terminals in targets, suggesting that the peptide may subserve an intraganglionic function.[9,10] Although the precise function of substance P (SP) in sympathetic neurons is not known, important clues are provided by studies of its regulation in the SCG. This report will describe a series of studies that have examined mechanisms governing the expression of substance P by SCG neurons.

There are a number of different types of signals in the cellular microenvironment that might influence neurotransmitter metabolism (FIGURE 1), including presynaptic nerve impulse activity, contact of the neuron with other cells or with extracellular matrix, target-derived factors, factors derived from other nonneuronal cells (Schwann cells, macrophages, astrocytes, etc.), and circulating factors (glucocorticoids, thyroid hormone, sex steroids, etc.). There is a distinct hierarchy among these regulatory influences with the effects of some factors superseding others.[6] However, before considering the role of these different categories of signals in substance P regulation, it may be helpful to enunciate several of the broad questions that the studies described in this discussion will address. First, what mechanisms regulate substance P expression? Are coexpressed transmitters regulated independently? Are all peptide transmitters similarly regulated or are there specific mechanisms governing substance P metabolism? Finally, what is the function of substance P in autonomic neurons?

Neuronal development and neurotransmitter expression may be regulated trans-synaptically by innervating neurons. For example, it is well documented that transsynaptic nerve impulse activity stimulates noradrenergic characters, such as the biosynthetic enzymes, tyrosine hydroxylase (TH) and dopamine-β-hydroxylase (DBH), in the SCG (for review, see references 1 and 11). Conversely, decentralization (denervation) results in diminished catecholaminergic functions. The effects of transsynaptic nerve impulse activity on substance P, though, differed dramatically. We found that decentralization resulted in significant increases in preprotachykinin (PPT) mRNA, which encodes substance P, as well as in the peptide itself (FIGURE 2), suggesting that the preganglionic nerve normally suppresses ganglion substance P expression.[12,13] Moreover, treatment with the specific nicotinic blocking agent chlorisondamine similarly increased substance P and PPT mRNA, suggesting that presynaptic impulse activity decreased peptide levels through the mediation of synaptic transmission.[13] In contrast, levels of TH mRNA as well as enzyme activity

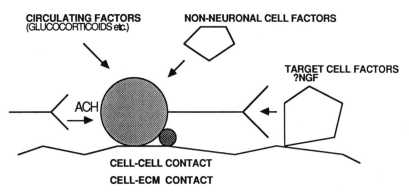

FIGURE 1. Regulation of neuronal transmitter expression by the cellular microenvironment. The neuron is exposed to a variety of categories of regulatory influences as depicted.

were slightly reduced after decentralization, indicating that the divergent effects on peptide and catecholamine traits occurred at the mRNA level. In further contrast to effects on substance P, nerve impulse activity did not alter levels of the peptide transmitter neuropeptide Y (NPY) and slightly increased levels of NPY mRNA. Thus, substance P and NPY are regulated differently in the ganglion.

To further characterize factors regulating sympathetic ganglion substance P, the SCG was examined in tissue culture. Substance P levels rose dramatically in ganglion explants, increasing more than 20-fold by 24 hours and more than 50-fold by 48 hours.[12] The increase in peptide reflected elevated levels of preprotachykinin mRNA, which rose rapidly to a peak at 24 hours (> 60-fold increase) and then decreased slightly to an elevated plateau at 48 hours. Because preganglionic impulse activity decreased substance P *in vivo*, the effects of membrane depolarization were examined in culture. Veratridine, which increases sodium influx by binding to sodium channels, prevented the rise of substance P seen after explantation. Veratridine treatment had no effect on tyrosine hydroxylase activity or on total protein, indicating the specificity of the effect on substance P. Moreover, addition of tetrodotoxin,

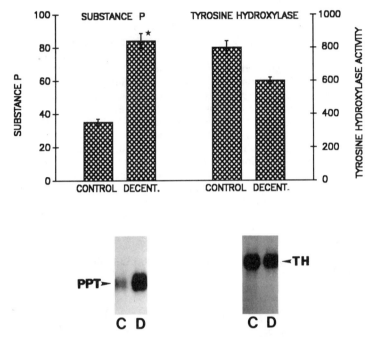

FIGURE 2. Effects of decentralization (denervation) on transmitter expression in the adult rat SCG. The preganglionic nerves innervating the SCG were cut and levels of substance P, TH, and their mRNAs were measured 10 days later in the ipsilateral (decentralized) and contralateral (control) SCG. Substance P is expressed as mean pg peptide per ganglion ± SEM ($N = 7$). The asterisk indicates a difference from control at $p < 0.005$. Effects on preprotachykinin (PPT) and TH mRNAs in decentralized (D) versus control (C) ganglia are shown in a representative Northern blot analysis. The PPT and TH blots are the same blot sequentially hybridized to the PPT probe, washed, and rehybridized to the TH probe.

which antagonizes the sodium ion effects of veratridine, blocked the actions of veratridine on substance P, whereas tetrodotoxin alone had no effect. Consequently, the inhibitory effects of veratridine on substance P elevation appeared to be specifically related to increased sodium ion influx and to the resultant membrane depolarization. Furthermore, the decrease in substance P resulted primarily from decreased net synthesis of the peptide rather than from depolarization-induced release.[14] To determine whether the depolarization-induced decrease in substance P in sympathetic neurons reflected alterations in mRNA metabolism, levels of preprotachykinin mRNA were examined. Veratridine- or potassium-induced membrane depolarization dramatically reduced preprotachykinin mRNA in cultured sympathetic neurons; by contrast, the treatments elevated levels of TH and NPY mRNA. These observations, in conjunction with the findings *in vivo* (FIGURE 2), suggest that presynaptic nerve impulse activity, acetylcholine release, and the resultant sympathetic neuron membrane depolarization normally act to inhibit substance P expression. This paradoxical regulation of substance P led us to postulate that, in the SCG, substance P does not function as a transmitter, but rather mediates other intraganglionic functions.[9,13] This hypothesis is supported by the observation that substance P is not transported to nerve terminals in target organs of the SCG[9] and by the mode of regulation of the peptide by cytokines (discussed later).

To define other intercellular interactions that regulate peptide expression, substance P development was compared in explants and in dissociated cell cultures of the SCG. As noted earlier, substance P levels increased more than 50-fold within 72 hours in ganglion explants. In dissociated cell cultures containing both neurons and ganglion nonneuronal cells, levels of PPT mRNA and substance P also increased dramatically, although the increase was smaller than that observed in explants.[14] Immunocytochemical examination demonstrated substance P–like immunoreactivity in virtually all neurons, but not in nonneuronal cells. However, pure sympathetic neuron cultures contained virtually no substance P or preprotachykinin mRNA, suggesting that nonneuronal cells fostered neuronal expression of the peptide (see FIGURE 3). In contrast, the sympathetic neuron content of NPY, tyrosine hydroxylase, and their mRNAs was higher in pure neuronal cultures than in cultures containing nonneuronal cells.[14] Consequently, nonneuronal cells apparently stimulate substance P, but suppress NPY expression by sympathetic neurons.

What mechanisms mediate the stimulatory effect of nonneuronal cells on substance P expression by sympathetic neurons? Previous studies by Patterson and

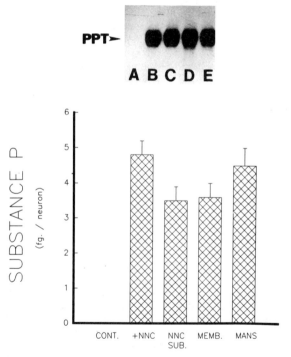

FIGURE 3. Effects of neuronal contact with nonneuronal cell membranes. Sympathetic neurons were examined for content of PPT mRNA and substance P after 10 days of (A) culture on a collagen substratum, (B) coculture with ganglion nonneuronal cells (+NNC), (C) culture on a substratum of killed nonneuronal cells (NNC SUB), (D) treatment with Schwann cell plasma membranes, or (E) treatment with MANS. Substance P is expressed as mean fg per neuron ± SEM ($N = 8$).

co-workers have shown that the stimulatory effects of nonneuronal cells on sympathetic cholinergic expression could be reproduced by treatment of neurons with medium conditioned by exposure to nonneuronal cells.[2] This suggested that similar mechanisms might regulate substance P expression. However, treatment of sympathetic neurons with the conditioned medium failed to induce detectable levels of preprotachykinin mRNA or substance P,[15] suggesting that the effects of nonneuronal cells on substance P were not mediated by a soluble factor. In turn, this raised the possibility that the effects might result from contact of the neurons with nonneuronal cells.

Two experiments were designed to test the hypothesis that direct neuronal contact with other cells fostered substance P expression. First, neurons were cultured on a substratum of nonneuronal cells that had been killed and lightly fixed. Culture on this substratum stimulated expression of PPT mRNA and substance P (FIGURE 3), reproducing the effects of coculture. Second, neurons were treated with plasma membranes isolated by density gradient centrifugation of cultured Schwann cells. PPT mRNA and substance P were stimulated by this treatment as well[16] (FIGURE 3). These observations suggested that nonneuronal cell membranes contained a molecule capable of stimulating neuronal SP expression.

Purification of the membrane molecule mediating the effects of cell-cell contact on transmitter expression required identification of a moderately abundant source of membranes containing high levels of the factor. After examining numerous tissues, we found that rat spinal cord was ideal because of the high abundance of bioactive factor and the ready availability of large amounts of tissue. Treatment of sympathetic neuron cultures with rat spinal cord membranes induced expression of preprotachykinin mRNA and substance P and elevated levels of the cholinergic biosynthetic enzyme, choline acetyltransferase (CAT).[17] More than 95% of the transmitter stimulating activity was associated with the P2 membrane fraction, and soluble extracts of spinal cord contained only low activity. Treatment of membranes with 4 M NaCl extracted transmitter stimulating activity; exposure of sympathetic neurons to this membrane-associated neurotransmitter stimulating factor (MANS) increased CAT activity and substance P in a dose-dependent manner.[17] The MANS factor was highly purified from spinal cord membranes using a three-column purification procedure and treatment of sympathetic neurons with purified MANS stimulated levels of PPT mRNA and substance P (FIGURE 3). Although MANS initially appeared to be a single 27-kDa protein, it is now apparent that there are two active molecules, one of which is antigenically related to ciliary neurotrophic factor (CNTF).

CNTF is a cytoplasmic protein produced by Schwann cells. CNTF lacks a signal sequence and there is no evidence that the protein is secreted.[18] Consequently, it has been hypothesized that CNTF is released during tissue injury and subsequent cell lysis and that the trophic protein helps to mediate recuperative responses to injury. Because MANS contained a CNTF-like constituent, we examined the effects of recombinant rat CNTF on substance P expression. Treatment of cultured sympathetic neurons with recombinant CNTF stimulated levels of PPT mRNA and substance P (FIGURE 4). Levels of CAT activity were also stimulated by CNTF, but TH activity was diminished. The striking effect of CNTF on substance P suggested that expression of the peptide by sympathetic neurons might reflect, in part, a response to injury.

We therefore sought to determine whether other proteins that help to mediate inflammatory responses also stimulated substance P expression by sympathetic neurons. Treatment of cultured neurons with interleukin-2 or with tumor necrosis factor did not alter levels of PPT mRNA or substance P either in pure neuron

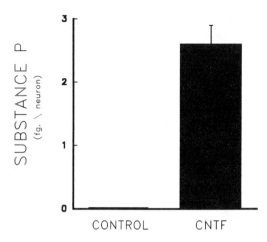

FIGURE 4. Effects of ciliary neurotrophic factor (CNTF). Sympathetic neurons were cultured for seven days in the absence (control) or presence of CNTF and were examined for content of substance P, which is expressed as mean fg per neuron ± SEM ($N = 6$).

cultures or in neurons cocultured with ganglion nonneuronal cells. Similarly, treatment of pure neuronal cultures with interleukin-1β (IL-1β) failed to stimulate preprotachykinin expression. However, IL-1β treatment of neurons cultured in the presence of ganglion nonneuronal cells significantly elevated levels of PPT mRNA and substance P (FIGURE 5). These observations suggest either that IL-1β stimulates neuronal substance P expression indirectly by stimulating nonneuronal cells or that a nonneuronal cell–derived cofactor is necessary for IL-1β actions on neurons. The

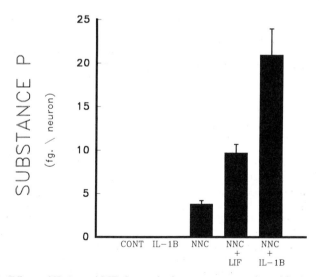

FIGURE 5. Effects of IL-1β and LIF. Sympathetic neurons were cultured for seven days on a collagen substratum in the presence of interleukin-1β (IL-1β), in coculture with nonneuronal cells (NNC), or in coculture with nonneuronal cells with added leukemia inhibitory factor (NNC + LIF) or interleukin-1β (NNC + IL-1β). The cultures were examined for content of substance P, which is expressed as mean fg per neuron ± SEM.

striking stimulation of substance P by IL-1β supports the hypothesis that increases in the peptide in sympathetic neurons may reflect a response to injury. It is interesting that treatment with IL-1β failed to elevate levels of CAT activity because other factors that stimulate substance P also stimulate cholinergic traits (TABLE 1). This suggests that the effects of IL-1β are not mediated by CNTF, MANS, or other known factors.

Leukemia inhibitory factor (LIF) is a protein that is apparently identical to the heart-derived factor of Patterson and co-workers that promotes cholinergic development in cultured sympathetic neurons.[19] In view of the association noted earlier between substance P and cholinergic expression (TABLE 1) and of the effects of other immunoregulators on preprotachykinin expression, we examined the effects of LIF. LIF treatment of neurons cocultured with nonneuronal cells significantly elevated levels of both substance P and CAT (FIGURE 5). The striking elevation of CAT activity after LIF treatment distinguishes its actions from those of IL-1β and indicates that effects of IL-1β are not mediated by LIF.

TABLE 1. Neurotransmitter Regulation in Cultured Sympathetic Neurons[a]

	Substance P	CAT	TH
coculture with Schwann cells	↑ *	↑	↓
cell-cell contact	↑ *	↑	↓
CNTF	↑ *	↑	↓
MANS	↑ *	↑	↓
LIF	↑	↑	↓
interleukin-1β	↑		
glucocorticoids	↓	↓	↑
depolarization	↓	↓	↑
NGF	↑	↑	↑

[a]The effects of different factors in the neuronal microenvironment on substance P, cholinergic (CAT), and noradrenergic (TH) expression are indicated. An upward-pointing arrow (↑) indicates stimulation of the transmitter trait, whereas a downward-pointing arrow (↓) means inhibition. An asterisk indicates that the culture condition can induce substance P expression by itself.

Because several mediators of immune responses stimulated preprotachykinin expression, we sought to determine whether immunosuppressive molecules might conversely diminish levels of PPT mRNA and substance P. Glucocorticoids have previously been shown to promote noradrenergic development in sympathetic neurons and to inhibit expression of cholinergic traits (see reference 1). Furthermore, we have previously shown that glucocorticoids inhibit the increase in substance P observed after explantation of the SCG.[20] We therefore examined the effects of glucocorticoids on the IL-1β stimulation of substance P. Dexamethasone treatment inhibited the stimulation of PPT mRNA and substance P caused either by IL-1β or by coculture with nonneuronal cells. In contrast, dexamethasone treatment elevated levels of TH mRNA and TH activity. Hence, dexamethasone treatment completely prevented the effects of IL-1β on sympathetic transmitter expression.

The foregoing observations indicate that substance P in sympathetic neurons is regulated by diverse factors in the cellular milieu. Nevertheless, the intracellular mechanisms mediating these effects remain unclear. Although the PPT gene has a cAMP responsive element (see discussion by Krause herein), drugs that stimulate intracellular levels of cAMP do not stimulate preprotachykinin mRNA expression.[14]

Calcium ionospheres do not stimulate levels of substance P, and physiologic manipulations that enhance transmembrane calcium flux (i.e., membrane depolarization; see earlier) actually reduce peptide expression. Thus, it seems unlikely that calcium influx mediates the stimulatory effects of CNTF, MANS, IL-1β, etc. We are currently examining the role of other known second messenger pathways in stimulating sympathetic neuron expression of substance P.

Our observations regarding the expression and regulation of transmitters coexpressed by sympathetic neurons suggest that there is no fixed relationship between substance P and any other transmitter system (TABLE 1), although the peptide is generally regulated in parallel with cholinergic traits. There appears to be no fundamental difference between mechanisms regulating substance P and conventional transmitter systems, which are regulated by the same factors (TABLE 1). However, there appears to be peptide-specific regulation for different peptides colocalized with the same neurons because NPY and substance P were regulated so differently.

There is also a distinct hierarchy among the types of regulatory influences depicted in FIGURE 1. For example, veratridine- or potassium-induced membrane depolarization suppresses expression of PPT mRNA and SP even in neurons treated with CNTF, MANS, or IL-1β. This suggests that these regulatory molecules may only influence developing (and not yet innervated) neurons or denervated neurons in a damaged ganglion. Similarly, glucocorticoid treatment inhibits SP expression in neurons treated with IL-1β, MANS, or CNTF. These observations indicate that the complement of transmitters expressed by a neuron depend upon multiple regulatory influences in the cellular microenvironment. Thus, neurotransmitter expression is a dynamic process that reflects the physiologic state and environment of the neuron.

REFERENCES

1. BLACK, I. B. 1982. Stages of neurotransmitter development in autonomic neurons. Science **215:** 1198.
2. PATTERSON, P. H. & L. L. Y. CHUN. 1977. The induction of acetylcholine synthesis in primary cultures of dissociated sympathetic neurons. I. Effects of conditioned medium. Dev. Biol. **56:** 263.
3. JOHNSON, M., D. ROSS, M. MYERS, R. BUNGE, E. WAKSHULL & H. BURTON. 1976. Synaptic vesicle cytochemistry changes when cultured sympathetic neurons develop cholinergic interactions. Nature (London) **262:** 308.
4. LEDOUARIN, N. M., M. TEILLET, C. ZILLER & J. SMITH. 1978. Adrenergic differentiation of cells of the cholinergic ciliary and Remak ganglia in avian embryos after in vivo transplantation. Proc. Natl. Acad. Sci. U.S.A. **75:** 2030.
5. KESSLER, J. A. 1987. Environmental regulation of neurotransmitter phenotypic expression in sympathetic neurons. In Somatostatin—Basic and Clinical Status. S. Reichlin, Ed.: 71–82. Plenum. New York.
6. KESSLER, J. A. 1984. Environmental co-regulation of substance P, somatostatin, and neurotransmitter synthesizing enzyme in cultured sympathetic neurons. Brain Res. **321:** 155.
7. LUNDBERG, J. M., L. TERENIUS, T. HÖKFELT, C. R. MARTLING, K. TATEMOTO, V. MUTT, J. POLAK, S. BLOOM & M. GOLDSTEIN. 1982. Neuropeptide Y (NPY)–like immunoreactivity in peripheral noradrenergic neurons and effects of NPY on sympathetic function. Acta Physiol. Scand. **116:** 477–480.
8. LUNDBERG, J. M., J. PERNOW, K. TATEMOTO & C. DAHLÖF. 1985. Pre- and post-junctional effects of NPY on sympathetic control of rat femoral artery. Acta Physiol. Scand. **123:** 511–513.
9. KESSLER, J. A., W. O. BELL & I. B. BLACK. 1983. Substance P levels differ in sympathetic target organ terminals and ganglion perikarya. Brain Res. **258:** 144–146.

10. KESSLER, J. A. 1985. Parasympathetic, sympathetic, and sensory interactions in the iris: nerve growth factor regulates cholinergic ciliary ganglion innervation *in vivo.* J. Neurosci. **5:** 2719–2725.

11. THOENEN, H., R. A. MUELLER & J. AXELROD. 1969. Transsynaptic induction of adrenal tyrosine hydroxylase. J. Pharmacol. Exp. Ther. **169:** 249.

12. KESSLER, J. A., J. ADLER, M. C. BOHN & I. B. BLACK. 1981. Substance P in principal sympathetic neurons: regulation by impulse activity. Science **214:** 335.

13. KESSLER, J. A. & I. B. BLACK. 1982. Regulation of substance P in adult rat sympathetic ganglia. Brain Res. **234:** 182–187.

14. KESSLER, J. A. 1985. Differential regulation of peptide and catecholamine characters in cultured sympathetic neurons. Neuroscience **15:** 827.

15. KESSLER, J. A. 1984. Nonneuronal cell conditioned medium stimulates peptidergic expression in sympathetic and sensory neurons *in vitro.* Dev. Biol. **106:** 61.

16. KESSLER, J. A., G. CONN & V. B. HATCHER. 1986. Isolated plasma membranes regulate neurotransmitter expression and facilitate effects of a soluble brain cholinergic factor. Proc. Natl. Acad. Sci. U.S.A. **83:** 3528–3532.

17. WONG, V. & J. A. KESSLER. 1987. Solubilization of a membrane factor that stimulates levels of substance P and choline acetyltransferase in sympathetic neurons. Proc. Natl. Acad. Sci. U.S.A. **84:** 8726–8729.

18. STÖCKLI, K., F. LOTTSPEICH, M. SENDTNER, P. MASIAKOWSKI, P. CARROLL, R. GÖTZ, D. LINDHOLM & H. THOENEN. 1989. Molecular cloning, expression, and regional distribution of rat ciliary neurotrophic factor. Nature **342:** 21–28.

19. YAMAMORI, T., K. FUKADA, R. AEBERSOLD, S. KORSCHING, J-J. FANN & P. H. PATTERSON. 1989. The cholinergic neuronal differentiation factor from heart cells is identical to leukemia inhibitory factor. Science **246:** 1412–1416.

20. KESSLER, J. A., J. E. ADLER, W. O. BELL & I. B. BLACK. 1983. Substance P and somatostatin metabolism in sympathetic and special sensory ganglia *in vitro.* Neuroscience **9:** 309–318.

Effects of Lymphokines on Substance P in Injured Ganglia of the Peripheral Nervous System

G. MILLER JONAKAIT, SANDRA SCHOTLAND, AND
RONALD P. HART

Department of Biological Sciences
Rutgers University
Newark, New Jersey 07102

INTRODUCTION

Because the nervous system requires flexibility in responding to external stimuli, it maintains an extensive repertoire of reactions to its environment. One such reaction that has been widely studied is the change in the biosynthesis of new neurotransmitter molecules. The neonatal superior cervical ganglion (SCG) of the rat has been used extensively as a model system in which to study the ability of the neurons to alter their neurotransmitter complement in response to changing environmental signals.[1-5] In one instance of dramatic neurotransmitter plasticity, substance P (SP) and the mRNA coding for its prohormone precursor are increased in response to ganglion deafferentation[6] or explantation into culture.[7,8] The ganglionic increase in SP occurs, at least in part, in response to the loss of presynaptic electrical activity because depolarizing stimuli depress the increase *in vitro*.[7,8] Whereas the increase of SP is notable, the functional significance of such an increase has remained obscure.

RESULTS

Conditioned Medium from Activated Splenocytes Increases SP

In studying the response of the SCG to a traumatic injury of this type, we found that conditioned medium from activated splenocytes elicits a dramatic increase in SP in cultured neonatal SCGs, mimicking deafferentation *in vivo*.[9] In initial studies,[9] explants of neonatal SCGs were cultured for five days with and without medium supplemented with conditioned medium from concanavalin A–stimulated rat splenocytes (Rat T-Cell Polyclone; Collaborative Research; abbreviated "PC" in our studies). Control cultures lacking PC attached quickly to the collagen substrate, sent out luxuriant neurite outgrowth, and developed modest levels of SP. However, in cultures supplemented with conditioned medium from con A–stimulated splenocytes, the increase in SP peptide content was dramatic and dose-dependent (FIGURE 1).

NGF Is Not Involved in Mediating the Action of PC

NGF is a requirement for the normal growth and development of the neonatal SCG both *in vivo*[10] and *in vitro*.[11,12] Moreover, in other models of peripheral neuronal

19

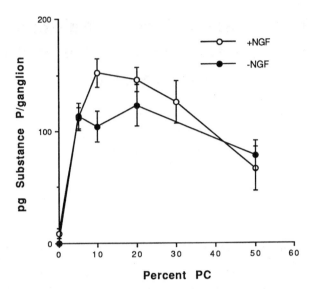

FIGURE 1. SP levels in SCG explants grown for five days in Ham's F12 medium, supplemented with 10% fetal calf serum and various concentrations of PC. Each data point represents the mean ± SEM for six or more determinations.

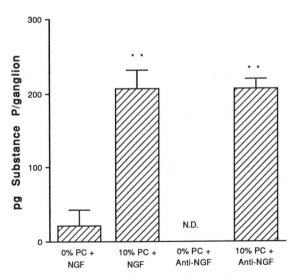

FIGURE 2. Antibodies to NGF (5%) were added to medium with or without 10% PC: ∗∗ = $p < 0.001$ when compared to 0% PC + NGF control; N.D. = not detectable.

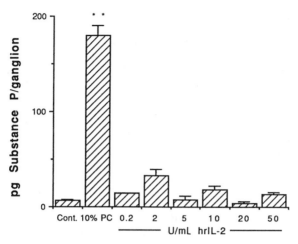

FIGURE 3. Dose response of hrIL-2: ✴✴ = $p < 0.001$ when compared to control.

injury, interleukin-1 was shown to stimulate the production of mRNA for both NGF and its receptor.[13,14] The stimulation by a lymphokine of a growth factor needed for tissue regeneration further suggested an important interaction between the immune system and the regenerating axons. Therefore, we tested the requirement for NGF in the mediation of a PC-induced increase in SP. Cultures lacking additional NGF were grown in the presence and absence of antibody to NGF. In the presence of antibody, ganglia did not send out neurites, failed to attach properly to the collagen substrate, and had no detectable SP. However, PC-treated ganglia displayed elevated SP levels even when unattached and free-floating (FIGURE 2), strongly suggesting that NGF was not a required intermediary for the PC-induced increase in SP.

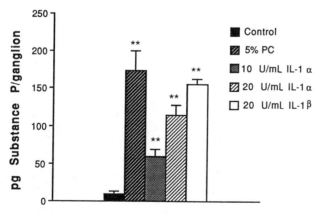

FIGURE 4. SCG cultures were grown for five days in medium supplemented with 5% PC, 10 or 20 U/mL hrIL-1α, or 20 U/mL hrIL-1β. SP levels in all groups were significantly higher than in untreated controls ($p < 0.001$).

The Effect of Conditioned Medium Is Somewhat Specific for SP

However, if PC were acting solely as a growth- or survival-promoting factor (like NGF), we might have expected other neurotransmitter-related molecules to be increased. Measurements of tyrosine hydroxylase (TOH) activity, though, indicated that PC did not affect this noradrenergic-specific enzyme (data not shown), suggesting that the action on SP induction was specific and probably not related to a generalized effect on neuronal survival. Moreover, levels of choline acetyltransferase (ChAT) and tryptophan hydroxylase (TPH)—enzymes in the biosynthetic pathways of acetylcholine and serotonin, respectively—were unchanged by the addition of PC (data not shown), suggesting further that the effect is somewhat specific for SP.

Effects of Conditioned Medium on Dorsal Root Ganglia

Neonatal dorsal root ganglia (DRG), which normally produce SP for use as a sensory neurotransmitter, were compared with SCGs for their responsiveness to PC. As expected, control ganglia grown for five days in culture were found to contain substantial amounts of SP. Moreover, just as with SCGs, SP levels were significantly increased by growth in medium supplemented with PC. However, the increase was not nearly as dramatic as that seen in sympathetic ganglia; in contrast to the 3-fold to 12-fold increase in SP levels seen in sympathetic ganglia, SP levels in DRG were not even doubled.[9]

Interleukin-1 (but Not Interleukin-2) Mimics the Action of Conditioned Medium

In order to begin to identify the active molecule(s) responsible for the observed increase in sympathetic SP, we grew SCG cultures in human recombinant interleu-

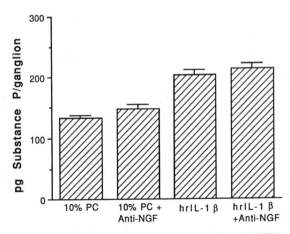

FIGURE 5. SCG explants were grown with or without antibodies to NGF in medium supplemented with either 10% PC or 20 U/mL IL-1β.

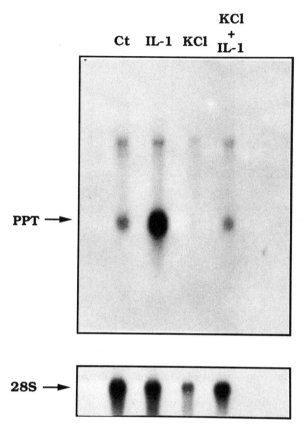

FIGURE 6. Northern blot analysis on SCG cultures grown for five days with and without IL-1β. For each lane, total RNA was prepared from a pool of eight cultures and 1 μg was loaded on a 1.5% agarose–1 M formaldehyde gel. The gel was blotted and probed with ^{32}P-cRNA specific for PPT cDNA and was then washed and exposed. The filters were then stripped and reprobed with nick-translated 28S rRNA gene sequences: Ct, no treatment; IL-1, 10 U/mL IL-1β; K⁺, 40 mM KCl; K⁺ + IL-1, 10 U/mL IL-1β and 40 mM KCl.

kin-2 (hrIL-2; Collaborative Research, Bedford, Massachusetts) because IL-2 was an expected constituent of PC and because there had been a report that IL-2 promoted neurite outgrowth in cultured sympathetic ganglia.[15] However, hrIL-2 did not increase SP above control levels, suggesting that the active molecule in PC was probably not IL-2 (FIGURE 3).

Both IL-1α and IL-1β were tested for their efficacy in stimulating SP in SCG cultures. Both succeeded in mimicking the effects of PC on cultured ganglia, with hrIL-1β being slightly more potent than IL-1α (FIGURE 4). Antibodies to NGF included in the medium did not diminish the IL-1β-stimulated increase in SP (FIGURE 5), suggesting an additional point of coincidence between the actions of IL-1β and PC.

1 hr **3 hr**

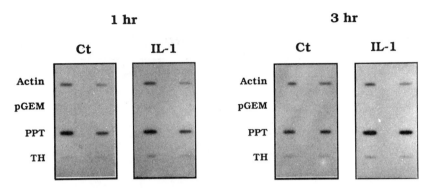

FIGURE 7. Nuclear transcription assay. Eight ganglia were cultured in the absence (Ct) or presence (IL-1) of 10 U/mL IL-1β. After one or three hours, the ganglia were washed, nuclei were isolated, and transcription was allowed to proceed for 30 min at 30 °C. Total RNA was isolated and was used to probe filters containing slot-blotted, linearized clones in duplicate specific for the following genes: actin, cytoplasmic actin; pGEM, pGEM1 control plasmid; PPT, preprotachykinin; TH, tyrosine hydroxylase. Filters were washed to a high stringency and exposed.

Interleukin-1 Increases PPT mRNA

Whereas initial studies showed that IL-1 increased the level of SP in cultured SCGs (mentioned earlier), a variety of processes including decreased release, decreased degradation, increased transcription, and alternative processing of the prohormone molecule might have accounted for the increase in peptide. Because changes in peptide levels are often accompanied by changes in the steady-state levels of the mRNA, we began to address this issue directly by measuring mRNA encoding the SP prohormone precursor, preprotachykinin (PPT).[16,17]

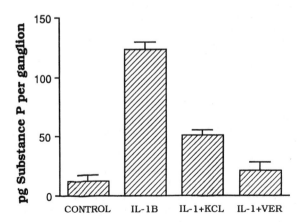

FIGURE 8. SP peptide levels in SCG explants grown with and without 10 U/mL IL-1β and/or under depolarizing conditions. The KCl concentration was 40 mM; veratrine (VER) concentration was 20 μg/mL.

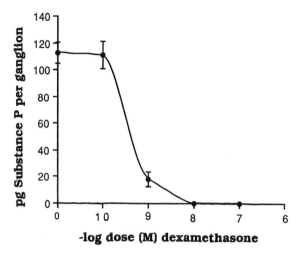

FIGURE 9. Effect of dexamethasone on SP peptide levels in SCGs grown in IL-1-containing medium. Dexamethasone in various concentrations was added at explantation.

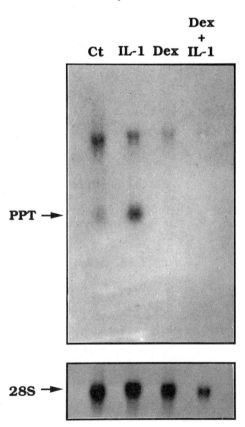

FIGURE 10. Northern blot analysis of PPT mRNA in cultured SCGs following treatment with IL-1β and/or dexamethasone: Ct, no treatment; IL-1, 10 U/mL IL-1β; Dex, 0.1 μM dexamethasone; Dex + IL-1, 10 U/mL IL-1β and 0.1 μM dexamethasone.

Northern blot analysis was performed on SCG cultures grown for five days with and without IL-1β (FIGURE 6, control and IL-1 lanes; see also reference 16). Exposure to IL-1β resulted in a 4-fold to 5-fold increase in PPT mRNA, suggesting that the increase in mRNA coding for the precursor molecule accounted for the increase in SP itself.

Interleukin-1 Increases PPT Gene Transcription

In order to determine whether changes in steady-state levels of PPT mRNA were due to changes in gene transcription, nuclear run-on assays were performed on cultured ganglia after a one- or three-hour exposure to IL-1 (FIGURE 7). Densitometry (not shown) of the resulting autoradiograms revealed that the PPT gene was transcribed at a 2-fold higher rate in the presence of IL-1 after three hours. No change in PPT transcription was seen after only one hour and no change was seen in the cytoplasmic actin gene or in the gene encoding tyrosine hydroxylase. This shows that the change in steady-state levels of PPT mRNA is at least partially due to changes in gene activity.

Electrical Activity in the Ganglia Inhibits the Response to IL-1

Ganglionic increases in SP occur only following deafferentation, suggesting that presynaptic electrical activity normally suppresses peptide expression.[7,8] In order to test whether depolarization affected the ability of IL-1 to induce peptide, we grew SCGs in depolarizing agents (40 mM KCl or 20 µg/mL veratrine) to mimic presynaptic input.

Inclusion of either of these depolarizing agents in the cultures impaired the IL-1-induced increase in SP (FIGURE 8), suggesting that electrical status of the ganglion affects responsiveness to IL-1. Moreover, KCl in the cultures prevented the

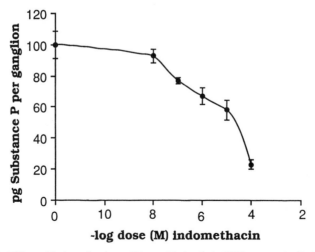

FIGURE 11. Effect of indomethacin on SP peptide levels in SCGs grown in IL-1-containing medium. Indomethacin in various concentrations was added at explantation.

TABLE 1. Effects of SP on the Immune System

Effects	References
↑ hPBL proliferation	20
↑ Proliferation of con A–stimulated splenocytes	21
↑ IgA and IgM production by splenocytes	21
↑ IgA production in lymph nodes and Peyer's patches	21
↑ Lymph flow	22
Activates macrophages	23–25
Stimulates production of IL-1, TNFα, and IL-6	26
Chemotactic for human monocytes	27
Degranulates mast cells	28
Releases histamine from peritoneal mast cells	29
Cells with SP receptors:	
human T8+	30
human T4+	30
murine lymphocytes	31
human IM-9 lymphocytes	32
murine B cells	31
guinea pig macrophages	24

IL-1-induced increase in PPT mRNA, suggesting an action on biosynthesis rather than, for example, release (FIGURE 6).

Glucocorticoid Hormones Inhibit the Ganglionic Response to IL-1

Stress in general and glucocorticoid hormones in particular suppress many aspects of the immune response (see reference 18 for review). In order to determine whether glucocorticoid hormones affect these neuroimmune interactions in the SCG, we included the synthetic glucocorticoid dexamethasone (dex) with IL-1β at the time of explantation. The ability of dex to inhibit the IL-1-induced increase in SP was dose-dependent, with complete inhibition occurring at 10 nM, with a K_i approximating 0.5 nM (FIGURE 9).

In order to determine whether dex had an effect on PPT mRNA accumulation, Northern blots were prepared from cultures treated with IL-1 in the presence and absence of 0.1 mM dex (FIGURE 10). Similar to its effects on SP itself, dex completely abolished the IL-1-induced increase in PPT mRNA, suggesting that the loss of SP levels was secondary to the loss of mRNA coding for the precursor molecule.

Prostaglandin Synthesis Inhibitors Inhibit the Ganglionic Response to IL-1

Many actions of IL-1 are mediated in part through prostaglandins (PGs), which are arachidonic acid metabolites in the cyclooxygenase pathway. In order to determine whether prostaglandin synthesis played a role in mediating the IL-1-induced increase in sympathetic SP, we included indomethacin (a cyclooxygenase inhibitor) with IL-1 at the time of explantation.

Indomethacin inhibited the action of IL-1β (20 U/mL) in a dose-dependent manner with a K_i approximating 50 μM, suggesting an involvement of PGs in mediating this action of IL-1. However, a dose of 0.1 mM was required to restore SP to control levels (FIGURE 11).

DISCUSSION

The up-regulation of SP expression that occurs in response to sympathetic deafferentation *in vivo* suggested to us that SP might have a role to play in promoting recovery following neuronal injury. This idea was bolstered by mounting evidence of the involvement of neuropeptides in general (see reference 19 for review) and SP in particular (TABLE 1) in modulating immune function. Moreover, SP is contained in fibers that innervate the spleen, thymus, and lymph nodes[33-38] and that contact mast cells in the intestine,[39] suggesting that SP is anatomically poised, ready to exert an influence on the immune system when necessary. Whereas these SP-positive nerve fibers have generally been thought to arise from sensory systems, sympathetic innervation of lymphoid organs is also well described.[40-42] Furthermore, activity in the sympathetic nervous system is generally inhibitory to immune function.[41,42] Intact sympathetic innervation would thus tend to keep the immune system suppressed.

Splicing this information together with our own data, a testable model of neuroimmune interaction emerges that may occur following injury to the sympathetic nervous system: Failure in the sympathetic nervous system (in this case, deafferentation) would result in an immediate loss of noradrenergic neurotransmission in lymphoid organs. Inhibitions of immune function facilitated by noradrenergic innervation would be lifted. Moreover, IL-1, released by invading macrophages (or thoughtfully provided by us in organ culture), would increase SP via an effect on PPT transcription. Newly elaborated SP may then be transported to lymphoid organs where its location in and release from sympathetic terminals could facilitate activation of the immune system. This, in turn, might facilitate neuronal regeneration and/or equip the animal to ward off infection or overwhelming inflammatory responses accompanying injury. In this model, then, SP plays a pivotal role as an intermediary between the neuronal and immune systems.

REFERENCES

1. PATTERSON, P. H. & L. L. Y. CHUN. 1977. The induction of acetylcholine synthesis in primary cultures of dissociated rat sympathetic neurons. I. Effects of conditioned medium. Dev. Biol. **56:** 263–280.
2. JOHNSON, M., D. ROSS, M. MEYERS, R. REES, R. BUNGE, E. WAKSHULL & H. BURTON. 1976. Synaptic vesicle cytochemistry changes when cultured sympathetic neurons develop cholinergic interactions. Nature (London) **262:** 308–310.
3. KESSLER, J. A. 1984. Nonneuronal cell conditioned medium stimulates peptidergic expression in sympathetic and sensory neurons *in vitro.* Dev. Biol. **106:** 61–69.
4. JONAKAIT, G. M. & I. B. BLACK. 1989. Regulation of catecholamine development. *In* Handbook of Experimental Pharmacology. U. Trendelenburg & N. Weiner, Eds.: 137–179. Springer-Verlag. New York/Berlin.
5. NAWA, H. & D. W. Y. SAH. 1990. Different biological activities in conditioned media

control the expression of a variety of neuropeptides in cultured sympathetic neurons. Neuron **4:** 279–287.

6. KESSLER, J. A. & I. B. BLACK. 1982. Regulation of substance P in adult rat sympathetic ganglia. Brain Res. **234:** 182–187.

7. KESSLER, J. A., J. E. ADLER, M. C. BOHN & I. B. BLACK. 1981. Substance P in principal sympathetic neurons: regulation by impulse activity. Science **214:** 335–336.

8. ROACH, A., J. E. ADLER & I. B. BLACK. 1987. Depolarizing influences regulate preprotachykinin mRNA in sympathetic neurons. Proc. Natl. Acad. Sci. U.S.A. **84:** 5078–5081.

9. JONAKAIT, G. M. & S. SCHOTLAND. 1990. Conditioned medium from activated splenocytes increases substance P in sympathetic ganglia. J. Neurosci. Res. **26:** 24–30.

10. LEVI-MONTALCINI, R. & P. U. ANGELETTI. 1963. Essential role of nerve growth factor in the survival and maintenance of dissociated sensory and sympathetic embryonic nerve cells *in vitro*. Dev. Biol. **7:** 653–659.

11. LEVI-MONTALCINI, R. & B. BOOKER. 1960. Destruction of the sympathetic ganglia in mammals by antiserum to a nerve growth factor. Proc. Natl. Acad. Sci. U.S.A. **46:** 384–391.

12. COHEN, A., E. C. NICOL & W. RICHTER. 1964. Nerve growth factor requirement for development of dissociated embryonic sensory and sympathetic ganglia in culture. Proc. Soc. Exp. Biol. Med. **116:** 784–789.

13. LINDHOLM, D., R. HEUMANN, M. MEYER & H. THOENEN. 1987. Interleukin-1 regulates synthesis of nerve growth factor in non-neuronal cells of rat sciatic nerve. Nature **330:** 658–659.

14. LINDHOLM, D., R. HEUMANN, R. HENGERER & H. THOENEN. 1988. Interleukin-1 increases stability and transcription of mRNA encoding nerve growth factor in cultured rat fibroblasts. J. Biol. Chem. **263:** 16348–16351.

15. HAUGEN, P. K. & P. C. LETOURNEAU. 1990. Interleukin-2 enhances chick and rat sympathetic, but not sensory, neurite outgrowth. J. Neurosci. Res. **25:** 443–452.

16. JONAKAIT, G. M., S. SCHOTLAND & R. P. HART. 1990. Interleukin-1 specifically increases substance P in injured sympathetic ganglia. *In* Neuropeptides and Immunopeptides: Messengers in a Neuroimmune Axis. Volume 594. M. S. O'Dorisio & A. Panerai, Eds.: 222–230. Ann. N.Y. Acad. Sci. New York.

17. HART, R. P. & G. M. JONAKAIT. 1990. Substance P gene expression is regulated by interleukin-1 in cultured sympathetic ganglia. Neuron. Submitted.

18. MUNCK, A., P. M. GUYRE & N. J. HOLBROOK. 1984. Physiological functions of glucocorticoids in stress and their relation to pharmacological actions. Endocr. Rev. **5:** 25–44.

19. O'DORISIO, M. S. & A. PANERAI, Eds. Neuropeptides and Immunopeptides: Messengers in a Neuroimmune Axis. Volume 594. Ann. N.Y. Acad. Sci. New York.

20. PAYAN, D. G., D. R. BREWSTER & E. J. GOETZL. 1983. Specific stimulation of human T lymphocytes by substance P. J. Immunol. **131:** 1613–1615.

21. STANISZ, A. M., D. BEFUS & J. BIENENSTOCK. 1986. Differential effects of vasoactive intestinal peptide, substance P, and somatostatin on immunoglobulin synthesis and proliferation by lymphocytes from Peyer's patches, mesenteric lymph nodes, and spleen. J. Immunol. **136:** 152–156.

22. MOORE, T. C., J. L. LAMI & C. H. SPRUCK. 1989. Substance P increases lymphocyte traffic and lymph flow through peripheral lymph nodes of sheep. Immunology **67:** 109–114.

23. BAR-SHAVIT, Z., R. GOLDMAN, Y. STABINSKY, P. GOTTLIEB, M. FRIDKIN, V. I. TEICHBERT & S. BLUMBERG. 1980. Enhancement of phagocytosis—a newly found activity of substance P residing in its N-terminal tetrapeptide sequence. Biochem. Biophys. Res. Commun. **94:** 1445.

24. HARTUNG, H. P., K. WOLTERS & K. V. TOYKA. 1986. Substance P: binding properties and studies on cellular responses in guinea pig macrophages. J. Immunol. **136:** 3856–3863.

25. LOTZ, M., D. A. CARSON & J. H. VAUGHAN. 1987. Substance P activation of rheumatoid synoviocytes: neural pathway in pathogenesis of arthritis. Science **235:** 893–895.

26. LOTZ, M., J. H. VAUGHAN & D. A. CARSON. 1988. Effects of neuropeptides on production of inflammatory cytokines by human monocytes. Science **241:** 1218–1221.

27. RUFF, M. R., S. M. WAHL & C. B. PERT. 1985. Substance P receptor–mediated chemotaxis of human monocytes. Peptides 2(suppl. 6): 107–111.

28. MATSUDA, H., K. KAWAKITA, Y. KISO, T. NAKANO & Y. KITAMURA. 1989. Substance P induces granulocyte infiltration through degranulation of mast cells. J. Immunol. **142:** 927–931.
29. FEWTRELL, C. M. S., J. C. FOREMAN, C. C. JORDAN, P. OEHME, H. RENNER & J. M. STEWART. 1982. The effects of substance P on histamine and 5-hydroxytryptamine release in the rat. J. Physiol. **330:** 393–411.
30. PAYAN, D. G., D. R. BREWSTER, A. MISSIRIAN-BASTIAN & E. J. GOETZL. 1984. Substance P recognition by a subset of human T lymphocytes. J. Clin. Invest. **74:** 1532–1539.
31. STANISZ, A. M., R. SCICCHITANO, P. DAZIN, J. BIENENSTOCK & D. G. PAYAN. 1987. Distribution of substance P receptors on murine spleen and Peyer's patch T and B cells. J. Immunol. **139:** 749–754.
32. PAYAN, D. G., D. R. BREWSTER & E. J. GOETZL. 1984. Stereospecific receptors for substance P on cultured human IM-9 lymphoblasts. J. Immunol. **133:** 3260–3265.
33. FELTEN, D. L., S. Y. FELTEN, S. L. CARLSON, J. A. OLSCHOWKA & S. LIVNAT. 1985. Noradrenergic and peptidergic innervation of lymphoid tissue. J. Immunol. **135:** 755s–765s.
34. FINK, T. & E. WEIHE. 1988. Multiple neuropeptides in nerves supplying mammalian lymph nodes: messenger candidates for sensory and autonomic neuroimmunomodulation? Neurosci. Lett. **90:** 39–44.
35. WEIHE, E., S. MULLER, T. FINK & H. J. ZENTEL. 1989. Tachykinins, calcitonin gene-related peptide, and neuropeptide Y in nerves of the mammalian thymus: interactions with mast cells in autonomic and sensory neuroimmunomodulation? Neurosci. Lett. **100:** 77–82.
36. POPPER, P., C. R. MANTYH, S. R. VIGNA, J. E. MAGIOOS & P. W. MANTYH. 1988. The localization of sensory nerve fibers and receptor binding sites for sensory neuropeptides in canine mesenteric lymph nodes. Peptides **9:** 257–267.
37. BELLINGER, D. L., D. LORTON, T. D. ROMANO, J. A. OLSCHOWKA, S. Y. FELTEN & D. L. FELTEN. 1990. Neuropeptide innervation of lymphoid organs. *In* Neuropeptides and Immunopeptides: Messengers in a Neuroimmune Axis. Volume 594. M. S. O'Dorisio & A. Panerai, Eds.: 17–33. Ann. N.Y. Acad. Sci. New York.
38. KURKOWSKI, R., W. KUMMER & C. HEYM. 1990. Substance P–immunoreactive nerve fibers in tracheobronchial lymph nodes of the guinea pig: origin, ultrastructure, and coexistence with other peptides. Peptides **11:** 13–20.
39. BIENENSTOCK, J., M. TOMIOKA, H. MATSUDA, R. H. STEAD, G. QUINONEZ, G. T. SIMON, M. D. COUGHLIN & J. A. DENBURG. 1987. The role of mast cells in inflammatory processes: evidence for nerve/mast cell interactions. Int. Arch. Allergy Appl. Immunol. **82:** 238–243.
40. FELTEN, D. L., S. Y. FELTEN, D. L. BELLINGER, S. L. CARLSON, K. D. ACKERMAN, K. S. MADDEN, J. A. OLSCHOWKA & S. LIVNAT. 1987. Noradrenergic sympathetic neural interactions with the immune system: structure and function. Immunol. Rev. **100:** 225–258.
41. MADDEN, K. S., K. D. ACKERMAN, S. LIVNAT, S. Y. FELTEN & D. L. FELTEN. 1989. Patterns of noradrenergic innervation of lymphoid organs and immunological consequences of denervation. *In* Neuroimmune Networks: Physiology and Diseases. E. J. Goetzl & N. H. Spector, Eds.: 1–8. Alan R. Liss. New York.
42. REDER, A. T., J. W. KARASZEWSKI & B. G. W. ARNASON. 1989. Sympathetic nervous system involvement in immune responses of mice and in patients with multiple sclerosis. *In* Neuroimmune Networks: Physiology and Diseases. E. J. Goetzl & N. H. Spector, Eds.: 137–148. Alan R. Liss. New York.

Preprotachykinin Gene Expression in the Forebrain: Regulation by Dopamine[a]

MICHAEL J. BANNON,[b] DORIS M. HAVERSTICK,
KAZUHIKO SHIBATA, AND MICHAEL S. POOSCH

Center for Cell Biology
Sinai Hospital of Detroit
Detroit, Michigan 48235
and
Departments of Psychiatry (Cellular and Clinical
Neurobiology Program) and Pharmacology
Wayne State University School of Medicine
Detroit, Michigan 48201

Neurons in the basal ganglia and various limbic nuclei that express the substance P (SP) neurotransmitter phenotype are intimately associated with dopamine (DA)–containing neurons.[1] In animal studies, either chronic blockade of DA receptors or lesioning of DA neurons decreases basal ganglia SP content as a result of decreased striatal tachykinin biosynthesis, with a time course that apparently parallels the period of maximum risk for drug-induced parkinsonism seen clinically.[2-4] Decreased postmortem SP content is also seen in the basal ganglia of patients with Parkinson's disease concurrent with DA cell death.[5-7] Thus, it is conceivable that motor movement deficits seen in Parkinson's disease and in patients receiving antipsychotic drug (DA antagonist) treatment may be related in some manner to decreased striatal preprotachykinin (PPT) gene expression. In contrast, few studies have investigated the potential regulation by DA of PPT gene expression in limbic regions and its possible relationship to the antipsychotic drug mechanism of action.

Multiple PPT mRNAs arising from alternative RNA splicing of the PPT primary transcript encode different combinations of tachykinin peptides[8-10] (FIGURE 1). Alpha-PPT mRNA (minus exon 6) encodes SP alone. Beta-PPT mRNA (full length, derived from exons 1–7) encodes SP, neurokinin A (NKA), and neuropeptide K, which is an N-terminally extended form of NKA. Gamma-PPT mRNA (minus exon 4) encodes SP, NKA, and neuropeptide gamma, which is an extended form of NKA truncated in comparison to neuropeptide K. Because PPT mRNA splicing is regulated in a species- and tissue-specific manner, the regulation of tachykinin production might occur at a transcriptional and/or posttranscriptional level. The series of experiments outlined below assessed the content and nature of the PPT mRNAs in various rat and human forebrain nuclei, the transcriptional/posttranscriptional regulation of rat PPT gene expression by DA receptor activation, and the relationship between the clinical effects of various typical or atypical antipsychotic drugs and their effects on PPT gene expression in rat forebrain nuclei.

A sensitive solution hybridization/nuclease protection protocol[11-13] facilitated the quantitation of the various PPT mRNAs in rat forebrain nuclei (FIGURE 2). The upper band represents radiolabeled antisense PPT RNA probe protected by beta-

[a]This work was supported in part by USPHS Grant No. MH43026, by the Scottish Rite Schizophrenia Research Program, and by Sinai Hospital.
[b]M. J. Bannon is an Alfred P. Sloan Fellow.

31

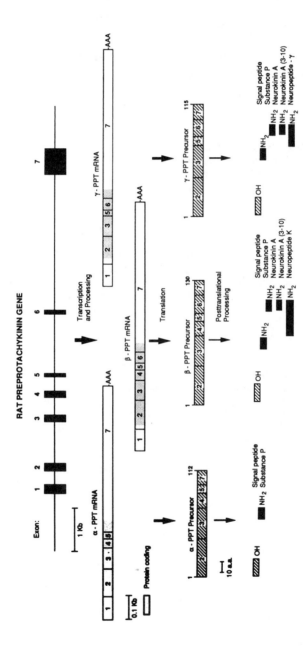

FIGURE 1. Schematic illustration of the transcription, alternate RNA splicing, and translation of the rat preprotachykinin (PPT) gene. The PPT gene is pictured at the top, with the exons as numbered boxes and the introns as connecting lines. PPT gene transcription and alternate RNA splicing result in three PPT mRNAs. Translation of mRNAs results in three distinct precursors that, when processed, yield differing combinations of tachykinin peptides. Modified from reference 23.

PPT mRNA, whereas the lower bands are derived from probe protected by gamma-PPT mRNA. No alpha-PPT mRNA was visualized. Although the absolute amounts of PPT mRNA (quantitated by sample comparisons with synthetic PPT RNA standards) ranged from 0.5 pg PPT/μg RNA (septum) to 3.5 pg PPT/μg RNA (striatum), the proportion of beta/gamma PPT (estimated using this protocol to be approximately 40% beta/60% gamma) varied less than 10% among brain regions or other tissues.[14,15] Thus, the proportions of PPT mRNAs in the rat are strikingly different from the reported predominance of alpha-PPT in bovine brain[8,9] and no tissue-specific splicing is observed.[10,14,15] In the rat, virtually all PPT mRNA encodes both SP and NKA.

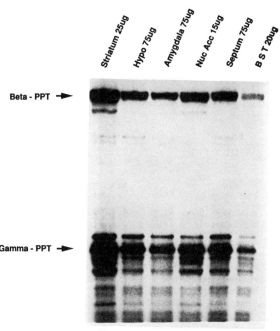

FIGURE 2. A representative solution hybridization experiment to determine the nature and quantity of preprotachykinin (PPT) mRNAs in various rat forebrain tissues. Tissue RNA was hybridized with an antisense RNA probe, nuclease treated, and the protected fragments were resolved in a urea/acrylamide gel prior to autoradiography. The two major PPT mRNA species, beta-PPT (full length) and gamma-PPT (minus exon 4), are indicated by arrows. Terms: Hypo, hypothalamus; Nuc Acc, nucleus accumbens; BST, bed nucleus of the stria terminalis. The RNA aliquots analyzed are indicated at the top of the figure. For more details, see reference 14.

The developmental profile of PPT gene expression has been determined in the rat striatum. At embryonic day 20, striatal PPT mRNA content was approximately 8% of adult values, with striatal PPT content approaching adult levels by postnatal days 12–15.[13] In many instances, alternate RNA splicing is regulated during development.[16] In the case of PPT mRNA, at those ages at which PPT content was significantly less than adult levels, a slight (10%), but significantly higher proportion of gamma-PPT mRNA relative to beta-PPT mRNA was seen.[13]

The DA receptor(s) mediating DA modulation of striatal PPT gene expression has been investigated. Administration to rats of the potent indirect DA agonist methamphetamine rapidly increases striatal PPT mRNA, with a maximal effect within 3 h. Increased striatal PPT mRNA is prevented by concurrent systemic administration of either a D-1 or a D-2 DA selective antagonist (SCH 23390 or sulpiride, respectively).[11] The D-2 agonist quinpirole, but not the D-1 agonist SKF 38393, mimicked the methamphetamine-induced increase. The D-2 agonist–induced increase in striatal PPT mRNA was dependent upon tonic D-1 receptor activation, as either coadministration of SCH 23390 or pretreatment with the DA synthesis inhibitor alpha-methyltyrosine blocked the effects of quinpirole.[11] These studies provided evidence (at a systems level) that D-1 DA receptors enable D-2 receptor modulation of PPT gene expression.

The mechanism(s) whereby methamphetamine activation of DA receptors increased rat striatal PPT mRNA was also studied.[12] Cell fractionation experiments showed that the earliest drug-induced increases in PPT mRNA occurred in cell

TABLE 1. Effect of Methamphetamine on PPT mRNA and Primary Transcript Content and on the PPT Gene Transcription Rate in Rat Striatum[a]

Time	PPT mRNA	Primary Transcript	PPT Gene Transcription Rate
0	100 ± 7	100 ± 7	100 ± 33
20	102 ± 9	48 ± 4*	ND
30	ND	ND	300 ± 50*
40	138 ± 8	53 ± 4*	ND
60	224 ± 10*	51 ± 3*	226 ± 40*
90	294 ± 10*	47 ± 3*	187 ± 33
120	292 ± 8*	48 ± 5*	125 ± 40
180	296 ± 7*	49 ± 4*	ND
240	300 ± 10*	42 ± 3*	ND

[a] Data are expressed as a percentage of control values (means ± SEM): $N = 7-10$ for PPT mRNA and PPT primary transcript levels; $N = 3$ for the PPT gene transcription rates. An asterisk indicates a difference from control, $p < 0.05$; ND = not determined. For more details, see the text and reference 12.

nuclei, ruling out stabilization of cytoplasmic PPT mRNA as a primary mechanism for increased PPT expression. Striatal PPT mRNA content was increased approximately threefold within 1.5 h after methamphetamine and was sustained for at least 4 h (TABLE 1). A unique rat PPT gene intron 6 sequence was used to specifically quantitate the PPT primary transcript (which contains both transcribed exon and intron sequences). Under basal conditions, the molar ratio of PPT mRNA to PPT primary transcript was approximately 125:1. Whereas mature PPT mRNA content was rapidly increasing in response to methamphetamine injection, PPT gene primary transcript levels were paradoxically decreased by 50% within 20 min and remained suppressed for at least 4 h postmethamphetamine (TABLE 1). Nuclear transcription assays indicated a twofold to threefold increase in the rate of PPT gene transcription that lasted 60–90 min after methamphetamine, with normal transcription rates reestablished by 2 h after drug treatment (TABLE 1). Taken together, these data suggest that activation of DA receptors by the indirect DA agonist methamphetamine alters striatal PPT gene expression at two levels: a transient increase in PPT

TABLE 2. Effects of Repeated Dopamine Antagonist Treatment on Preprotachykinin mRNA in Rat Striatum and Limbic Nuclei[a]

Drug	Striatum	Nucleus Accumbens	Bed Nucleus of Stria Terminalis	Septum
haloperidol	51 ± 8*	100 ± 10	95 ± 11	119 ± 5*
chlorpromazine	79 ± 6*	114 ± 20	98 ± 23	147 ± 7*
l-sulpiride	121 ± 17	161 ± 7*	148 ± 27*	87 ± 20
clozapine	110 ± 26	191 ± 28*	154 ± 19*	124 ± 18

[a] Data are expressed as a percentage of control values (means ± SEM); N = 3–5. An asterisk indicates a difference from control, $p < 0.05$. For more details, see the text and reference 14.

gene transcription and a more sustained increase in the rate at which PPT primary transcript is processed to mature PPT mRNA.[12]

It is widely believed that antipsychotic drugs effect clinical improvement through interaction with DA receptors located in limbic nuclei, whereas DA receptor antagonism in the basal ganglia is associated with drug-induced extrapyramidal side effects.[17] Given the close association in these brain regions between tachykinin and DA neurons, the effects of antipsychotic drugs on PPT gene expression were investigated.[14] Repeated administration of prototypical DA antagonists such as haloperidol and chlorpromazine significantly decreased striatal PPT mRNA, whereas the atypical antipsychotic drugs, sulpiride and clozapine, were without effect (TABLE 2). Neither repeated haloperidol nor chlorpromazine altered PPT mRNA in the

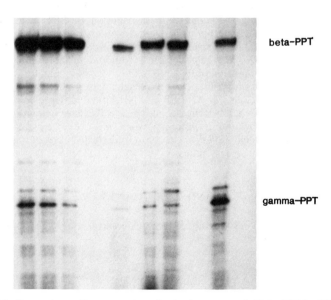

FIGURE 3. Comparison of human and rat forebrain preprotachykinin (PPT) mRNAs. Samples were analyzed by solution hybridization as described in FIGURE 2 and the text. Equal aliquots were run in the following order: human medial head caudate, posterior head caudate, nucleus accumbens, anterolateral putamen, posteromedial putamen, posterolateral putamen, and rat caudate-putamen. Note the predominance of beta-PPT mRNA in the human in comparison to the rat.

nucleus accumbens or in the bed nucleus of the stria terminalis, but sulpiride and clozapine increased PPT mRNA in these nuclei (TABLE 2). In the septum, repeated haloperidol and chlorpromazine significantly increased PPT mRNA, whereas sulpiride and clozapine were without effect (TABLE 2). Hence, in the striatum, as well as in three limbic nuclei (nucleus accumbens, bed nucleus of the stria terminalis, and septum), the prototypical antipsychotic drugs, haloperidol and chlorpromazine, exhibited a pharmacological profile distinct from that of the atypical drugs, sulpiride and clozapine.[14] The atypical antipsychotic agents, clozapine and sulpiride, which are associated with a greatly diminished risk of extrapyramidal side effects,[17,18] did not decrease striatal PPT gene expression, strengthening the observed correlation between the reduced striatal tachykinin biosynthesis and the parkinsonian symptoms outlined earlier. On the other hand, it is apparent that the distinct effects of typical versus atypical antipsychotic drugs on limbic PPT gene expression do not correlate with their common clinical efficacy. It has been shown that a significant proportion of otherwise treatment-resistant schizophrenics respond to atypical antipsychotics.[19] Although speculative, it is conceivable that the distinctive effects of atypical antipsychotic agents on limbic PPT gene expression might provide a potential model for the development of adjunct therapies directed at these treatment-resistant patients.

In the present study and in published reports,[11,12,14,20,21] various pharmacological manipulations, including alterations in DA receptor stimulation, did not alter the proportion of the PPT mRNA variants found in rat brain. Thus, evidence for stimulus-specific splicing of rat PPT gene transcripts has not been forthcoming (apart from the slight developmentally regulated shift discussed earlier).

Northern blot analysis of human basal ganglia RNA probed with human PPT cDNA clones has confirmed the postmortem stability of PPT mRNA.[22] Analysis of dissected tissues suggests a roughly even distribution of PPT gene expression throughout the entire caudate-putamen, with an absence of PPT mRNA in the globus pallidus. Solution hybridization experiments reveal that human PPT mRNA is approximately 80% beta/20% gamma forms, with no detectable alpha-PPT (FIGURE 3). Although the proportion of PPT mRNA variants in human forebrain differs from both bovine and rat brain, it most resembles the pattern seen in the rat because virtually all PPT mRNAs encode both SP and NKA-related peptides. Postmortem analyses of neuropathological specimens, along with the development of chemical probes specific for tachykinin receptor subtypes and the cloning of tachykinin receptors,[23] will aid in elucidating the role of forebrain tachykinin neurons in normal neurotransmission and in disease states.

ACKNOWLEDGMENTS

We thank Rolf Hanson for excellent technical assistance and Cheryl Jackson for skilled secretarial assistance.

REFERENCES

1. WARDEN, M. K. & W. S. YOUNG III. 1988. Distribution of cells containing mRNAs encoding substance P and neurokinin B in the rat central nervous system. J. Comp. Neurol. 227: 90–113.
2. HONG, J-S., H-Y. T. YANG & E. COSTA. 1978. Substance P content of substantia nigra after chronic treatment with antischizophrenic drugs. Neuropharmacology 17: 83–85.
3. BANNON, M. J., J-M. LEE, P. GIRAUD, A. YOUNG, H-U. AFFOLTER & T. I. BONNER. 1986.

The dopamine antagonist haloperidol decreases substance P, substance K, and prepro-tachykinin mRNAs in rat striatonigral neurons. J. Biol. Chem. **261:** 6640–6644.

4. YOUNG, W. S., III, T. I. BONNER & M. R. BRANN. 1986. Mesencephalic dopamine neurons regulate the expression of neuropeptide mRNAs in the rat forebrain. Proc. Natl. Acad. Sci. U.S.A. **83:** 9827–9831.

5. MAUBORGNE, A., F. JAVOY-AGID, J. C. LEGRAND, Y. AGID & F. CESSETIN. 1983. Decrease of substance P–like immunoreactivity in the substantia nigra and pallidum of parkinsonian brains. Brain Res. **268:** 167–170.

6. TENOVNO, O., V. K. RUNNE & M. K. VILJANEN. 1984. Substance P immunoreactivity in the postmortem parkinsonian brain. Brain Res. **303:** 113–116.

7. CLEVENS, R. A. & M. F. BEAL. 1989. Substance P–like immunoreactivity in brains with pathological features of Parkinson's and Alzheimer's diseases. Brain Res. **486:** 398–390.

8. NAWA, H., T. HIROSE, H. TAKESHIMA, S. INAYAMA & S. NAKANISHI. 1983. Nucleotide sequences of cDNAs for two types of bovine brain substance P precursor. Nature **306:** 32–34.

9. NAWA, H., H. KOTANI & S. NAKANISHI. 1984. Tissue-specific generation of two preprotachy-kinin mRNAs from one gene by alternate RNA splicing. Nature **312:** 729–734.

10. KRAUSE, J. E., J. M. CHIRGWIN, M. S. CARTER, Z. S. XU & A. D. HERSHEY. 1987. Three rat preprotachykinin mRNAs encode the neuropeptides substance P and neurokinin A. Proc. Natl. Acad. Sci. U.S.A. **84:** 881–885.

11. HAVERSTICK, D. M., A. RUBENSTEIN & M. J. BANNON. 1989. Striatal tachykinin gene expression regulated by interaction of D-1 and D-2 dopamine receptors. J. Pharmacol. Exp. Ther. **248:** 858–862.

12. HAVERSTICK, D. M. & M. J. BANNON. 1989. Evidence for dual mechanisms involved in methamphetamine-induced increases in striatal preprotachykinin mRNA. J. Biol. Chem. **264:** 13140–13144.

13. HAVERSTICK, D. M., M. JEZIORSKI & M. J. BANNON. 1990. Developmental profile of striatal preprotachykinin gene expression. J. Neurochem. **55:** 764–768.

14. SHIBATA, K., D. M. HAVERSTICK & M. J. BANNON. 1990. Tachykinin gene expression in rat limbic nuclei: modulation by dopamine antagonists. J. Pharmacol. Exp. Ther. **255:** 388–392.

15. STERNINI, C., K. ANDERSON, G. FRANTZ, J. E. KRAUSE & N. BRECHA. 1989. Expression of substance P/neurokinin A–encoding preprotachykinin mRNAs in the rat enteric nervous system. Gastroenterology **97:** 348–356.

16. LEFF, S. E. & M. G. ROSENFELD. 1986. Complex transcriptional units: diversity in gene expression by alternative RNA processing. Annu. Rev. Biochem. **55:** 1091–1117.

17. BALDESSARINI, R. J. 1985. Drugs and the treatment of psychiatric disorders. *In* The Pharmacological Basis of Therapeutics. A. S. Gilman, L. S. Goodman, T. W. Rall & F. Mural, Eds. Macmillan Co. New York.

18. COFFIN, V. L., M. B. LATRANYI & R. E. CHIPKIN. 1989. Acute extrapyramidal syndrome in cebus monkeys: development mediated by dopamine D2, but not D1 receptors. J. Pharmacol. Exp. Ther. **249:** 769–774.

19. MELTZER, H. Y. 1988. New insights into schizophrenia through atypical antipsychotic drugs. Neuropsychopharmacology **1:** 193–196.

20. SIVAM, S. P., J. E. KRAUSE, K. TAKEUCHI, S. LI, J. F. MCGINTY & J-S. HONG. 1989. Lithium increases rat striatal beta- and gamma-preprotachykinin messenger RNAs. J. Pharmacol. Exp. Ther. **248:** 1297–1301.

21. BROWN, E. R., R. E. HARLAN & J. E. KRAUSE. 1990. Gonadal steroid regulation of substance P (SP) and SP-encoding messenger ribonucleic acid in the rat anterior pituitary and hypothalamus. Endocrinology **126:** 330–340.

22. POOSCH, M. S., D. M. HAVERSTICK, A. MANDAL, I. C. XUE, K. SHIBATA, L. J. DRAGOVIC & M. J. BANNON. 1990. Nature and distribution of preprotachykinin mRNAs in human basal ganglia. Soc. Neurosci. Abstr. **16:** 1171.

23. HELKE, C. J., J. E. KRAUSE, P. W. MANTYH, R. COUTURE & M. J. BANNON. 1990. Diversity in mammalian tachykinin peptidergic neurons: multiple peptides, receptors, and regulatory mechanism. FASEB J. **4:** 1606–1615.

Differential Changes in Tachykinins in the Rat Brain after Drug-induced Seizures[a]

A. SARIA,[b] G. SPERK,[c] J. MARKSTEINER,[c] C. HUMPEL,[b]
AND R. BELLMANN[c]

[b]Neurochemistry Unit
Department of Psychiatry
[c]Department of Pharmacology
University of Innsbruck Medical School
A-6020 Innsbruck, Austria

INTRODUCTION

Support for a possible role of neuropeptides in epilepsy comes from experiments using systemic injection of the neurotoxin kainic acid or from kindling with repeated administration of initially subconvulsive electrical or chemical stimuli. The use of kainic acid (KA) is associated with severe limbic seizures[1] and with subsequently increased seizure susceptibility[2,3] and results in increased levels of several neuropeptides,[4–7] presumably as a consequence of enhanced peptide synthesis.[8–10] Kindling was recently reported to result in elevated brain levels of the neuropeptides, met-enkephalin,[11–13] somatostatin,[14,15] neuropeptide Y,[3] and cholecystokinin-octapeptide.[13,16]

In the present discussion, we report in detail changes in tissue levels of tachykinins (TK) such as substance P (SP), neurokinin A (NKA), neurokinin B (NKB), neuropeptide K (NPK), and γ-PPT-A$_{72-92}$ after intraperitoneal kainic acid injection or after kindling with pentylenetetrazol (PTZ). The preprotachykinin-B (PPT-B) mRNA, coding for neurokinin B,[17] and the preprotachykinin-A (PPT-A) mRNA, coding for either SP (alpha-species) or SP and NKA (beta- and gamma-species), were measured to determine if changes in TK tissue levels reflect altered biosynthesis.

METHODS

Injection of Kainic Acid and Evaluation of Behavior

Male Sprague-Dawley rats were injected intraperitoneally with kainic acid (10 mg/kg).[18] Control animals received saline in the same volume. The rats were observed for 3 h and their behavior was rated according to a scale from 0 to 4.[5]

[a]This study was supported by the Austrian Scientific Research Funds (Grant No. P7029M to G. Sperk and Grant No. P7573M to A. Saria) and by the Dr. Legerlotz Foundation.

Pentylenetetrazol Kindling

Male Sprague-Dawley rats received daily injections of 30 mg/kg ip pentylenetetrazol (PTZ) over a period of five weeks as described.[16] Briefly, the animals were observed for 30 min after each injection and convulsions were rated according to a scale described,[16] ranging from 0 to 5.

Neurochemical Procedures

The animals were killed by decapitation at various time points after kainic acid injection or after the last PTZ injection. Brains were removed and stored at $-70\,°C$ for determination of peptide levels. Frontal cortex, striatum, dorsal hippocampus, substantia nigra, and amygdala/pyriform cortex were dissected from frozen brains as described previously.[5,18] For mRNA measurements, brains were dissected freshly.

Determination of Neuropeptides

Brain samples were extracted by ultrasonication in 2 M acetic acid (1:50, w/v) and by centrifugation.[19]

Radioimmunoassays and HPLC analyses for individual peptides were performed as described in detail elsewhere.[3,6,7,20,21] For neurokinin-like immunoreactivity, the antibody K12 (donated by E. Theodorsson) was used. This antibody recognizes neurokinin A, neurokinin B, neuropeptide K, γ-PPT-A$_{72-92}$, and the respective sulfoxides, but not substance P. The antisera for substance P (RD$_2$, donated by S. Leeman) and NPY[7] were highly specific and recognized only single HPLC peaks. The antisera for VIP (AC115, Cambridge Research Chemicals) and calcitonin gene–related peptide (CGRP) (antiserum RAS6009, Peninsula) were obtained commercially and also recognized only single major HPLC peaks.[7,21] Therefore, neurokinin-like immunoreactivities were further characterized by reversed-phase HPLC,[19] separating NKA, NKB, NPK, γ-PPT-A$_{72-92}$, and the respective sulfoxides.

Determination of Preprotachykinin mRNAs

Immediately after dissection, each brain sample was homogenized in 1 mL of 7.6 M guanidine-HCl.[22] Total RNA was extracted and its concentration was determined photometrically. Equal aliquots of 7.5 or 20 μg of total RNA were run on denaturating agarose-formaldehyde gels, blotted onto nylon membranes, and fixed at 80 °C for 2 h.[22] Blotted mRNAs were hybridized with a ^{32}P-labeled probe for PPT-A or PPT-B at 65 °C for 16 h. The probes had been cloned into a pGI vector. Labeled, complementary RNAs were synthesized in a transcription system (Clontech) containing ^{32}UTP (800 Ci/mmol) and T-7 or SP-6 polymerase for transcription of the PPT-A and PPT-B probes, respectively. The blots were washed, sealed into plastic covers, and autoradiographed, and mRNA signals were quantified by densitometric scanning.[22]

RESULTS

Changes in Neuropeptide Levels after Kainic Acid Treatment

The time course of changes in total neurokinin immunoreactivity (NK-IR) subsequently to KA-induced seizures is shown in FIGURE 1. Significant decreases were found in the frontal cortex, striatum, and dorsal hippocampus after 3 h. During the subsequent 3 days, NK-IR recovered to values not significantly different from controls. At subsequent time intervals, NK-IR was found to be markedly increased in the cortex and hippocampus. Only slight increases were observed in the amygdala and in the striatum (FIGURE 1).

The tachykinins (TK) investigated in this study were well separated by high performance liquid chromatography (HPLC) (FIGURE 2). Using an acetonitrile gradient (18–40%), synthetic NKA and NKB eluted at 22% and 36% acetonitrile, respectively. NPK eluted five fractions in front of NKB and γ-PPT-A$_{72-92}$ could be found at approximately six fractions in front of NKA. Substance P eluted at 28% acetonitrile, but was not detected with the NK-antiserum K12. The respective peptides oxidized with H_2O_2 eluted earlier than the peptides from which they were derived. Under the oxidizing conditions used, only one peak of oxidized NKB

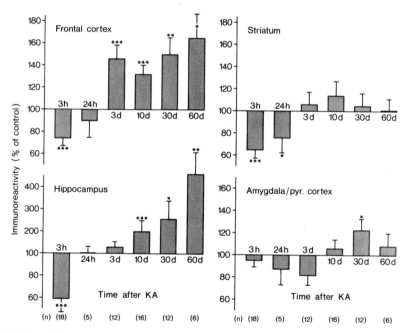

FIGURE 1. Time course of the changes in neurokinin immunoreactivity after kainic acid–induced seizures. Neurokinin immunoreactivity was determined in tissue extracts using the K12 antiserum, which detects almost equally all known mammalian tachykinins except substance P, and is expressed as percentage immunoreactivities ± SEM. The number of animals is given in the parentheses. No significant changes in neurokinin immunoreactivity were found in the substantia nigra. Key: ($***$) $p < 0.001$, ($**$) $p < 0.05$ versus controls; Student's t test. (From reference 19, with permission.)

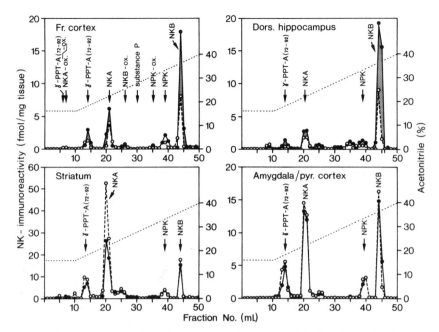

FIGURE 2. Reversed-phase HPLC of neurokinin immunoreactivity in individual brain areas 30 days after KA. Neurokinin immunoreactivity was determined in HPLC fractions obtained after separation of brain extracts from KA-treated (●) and control (○) rats and was corrected for the recovery of total immunoreactivity. The arrows indicate the retention times of the respective synthetic peptides. The shaded areas represent the peak areas increased after KA treatment. The dotted lines show the acetonitrile concentration in the mobile phase. The antiserum K12 and the synthetic NKA as standard were used for the radioimmunoassays. There were no differences in the relative peak heights when NKB and NPK were used alternatively for standardization. (From reference 19, with permission.)

(probably bisoxidized material) was found. In untreated animals, the relative amounts of NKA and NKB varied depending on the brain area (FIGURE 2). More NKA was detected in the striatum and more NKB was detected in the hippocampus, whereas the cortex and the amygdala contained about equal amounts of NKA and NKB and apparently lower amounts of NPK. Thirty days after KA, strong increases of IR associated with the NKB peak occurred in the cortex and hippocampus (FIGURE 2, TABLE 1). The NKA peak was markedly increased only in the hippocampus. Only slight elevations of NPK and γ-PPT-A$_{72-92}$ (in the cortex and hippocampus, FIGURE 2) or of SP (in the cortex, TABLE 1) were observed. Three days after KA, NKB (but not NKA) was increased similarly to that after 30 days (not shown). Decreases in SP tissue concentrations were previously found 3 h after KA[5] (data not shown). After 30 days, increased SP levels could be detected in the frontal cortex, in the striatum, and (although not statistically significant) in the hippocampus (TABLE 1). The increase in the frontal cortex could also be verified by HPLC (FIGURE 3). Calcitonin gene–related peptide (CGRP), another neuropeptide, markedly increased 3 days after KA in the cortex, striatum, and hippocampus (TABLE 2). However, this increase declined during the following 4 weeks, thereby reaching nearly control values[21] (data not shown).

TABLE 1. Changes in Individual Neuropeptide Levels 30 Days after KA-induced Seizures[a]

	Neurokinin B	Substance P
Frontal cortex	238 ± 27**	128 ± 11**
Hippocampus	318 ± 83*	131 ± 35
Amygdala/pyr. cortex	190 ± 123	103 ± 8
Striatum	122 ± 33	116 ± 7*

[a]Data are expressed as percentage of controls ± SEM. Mean NKB immunoreactivities were determined by three individual HPLC runs and were compared with three controls using synthetic NKB for the standard curve. Substance P ($n = 12$ versus 15 controls) was determined directly in the tissue extract with the respective antiserum. Key: (**) $p < 0.01$, (*) $p < 0.05$ versus controls; Student's t test. Data from reference 19.

Changes in Neuropeptide Levels after PTZ Kindling

In animals that were killed 10 days after the last injection of PTZ, significant increases in total NK-IR and also in neuropeptide Y (NPY)–IR were observed in all four brain regions investigated (TABLE 3). In the same rats, no significant changes could be detected for SP-IR, VIP-IR, or CGRP-IR (TABLE 3). The increase in NPY-IR and NK-IR was found to be dependent on the kindling state. Thus, statistically increased concentrations of these peptides were observed only in animals that exhibited a mean rating of the last five kindling sessions of >4.5 (data not shown).[16] When a group of such animals was allowed to survive for three more months, the peptide levels markedly declined again (TABLE 3), although the seizure threshold was still decreased to a similar extent as immediately after the last kindling session. HPLC analysis of cortical NK-IR in controls and at 10 days after the last kindling session indicated an increase in NKB, but not in NKA, NPK, or γ-PPT-A$_{72-92}$ (not shown).

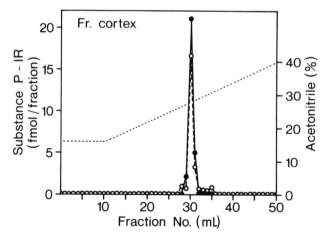

FIGURE 3. Reversed-phase HPLC of substance P immunoreactivity in the frontal cortex 30 days after KA for KA-treated (●) and control (○) rats. The RD$_2$ antiserum was used. (From reference 19, with permission.)

TABLE 2. Levels of CGRP 3 Days after Kainic Acid Treatment[a]

| | (n) | CGRP (fmol/mg wet tissue weight) | | |
		Frontal Cortex	Striatum	Hippocampus
Controls	(7)	3.5 ± 0.35	5.5 ± 1.03	6.0 ± 0.44
Kainic acid	(9)	56.0 ± 8.79**	12.1 ± 1.17*	22.7 ± 3.26**

[a]Data are expressed as the mean ± SEM. Key: (**) $p < 0.01$, (*) $p < 0.05$ versus controls; Student's *t* test. Data from reference 21.

Changes in PPT-A and PPT-B mRNAs after Kainic Acid Treatment

In the frontal cortex, the concentration of PPT-B mRNA was increased by approximately 150% at 2 and 30 days after KA (TABLE 4). In the hippocampus, PPT-B mRNA elevations were most pronounced at 30 days (TABLE 4) after KA. In the striatum, PPT-B mRNA was increased 2 days after KA, but declined to basal

TABLE 3. Changes in Neuropeptide Immunoreactivities 10 and 90 Days after the Last PTZ Kindling Session[a]

	Frontal Cortex	Hippocampus	Amygdala
		Neurokinins	
Controls (fmol/mg wet weight)	26 ± 1.7	11 ± 0.9	64 ± 3.5
10 days after kindling (% of control)	144 ± 9.0***	194 ± 40.6**	180 ± 47.9*
90 days after kindling (% of control)	117 ± 8.3*	152 ± 33.1	107 ± 11.1
		Somatostatin	
Controls (fmol/mg wet weight)	298 ± 5.4	121 ± 5.4	426 ± 12.3
10 days after kindling (% of control)	156 ± 6.3***	113 ± 11.1	137 ± 5.8***
90 days after kindling (% of control)	116 ± 5.5**	102 ± 4.8	106 ± 4.2
		Neuropeptide Y	
Controls (fmol/mg wet weight)	132 ± 6.6	69 ± 2.49	157 ± 5.5
10 days after kindling (% of control)	241 ± 22.4***	152 ± 11.0***	204 ± 17.9***
90 days after kindling (% of control)	119 ± 5.0***	125 ± 8.7**	120 ± 10.7
		Substance P	
Controls (fmol/mg wet weight)	66 ± 3.3	13 ± 1.5	183 ± 15.1
10 days after kindling (% of control)	89 ± 7.7	115 ± 21.5	91.3 ± 9.2
		Vasoactive Intestinal Peptide	
Controls (fmol/mg wet weight)	88 ± 9.7	27 ± 3.3	122 ± 7.8
10 days after kindling (% of control)	103.4 ± 8.5	85.2 ± 17.0	95.9 ± 16.1
		Calcitonin Gene–related Peptide	
Controls (fmol/mg wet weight)	2.3 ± 0.27	2.3 ± 0.38	25.9 ± 2.29
10 days after kindling (% of control)	100 ± 4.8	104.3 ± 21.7	97.3 ± 20.6

[a]Only animals exhibiting a full seizure rating (4.5–5.0) were included. They were sacrificed 10 or 90 days after the last kindling session. For all time points, individual control groups were used. Control values shown represent the mean of all individual control groups ($n = 24$) and are given as absolute values ± SEM. Data for kindled animals represent the percentage of the respective control group ($n = 6$–10). Key: (*) $p < 0.05$, (**) $p < 0.01$, (***) $p < 0.001$ versus controls; Student's *t* test. Data from reference 16.

levels at 30 days after KA. PPT-A mRNA was increased 2 days after KA in the hippocampus (TABLE 4). Although it could be well detected in all other brain regions and at all time intervals investigated, no other significant changes apart from the early increase in the hippocampus could be observed.

DISCUSSION

The present data demonstrate pronounced changes in NK-IR in the frontal cortex, hippocampus, and striatum after KA-induced seizures. The early decreases may reflect increased release and subsequent metabolism of the peptides during the acute seizures. This is consistent with the changes in the levels of, for example, SP, NPY, somatostatin, or CGRP[3,6,7,21] and with the augmented amine turnover[18] during the acute seizures. The gradual increases in NK-IR in the cortex and hippocampus at 3–60 days after KA were striking and resembled the increases in tissue concentrations of somatostatin, NPY, and cholecystokinin-octapeptide.[6,7] This long-term effect may be explained by decreased release or increased biosynthesis of the respective peptides. For the latter peptides, it could be demonstrated that the rise in peptide

TABLE 4. Preprotachykinin mRNA after ip Kainic Acid Treatment[a]

	Cortex	Hippocampus	Striatum
		2 Days	
Preprotachykinin A	143 ± 30	234 ± 26	104 ± 21
Preprotachykinin B	236 ± 96	187 ± 35	292 ± 64
		30 Days	
Preprotachykinin A	94 ± 20	100 ± 20	87 ± 20
Preprotachykinin B	246 ± 69	481 ± 124	134 ± 41

[a]Response is expressed as % of controls ± SEM; $n = 7$. Data from reference 22.

levels was associated with increased mRNA synthesis of the respective prepropeptides.[23] The increased concentrations of PPT mRNAs[22] also point to enhanced biosynthesis of the neuropeptides as the reason for increased tissue levels.

Based on HPLC analyses, all three final TK gene products (SP, NKA, and NKB), as well as the PPT-A gene–related precursor peptides (NPK and γ-PPT-A$_{72-92}$), were found to be present in all brain areas investigated. This indicates that both routes of NKA synthesis, through the formation of β- and γ-PPT-A, may be used. KA-induced seizures led to an accumulation of all three final TK gene products, that is, SP, NKA, and NKB, although apparently quantitatively different in different brain regions. Thus, in the frontal cortex and hippocampus, NKB rather than the other neurokinins was increased. This is consistent with the findings after PTZ kindling, that is, increased tissue levels of NKB, but not of NKA or its precursors in the frontal cortex and hippocampus. In this context, the differences in the changes of PPT-A and PPT-B mRNAs are striking as well. These results point to the fact that TKs are differentially involved in two phases of neuropathological and neurochemical changes as a consequence of seizures produced by KA.[18] Hence, the early moderate increases of PPT-B mRNA in both the cortex and striatum and of PPT-A mRNA in the hippocampus could be a result of the acute status epilepticus and may fade away at later time intervals.

In a second phase, neuronal cell loss occurs in limbic areas and also in the hippocampus and other brain regions.[2,18] Moreover, this is accompanied by an increasing rate of spontaneous seizures.[24] These may induce enhanced expression of NKB via PPT-B mRNA. This hypothesis is further supported by the data obtained from the kindling model where the initial status epilepticus is missing and, as a consequence, only the late increase in NKB tissue levels can be observed. Additionally, the rapid transient increases in CGRP and VIP levels that were found after KA do not occur after PTZ kindling. The increased peptide levels after PTZ kindling seem to be linked ultimately to the repeated seizures during kindling rather than to the decreased seizure threshold per se because they declined three months after the last kindling session, where the seizure threshold is still reduced, without frequent spontaneous convulsions.

The different responses of various neuropeptides may also reflect different responses of the respective neurons. It is interesting to note that TK, NPY, somatostatin, and cholecystokinin-octapeptide partly coexist with GABA.[25-27] These peptides exhibit sustained increases in their levels in both seizure models (at least in the cortex), pointing to an activation of the respective subpopulations of GABA neurons. VIP and CGRP, which exhibit different responses after KA or after PTZ kindling, have been suggested to coexist with acetylcholine in the cortex[28] and brain stem.[29] Recently, a marked accumulation of met-enkephalin and NPY has been found in the hippocampal mossy fiber pathway after KA.[30,31] This accumulation may be accompanied by sprouting of this pathway to the supragranular layer,[31,32] which may contribute to some extent to the persisting increases in NKB levels and PPT-B mRNA in hippocampal mossy fibers (preliminary observation).

In summary, the present results indicate that PPT-A and PPT-B gene products, like other neuropeptides, are regulated differently upon seizure-induced neurochemical and neuropathological alterations depending on the seizure model applied. Concerning tachykinins, long-term adaptation to seizures due to reduced seizure threshold after kainic acid or due to kindling with pentylenetetrazol mainly involves increased synthesis of PPT-B mRNA and NKB presumably contained in cortical and hippocampal GABA neurons.

ACKNOWLEDGMENTS

The skillful technical assistance of D. Maas, I. Berger, and A. Gran is gratefully acknowledged. We further thank S. Leeman and E. Theodorsson for providing antisera and J. Krause for providing the PPT probes.

REFERENCES

1. BEN-ARI, Y. 1985. Limbic seizures and brain damage produced by kainic acid: mechanisms and relevance to human temporal lobe epilepsy. Neuroscience **14:** 375–403.
2. NADLER, J. V. 1981. Kainic acid as a tool for the study of temporal lobe epilepsy. Life Sci. **29:** 2031–2042.
3. MARKSTEINER, J. & G. SPERK. 1988. Concomitant increase of somatostatin, neuropeptide Y, and glutamate decarboxylase in the frontal cortex of rats with decreased seizure threshold. Neuroscience **26:** 379–385.
4. HONG, J. S., P. L. WOOD, J. C. GILLIN, H. Y. T. YANG & E. COSTA. 1980. Changes of hippocampal met-enkephalin content after recurrent motor seizures. Nature **285:** 231–232.

5. SPERK, G., R. WIESER, R. WIDMANN & E. A. SINGER. 1986. Kainic acid–induced seizures: changes in somatostatin, substance P, and neurotensin. Neuroscience **17:** 1117–1126.
6. MEYER, D. K., R. WIDMANN & G. SPERK. 1986. Increased brain levels of cholecystokinin octapeptide after kainic acid–induced seizures in the rat. Neurosci. Lett. **69:** 208–211.
7. MARKSTEINER, J., G. SPERK & D. MAAS. 1989. Differential increases in brain levels of neuropeptide Y and vasoactive intestinal polypeptide after kainic acid–induced seizures in the rat. Naunyn-Schmiedeberg's Arch. Pharmacol. **339:** 173–177.
8. KANAMATSU, T., J. OBIE, L. GRIMES, J. F. MCGINTY, K. YOSHIKAWA, S. SABOL & J. S. YONG. 1986. Kainic acid alters the metabolism of met^5-enkephalin and the level of dynorphin A in the rat hippocampus. J. Neurosci. **6:** 3094–3102.
9. WHITE, J. D., C. M. GALL & J. F. MCKELVY. 1987. Enkephalin biosynthesis and enkephalin gene expression are increased in hippocampal mossy fibers following a unilateral lesion of the hilus. J. Neurosci. **7:** 753–759.
10. OLENIK, C., D. K. MEYER, J. MARKSTEINER & G. SPERK. 1989. Concentrations of mRNAs encoding for preprosomatostatin and preprocholecystokinin are increased after kainic acid–induced seizures. Synapse **4:** 223–228.
11. VINDROLA, O., R. BRIONES, M. ASAI & A. FERNANDEZ-GUARDIOLA. 1981. Amygdaloid kindling enhances the enkephalin content in the rat brain. Neurosci. Lett. **21:** 39–43.
12. MCGINTY, J. F., T. KANAMATSU, J. OBIE, R. S. DYER, C. L. MITCHELL & J. S. HONG. 1986. Amygdaloid kindling increases enkephalin-like immunoreactivity, but decreases dynorphin-A-like immunoreactivity in rat hippocampus. Neurosci. Lett. **71:** 31–36.
13. IADAROLA, M. J., C. SHIN, J. O. MCNAMARA & H. Y. T. YANG. 1986. Changes in dynorphin, enkephalin, and cholecystokinin content of hippocampus and substantia nigra after amygdala kindling. Brain Res. **365:** 185–191.
14. KATO, N., T. HIGUCHI, H. G. FRIESEN & J. A. WADA. 1983. Changes of immunoreactive somatostatin and β-endorphin content in rat brain after amygdaloid kindling. Life Sci. **32:** 2415–2422.
15. PITKÄNEN, A., J. JOLKKONEN, J. SIRVIÖ & P. RIEKKINEN. 1988. Somatostatin-like immunoreactivity and somatostatin receptor binding in rat brain in pentylenetetrazol-induced kindling. Peptides **9:** 105–107.
16. MARKSTEINER, J., H. LASSMANN, A. SARIA, C. HUMPEL, D. K. MEYER & G. SPERK. 1990. Neuropeptide levels after pentylenetetrazol kindling in the rat. Eur. J. Neurosci. **2:** 98–103.
17. KOTANI, H., M. HOSHIMARU, H. NAWA & S. NAKANISHI. 1986. Structure and gene organization of bovine neuromedin K precursor. Proc. Natl. Acad. Sci. U.S.A. **83:** 7074–7078.
18. SPERK, G., H. LASSMANN, H. BRAN, S. J. KISH, F. SEITELBERGER & O. HORNYKIEWICZ. 1983. Kainic acid–induced seizures: neurochemical and histopathological changes. Neuroscience **10:** 1301–1315.
19. SPERK, G., J. MARKSTEINER, A. SARIA & C. HUMPEL. 1990. Differential changes in tachykinins after kainic acid–induced seizures in the rat. Neuroscience **34:** 219–224.
20. SPERK, G. & R. WIDMANN. 1985. Somatostatin precursor in the striatum: changes after local injection of kainic acid. J. Neurochem. **45:** 1441–1447.
21. SARIA, A., J. MARKSTEINER, C. HUMPEL & G. SPERK. 1989. Pronounced increases in brain levels of calcitonin gene–related peptide after kainic acid–induced seizures. Regulat. Peptides **26:** 215–227.
22. BELLMANN, R., C. HUMPEL, J. E. KRAUSE, J. MARKSTEINER, A. SARIA & G. SPERK. 1991. Differential changes in mRNAs encoding for preprotachykinin A and B after kainic acid–induced seizures in the rat. Synapse. In press.
23. MEYER, D. K., C. OLENIK & G. SPERK. 1988. Chronic effects of systemic applications of kainic acid on mRNA levels of neuropeptides in rat brain. Soc. Neurosci. Abstr. **14:** 6.
24. BARAN, H., H. LASSMANN & O. HORNYKIEWICZ. 1988. Behaviour and neurochemical changes six months after kainic acid. Soc. Neurosci. Abstr. **14:** 194.
25. HENDRY, S. H. C., E. G. JONES, J. DEFELIPE, D. SCHMECHEL, C. BRANDON & P. C. EMSON. 1984. Neuropeptide-containing neurons of the cerebral cortex are also GABAergic. Proc. Natl. Acad. Sci. U.S.A. **81:** 6526–6530.
26. SOMOGYI, P., A. J. HODGSON, A. D. SMITH, G. M. NUNZI, A. GORI & J-Y. WU. 1984. Different populations of GABAergic neurons in the visual cortex and hippocampus of

cat contain somatostatin- or cholecystokinin-immunoreactive material. J. Neurosci. **4:** 2590–2603.

27. VINCENT, S. R., O. JOHANSSON, T. HÖKFELT, L. SKIRBOLL, R. P. ELDE, L. TERENIUS, J. KIMMEL & M. GOLDSTEIN. 1983. NADPH-diaphorase: a selective histochemical marker for striatal neurons containing both somatostatin- and avian pancreatic polypeptide (APP)–like immunoreactivities. J. Comp. Neurol. **217:** 252–263.

28. ECKENSTEIN, F. & R. W. BAUGHMAN. 1984. Two types of cholinergic innervation in cortex, one co-localized with vasoactive intestinal polypeptide. Nature **309:** 153–155.

29. KAWAI, Y., K. TAKAMI, S. SHIOSAKA, P. C. EMSON, C. J. HILLYARD, S. GIRGIS, I. MCINTYRE & M. TOHYAMA. 1985. Topographic localization of calcitonin gene–related peptide in the rat brain: an immunohistochemical analysis. Neuroscience **15:** 747–763.

30. GALL, C. 1988. Seizures induce dramatic and distinctly different changes in enkephalin, dynorphin, and CCK immunoreactivities in mouse hippocampal mossy fibers. J. Neurosci. **8:** 1852–1862.

31. MARKSTEINER, J., M. ORTLER, R. BELLMANN & G. SPERK. 1990. Neuropeptide Y biosynthesis is markedly induced in mossy fibers during temporal lobe epilepsy of the rat. Neurosci. Lett. **112:** 143–148.

32. REPRESSA, A., G. LEGALL LASALLE & Y. BEN-ARI. 1989. Hippocampal plasticity in the kindling model of epilepsy in rats. Neurosci. Lett. **99:** 345–350.

Functional Role of Substance P for Respiratory Control during Development

HUGO LAGERCRANTZ,[a,b] MEERA SRINIVASAN,[b]
YUJI YAMAMOTO,[b] AND NANDURI PRABHAKAR[c]

[a]Department of Pediatrics
Karolinska Hospital
104 01 Stockholm, Sweden

[b]Nobel Institute for Neurophysiology
Karolinska Institute
60 Stockholm, Sweden

[c]Department of Medicine
University Hospital
Case Western Reserve University
Cleveland, Ohio 44106

Substance P (SP) was demonstrated to stimulate breathing when injected intraventricularly in cats and rabbits by von Euler and Pernow.[1] SP immunoreactivity has been detected in the peripheral chemoreceptors, in the petrosal and nodose ganglia, and in the nucleus tractus solitarius (nTS) where the respiratory movements are integrated. Thus, SP has been suggested to be a putative neurotransmitter or possibly a neuromodulator in the primary chemoreceptor afferent neurons.[2] Some of the criteria to establish a physiological role for a neurotransmitter will be discussed in this article with particular emphasis on developmental aspects.

ANATOMICAL LOCALIZATION OF SP

There is a considerable body of evidence indicating the presence of SP-like immunoreactivity (SP-LI) in the glomus cells of the cat carotid body.[3-6] However, these studies also show that not all glomus cells display SP-LI. A recent electron microscopic study has demonstrated that SP-LI is localized primarily in glomus cells that form synaptic contacts with afferent nerve. In contrast, the glomus cells that do not possess sensory innervation lack endings.[7] In a recent investigation, Scheibner and colleagues studied the development of SP-LI in the carotid bodies from the fetal to the adult state in cats.[6] The appearance of SP-LI glomus cells coincided with the development of hypoxic response.

In addition, high SP-like concentration has been found in the brain stem,[8] particularly in the nucleus tractus solitarius (nTS),[9] where the afferents from the peripheral chemoreceptors terminate.[10]

SYNAPTIC MIMICRY

SP has been demonstrated to increase ventilation by administration intra-arterially at the peripheral chemoreceptors, intraventricularly,[1,11,12] and also locally with a dialysis probe in the region of nTS.[13] SP was found to increase mainly the tidal volume, whereas the respiratory rate was unaffected in adult rats.[11] However, a stimulatory effect of SP was seen on both tidal volume and frequency in rabbit pups; SP caused a stronger respiratory stimulatory effect in younger pups, which was even more pronounced in decerebrate animals, possibly due to removal of some suprapontine inhibitory mechanisms.[12] SP did not significantly change the slope of the CO_2-response curve, but shifted it to the left, that is, lowered the threshold.[2]

BLOCKING AND DEPLETING

Although these findings are essential, they do not prove that the respiratory effects of SP have a significant bearing on the chemoreceptor transduction process. By the synthesis of specific SP antagonists, it became possible to block endogenous SP activity.[14] The specific SP analogue antagonist (D-Arg^1-D-Trp^{7,9},Leu^{11})-SP was administered close to the carotid bodies of adult cats and sinus nerve activity was recorded from a single or few fibers.[15] The antagonist was found to block the effect of externally administrated SP and the hypoxic ventilatory response completely,[15] but not the response to CO_2.[16] In another series of experiments, the antagonist (D-Arg^1-D-Pro^2,D-Trp^{7,9},Leu^{11})-SP was applied on the exposed surface of the fourth ventricle of rabbit pups. The ventilatory response to hypoxia[12] was completely blocked.

These experiments support the idea of SP as a putative mediator of the hypoxic drive. However, the specificities of the SP antagonists have been questioned and the effects of the SP antagonists have been attributed to possible local anesthetic effects of the antagonists. However, as stated in the preceding paragraph, chemosensory excitation produced by CO_2 was unaffected by the SP antagonist (D-Pro^2-D-Trp^{7,9}, SP DPDT)[14] and the effects of DPDT were reversible. These data thus exclude the possible local anesthetic or neurotoxic effects of these antagonists in the *in vivo* carotid body preparation. In a recent study, it was further demonstrated that neurokinin-1 (NK-1), but not the NK-2 receptor antagonist blocks the hypoxic response.[17]

Furthermore, SP has been found to be depleted in the nTS after denervation of the ninth and tenth cranial nerves that innervate the peripheral chemoreceptors.[2,18] Capsaicin has been found to decrease the SP content in the nTS by about 60%, but the effect on hypoxic ventilatory response has not been tested.[19]

RELEASE OF SP DURING HYPOXIA

If SP is the mediator of the hypoxic respiratory drive, it should be possible to detect increased release of SP during hypoxia in respiratory-related structures. The microdialysis probe was found to be suitable for such studies. The localization of the probe was tested by recording respiratory-related activity by implanting a tungsten microelectrode stereotaxically in the nTS. After confirmation of inspiration-related neuronal activity, the microdialysis probe was inserted in the same position.[20]

Krebs-Ringer solution (pH 7.5) was pumped at a rate of 3.6 μL/min to the tip of the dialysis probe inside the tubule. Fractions were collected for 30 minutes. SP was analyzed by radioimmunoassay.[21] The first sample collected after insertion of the probe contained relatively high levels of SP, possibly due to some mechanical effects caused by implantation. After that, a low resting level of SP was seen. A significant increase of SP concentration was found during hypoxia, which decreased to the resting level after provocation.[20]

In another series of experiments, SP was analyzed during hypoxia in intact and sinus nerve–denervated adult rabbits.[13] Sinus denervation prevented hypoxia-induced enhanced SP release in the nTS, strongly indicating that this effect is mediated via the carotid chemoreceptors.

The basal levels of SP in the dialysates of the nTS of the rabbit are at least 50 times higher than in the cat. Thus, there appears to be a remarkable species variation.

DEVELOPMENTAL ASPECTS

SP has been detected at an early stage during ontogeny[22] long before the establishment of synaptic transmission.[23] SP immunoreactivity has been studied during development in the brain stem nuclei of rabbits.[24] The highest concentration of SP was found in the nTS. It reached a peak at a postnatal age of seven days. The innervation of carotid bodies with SP neurons has been studied in kittens.[6] In newborn kittens, only some unmyelinated nerves contained SP-like immunoreactivity and, after two weeks, the glomus cells were found to contain high immunofluorescent reactivity to SP.

To further examine the ontogenesis of SP neurons in the nTS, the expression of preprotachykinin-A (PPT-A) mRNA was investigated in respiratory-related structures of rabbit fetuses and pups of various ages.[25] The dorsal respiratory group containing the nTS, the ventral medullary surface structure, and the striatum were all dissected out. Tissues from 4–6 pups were pooled for each age and the RNA was isolated by the conventional CsCl density centrifugation technique; mRNA for PPT-A was determined by the Northern blot technique.

One day before estimated birth, a very thin PPT-A mRNA band was observed in the region of nTS. On the day of birth, a 380% increase in the level of PPT-A mRNA was observed. The level decreased 25% on day 2 and a further decrease was seen on day 3. The postnatal values were, in general, higher than in adults. In the ventral structures of the medulla, the prenatal expression was higher than on the day of birth, but a gradual increase occurred after a few days of birth until adulthood. To study whether this increased PPT-A mRNA expression was related to breathing, a litter of rabbit fetuses was delivered by cesarean section one day before expected birth. Half of the litter was sacrificed immediately, whereas the other half was allowed to breathe for two hours. The pups that were allowed to breathe showed a 370% increase in the level of PPT-A mRNA as compared with the nonbreathers. No difference in PPT-A mRNA expression was seen in the striatum, which was used as the hybridizing control.

CLINICAL STUDIES

We have also been interested in studying and determining the SP content in peripheral chemoreceptors and in the brain stem from human fetuses and infants, with special reference to see how the levels are affected by hypoxia and in infants succumbing to sudden infant death (SIDS). However, we were not able to see any difference in SP content in peripheral chemoreceptors of infants who had died of SIDS as compared to controls.[26] On the other hand, three infants who had sustained chronic hypoxia had remarkably high dopamine concentrations in the carotid bodies. In another series of studies, SP, enkephalin, and neuropeptide Y were analyzed in various parts of the brains of infants who had died of SIDS and other causes.[27] We were not able to see any significant difference in the content of enkephalin between the SIDS and control infants, which had earlier been postulated. However, the SP level was significantly higher in the medulla of SIDS infants as compared with controls. A tentative explanation is that some of these infants had suffered from chronic hypoxia, which stimulated SP synthesis.

CONCLUDING REMARKS

SP fulfills a number of classical criteria as the neurotransmitter of the hypoxic ventilatory drive both in the carotid bodies and from their afferents into the respiratory nuclei: for example, anatomical localization, synaptic mimicry, blocking the effect with SP antagonists, release of SP in the nTS during hypoxia, and its abolishment by denervation.

REFERENCES

1. VON EULER, U. S. & B. PERNOW. 1956. Neurotropic effects of substance P. Acta Physiol. Scand. **36:** 265–275.
2. GILLIS, R. A., C. J. HELKE, B. L. HAMILTON, W. P. NORMAN & D. M. JACOBOWITZ. 1980. Evidence that substance P is a neurotransmitter of baro- and chemo-receptor afferents in nucleus tractus solitarius. Brain Res. **181:** 476–481.
3. LUNDBERG, J. M., T. HÖKFELT, J. FAHRENKRUG, G. NILSSON & L. TERENIUS. 1979. Peptides in the cat carotid body (glomus caroticum): VIP-enkephalin and substance P–like immunoreactivity. Acta Physiol. Scand. **107:** 279–281.
4. CUELLO, A. C. & D. S. MCQUEEN. 1980. Substance P: a carotid body peptide. Neurosci. Lett. **17:** 215–219.
5. PRABHAKAR, N. R., S. C. LANDIS, G. K. KUMAR, D. MULLIKIN-KILPATRICK, N. S. CHERNIACK & S. LEEMAN. 1989. Substance P and neurokinin A in the cat carotid body: localization, exogenous effects, and changes in content in response to arterial pO_2. Brain Res. **481:** 205–214.
6. SCHEIBNER, T., D. J. C. READ & C. E. SULLIVAN. 1988. Distribution of substance P–immunoreactive structures in the developing cat carotid body. Brain Res. **453:** 72–78.
7. CHEM, L. I., R. D. YATES & J. I. HANSEN. 1986. Substance P–like immunoreactivity in rat and cat carotid bodies: light and electron microscopic studies. Histol. Histopathol. **1:** 203–212.
8. MROZ, E. A. & S. E. LEEMAN. Substance P. *In* Methods of Hormone Radioimmunoassay. Vol. 2: 121–137. Academic Press. New York.
9. LJUNGDAHL, Å., T. HÖKFELT & G. NILSSON. 1978. Distribution of substance P–like immunoreactivity in the central nervous system of the rat. I. Cell bodies and nerve terminals. Neuroscience **3:** 861–943.
10. MALEY, B. & R. ELDE. 1981. Immunohistochemical localization of putative neurotransmitters within the feline nucleus tractus solitarii. Neuroscience **7:** 2469–2490.
11. HEDNER, T., J. HEDNER, J. JONASON & D. LUNDBERG. 1981. Evidence suggesting a role for substance P in central respiratory regulation in the rat. Acta Physiol. Scand. **112:** 487–489.
12. YAMAMOTO, Y. & H. LAGERCRANTZ. 1985. Some effects of substance P on central respiratory control in rabbit pups. Acta Physiol. Scand. **124:** 449–455.
13. SRINIVASAN, M., M. GOINY, T. PANTALEO, E. BRODIN & Y. YAMAMOTO. 1991. Enhanced *in vivo* release of substance P in the nucleus tractus solitarius during hypoxia in the rabbit: role of peripheral input. Brain Res. In press.

14. ROSELL, S. & K. FOLKERS. 1982. Substance P–antagonists: a new type of pharmacological tool. TINS (May), p. 211–212.
15. PRABHAKAR, N. R., M. RUNOLD, Y. YAMAMOTO, H. LAGERCRANTZ & C. VON EULER. 1984. Effect of substance P antagonist on the hypoxia-induced carotid chemoreceptor activity. Acta Physiol. Scand. **121:** 301–303.
16. PRABHAKAR, N. R., J. MITRA & N. S. CHERNIACK. 1986. Role of substance P in hypercapnic excitation of carotid chemoreceptors. J. Appl. Physiol. **63:** 2418–2425.
17. PRABHAKAR, N. R., M. RUNOLD, N. S. CHERNIACK & G. K. KUMAR. 1990. Analysis of chemoreceptor responses to tachykinins in rats, cats, and rabbits. *In* Chemoreceptors and Chemoreceptor Reflexes. H. Acker *et al.*, Eds.: 103–106. Plenum. New York.
18. HELKE, C. J., T. L. O'DONOHUE & D. M. JACOBOWITZ. 1980. Substance P as a baro- and chemo-receptor afferent neurotransmitter: immunocytochemical and neurochemical evidence in the rat. Peptides **1:** 1–9.
19. LOREZ, H. P., G. HAEUSLER & L. AEPPLI. 1983. Substance P neurons in medullary baroreflex area and bororeflex function of capsaicin-treated rats—comparison with other primary afferent systems. Neuroscience **8:** 507–523.
20. LINDEFORS, N., Y. YAMAMOTO, T. PANTALEO, H. LAGERCRANTZ, E. BRODIN & U. UNGERSTEDT. 1986. *In vivo* release of substance P in the nucleus tractus solitarii increases during hypoxia. Neurosci. Lett. **69:** 94–97.
21. LINDEFORS, N., E. BRODIN, E. THEODORSSON-NORHEIM & U. UNGERSTEDT. 1985. Regional distribution and *in vivo* release of tachykinin-like immunoreactivities in rat brain: evidence for regional differences in relative proportions of tachykinins. Regulat. Peptides **10:** 217–230.
22. SAKANAKA, M., S. INAGAKI, S. SHIOSAKA, E. SENBA, H. TAKAGI, K. TAKATSUKI, Y. KAWAI, H. IIDA, Y. HARA & M. TOHYAMA. 1982. Ontogeny of substance P containing neuron system of the rat: immunohistochemical analysis. II. Lower brain stem. Neuroscience **7:** 1097–1126.
23. ALTMAN, J. & S. A. BAYER. 1980. Development of the brain stem in the rat. I. Thymidine-radiographic study of the time of origin of neurons of the lower medulla. J. Comp. Neurol. **194:** 1–35.
24. GINGRAS, J. L., S. L. BRUNNER & M. C. MCNAMARA. 1988. Developmental characteristics of substance P immunoreactivity within specific rabbit brain stem nuclei. Regulat. Peptides **23:** 183–192.
25. SRINIVASAN, M., Y. YAMAMOTO, H. PERSSON & H. LAGERCRANTZ. 1991. Birth-related activation of preprotachykinin-A mRNA in the respiratory neural structures of the rabbit. Pediatr. Res. In press.
26. HERTZBERG, T., M. SRINIVASAN, T. SCHEIBNER, C. SULLIVAN & H. LAGERCRANTZ. Catecholamines and substance P in carotid bodies from succumbed human fetuses and infants (manuscript).
27. BERGSTRÖM, L., H. LAGERCRANTZ & L. TERENIUS. 1984. Post-mortem analyses of neuropeptides in brains from sudden infant death victims. Brain Res. **323:** 279–285.

PART II

Molecular Characterization of the Three Tachykinin Receptors

HIROAKI OHKUBO[a] AND SHIGETADA NAKANISHI

Institute for Immunology
Faculty of Medicine
Kyoto University
Kyoto 606, Japan

INTRODUCTION

The mammalian tachykinin system represents a typical example of biologically active peptides that exhibit a high degree of functional diversity within the same group of peptides. It consists of three distinct peptides: substance P, substance K, and neuromedin K.[1,2] The three peptides possess a common spectrum of biological activities including a sensory transmission in the nervous system and contraction/relaxation of peripheral smooth muscles. However, their biological potencies differ markedly, depending on the pharmacological preparations tested.[3-6] These pharmacological studies as well as ligand-binding experiments suggest that there are at least three distinct tachykinin receptors, each specific for the respective peptide. Thus, the regulation at the level of not only peptide production, but also of peptide-receptor interaction plays an important role in expressing the functional diversity of the mammalian tachykinin system.

Recently, we isolated and characterized functional cDNA clones for the three rat tachykinin receptors by molecular cloning in combination with electrophysiology. These studies have revealed the primary structure of the three receptors and have enabled the characterization of the properties and the distributions of the individual tachykinin receptors. This article deals with our recent studies concerning the molecular characterization of multiple forms of the tachykinin receptors.

MOLECULAR CLONING OF TACHYKININ RECEPTOR cDNA

In our previous study,[7] we isolated a functional cDNA clone for the bovine substance K receptor by developing a new strategy, which combined molecular cloning with an electrophysiological assay in *Xenopus* oocytes. This strategy was based on our observation[8] that oocytes injected with brain and stomach mRNAs produced clear electrophysiological responses to the application of substance P and substance K, respectively. The oocyte expression system in combination with electrophysiological measurements thus provides a sensitive and powerful tool for identifying the tachykinin receptor mRNAs. The principle of the new cloning strategy is briefly summarized as follows: an mRNA fraction expressing a potent substance K receptor in *Xenopus* oocytes was isolated from bovine stomach poly(A)$^+$ RNA by sucrose density gradient centrifugation and was used for the cDNA synthesis. The

---

[a] Present address: Institute for Medical Genetics, Kumamoto University Medical School, Kuhonji 4-24-1, Kumamoto 862, Japan.

double-stranded cDNAs were then synthesized and inserted immediately down-stream of the SP6 promoter in the vector DNA. A cDNA library was constructed and a clonal cDNA mixture was extracted and subjected to *in vitro* transcription by specific SP6 RNA polymerase in the presence of the capping nucleotide. The mRNA mixture thus synthesized was injected into oocytes, which were examined for the expression of the receptor by measuring the electrophysiological response to applica-tion of substance K. A single cDNA clone that encodes the substance K receptor was thus isolated after repeated subdivision of the response-evoking cDNA mixture in the library.

A functional cDNA clone for the rat substance P receptor was subsequently isolated from a rat brain cDNA library constructed with an RNA expression vector.[9] We first identified a cDNA mixture containing a functional substance P receptor cDNA by electrophysiologically examining a receptor expression following injection of the mRNAs synthesized *in vitro* into *Xenopus* oocytes. A receptor cDNA clone was then isolated by cross-hybridization with the bovine substance K receptor cDNA. Functional cDNA clones for the rat substance K[10] and neuromedin K[11] receptors were also isolated by cross-hybridization with the same cDNA from rat stomach and brain cDNA libraries, respectively. The sequence analyses of these cloned cDNAs indicate that the rat substance P, substance K, and neuromedin K receptors consist of 407, 390, and 452 amino acid residues, respectively.

STRUCTURAL FEATURES OF TACHYKININ RECEPTORS

The comparison of the amino acid sequences of the three rat tachykinin recep-tors is shown in FIGURE 1.[9-13] The three receptors have seven hydrophobic, presum-ably membrane-spanning, domains and share a significant sequence similarity with G protein–coupled receptors.[14-16] Although the amino- and carboxy-terminal regions of the three receptors diverge in their sizes and amino acid sequences, they retain some structural features common to those of the G protein–coupled receptors. All three receptors possess potential N-glycosylation sites at their amino termini and many serine and threonine residues as possible phosphorylation sites at their carboxyl termini. Hence, all three tachykinin receptors belong to the family of G protein–coupled receptors and possess seven transmembrane domains with extracellular amino termini and cytoplasmic carboxyl termini. This indicates that both the structure and the function of these peptide receptors are fundamentally similar to those of the receptors for classical small molecule neurotransmitters such as catechol-amines and acetylcholine.

FIGURE 2 shows a seven-transmembrane model of the substance P receptor indicating the amino acid identity with the neuromedin K and substance K receptors. The core sequences covering the seven putative transmembrane domains and cytoplasmic portions adjacent to these transmembrane helices are highly conserved among the three tachykinin receptors[11,12] and the similarity in these core segments (54–66%) is comparable to that of the adrenergic or muscarinic receptor sub-types.[11,14] Furthermore, some amino acids of the three tachykinin receptors are also conserved in the sequences of all the members of the adrenergic and muscarinic receptors. The structural analysis of the β_2-adrenergic receptor suggests that two cysteine residues in the first and second extracellular loops are involved in joining these two loops through the formation of a disulfide bridge.[17] Another cysteine residue that immediately follows transmembrane segment VII is evidenced to be palmitoylated and this palmitoylation results in the anchoring of the receptor to the plasma membrane.[18] These three cysteine residues are all conserved in the three tachykinin receptors. In addition, certain glycine, proline, and aromatic amino acids are conserved in the members of G protein–coupled receptors including the three tachykinin receptors. Therefore, these conserved amino acids should play a crucial role in the formation of a basic architecture of the G protein–coupled receptor proteins.

In addition to the aforementioned structural features, several interesting sequence characteristics are also notable in the three receptors.[9-13] Among the seven putative transmembrane domains, each consisting of 20–25 almost uncharged amino acids, transmembrane segment II of both substance K and neuromedin K receptors contains an aspartic acid, as observed for other G protein–coupled receptors. In contrast, this aspartic acid is replaced with a glutamic acid in the substance P

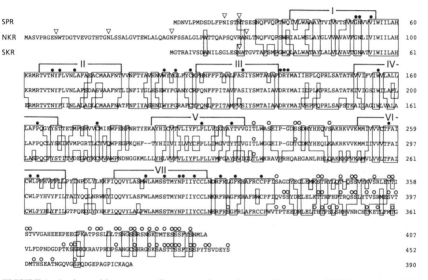

FIGURE 1. Amino acid sequence alignment of rat substance P receptor (SPR), neuromedin K receptor (NKR), and substance K receptor (SKR): boxed amino acids, identical residues in two or all of the three sequences; dashes, deletions of amino acid residues; solid circles, amino acid residues conserved in the sequences of the tachykinin, adrenergic, and muscarinic receptors; open circles, serine and threonine residues as possible phosphorylation sites in the cytoplasmic regions; triangles, potential N-glycosylation sites.

receptor. All three receptors contain one histidine residue each in transmembrane segments V and VI, and the presence of these two histidine residues is characteristic of the tachykinin receptors. The third cytoplasmic loops as well as portions of the carboxy-terminal regions are highly conserved between the substance P and neuromedin K receptors, but most of these regions diverge between the substance K receptor and each of the other two receptors. All three receptors are thought to be coupled to a G protein involved in a phosphatidylinositol-calcium second messenger system (see the discussion described later). Therefore, as reported for β-adrenergic[19] and muscarinic receptors,[20] the conserved sequences on the cytoplasmic side, particularly on the short homologous sequences near transmembrane segments V and VI, could be important in the coupling of the receptors to a G protein.

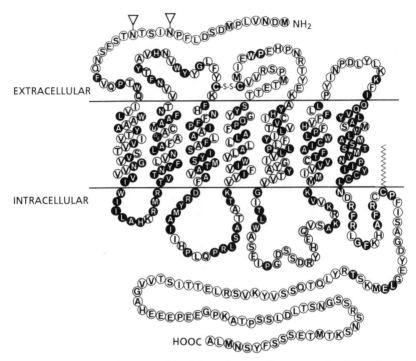

FIGURE 2. A transmembrane model of the substance P receptor showing amino acids identical among the three tachykinin receptors: solid circles, amino acids conserved among the three tachykinin receptors; triangles, potential N-glycosylation sites; zigzag line, possible palmitoylation site; D/E in transmembrane II, E for the substance P receptor and D for the substance K and neuromedin K receptors.

The number and distribution of serine and threonine residues in the third cytoplasmic loops and in the carboxy-terminal cytoplasmic regions also differ among the three tachykinin receptors. The adrenergic and muscarinic receptors and rhodopsin are desensitized as a result of phosphorylations of serine and threonine residues in analogous regions.[14,15,21] The three tachykinin receptors show differing desensitization behaviors in response to repeated application of agonists.[8,11] Thus, it is possible that the sequence divergence and/or the different distribution of serine and threonine residues in the aforementioned cytoplasmic regions may participate in evoking differing desensitization behaviors of the three tachykinin receptors through different phosphorylations.

FUNCTIONAL PROPERTIES, DISTRIBUTION, AND EXPRESSION OF TACHYKININ RECEPTORS

The precise analysis of the functional properties and tissue distribution of the individual tachykinin receptors has been hindered by several reasons. For example, selective pure antagonists, specific radioligands, and antibodies are not readily available. In addition, the three tachykinin peptides all interact to varying degrees with each of the receptors and many tissue preparations used for pharmacological and ligand-binding studies often contain more than one type of receptor. Therefore, we characterized the functional properties and expression sites of the individual tachykinin receptors by using the functional cDNA clone for each of the three tachykinin receptors. Some of these properties as well as the structural features of the three rat tachykinin receptors are summarized in TABLE 1.

To determine the ligand specificity of each tachykinin receptor, we examined the ligand-binding properties[9,11,22] and the stimulation of phosphatidylinositol turnover[23] of the receptor expressed in mammalian cells. We also investigated electrophysiological responses in the oocyte expression system.[7,9–11] For the ligand-binding study, the tachykinin receptor cDNA inserted into a eukaryotic expression vector was introduced into COS cells. These cells or membranes prepared from these cells were analyzed by displacement of radiolabeled tachykinin binding with the three tachykinins. The K_i values determined for each receptor[11,12,22] are shown in TABLE 1. The results explicitly demonstrate that the three receptors differ in the rank orders of affinities to the three tachykinins. For substance P receptor, the rank order of affinities is substance P, substance K, and neuromedin K; for substance K receptor, it is substance K, neuromedin K, and substance P; for neuromedin K receptor, it is neuromedin K, substance K, and substance P. Similar results were obtained by the two other functional assays described earlier. Thus, the substance K and neuromedin K receptors are more closely related to each other than to the substance P receptor in terms of agonist specificity, although the structural similarity between the former two receptors is lower than that between the substance P and neuromedin K receptors.[13]

Electrophysiological examination indicated that the chloride ions are the major ions involved in the activation of the tachykinin receptor expressed in the oocyte

TABLE 1. Structure and Properties of Rat Tachykinin Receptors

	Substance P Receptor	Neuromedin K Receptor	Substance K Receptor
Amino acid residues	407	452	390
Molecular weight	46,364	51,104	43,851
Homology in the core sequence	66.3% (to NKR) 53.7% (to SKR)	54.9% (to SKR)	
Possible N-glycosylation sites	2	4	1
Ser/Thr residues as possible phosphorylation sites: third loop	5	2	1
C-terminus	26	28	14
Second messenger	IP_3-Ca^{2+}	IP_3-Ca^{2+}	IP_3-Ca^{2+}
Ligand specificity (K_i; M)	SP, 1.6×10^{-10} SK, 1.7×10^{-8} NK, 5.3×10^{-8}	NK, 2.9×10^{-10} SK, 2.2×10^{-8} SP, 5.4×10^{-8}	SK, 2.9×10^{-10} NK, 5.0×10^{-9} SP, 9.2×10^{-8}
Desensitization	+++	++	+
Expression sites: nervous system	++	+++	−
peripheral tissues	+++	+	+++

system.[8] Based on this result as well as others, the following model can be proposed for the signal transduction and ionic mechanisms coupled with the tachykinin receptors in the oocyte expression system.[12] The tachykinin receptor expressed in an oocyte acts through a G protein to stimulate production of IP_3, which in turn elevates cytoplasmic Ca^{2+}. This Ca^{2+} then activates a Ca^{2+}-dependent chloride channel in the oocyte plasma membrane.

The desensitization effect observed in electrophysiological responses after repeated application of agonists also differs among the three receptors expressed in oocytes[8,11] and this effect is manifested in the order of substance P, neuromedin K, and substance K receptors.[12,13] The mechanisms underlying the different desensitization behaviors of the three tachykinin receptors remain to be elucidated (see the discussion described earlier).

The distribution of the three tachykinin receptor mRNAs in various tissues of the rat was investigated by RNA blot hybridization using each of the three receptor cDNAs.[24] The substance P receptor mRNA is widely distributed both in the nervous system and in peripheral tissues. This mRNA is mainly expressed in the hypothalamus, olfactory bulb, spinal cord, and striatum in the nervous system and in the urinary bladder, salivary glands, and small and large intestines in peripheral tissues. The neuromedin K receptor mRNA is also distributed in various tissues, but it is more predominantly expressed in the nervous system than in peripheral tissues. Within the central nervous system, this mRNA is most abundant in the hypothalamus, cerebellum, and cortex. In contrast, the expression of the substance K receptor mRNA is localized in peripheral tissues, particularly in the urinary bladder, stomach, large intestine, and adrenal gland. These results clearly demonstrate that the mRNAs for the three receptors are differently expressed in the nervous system and peripheral tissues. Interestingly, the mRNA for the substance K receptor was undetectable in the nervous system,[10] although substance K[25] and its precursor mRNA[26,27] were identified in the same tissues. It has already been pointed out that there is a discrepancy between the distribution of the tachykinin peptides and their binding sites.[28,29] Thus, the biological role of the tachykinin peptides in neural function deserves careful consideration.

Substance P is not only thought to function as a peptidergic neuromediator, but also is thought to act as a neurogenic inflammatory factor. Besides, glucocorticoids are known to be potent anti-inflammatory agents. Therefore, we investigated the possible regulation of gene expression of the substance P receptor by glucocorticoids. The mRNA of the substance P receptor expressed in AR42J cells (rat pancreatic acinar cells) was strongly and selectively decreased by glucocorticoids.[30] The result thus provides the first evidence indicating that the peptide receptor is regulated at the mRNA level.

DIVERSITY OF THE TACHYKININ SYSTEM

The diversity of the mammalian tachykinin system is schematically illustrated in FIGURE 3, which is based on the studies described earlier as well as on our previous studies on the expression of the tachykinin peptides. The three mammalian tachykinins are derived from two peptide precursor genes: the preprotachykinin A and B (PPT-A and PPT-B) genes.[1,2,26,27,31–33] The PPT-A gene encodes the precursors common to substance P and substance K, whereas the precursor for neuromedin K is produced from the PPT-B gene. The structural organization of these two genes is remarkably similar in terms of exon-intron arrangements, indicating that both genes have evolved from a common ancestral gene by duplication events.[32] The distribution

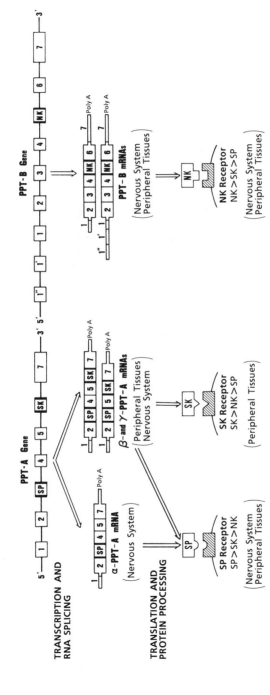

FIGURE 3. Expression and reception of the mammalian tachykinin system. Numbered boxes and the boxes labeled as SP, SK, and NK stand for exons; SP, substance P; SK, substance K; NK, neuromedin K; PPT, preprotachykinin.

of the mRNAs derived from the PPT-A and PPT-B genes differs in tissues and in regions of the nervous system. The PPT-A mRNAs are most abundant in the trigeminal ganglion and in the striatum,[26] whereas the PPT-B mRNAs are expressed in the hypothalamus and intestines.[32] Alternative RNA processing is closely associated with the expression of both genes and is involved in the formation of their multiple species of mRNAs.[26,32] Substance K is specified by a discrete genomic segment of the PPT-A gene and its generation is regulated through the specific inclusion and exclusion of the substance K–coding region by alternative splicing. The mRNA encoding substance P alone is mainly produced in the central nervous system, whereas the mRNAs encoding both substance P and substance K are synthesized in peripheral tissues as well as in the nervous system. This alternative splicing is thus controlled in a tissue-specific manner.[26] The generation of two forms of the mRNA from the PPT-B gene also involves alternative RNA splicing combined with differential usage of two different promoters.[32] Hence, the production of tachykinin peptides is diversified by using various cellular mechanisms, including gene duplication, differential expression of duplicated genes, and alternative RNA processing.

The three mammalian tachykinins exhibit different biological activities on a wide range of mammalian tissues, depending on the presence of different types of tachykinin receptors. As summarized in TABLE 1, the three tachykinin receptors have different affinities for the tachykinins and are distributed differently in various mammalian tissues. Thus, the differing physiological responses of the three tachykinins occur as a result of the selectivity and different distribution of the different types of receptors. The tachykinin receptors all belong to the family of G protein–coupled receptors and effect their functions through the activation of the second messenger pathway, which is thought to be a phosphatidylinositol-Ca^{2+} system. These receptors show differing desensitization behaviors in response to agonists and these differences may cause a different onset and duration of the tachykinin responses. Therefore, it is clear that the tachykinin system exhibits its functional diversity through various cellular mechanisms involved in both peptide production and peptide reception.

CONCLUSIONS

Recent advancements in molecular characterization of the multiple tachykinin receptors have contributed greatly to our understanding of the diversity of transmembrane signaling mechanisms in the mammalian tachykinin system. This is the first example of a comprehensive molecular analysis of the multiple peptide receptors exhibiting similar, but clearly distinguishable biological activities. These similar, but distinct properties of the three receptors should result from the sequence similarities and divergences observed among the three receptors. The tachykinin receptors thus provide an interesting system to characterize the structure-function relationships of the diversified multiple peptide receptors. Further investigations on the cellular localization and on the regulation of gene expression for the three tachykinin receptors will also be interesting and important for understanding the biological role of these peptides.

REFERENCES

1. NAKANISHI, S. 1986. Structure and regulation of the preprotachykinin gene. Trends Neurosci. **9:** 41–44.

2. NAKANISHI, S. 1987. Substance P precursor and kininogen: their structures, gene organizations, and regulation. Physiol. Rev. **67:** 1117–1142.
3. NAWA, H., M. DOTEUCHI, K. IGANO, K. INOUYE & S. NAKANISHI. 1984. Substance K: a novel mammalian tachykinin that differs from substance P in its pharmacological profile. Life Sci. **34:** 1153–1160.
4. QUIRION, R. 1985. Multiple tachykinin receptors. Trends Neurosci. **8:** 183–185.
5. BUCK, S. H. & E. BURCHER. 1986. The tachykinins: a family of peptides with a brood of "receptors". Trends Pharmacol. Sci. **7:** 65–68.
6. REGOLI, D., G. DRAPEAU, S. DION & R. COUTURE. 1988. New selective agonists for neurokinin receptors: pharmacological tools for receptor characterization. Trends Pharmacol. Sci. **9:** 290–295.
7. MASU, Y., K. NAKAYAMA, H. TAMAKI, Y. HARADA, M. KUNO & S. NAKANISHI. 1987. cDNA cloning of bovine substance-K receptor through oocyte expression system. Nature **329:** 836–838.
8. HARADA, Y., T. TAKAHASHI, M. KUNO, K. NAKAYAMA, Y. MASU & S. NAKANISHI. 1987. Expression of two different tachykinin receptors in *Xenopus* oocytes by exogenous mRNAs. J. Neurosci. **7:** 3265–3273.
9. YOKOTA, Y., Y. SASAI, K. TANAKA, T. FUJIWARA, K. TSUCHIDA, R. SHIGEMOTO, A. KAKIZUKA, H. OHKUBO & S. NAKANISHI. 1989. Molecular characterization of a functional cDNA for rat substance P receptor. J. Biol. Chem. **264:** 17649–17652.
10. SASAI, Y. & S. NAKANISHI. 1989. Molecular characterization of rat substance K receptor and its mRNAs. Biochem. Biophys. Res. Commun. **165:** 695–702.
11. SHIGEMOTO, R., Y. YOKOTA, K. TSUCHIDA & S. NAKANISHI. 1990. Cloning and expression of a rat neuromedin K receptor cDNA. J. Biol. Chem. **265:** 623–628.
12. NAKANISHI, S., H. OHKUBO, A. KAKIZUKA, Y. YOKOTA, R. SHIGEMOTO, Y. SASAI & T. TAKUMI. 1990. Molecular characterization of mammalian tachykinin receptors and a possible epithelial potassium channel. Recent Prog. Horm. Res. **46:** 59–84.
13. NAKANISHI, S. 1991. Mammalian tachykinin receptors. Annu. Rev. Neurosci. **14:** 123–136.
14. DIXON, R. A. F., C. D. STRADER & I. S. SIGAL. 1988. Structure and function of G-protein coupled receptors. *In* Annual Reports in Medicinal Chemistry. Volume 23. R. C. Allen, Ed.: 221–233. Academic Press. New York.
15. O'DOWD, B. F., R. J. LEFKOWITZ & M. G. CARON. 1989. Structure of the adrenergic and related receptors. Annu. Rev. Neurosci. **12:** 67–83.
16. BONNER, T. I. 1989. The molecular basis of muscarinic receptor diversity. Trends Neurosci. **12:** 148–151.
17. DIXON, R. A. F., I. S. SIGAL, M. R. CANDELORE, R. B. REGISTER, W. SCATTERGOOD, E. RANDS & C. D. STRADER. 1987. Structural features required for ligand binding to the β-adrenergic receptor. EMBO J. **6:** 3269–3275.
18. O'DOWD, B. F., M. HNATOWICH, M. G. CARON, R. J. LEFKOWITZ & M. BOUVIER. 1989. Palmitoylation of the human β_2-adrenergic receptor. J. Biol. Chem. **264:** 7564–7569.
19. STRADER, C. D., R. A. F. DIXON, A. H. CHEUNG, M. R. CANDELORE, A. D. BLAKE & I. S. SIGAL. 1987. Mutations that uncouple the β-adrenergic receptor from G_s and increase agonist affinity. J. Biol. Chem. **262:** 16439–16443.
20. KUBO, T., H. BUJO, I. AKIBA, J. NAKAI, M. MISHINA & S. NUMA. 1988. Location of a region of the muscarinic acetylcholine receptor involved in selective effector coupling. FEBS Lett. **241:** 119–125.
21. BOUVIER, M., W. P. HAUSDORFF, A. DE BLASI, B. F. O'DOWD, B. K. KOBILKA, M. G. CARON & R. J. LEFKOWITZ. 1988. Removal of phosphorylation sites from the β_2-adrenergic receptor delays onset of agonist-promoted desensitization. Nature **333:** 370–373.
22. INGI, T. & S. NAKANISHI. 1990. Manuscript in preparation.
23. NAKAJIMA, Y., S. ITO, M. NEGISHI & S. NAKANISHI. 1990. Manuscript in preparation.
24. TSUCHIDA, K., R. SHIGEMOTO, Y. YOKOTA & S. NAKANISHI. 1990. Eur. J. Biochem. **193:** 751–757.
25. MAGGIO, J. E. & J. C. HUNTER. 1984. Regional distribution of kassinin-like immunoreactivity in rat central and peripheral tissues and the effect of capsaicin. Brain Res. **307:** 370–373.

26. NAWA, H., H. KOTANI & S. NAKANISHI. 1984. Tissue-specific generation of two preprotachykinin mRNAs from one gene by alternative RNA splicing. Nature **312:** 729–734.
27. KAWAGUCHI, Y., M. HOSHIMARU, H. NAWA & S. NAKANISHI. 1986. Sequence analysis of cloned cDNA for rat substance P precursor: existence of a third substance P precursor. Biochem. Biophys. Res. Commun. **139:** 1040–1046.
28. MAGGIO, J. E. 1988. Tachykinins. Annu. Rev. Neurosci. **11:** 13–28.
29. SAFFROY, M., J-C. BEAUJOUAN, Y. TORRENS, J. BESSEYRE, L. BERGSTRÖM & J. GLOWINSKI. 1988. Localization of tachykinin binding sites (NK$_1$, NK$_2$, NK$_3$ ligands) in the rat brain. Peptides **9:** 227–241.
30. IHARA, H. & S. NAKANISHI. 1990. J. Biol. Chem. **265:** 22441–22445.
31. NAWA, H., T. HIROSE, H. TAKASHIMA, S. INAYAMA & S. NAKANISHI. 1983. Nucleotide sequences of cloned cDNAs for two types of bovine brain substance P precursor. Nature **306:** 32–36.
32. KOTANI, H., M. HOSHIMARU, H. NAWA & S. NAKANISHI. 1986. Structure and gene organization of bovine neuromedin K precursor. Proc. Natl. Acad. Sci. U.S.A. **83:** 7074–7078.
33. KRAUSE, J. E., J. M. CHIRGWIN, M. S. CARTER, Z. S. XU & A. D. HERSHEY. 1987. Three rat preprotachykinin mRNAs encode the neuropeptides substance P and neurokinin A. Proc. Natl. Acad. Sci. U.S.A. **84:** 881–885.

Molecular and Genetic Characterization, Functional Expression, and mRNA Expression Patterns of a Rat Substance P Receptor[a]

A. D. HERSHEY,[b] L. POLENZANI,[c] R. M. WOODWARD,[c] R. MILEDI,[c] AND J. E. KRAUSE[b]

[b]Department of Anatomy and Neurobiology
Washington University School of Medicine
St. Louis, Missouri 63110

[c]Laboratory of Cellular and Molecular Neurobiology
Department of Psychobiology
University of California
Irvine, California 92717

Substance P (SP) is a neuropeptide that elicits excitatory effects as a neurotransmitter or neuromodulator in both the central and peripheral nervous systems. It is a member of a family of neuropeptides known as the tachykinins and it has been well characterized in terms of distribution, sites of release, and biological actions.[1] These actions of SP are mediated by the substance P receptor (SPR) and by its subsequent activation of a second messenger system. Evidence suggests that the receptor is coupled to a GTP binding protein (G protein) that is positively coupled to phospholipase C,[2,3] catalyzing the hydrolysis of inositol phospholipids into diacylglycerol and inositol polyphosphates[2,4,5] with a concomitant mobilization of intracellular calcium.[2,6] All these observations strongly suggest that the SPR is a member of the G protein–coupled receptor superfamily. Activation of the SPR regulates a number of diverse biological processes that include sensory perception (e.g., olfaction, vision, audition, and pain), movement control, gastric motility, vasodilation, salivation, and micturition.[1,7] These diverse biological properties can be attributed to activation of SPRs that are widely distributed throughout the nervous system and in peripheral tissues. This distribution has been analyzed by identifying the location of binding sites for radiolabeled SP and its analogues. The pharmacological properties of this binding site have also been determined and the rank order of binding of the various tachykinins has been used to define this binding site [SP > neurokinin A (NKA) > neurokinin B (NKB)].[8] Additionally, these pharmacological and functional studies have demonstrated that the SPR rapidly desensitizes both in tissues[9–12] and in expression studies using *Xenopus* oocytes.[13]

In order to define better the molecular characteristics of the SPR and to define also the functional responses due to its activation, we have cloned an SPR cDNA, determined its nucleotide and amino acid sequence, and analyzed the ligand binding properties of the expressed protein.[14] This analysis revealed that the expressed protein had (1) the binding properties expected of an SP binding site (i.e., NK-1

[a]This work was supported by USPHS Grant Nos. NS21937 (to J. E. Krause) and NS23294 (to R. Miledi). L. Polenzani was supported by a fellowship from FIDIA.

receptor), (2) a distribution of mRNA similar to previously identified high affinity SP binding sites, and (3) an amino acid sequence that identified the SPR as a member of the G protein–coupled receptor superfamily. This G protein–coupled receptor superfamily is an extremely diverse group of receptors in terms of activating ligands and biological functions; however, they all appear to share common structural features (i.e., seven α-helical hydrophobic membrane-spanning domains) and methods of intracellular signal transduction (i.e., activation of specific G proteins). Specific structural features now provide a testable model for determining areas of functional relevance. For example, the presence of specific serine, threonine, and tyrosine residues in the third cytoplasmic loop and in the intracellular carboxyl tail can now be tested for their potential role in desensitization mechanisms as performed previously with the β-adrenergic receptor[15] and the role of the transmembrane regions can be analyzed for establishing possible sites of ligand interaction.

One feature that certain G protein–coupled receptors have in common is their genomic arrangement. The organization of exons has often been hypothesized to represent distinct functional and structural units.[16,17] Many receptor genes in this superfamily lack introns within their coding region, which has greatly aided the isolation of many receptor genes (e.g., muscarinic receptor gene sequences[18]). A distinction within this superfamily is that only three members to date have been shown to contain introns within the coding region of their genes: the SPR,[19] the opsins,[20–22] and the D_2 dopamine receptor.[23,24] Because this superfamily of receptors has distinct structural domains (i.e., the membrane-spanning domains interrupted by cytoplasmic and extracellular loops) and potentially distinct functional domains, a comparison of the genes that contain introns may establish the genetic/molecular limits of functional units. Additionally, the presence of introns in only a few of these receptors allows for a subdivision of the superfamily that may be related to the establishment of the diversity of G protein–coupled receptors in evolutionary time.

Another important question is to find out where SPRs are synthesized and at what level. The distribution of putative SP binding sites has been examined using *in vitro* autoradiographic analysis with SP selective ligands[25–29] and has shown where the potential final location of the SPR may be; however, it does not determine where the SPR gene is transcribed. With the availability of a cDNA encoding the SPR, the distribution and levels of expression of the mRNA for SPR can be resolved, thus determining the timing, locations, and levels of synthesis. This determination allows for a direct comparison of where the binding sites are for the SPR, which is particularly important in cases of axonal transport and potential regulation of synthesis at the transcriptional level in which the cell bodies may be located in a different area. With the isolation of a cDNA for the SPR, these questions can now be addressed.

MOLECULAR CHARACTERIZATION OF A RAT SUBSTANCE P RECEPTOR

Previous work has established that high affinity substance P binding sites could be modulated by nonhydrolyzable GTP analogues.[30–32] Furthermore, the characteristic oscillatory membrane current responses of SPRs expressed in *Xenopus* oocytes[13] implied activation of phospholipase C and suggested involvement of a G protein–coupled receptor. The expression cloning in oocytes of the bovine NKA (i.e., substance K or NK-2) receptor provided the structural conformation of this idea.[33] We hypothesized that conserved sequences of amino acids would exist among G protein–coupled receptors, particularly among the tachykinin receptor subfamily.

Consequently, we designed two oligonucleotides of 20 and 17 bases with 128- and 64-fold degeneracy that corresponded to areas within the second and seventh membrane-spanning domains of the bovine NKAR.[33] These two oligonucleotides were then used in a polymerase chain reaction (PCR)[34] with rat stomach mRNA to generate a putative tachykinin receptor fragment. The strategy is outlined in FIGURE 1. One cDNA fragment generated was 671 base pairs (bp) and contained only one open reading frame that encoded a protein fragment with six potential α-helical membrane-spanning domains. Sequence analysis demonstrated that the putative transmembrane domains were similar to the bovine NKAR (e.g., 83%); however, the similarity of the putative extracellular and intracellular domains was much lower

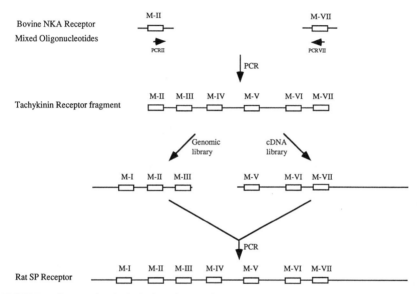

FIGURE 1. Strategy for the isolation of a rat substance P receptor cDNA. The rat SPR cDNA was isolated by using two mixed oligonucleotides based on the bovine neurokinin A receptor and the polymerase chain reaction (PCR) (top). A tachykinin receptor–specific fragment was generated and was used to screen both a rat genomic DNA library and a rat hippocampal cDNA library (middle). Using results obtained from sequence analysis of these cDNAs, the PCR was used to generate a fragment containing the entire coding region of the rat SPR (bottom), which was used for expression studies.

(e.g., 57% and 51%, respectively). When this fragment was compared to other established members of the G protein–coupled receptor superfamily, the similarity was very low, although specific amino acids were observed to be conserved throughout this superfamily. Not only did this help to confirm that the cDNA fragment encoded a G protein–coupled receptor, but it also emphasized the potential importance of these residues for structural or functional reasons. It is apparent that this strategy could therefore be very useful in isolating other G protein–coupled receptors, but it is dependent on the proper selection of oligonucleotides. This strategy has also been used recently by Libert and co-workers[35] to clone other receptors of the G protein–coupled receptor superfamily.

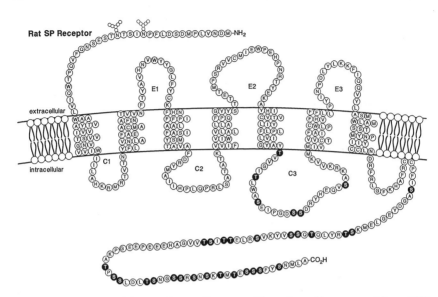

FIGURE 2. Schematic of the rat substance P receptor. The amino acid sequence of the rat SPR is depicted with its seven membrane-spanning α-helices. The upper portion of the figure represents the extracellular portion of the cell, whereas the lower portion represents the intracellular environment. The extracellular loop domains are labeled E1, E2, and E3, whereas the cytoplasmic loop domains are labeled C1, C2, and C3. Potential glycosylation sites are depicted for the amino terminus by a branched set of open circles, whereas potential phosphorylation sites in C3 and the cytoplasmic tail are identified by darkened circles.

The tachykinin receptor–specific cDNA fragment was next used to isolate the remainder of the cDNA encoding the entire protein. In order to do this, both a rat genomic library and a rat hippocampal cDNA library were screened for the presence of tachykinin receptor clones with the 671–base pair cDNA fragment.[14] Partial cDNA clones and five exons were isolated, revealing the 5′ and 3′ extents of the coding region for this receptor. The 5′ extent was determined by the presence of a start methionine preceded by a consensus ribosome 40s binding sequence,[36] whereas the 3′ extent was determined by the presence of a stop codon after a long open reading frame. Oligonucleotides specific to these regions were synthesized and the PCR was used to generate a cDNA encoding the complete SPR coding region. The predicted protein sequence encoded by this cDNA is shown in FIGURE 2. The protein encoded by this cDNA is 407 amino acids long and contains seven potential membrane-spanning domains characteristic of a G protein–coupled receptor. Within this protein, there are three areas of potential posttranslational modifications—2 potential glycosylation sites in the amino terminus; a cysteine residue in the carboxyl tail that may be palmitoylated; and 36 potential serine, threonine, and tyrosine phosphorylation sites in the third cytoplasmic loop region and in the carboxyl terminus. The functional roles of these potential modification sites are not yet known for the SPR, but they are believed to be important in other systems; for example, the phosphorylation sites appear to be related to desensitization in the β-adrenergic receptor.[15] Thus, it appeared that we had isolated a cDNA for a G protein–coupled receptor that was most similar to the bovine NKAR when compared to other G protein–coupled receptors (e.g., the adrenergic receptors,[37] the muscarinic receptors,[18,38–43] the D_2 dopamine receptor,[44] the opsins,[20] etc.). However, our cloned receptor does not appear to be the rat homologue of the bovine NKAR because it has <80% identity with this receptor at the amino acid level. Hence, we hypothesized that it was a different tachykinin receptor.

BINDING PROPERTIES OF THE SPR EXPRESSED IN COS-7 CELLS

In order to determine which G protein–coupled receptor this cDNA encoded, tachykinin ligand binding characteristics were determined. The cDNA was cloned into the mammalian expression vector pBC12BI[45] and this plasmid was used in gene transfer experiments to transfect the COS-7 mammalian cell line.[14] The expression vector contains the Rous sarcoma virus long-terminal repeat oriented such that the cloned sequence is under its control. When the cDNA for the SPR was transiently expressed in this system, the COS-7 cells expressed binding sites selective for SP versus NKA and NKB when examined by displacement of ^{125}I-Tyr^8-SP (FIGURE 3). When nontransfected COS-7 cells were analyzed, specific SP binding sites were not detected. A Scatchard analysis[46] of these binding sites yielded a dissociation constant (K_d) for SP of 3.5 nM with 5.4 fmol of binding sites per 200,000 cells or, on average, 16,200 sites per cell. When these transiently expressed binding sites were analyzed in displacement studies using ^{125}I-labeled Tyr^8-SP, the IC$_{50}$ for SP was approximately 1 nM, whereas the IC$_{50}$ values for NKA and NKB were 300 nM and 1 μM, respectively. This analysis confirmed that the cDNA, when expressed in COS-7 cells, encodes a

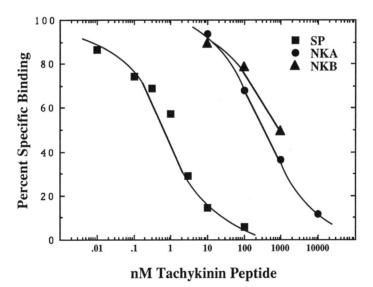

nM Tachykinin Peptide

FIGURE 3. Pharmacology of ligand binding to the SPR in transfected COS-7 cells. COS-7 cells were transfected with an expression vector containing the SPR cDNA and whole cells were used for ligand binding studies. Cells were incubated at 4 °C in PBS containing ^{125}I-Tyr^8-SP (0.05 nM) and the indicated concentration of unlabeled SP, NKA, or NKB. Nontransfected cells did not express any specific ^{125}I-Tyr^8-SP binding. Nonspecific binding of ^{125}I-Tyr^8-SP was determined by the binding of ligand to cells incubated with 1000-fold excess unlabeled SP.

high affinity SP binding site characteristic of the SPR. The high affinity SP binding site from tissues was previously shown to have a K_d of 0.4 to 4.0 nM.[47,48] The coupling of the SPR to a specific G protein promotes the high affinity state of the receptor and the difference in the K_d values observed in tissue preparations and in the transfected cells may be partly due to coupling of the SPR to different G proteins.

EXPRESSION OF THE SPR IN THE *XENOPUS* OOCYTE SYSTEM

Once it was established that we had isolated a cDNA clone for an SP binding site, the functional nature of this cDNA was assessed in the *Xenopus* oocyte expression

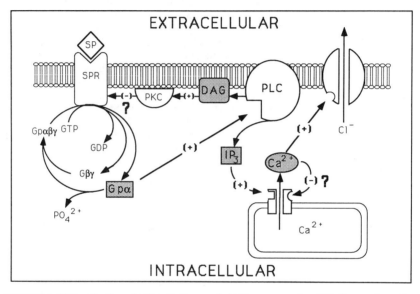

FIGURE 4. SPR activation of a G protein cascade in *Xenopus* oocytes. This figure schematizes the sequence of events following SPR activation by ligand. See the text for discussion. Intracellular messenger molecules are shaded. The proposed feedback inhibitions by protein kinase C on the substance P receptor and by Ca^{2+} on the Ca^{2+}-release channel remain tentative. Abbreviations: SP, substance P; SPR, substance P receptor; Gp, G protein and its constituent subunits (α, β, and γ); PLC, phospholipase C; IP_3, inositol-1,4,5-trisphosphate; DAG, diacylglycerol; PKC, protein kinase C.

system. In the 1970s and early 1980s, R. Miledi and his co-workers developed this oocyte system for the functional expression of exogenous RNAs encoding receptor and channel proteins and for their detection by sensitive electrical assays.[49] Subsequently, it was shown that sensitivity to SP could be induced by injection of exogenous RNA.[13] Using this system, the activation of the SPR, depicted in FIGURE 4, initiates a G protein cycle that has been well characterized in many systems (for reviews, see reference 50). Activation of the G protein leads to the activation of a particular isoform of phospholipase C, which catalyzes the breakdown of inositol phospholipids to inositol-1,4,5-trisphosphate (IP_3). IP_3 in turn stimulates the release of Ca^{2+} from internal reticular stores and the Ca^{2+} gates a specific Cl^- channel in the oocyte plasma membrane.[51] As a result of this second messenger cascade, a chloride conductance is activated. The oscillatory nature of this conductance is believed to be due to feedback inhibition of Ca^{2+} on the IP_3 receptor, thus modulating the Ca^{2+} release.[52,53]

The cloned SPR was analyzed in the *Xenopus* oocyte system after injecting 0.5–50 ng of synthetic mRNA transcribed from a plasmid vector containing the SPR cDNA. After culturing the injected oocytes for 1 to 6 days, they were screened for membrane current responses by application of 1 nM to 1 μM SP. At a holding potential of −60 mV, SP evoked an oscillatory inward membrane current ranging from 50 nA to greater than 2 μA (FIGURE 5A). This current appeared with a latency of seconds following administration of SP, which is consistent with responses mediated by a second messenger system. Subsequent responses to applications of SP 10 minutes later were much lower in amplitude, but recovered fully from this "desensitization" after washout periods of 30–50 minutes, as depicted in the right trace in FIGURE 5A. The current/voltage relationship of this current response was also examined. The oocytes were held at a resting potential of −60 mV and then a low dose of SP (e.g., 5 nM), which evoked a relatively sustained response, was applied. The voltage dependence was then measured by briefly stepping the voltage to various holding potentials during the oscillatory current (FIGURE 5B). From this analysis, it was determined that the SP-evoked current reverses at approximately −25 mV, which is the characteristic reversal potential of Cl^- in oocytes,[54] and rectifies strongly at potentials more negative than −40 to −50 mV, which is a characteristic of Ca^{2+}-gated Cl^- channels.[55] Uninjected oocytes from the same frogs gave little or no electrical response to SP, thus demonstrating the specificity of this SP-mediated response.

The desensitization of the SP-mediated response was further analyzed by comparing it with that of serotonin for its receptor, which is a different G protein–coupled receptor that, like other receptors, is linked to the same second messenger system in the *Xenopus* oocyte.[56] Exposing oocytes that express each receptor to either SP or serotonin at 10-minute intervals demonstrates that the response to SP rapidly and completely desensitizes, whereas desensitization of the responses to serotonin is much less marked (FIGURE 6). These experiments not only demonstrate that two different receptors can evoke similar responses within this oocyte system, but also that the desensitization of these responses can vary substantially in magnitude and is therefore dependent upon the specific receptor type expressed. This makes direct study of the molecular mechanisms of desensitization of the SPR system feasible, given the ability to prepare essentially unlimited amounts of SPR mRNA from the cloned cDNA.

Overall, the studies carried out so far clearly demonstrate that the cDNA that we have isolated expresses an SPR that binds ligand with high affinity and expresses a pharmacological profile expected for the NK-1 class of tachykinin receptors. Moreover, in the *Xenopus* oocyte system, the expressed protein functions by activating a receptor-channel coupling mechanism that involves the production of inositol trisphosphate, which releases Ca^{2+} from internal stores and generates an oscillatory chloride current. Once activated, the receptor is rapidly, potently, and selectively desensitized.

DISTRIBUTION OF THE mRNA ENCODING THE SPR

The distribution of an mRNA species in a tissue can be used to identify the probable location of the synthesis of the corresponding protein. In many cases, this is

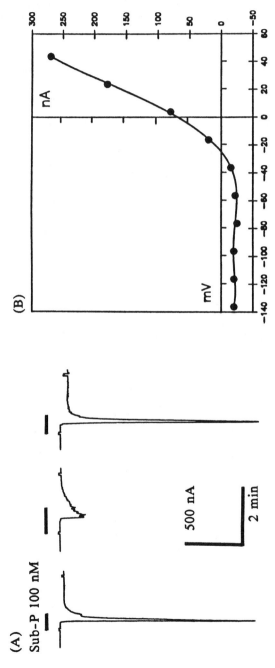

FIGURE 5. Membrane current responses elicited by substance P in *Xenopus* oocytes expressing the cloned rat substance P receptor. (A) Examples of membrane current responses evoked by 100 nM SP. The bars above the traces indicate the length of exposure to SP. The second trace follows the first trace by 10 min, demonstrating desensitization of the responses, whereas the third trace was generated after a 50-min wash sufficient to allow complete resensitization. For all cases, the holding potential was −60 mV and inward current is denoted by downward deflection. (B) Current/voltage relationship of the response elicited by SP in oocytes injected with SPR mRNA. The voltage dependence was determined by applying 5 nM SP, thus evoking a relatively sustained response, and by briefly stepping to different holding potentials.

the same site where the mature protein is seen. However, in the nervous system where axonal transport occurs, the final location of a protein may be quite different from its location of synthesis. Additionally, the level of mRNA expression may give an indication of the level of receptor synthesis for these tissues. Using a highly sensitive solution hybridization/nuclease protection assay that has been standardized in our laboratory,[57] the distribution of the SPR mRNA was determined.[19] This method involves synthesizing ^{32}P-labeled antisense RNA probes, annealing these probes to total tissue RNAs, and enzymatically digesting nonannealed probe with either S_1 nuclease or RNases A and T_1.[14,19,57,58] The antisense RNA probes, protected by the cognate tissue mRNA, are then examined by gel electrophoresis and autoradiography. Quantitation of the resultant signal is performed by densitometric analysis. This assay, using antisense ^{32}P-probes corresponding to the 5′ or 3′ coding regions of the SPR mRNA, has been validated such that the signals obtained are linear with respect to the mass of the specific mRNA analyzed.

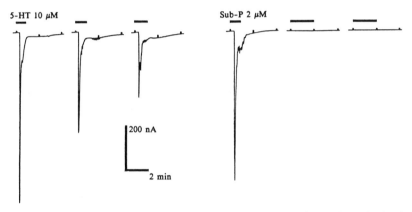

FIGURE 6. Desensitization of the SPR in *Xenopus* oocytes. This figure shows the levels in desensitization of responses elicited by either serotonin (5-HT) or substance P (SP) using oocytes injected with poly(A)+ RNA isolated from rat cerebral cortex and bovine retina, respectively. In both cases, agonist concentrations were selected to elicit maximum responses and were applied as indicated by the bars with 10-min washes between applications.

Consequently, this method can be used to determine the relative abundance of SPR mRNA in a given RNA preparation. Using this method with RNA preparations isolated from ten regions of the central nervous system of the rat, the steady-state levels of SPR mRNA were found to differ by some 13-fold.[19] This distribution of the SPR mRNA follows fairly closely that seen for high affinity SP binding sites in CNS regions.[25,26,28,29] In addition to the striatum in which SPR mRNA abundance is highest, SPR mRNA occurs at relatively high levels in hippocampal, midbrain, and olfactory bulb RNA preparations. The high levels in the striatum and midbrain appear to represent the expression of the SPR in the nigrostriatal tract. The striatonigral SP projection is one of the major SP systems in the CNS, where SP-expressing cell bodies project to an extensive nerve terminal field within the substantia nigra. However, relatively low levels of SP binding sites are present within the substantia nigra,[26,59,60] presumably due to ligand-receptor mismatch. It has also been reported that the hippocampus contains a large number of binding sites, but relatively little

SP,[26] although it is sometimes difficult to reveal sites of SP synthesis in the CNS unless colchicine is used to block axonal transport. Further analysis with *in situ* hybridization using peptide and receptor probes in conjunction with immunohistochemistry should allow for a better determination. The wide distribution of the mRNA for the SPR in the central nervous system may reflect its potential role in a wide variety of systems including pain perception, olfaction, vision, and motor control, among others.

In the periphery, the SPR mRNA has a more limited distribution. Much of the distribution can be generally attributed to SPR expression in tissues containing smooth muscle (urinary bladder and gastrointestinal tissues). In these systems, there exists extensive evidence for a role of SP in gastric motility[1,61] and in the micturition reflex.[7,62] It is interesting that the highest level of SPR mRNA is in the urinary bladder (400 pg per 25 μg of total RNA), a tissue where a high degree of specific binding is also observed with both SP and NKA,[63,64] suggesting an important role for both tachykinins and their respective receptors in urinary bladder function. The distribution of SPR mRNA in the gastrointestinal system is also interesting in that there is an increasing amount of SPR mRNA proceeding distally from the esophagus to the ileum, where the highest level is seen, with lower levels in the colon. The distribution of NKAR mRNA differs somewhat from that of the SPR mRNA distribution, where the level of NKAR mRNA progressively decreases from the stomach to the colon (Y. Takeda and J. E. Krause, unpublished). This fact, as well as differences throughout the gastrointestinal tract in ligand binding,[29,64] suggests that the two receptors may have different roles in gastrointestinal function. In addition, both the sublingual and submandibular salivary glands contain relatively large amounts of the SPR mRNA (355 pg and 270 pg per 25 μg of total RNA, respectively), whereas the parotid gland contains much lower levels of mRNA (50 pg per 25 μg of total RNA). Conversely, in the anterior pituitary, ligand binding studies have demonstrated the presence of an SPR,[65,66] whereas we have been unable to detect SPR mRNA using the nuclease protection method. Hence, either a different SPR exists in the anterior pituitary or the level of mRNA for the SPR is below the detection limit of the nuclease protection assay. Further cloning and expression experiments with mRNAs from this tissue will be necessary to determine whether multiple SPR-encoding mRNAs exist. For the most part, though, the SPR mRNA is widely distributed throughout the tissues of the rat and fairly closely follows the distribution of SP binding sites, thus suggesting that the cloned SPR cDNA encodes the major SPR in the rat.

GENOMIC ORGANIZATION OF THE RAT SPR

The genomic organization of the rat SPR was determined in order to begin studies of the molecular mechanisms regulating SPR gene expression. The characterization of the gene is also important for several additional reasons. Because a potential area for the regulation of expression of a protein is at the level of transcription, defining the 5' extent of the gene provides the DNA sequence that is involved in this regulation. This knowledge can be used to compare this sequence with known sequences that are used for controlling the level of expression of other proteins and for designing further experiments to analyze this control. Furthermore, knowledge of the organization of the exons and introns for a particular gene not only allows for the potential determination of individual structural or functional divisions within a protein, but, by comparison with related genes, it can also be used to determine the evolutionary nature of a group of proteins. Additionally, through the use of Southern blotting of genomic DNA, the isolation of a gene or cDNA can be used to look for the presence of another closely related gene or multiple genes and thus can aid in the isolation of related proteins. Finally, the sequence of the exons for a gene can be used to confirm the sequence of the cDNA.

The SPR gene was isolated from a rat genomic library and was initially characterized by restriction mapping. The individual exons were then isolated and subcloned and the nucleotide sequences were determined. A map of the gene is shown in FIGURE 7. The gene for the SPR is dispersed over greater than 45,000 bp and contains 5 exons (consisting of 965, 195, 151, 197, and 2010 bp, respectively). Exons 1 and 2 are separated from the remainder of the gene by two large introns (≥ 15 kb and > 23 kb, respectively), whereas the last 3 exons are clustered within ~ 3800 bp. All of the intron insertion positions of the SPR gene occur within the protein coding region. The first intron (intron A) is inserted between the sequence encoding the third membrane-spanning domain and the second intracellular loop region. The second intron (intron B) is positioned between the sequence encoding the second extracellular region and the fifth membrane-spanning domain. The third intron (intron C) is positioned between the sequence encoding the third extracellular domain and the sixth membrane-spanning domain. The final intron (intron D) is inserted between the sequence encoding the seventh membrane-spanning domain and the cytoplasmic tail. Therefore, the first interesting feature of the SPR gene is that, unlike many other members of the G protein–coupled superfamily, the portion of the gene containing the coding region of the SPR is interrupted by introns. Thus, this distinct organization of the genes for the G protein–coupled receptor superfamily allows for a subdivision of the members of this superfamily. Presently, only three members of this receptor superfamily have been discovered to contain introns within their protein coding region. These include the opsins,[20–22] the D_2 dopamine receptor,[23,24] and the SPR[19] (see FIGURE 8). The genes encoding adrenergic receptors, muscarinic receptors, certain serotonin receptors, yeast mating factor receptors, and the product of the oncogene c-*mas* have only one exon containing the coding region of the receptor, although the muscarinic receptors do contain a second exon within the 5' untranslated region of the receptor.[18,40,42] The presence of introns and their precise location should be useful in examining the evolutionary divergence of receptor genes within this receptor superfamily and the locations of introns may suggest potential functional/structural units within the receptors. Predicting functional/structural units within the receptor becomes important in ascertaining the specific roles that different portions of the receptor may play (i.e., what parts are involved in ligand recognition, G protein coupling and activation, and desensitization). Additionally, because it is very likely that the receptors in the superfamily function in a similar way, an understanding of the functional units within an individual receptor will aid in the understanding of functional units within others. Other genes have been seen to have their exons represent distinct functional units (for example, the gene encoding SP and NKA contains exons that are specific for NKA and SP;[67,68] however, the sequences of neuropeptide K and neuropeptide γ are encoded by parts of at least four and three exons, respectively[68]). Whether SPR sequences encoded by distinct exons correspond to functional units of this receptor remains to be determined.

The precise locations of introns within the SPR gene occur near potential structural motifs of the receptor primary structure and these intron locations allow for a comparison between additional receptor genes containing introns within their coding region. The first exon encodes the start methionine through the third membrane-spanning domain. The location of this splice site for intron A occurs at a similar location within the D_2 dopamine receptor gene sequence (FIGURE 8). The SPR gene also contains two novel splice sites when compared to other genes within

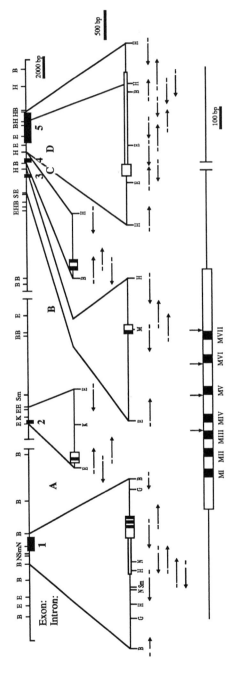

FIGURE 7. Genomic map of the rat substance P receptor gene. The upper portion represents the restriction map of the SPR gene. The line is interrupted at two locations, corresponding to gaps in introns A and B. The first interruption represents >1000 bp, whereas the second represents >4000 bp. Exons are indicated by solid boxes and are numbered 1 through 5, whereas restriction endonuclease sites are indicated by the vertical lines. The individual subcloned fragments for each exon are located beneath the genomic map. Within these fragments, the untranslated regions are represented by thin boxes and the coding region is represented by large boxes, with stripes indicating the location of the putative membrane-spanning domains. Dashes and arrows beneath these subcloned fragments indicate the sequencing primers and the sequences obtained, respectively. The lower portion of the figure is a schematic of the cDNA for the SPR with the coding region defined by a box and the membrane-spanning domains darkened. The arrows above this primary structure schematic illustrate the sites of intron insertion into the receptor coding region. Restriction endonucleases depicted are as follows: B, Bam HI; E, Eco RI; N, Nhe I; Sm, Sma I; K, Kpn I; H, Hind III; G, Bgl II; M, Mlu I. Not all enzyme sites are indicated for all subclones or for each of the three divisions of the genomic scheme; however, all sites within an individual DNA fragment are indicated.

this superfamily. These introns (B and C) interrupt the protein coding sequence immediately preceding the fifth and sixth membrane-spanning domains, respectively. Although the location for intron C is unique for the SPR, all of the receptor genes with introns contain one or more splice sites within this third cytoplasmic loop, which is a region that appears to play an important role in G protein coupling and perhaps desensitization. The fourth intron (intron D) occurs immediately after the seventh membrane-spanning domain, dividing the cytoplasmic tail from the remainder of the receptor structure. This splice site is nearly identically conserved, within one nucleotide, within the bovine and human opsin genes. This cytoplasmic tail region in the SPR has many potential sites for serine, threonine, and tyrosine phosphorylation (29 out of 99 amino acids) and, in the β-adrenergic system, these residues have been

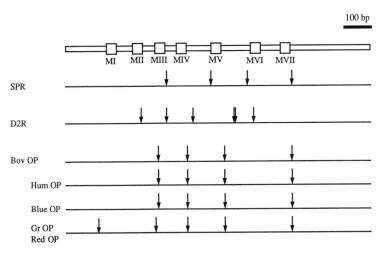

FIGURE 8. Comparison of the splice sites for selected G protein–coupled receptor genes. The locations of the exon/intron splice site are compared among the following genes: the substance P receptor (SPR); the D_2 dopamine receptor (D2R);[23,24] the bovine opsin (Bov OP);[20] the human opsin (Hum OP);[21] and the blue (Blue OP), red (Red OP), and green (Gr OP) human color opsins.[22] The upper portion of the figure depicts a schematic of the coding region of the rat SPR with the membrane-spanning domains highlighted. Beneath these are linear representations of the cDNA for the other G protein–coupled receptors containing introns, with arrows indicating the splice sites.

described to be involved in desensitization.[15,69] Because both the SPR[10,13] and the opsins[70] desensitize, the conserved location of this cytoplasmic tail splice site is an interesting observation. On the other hand, the gene encoding the β-adrenergic receptor does not contain introns, but it does desensitize extensively.

The SPR gene has a relatively long 5′ untranslated region (576 bp) in comparison to other members of the superfamily.[19] The extent of the 5′ end has been tentatively defined by nuclease protection[19] and is preceded by a single TATAAA sequence that presumably functions as an RNA polymerase II recognition sequence. A comparison of the 5′ flanking region with known promoter elements indicated a sequence at −52 to −45 (5′-TGACGTCT-3′) that resembles both the Ca^{2+} inducibility sequence of c-*fos* (5′-TGACGTTT-3′)[71] and the consensus sequence for the cAMP response element recognition (CRE) [5′-T(G/T)ACGTCA-3′].[72] The presence of this sequence may have interesting implications. Because stimulation of the SPR with agonist leads to IP_3 turnover with subsequent elevation in intracellular calcium in native cells where the SPR is expressed, a rise in cellular calcium levels may trigger an increase in SPR gene transcription. This may be of special importance in times of intense or sustained SPR stimulation because, in many systems, the SPR responses rapidly desensitize,[9,11,12] and a transcriptional mechanism for SPR resensitization may exist in addition to other short-term mechanisms of receptor sensitization. Except for the TATA box and the Ca^{2+}/CRE sequences, no other 5' flanking sequences closely match established promoter consensus sequences; however, a thorough analysis of the 5' flanking region in gene transfer transcriptional studies would be required to definitively establish the presence or absence of a control mechanism.

The 3' untranslated region of the SPR gene, which is encoded in exon 5, is also relatively large (1721 bp). There are two potential polyadenylation sites as defined by the sequence AATAAA (located at +44,865 and +44,909). The first of these is followed, 23 bases later, by the dinucleotide CA, which is then followed by two GT-rich stretches. These two features have been reported to represent conserved areas for transcription termination and 3' processing.[73] Additionally, in preliminary experiments, a nuclease protection analysis of this region in SPR mRNA has resulted in a protected fragment that coincides with the size expected if the first AATAAA sequence is used as the 3' processing signal (i.e., at +44,892 bp).[19] Overall, the genomic analysis of the SPR gene has revealed a gene divided into multiple exons dispersed over a large range with several introns present at locations similar to intron sites present in other G protein–coupled receptors. Furthermore, some potential regulatory elements in the SPR gene's 5' flanking region have been identified. These results will be useful in determining the mechanisms regulating SPR gene expression.

CONCLUSIONS

The SPR has been molecularly characterized using cDNA and genomic cloning methods. This has involved using degenerate oligonucleotides and the polymerase chain reaction to amplify a tachykinin receptor cDNA fragment. This cDNA was then used to isolate the remainder of the cDNA. Expression analysis has demonstrated that the cDNA encodes the rat SPR. In COS-7 cells, expression of the cDNA results in the appearance of a high affinity SP-specific binding site, and synthetic mRNA generated from this cDNA expresses a functional SPR that is coupled to the phosphatidyl inositol receptor-channel coupling system in *Xenopus* oocytes. In the *Xenopus* oocyte system, responses to SP desensitize rapidly, consistent with SPR responses in many systems. The distribution of the mRNA for this cDNA corresponds closely to previously described SP binding sites. This mRNA is distributed widely throughout many tissues of the rat and occurs in all CNS regions. These observations support further the conclusion that this cDNA encodes the primary SPR in rat tissues. The gene for the SPR has also been characterized. The SPR cDNA is encoded by five exons dispersed over ≥ 45,000 base pairs. This genomic organization makes the SPR unique among G protein–coupled receptors, although suggesting that it may be distantly related to the opsins and the D_2 dopamine receptor.

These results and the tools generated now allow for further studies on SPR structure-function relationships and mechanisms regulating SPR gene expression, whereas the PCR technique will allow for the isolation of additional novel G protein–coupled receptors. Further studies are now possible in terms of receptor–G protein activation/interaction and in terms of the molecular nature of desensitization in a defined, receptor-enriched system. Moreover, the mRNA analysis establishes the basal level of SPR mRNA in various tissues and the sensitive nuclease protection technique can be used for examining regulation of SPR gene expression.

REFERENCES

1. PERNOW, B. 1983. Pharmacol. Rev. **35:** 85–141.
2. ABDEL-LATIF, A. A. 1986. Pharmacol. Rev. **38:** 227–272.
3. SUGIYA, H., J. F. OBIE & J. W. PUTNEY, JR. 1988. Biochem. J. **253:** 459–466.
4. HANLEY, M. R., C. M. LEE, L. M. JONES & R. H. MICHELL. 1980. Mol. Pharmacol. **18:** 78–83.
5. WEISS, S. J., J. S. MCKINNEY & J. W. PUTNEY, JR. 1982. Biochem. J. **206:** 555–560.
6. PUTNEY, J. W., JR. 1977. J. Physiol. (London) **14:** 1046–1053.
7. MAGGI, C. A., S. GIULIANI, P. SANTICIOLI, D. REGOLI & A. MELI. 1987. J. Auton. Pharmacol. **7:** 11–32.
8. REGOLI, D., G. DRAPEAU, S. DION & P. D'ORLEANS-JUSTE. 1987. Life Sci. **40:** 109–117.
9. FRIEDMAN, Z. Y., U. WORMSER, E. RUBINI, M. CHOREV, C. GILON & Z. SELINGER. 1985. Eur. J. Pharmacol. **17:** 323–328.
10. SUGIYA, H., K. A. TENNES & J. W. PUTNEY, JR. 1987. Biochem. J. **244:** 647–653.
11. MCMILLIAN, M. K., S. P. SOLTOFF & B. R. TALAMO. 1987. Biochem. Biophys. Res. Commun. **148:** 1017–1024.
12. LAUFER, R., C. GILON, M. CHOREV & Z. SELINGER. 1988. J. Pharmacol. Exp. Ther. **245:** 639–643.
13. PARKER, I., K. SUMIKAWA & R. MILEDI. 1986. Proc. R. Soc. London **229:** 151–159.
14. HERSHEY, A. D. & J. E. KRAUSE. 1990. Science **247:** 958–962.
15. HAUSDORFF, W. P., M. G. CARON & R. J. LEFKOWITZ. 1990. FASEB J. **4:** 2881–2889.
16. DOUGLASS, J., O. CIVELLI & E. HERBERT. 1984. Annu. Rev. Biochem. **53:** 665–715.
17. TRAUT, T. W. 1988. Proc. Natl. Acad. Sci. U.S.A. **85:** 2944–2948.
18. BONNER, T. I., N. J. BUCKLEY, A. C. YOUNG & M. R. BRANN. 1987. Science **237:** 527–532.
19. HERSHEY, A. D., P. E. DYKEMA & J. E. KRAUSE. 1990. J. Biol. Chem. In press.
20. NATHANS, J. & D. S. HOGNESS. 1983. Cell **34:** 807–814.
21. NATHANS, J. & D. S. HOGNESS. 1984. Proc. Natl. Acad. Sci. U.S.A. **81:** 4851–4855.
22. NATHANS, J., D. THOMAS & D. S. HOGNESS. 1986. Science **232:** 193–202.
23. GRANDY, D. K., M. A. MARCHIONNI, H. MAKAM, R. E. STOFKO, M. ALFANO, L. FROTHINGHAM, J. B. FISCHER, K. J. BURKE-HOWIE, J. R. BUNZOW, A. C. SERVER & O. CIVELLI. 1989. Proc. Natl. Acad. Sci. U.S.A. **86:** 9762–9766.
24. O'MALLEY, K. L., K. J. MACK, K-Y. GANDELMAN & R. D. TODD. 1990. Biochemistry **29:** 1367–1371.
25. QUIRION, R., C. W. SHULTS, T. W. MOODY, C. B. PERT, T. N. CHASE & T. L. O'DONOHUE. 1983. Nature **303:** 714–716.
26. SHULTS, C. W., R. QUIRION, B. CHRONWALL, T. N. CHASE & T. L. O'DONOHUE. 1984. Peptides **5:** 1097–1128.
27. QUIRION, R. & T-V. DAM. 1986. J. Neurosci. **6:** 2187–2199.
28. SAFFROY, M., J-C. BEAUJOUAN, Y. TORRENS, J. BESSEYRE, L. BERGSTROM & J. GLOWINSKI. 1988. Peptides **9:** 227–241.
29. MANTYH, P. W., T. GATES, C. R. MANTYH & J. E. MAGGIO. 1989. J. Neurosci. **9:** 258–279.
30. CASCIERI, M. A. & T. LIANG. 1983. J. Biol. Chem. **258:** 5158–5164.
31. LEE, C-M., J. A. JAVITCH & S. H. SNYDER. 1983. Mol. Pharmacol. **23:** 563–569.
32. TAYLOR, C. W., J. E. MERRITT, J. W. PUTNEY, JR. & R. P. RUBIN. 1986. Biochem. Biophys. Res. Commun. **136:** 362–368.
33. MASU, Y., K. NAKAYAMA, H. TAMAKI, Y. HARADA, M. KUNO & S. NAKANISHI. 1987. Nature **329:** 836–838.
34. SAIKI, R. K., S. SCHARF, F. FALOONA, K. B. MULLIS, G. T. HORN, H. A. ERLICH & N. ARNHEIM. 1985. Science **230:** 1350–1354.
35. LIBERT, F., M. PARMENTIER, A. LEFORT, C. DINSART, J. VAS SANDE, C. MAENHAUT, M-J. SIMONS, J. E. DUMONT & G. VASSART. 1989. Science **244:** 569–572.

36. KOZAK, M. 1987. Nucleic Acids Res. **15:** 8125–8148.
37. LEFKOWITZ, R. J. & M. G. CARON. 1988. J. Biol. Chem. **263:** 4993–4996.
38. KUBO, T., K. FUKUDA, A. MIKAMI, A. MAEDA, H. TAKAHASHI, M. MISHINA, T. HAGA, K. HAGA, A. ICHIYAMA, K. KANGAWA, M. KOJIMA, H. MATSUO, T. HIROSE & S. NUMA. 1986. Nature **323:** 411–416.
39. KUBO, T., A. MAEDA, K. SUGIMOTO, I. AKIBA, A. MIKAMI, H. TAKAHASHI, T. HAGA, K. HAGA, A. ICHIYAMA, K. KANGAWA, H. MATSUO, T. HIROSE & S. NUMA. 1986. FEBS Lett. **209:** 367–372.
40. PERALTA, E. G., J. W. WINSLOW, G. L. PETERSON, D. H. SMITH, A. ASHKENAZI, J. RAMACHANDRAN, M. I. SCHIMERLIK & D. J. CAPON. 1987. Science **236:** 600–605.
41. PERALTA, E. G., A. ASHKENAZI, J. W. WINSLOW, D. H. SMITH, J. RAMACHANDRAN & D. J. CAPON. 1987. EMBO J. **6:** 3923–3929.
42. BONNER, T. I., A. C. YOUNG, M. R. BRANN & N. J. BUCKLEY. 1988. Neuron **1:** 403–410.
43. SHAPIRO, R. A., N. M. SCHERER, B. A. HABECKER, E. M. SUBERS & N. M. NATHANSON. 1988. J. Biol. Chem. **263:** 18397–18403.
44. BUNZOW, J. R., H. H. M. VAN TOL, D. K. GRANDY, P. ALBERT, J. SALON, M. CHRISTIE, C. A. MACHIDA, K. A. NEVE & O. CIVELLI. 1988. Nature **336:** 783–787.
45. CULLEN, B. R. 1987. Methods Enzymol. **152:** 684–704.
46. SCATCHARD, G., J. S. COLEMAN & A. L. SHEN. 1957. J. Am. Chem. Soc. **79:** 12.
47. VIGER, A., J-C. BEAUJOUAN, Y. TORRENS & J. GLOWINSKI. 1983. J. Neurochem. **40:** 1030–1039.
48. LIANG, T. & M. A. CASCIERI. 1981. J. Neurosci. **1:** 1133–1141.
49. MILEDI, R., I. PARKER & K. SUMIKAWA. 1989. Fidia Res. Found. Neurosci. Award Lect. **3:** 57–90.
50. BERRIDGE, M. J. 1987. Annu. Rev. Biochem. **56:** 159–193.
51. MILEDI, R. 1982. Proc. R. Soc. London **B215:** 491–497.
52. PARKER, I. & R. MILEDI. 1986. Proc. R. Soc. London **B228:** 307–315.
53. PARKER, I. & I. IVORRA. 1990. Proc. Natl. Acad. Sci. U.S.A. **87:** 260–264.
54. KUSANO, K., R. MILEDI & J. STINNAKRE. 1982. J. Physiol. **328:** 143–170.
55. MILEDI, R. & I. PARKER. 1984. J. Physiol. **357:** 173–183.
56. PARKER, I., K. SUMIKAWA & R. MILEDI. 1987. Proc. R. Soc. London **231:** 37–45.
57. KRAUSE, J. E., J. D. CREMINS, M. S. CARTER, E. R. BROWN & M. R. MACDONALD. 1989. Methods Enzymol. **168:** 634–652.
58. KRAUSE, J. E., J. M. CHIRGWIN, M. S. CARTER, Z. S. XU & A. D. HERSHEY. 1987. Proc. Natl. Acad. Sci. U.S.A. **84:** 881–885.
59. LJUNGDAHL, A., T. HÖKFELT & G. NILSSON. 1978. Neuroscience **3:** 861–943.
60. KRAUSE, J. E., A. J. REINER, J. P. ADVIS & J. F. MCKELVY. 1984. J. Neurosci. **4:** 775–785.
61. MAGGI, C. A., S. GIULIANI, S. MANZINI, P. SANTICIOLI & A. MELI. 1986. J. Pharmacol. Exp. Ther. **238:** 341–351.
62. MAGGI, C. A., M. PARLANI, M. ASTOLFI, P. SANTICIOLI, P. ROVERO, L. ABELLI, V. SOMMA, S. GIULIANI, D. REGOLI, R. PATACCHINI & A. MELI. 1988. J. Pharmacol. Exp. Ther. **246:** 308–315.
63. BURCHER, E. & S. H. BUCK. 1986. Eur. J. Pharmacol. **128:** 165–177.
64. BURCHER, E., S. H. BUCK, W. LOVENBERG & T. L. O'DONOHUE. 1986. J. Pharmacol. Exp. Ther. **236:** 819–831.
65. KERDELHUÉ, B., A. TARTAR, V. LENIOR, A. EL ABED, P. HUBLAU & R. P. MILLAR. 1985. Regulat. Peptides **10:** 133–143.
66. LARSEN, P. J., J. D. MIKKELSEN & T. SAERMARK. 1989. Endocrinology **124:** 2548–2557.
67. NAWA, H., H. KOTANI & S. NAKANISHI. 1984. Nature **312:** 729–734.
68. CARTER, M. S. & J. E. KRAUSE. 1990. J. Neurosci. **10:** 2203–2214.
69. VALIQUETTE, M., H. BONIN, M. HNATOWICH, M. G. CARON, R. J. LEFKOWITZ & M. BOUVIER. 1990. Proc. Natl. Acad. Sci. U.S.A. **87:** 5089–5093.
70. WILDEN, U., S. W. HALL & H. KÜHN. 1986. Proc. Natl. Acad. Sci. U.S.A. **83:** 1174–1178.
71. SHENG, M., S. T. DOUGAN, G. MCFADDEN & M. E. GREENBERG. 1988. Mol. Cell. Biol. **8:** 2787–2796.
72. ROESLER, W. J., G. R. VANDENBARK & R. W. HANSON. 1988. J. Biol. Chem. **263:** 9063–9066.
73. BIRNSTIEL, M. L., M. BUSSLINGER & K. STRUB. 1985. Cell **41:** 349–359.

Substance P Receptor

Biochemical Characterization and Interactions with G Proteins[a]

N. D. BOYD, S. G. MACDONALD, R. KAGE,
J. LUBER-NAROD, AND S. E. LEEMAN

Department of Physiology
University of Massachusetts Medical Center
Worcester, Massachusetts 01655

INTRODUCTION

The binding of substance P (SP) to its receptor leads to the hydrolysis of membrane-bound inositol phospholipids via the activation of a phosphoinositide-specific phospholipase C (PLC).[1-4] Two second messengers, inositol 1,4,5-trisphosphate and diacylglycerol, result from this hydrolysis and stimulate calcium release from intracellular stores and protein kinase C activation, respectively. Various biochemical studies,[5-8] as well as a shared amino acid sequence homology with the G protein–coupled receptor family,[9,10] indicate that a G protein is involved in the SP receptor signaling pathway. However, the identity of the relevant G protein is not known and the nature of its interaction with the SP receptor remains unclear. To obtain a better understanding of the molecular events leading to the physiologic actions of SP, we are studying the structural and regulatory characteristics of SP receptors in rat submaxillary gland. The questions we are particularly interested in are the following: What primary structures of the SP receptor are involved in peptide recognition and receptor activation? What are the biochemical and functional properties of the G protein that couples to SP receptors? How does the binding of SP regulate the interaction between the SP receptor and its G protein?

In this report, we describe recent progress in these areas that has been achieved through the development of (1) a highly efficient photoaffinity probe for the binding site of the SP receptor, (2) a modified binding assay permitting the measurement of rapidly dissociating low-affinity binding, and (3) a reconstitution procedure for the study of SP receptor–G protein interactions.

METHODS

[Phe[8](pBz)]SP was synthesized by solid-phase synthesis methodology to incorporate the amino acid, *p*-benzoyl-L-phenylalanine [L-Phe[8](pBz)], in place of the Phe[8] residue of SP.[11] Radioiodinated derivatives of [Phe[8](pBz)]SP and also of SP were prepared by conjugation with ^{125}I-labeled Bolton-Hunter reagent (2200 Ci/mmole).

[a] This work was supported by Grant Nos. NS25151 and DK29876 from the National Institutes of Health.

Preparation and Alkaline Treatment of Rat Submaxillary Gland Membranes

Submaxillary glands from adult Sprague-Dawley rats were used to prepare membranes as described previously.[8]

For alkaline treatment, rat submaxillary gland membranes were resuspended at 4 °C in 50 mM sodium phosphate (pH 11.5) at a concentration of 2.5–3.3 mg of membrane protein/mL and the pH of the suspension was adjusted to 11.5 with 1–3 drops of 1 M NaOH. Following a 30-min incubation on ice, the pH of the mixture was lowered to between 8 and 9 by addition of 50 mM Tris-HCl, pH 7.6. The membranes were collected by centrifugation at 35,000g for 35 min and were resuspended to a final concentration of 4 mg of protein/mL in 50 mM Tris-HCl buffer containing 1 mM EGTA and 10 mM $MgCl_2$, pH 7.4 (TME buffer).

Addition of G Proteins to pH 11.5–treated Membranes

Purified G proteins [G_o (a pertussis toxin–sensitive G protein having a 39,000-dalton α-subunit) and G_i] were purified from bovine brain by the procedure of Sternweis and Robishaw.[12]

A volume of the G protein preparation was added to the alkaline-treated membranes (16 mg of membrane protein/mL in TME buffer) to give a final concentration of ~80 pmol of GTPγS binding activity added/mg of membrane protein. The membranes were incubated on ice for 10 min before warming to room temperature. The cholate was then slowly diluted at least 20-fold by several additions of room-temperature TME buffer over a period of 30 min. Following the cholate dilution, the membranes were incubated for an additional 15 min at room temperature. Reconstituted membranes were collected by centrifugation at 35,000g for 35 min and were resuspended in TME buffer to a final concentration of 3 mg of membrane protein/mL for binding assays.

Binding Assays

The binding of ^{125}I-SP and ^{125}I-[Phe^8(pBz)]SP was as described previously.[11] Rat submaxillary gland membranes (50–100 μg of protein) were incubated with ^{125}I-SP or ^{125}I-[Phe^8(pBz)]SP (0.1–5 nM) for 30 min at 22 °C in a total volume of 200 μL of TME supplemented with 200 μg/mL crystalline bovine serum albumin, 3 μg/mL chymostatin, 5 μg/mL leupeptin, and 30 μg/mL bacitracin. For competition binding experiments, membranes were incubated with 0.5 nM ^{125}I-SP or ^{125}I-[Phe^8(pBz)]SP and with varying concentrations of peptides for 30 min at 22 °C in Tris buffer (as just described). In binding experiments utilizing ^{125}I-[Phe^8(pBz)]SP, the incubation mixtures were protected from light. For all experiments, nonspecific binding was defined by the addition of 1 μM SP. Binding was terminated by addition of 5 mL of ice-cold 50 mM Tris-HCl and 10 mM $MgCl_2$ (pH 7.4) and by rapid filtering through a glass fiber filter (Whatman GF/C) that had been soaked for >2 hours in 0.1% polyethyleneimine. The incubation tubes and filters were washed three times with 5 mL of the same ice-cold buffer.

This procedure for removing nonspecific binding could not be used if we were to be able to detect low-affinity, rapidly dissociable binding in the presence of guanine nucleotides. A Hoefer filtration apparatus allowed us to assay binding extremely rapidly using the following modifications. The metal wells were kept on ice until just prior to filtration and then they were filled with 10 mL of ice-cold TME. Aliquots of the incubation mixture at room temperature were then injected rapidly into the buffer in the wells and filtration was begun simultaneously. This was followed by a single 10-mL wash to TME. The mean time interval required for dilution, filtration, and wash steps was found to be 2.6 ± 0.4 s. Radioactivity retained by the glass fiber filters by either technique was determined by γ-radiation spectrometry.

Photoaffinity Labeling

Membranes (3–5 mg of protein/mL) were incubated in the dark with 0.5–1.0 nM ^{125}I-[Phe^8(pBz)]SP for 30 min at 22 °C in TME buffer supplemented with both protease inhibitors (see earlier discussion) and competing peptides at the concentrations indicated. Following incubation, the samples were diluted 10-fold with ice-cold buffer and were centrifuged at 40,000g for 15 min. The pellets were resuspended in the same volume of ice-cold buffer and were recentrifuged. This step was repeated twice. The membrane pellets obtained following the last centrifugation step were resuspended in ice-cold buffer at 1–2 mg of membrane protein/mL and were irradiated for 15 min on ice in polystyrene tissue culture dishes at a distance of 6 cm from a 100-watt long wave (365 nm) UV lamp (Blak-Ray). The photolabeled membranes were then obtained by centrifugation (40,000g for 15 min).

SDS-PAGE and Autoradiography

Photolabeled membranes were solubilized for 5 min at 60 °C in sample buffer (2% SDS, 10% glycerol, and 5% β-mercaptoethanol in 25 mM Tris-HCl, pH 6.8). Samples (50–100 μg of membrane protein) were electrophoresed in polyacrylamide slab gels according to the method of Laemmli.[13] Gels were dried using a Hoefer Scientific Instruments slab gel drier (Model SE540) and were exposed at −80 °C to Kodak XAR-5 film using one intensifying screen for various times (8–30 h).

To document quantitative photoincorporation of ^{125}I-Phe^8(pBz) into receptor polypeptides, the autoradiographs were aligned with the dried gels, the radiolabeled polypeptides were cut out, and the amount of radioactivity was measured. In the experiments to examine the inhibitory effect of SP and related tachykinin peptides on photolabeling by ^{125}I-Phe^8(pBz), individual lanes on the autoradiographs were analyzed densitometrically using a Hoefer (GS 300) scanning densitometer.

Enzymatic Treatment of Photolabeled Polypeptides

The 53-kDa and 46-kDa photolabeled peptides were resolved by preparative SDS-PAGE. The radioactive bands were located autoradiographically and the photolabeled peptides were obtained by electroelution of the excised gel strip. The photolabeled polypeptides were incubated with endoglycosidase F (5 units/mL) at 37 °C for 12 h in 50 mM sodium phosphate buffer, pH 6.0, containing 1% (wt/vol) Nonidet P-40.

RESULTS AND DISCUSSION

Photoaffinity Labeling of SP Receptors

Recently, we described the successful use of a novel photoreactive analogue of SP, [125]I-[Phe[8](pBz)]SP (FIGURE 1), for irreversibly labeling SP receptors in membrane preparations obtained from rat submaxillary glands.[11]

The photoaffinity label was synthesized by replacing the Phe[8] residue of SP with p-benzoyl-L-phenylalanine [L-Phe(pBz)] (FIGURE 1). This photoreactive amino acid was chosen on the basis of its chemical stability under peptide synthesis conditions and on the basis of its highly selective photochemistry.[14] The carboxyl-terminal region of SP was selected for introduction of L-Phe(pBz) to optimize the possibility that the photoreactive group would be in close proximity to amino acid residues comprising the peptide binding site of the SP receptor. The importance of the C-terminal region of SP for interaction with the binding site of the SP receptor has been established by the demonstration that C-terminal fragments of six amino acids or larger are capable of interacting with the SP receptor, whereas shorter C-terminal fragments and all N-terminal fragments have little or no affinity.[15] A further consideration in the design of the photoaffinity probe was the finding that, despite its location in the region of the peptide sequence critical for binding, Phe[8] can be structurally modified without causing a marked decrease in affinity.[5,16]

A radioiodinated derivative of Phe[8](pBz)-SP was prepared by conjugation with ^{125}I-labeled Bolton-Hunter reagent, a reagent that has been used previously to radiolabel SP[17] and other tachykinins.[18,19] The equilibrium binding of [125]I-[Phe[8](pBz)]SP to rat submaxillary gland membranes was attained at 22 °C in 20 min. The binding consisted of a specific, saturable component and a nonspecific component, identified by measuring the binding in the presence of a saturating amount of SP (FIGURE 2). Scatchard analysis of the saturable component indicated that [125]I-[Phe[8](pBz)]SP bound with high affinity ($K_D = 0.44 \pm 0.13$ nM) to an apparently homogeneous population of binding sites ($B_{max} = 240 \pm 80$ fmoles/mg protein). These equilibrium parameters are the same, within experimental error, as those characterizing the binding of the ^{125}I-Bolton-Hunter conjugate of SP, ^{125}I-SP, to the same membrane preparation.

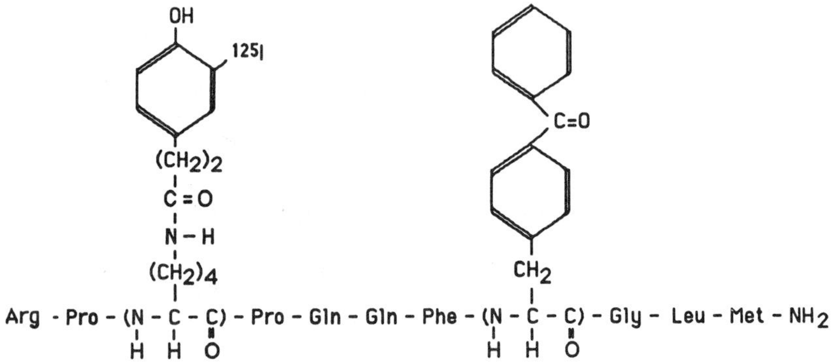

FIGURE 1. Chemical structure of the ^{125}I–Bolton Hunter conjugate of an SP analogue in which phenylalanine in position 8 has been replaced by the photoreactive amino acid, p-benzoyl-L-phenylalanine [L-Phe(pBz)].

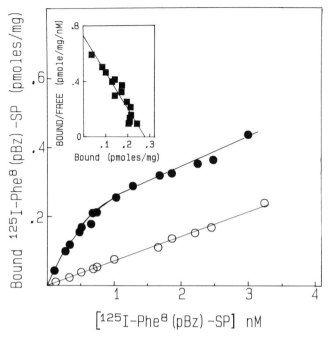

FIGURE 2. Saturation binding isotherm of ^{125}I-[Phe^8(pBz)]SP to rat submaxillary gland membranes. Increasing concentrations of ^{125}I-[Phe^8(pBz)]SP were incubated in the dark with rat submaxillary gland membranes (100 µg of protein/0.1 mL assay volume) and the binding was measured by ultrafiltration: total binding (●) and nonspecific binding (○) in the presence of 1 µM SP. Each point is the average of duplicate determinations. Inset: Scatchard analysis of the specific binding of ^{125}I-[Phe^8(pBz)]SP (■) (K_D = 0.4 nM, B_{max} = 0.28 pmoles/mg). The experiment was repeated three times with similar results.

Competitive binding assays were used to characterize further the peptide specificity of ^{125}I-[Phe^8(pBz)]SP binding to rat submaxillary gland membranes (FIGURE 3). SP competed for the binding sites occupied by ^{125}I-[Phe^8(pBz)]SP with an IC$_{50}$ = 1 nM. Deaminated SP (SP-free acid), which is inactive in various SP/NK-1 bioassays including stimulation of salivation,[17] inhibited ^{125}I-[Phe^8(pBz)]SP binding only when added at high concentrations (>100 nM). Neurokinin A (NKA), which is a more potent agonist than SP at NKA/NK-2 receptors, but is less active at SP/NK-1 receptors, exhibited a >10-fold lower potency than SP in competing for ^{125}I-[Phe^8(pBz)]SP binding. The development of selective agonists for the various neurokinin receptor classes[20] permitted further characterization of the binding specificity. Only the selective SP/NK-1 receptor agonist, [Sar^9,Met(O$_2$)^{11}]-SP, and not Nle^{10}-NKA(4–10) and MePhe^7-NKB [selective agonists for NK-2 and NK-3 receptors, respectively], was found to be a potent competitor of ^{125}I-[Phe^8(pBz)]SP binding (FIGURE 3).

The results of these competition binding experiments when considered together with the saturation binding experiments clearly document that ^{125}I-[Phe^8(pBz)]SP and ^{125}I-SP bind to the same sites on rat submaxillary gland membranes with a specificity that identifies these sites as SP receptors of the NK-1 type.

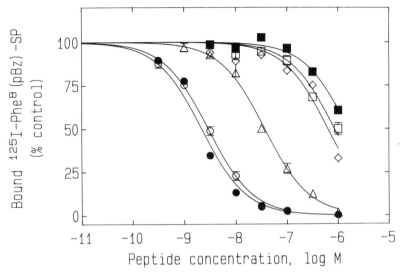

FIGURE 3. Inhibition of ^{125}I-[Phe^8(pBz)]SP binding to rat submaxillary gland membranes by SP and related peptides. A constant concentration of ^{125}I-[Phe^8(pBz)]SP (0.2 nM) was incubated in the dark at 22 °C for 30 min with rat submaxillary gland membranes (50 μg of protein/0.1 mL assay volume) in the presence of increasing concentrations of SP (●), [Sar^9,Met(O$_2$)^{11}]-SP (○), NKA (△), Nle^{10}-NKA(4–10) (□), MePhe^7-NKB (◇), and SPFA (■). Bound ^{125}I-[Phe^8(pBz)]SP was determined in triplicate and is represented as a percentage of the specific binding measured in the absence of competing peptide. The lines through the experimental points represent the computer-generated best fit to the data of a single representative experiment performed three times.

Upon exposure to UV light, the photoligand undergoes covalent attachment into these SP binding sites. A typical photolabeling experiment is shown in FIGURE 4. The autoradiograph of the dried Coomassie Blue–stained gel indicates that the photolabel was covalently and selectively incorporated into two polypeptides of $M_r = 53$ kDa and 46 kDa. The labeling of both polypeptides is specific because no labeling was observed in the presence of a saturating amount of SP. Quantitative measurements of the total amount of ^{125}I-[Phe^8(pBz)]SP that was covalently bound to the polypeptides at $M_r = 53$ kDa and 46 kDa indicated that 70 ± 5% ($n = 4$) of the ^{125}I-[Phe^8(pBz)]SP bound reversibly prior to photolysis had undergone covalent attachment. This remarkably efficient photolabeling is most likely a reflection of the highly selective photochemistry of the benzophenone group. Upon low-level ultraviolet light irradiation, the ketone carbonyl of the benzophenone moiety undergoes an n,π^* transition to give a triplet biradical that has been shown to possess high reactivity for C-H bonds,[14] but low reactivity towards water.[21]

Because analysis of the saturation and competition binding of the photoligand under nonphotolyzing conditions provided evidence for only one class of binding sites in rat submaxillary gland membranes, the finding of two photoaffinity-labeled proteins was somewhat surprising and implies that the binding properties of the 53-kDa and 46-kDa polypeptides are similar. To compare the binding properties of the two SP receptor polypeptides, a series of photolabeling protection experiments were conducted. SP inhibited the photolabeling of both polypeptides in a concentration-dependent manner (FIGURE 5, lanes 1–6). Densitometric scanning of the individual lanes on the autoradiograph indicated that the labeling at 53 kDa and 46 kDa was equally sensitive to SP inhibition ($IC_{50} \sim 1$ nM). The specific agonist of SP/NK-1 receptors, [Sar^9,Met(O_2)^{11}]-SP, was also found to be a potent inhibitor of photolabeling, with inhibition of each of the labeled bands exhibiting an $IC_{50} \sim 6$ nM. On the other hand, the specific NK-2 and NK-3 receptor agonists, Nle^{10}-NKA(4–10) and MePhe^7-NKB, respectively, when added at a concentration of 10 nM, had no detectable effect on the photolabeling of either the 53-kDa or 46-kDa polypeptides. These results establish that the photolabeled SP binding sites of $M_r = 53$ kDa and 46 kDa bind SP with the same affinity and have the same peptide specificity, that is, characteristic of SP/NK-1 receptors. Because the predicted primary sequence of the SP receptor has a relative molecular weight of 46,364 and contains (close to its amino-terminus) a possible site for attachment of N-linked carbohydrates,[9] the possibility was raised that the 53-kDa and 46-kDa polypeptides represent, respectively, glycosylated and nonglycosylated forms of the receptor. Alternatively, both photolabeled polypeptides might be glycosylated and the difference in molecular weight could be due to the action of an endogenous proteolytic enzyme.

To distinguish between these two possibilities, the two photolabeled polypeptides were resolved by preparative SDS-PAGE and were treated individually with endoglycosidase F, an enzyme that removes asparagine-linked carbohydrates from the polypeptide chain. Analysis of enzymatic products by SDS-PAGE and autoradiography has indicated that the 53-kDa and 46-kDa polypeptides both contain about 10 kDa of N-linked carbohydrates, but differ in the length of their polypeptide backbone (FIGURE 6). Thus, it appears likely that the smaller 46-kDa glycoprotein is derived proteolytically from the larger 53-kDa glycoprotein. Interestingly, several other G protein–linked receptors including β-adrenergic[22] and D$_2$ dopamine[23] recep-

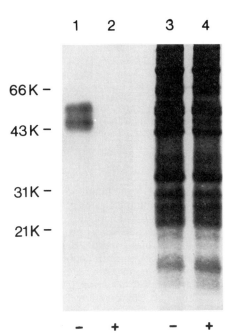

FIGURE 4. Photolabeling of rat submaxillary gland membranes with ^{125}I-[Phe^8(pBz)]SP. Rat submaxillary gland membranes (1 mg of membrane protein/mL) were equilibrated at 22 °C with ^{125}I-[Phe^8(pBz)]SP (0.3 nM) in the absence (−) and presence (+) of 1 μM SP, were washed with ice-cold buffer, and were photolyzed at 4 °C for 10 min with 350-nm light. Photolabeled membranes (100 μg of membrane protein) were subjected to SDS-PAGE. The resolved proteins were stained with Coomassie Blue (lanes 3 and 4) and radiolabeled bands were visualized by autoradiography of the dried gel (lanes 1 and 2).

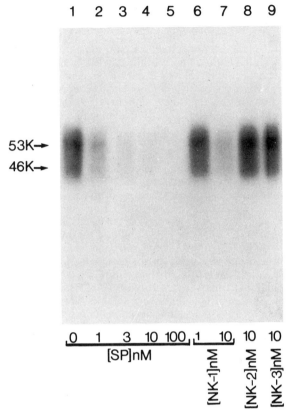

FIGURE 5. Peptide specificity of ^{125}I-[Phe^8(pBz)]SP photoincorporation into rat submaxillary gland membranes. Membranes were photoaffinity-labeled with ^{125}I-[Phe^8(pBz)]SP alone (lane 1) or in the presence of the specified concentrations of competing tachykinin peptides (lanes 2–9). Samples were subjected to SDS-PAGE and autoradiography. The amount of labeling at $M_r = 53$ kDa and at $M_r = 46$ kDa was assessed by densitometric scanning of the individual lanes of the autoradiogram (see text for details). The results are representative of at least three similar experiments. Terms: NK-1, [Sar^9,Met(O$_2$)^{11}]-SP; NK-2, [Nle^{10}]NKA(4–10); NK-3, [MePhe^7]NKB.

tors have also been found to be highly susceptible to proteolytic degradation. Inclusion of multiple classes of specific protease inhibitors shown to be effective in preventing degradation of these receptors did not, however, prevent radiolabeling of the lower molecular weight protein. At this time, we do not know whether both the intact and the proteolytically degraded forms of the SP/NK-1 receptor exist *in vivo* or whether proteolytic degradation of the receptor occurs during membrane preparation due to an inappropriate choice of protease inhibitor and/or to the high proteolytic activity of salivary gland tissue.

Although further study will be necessary before it can be established that the 53-kDa polypeptide alone represents the functional SP receptor, we can nevertheless conclude that this polypeptide contains the sites for both SP binding and interaction with G proteins. On the basis of the change in mobility observed following N-deglyco-sylation, the molecular weight of the deglycosylated, but otherwise intact polypeptide backbone of the SP receptor is estimated to be about 43 kDa, a value that is similar to the value predicted by nucleotide sequence analysis of a cDNA clone for the rat SP receptor.[9,10]

The highly efficient photolabeling achieved using ^{125}I-[Phe^8(pBz)]SP suggests that, in addition to its use in characterizing the SP receptor polypeptide, it will also be useful for identifying peptide fragments derived from the binding site. Purification and sequence analysis can then be used to position the photolabeled fragment within the primary amino acid sequence of the receptor and to determine the particular amino acid residue that serves as the site of covalent attachment. Through the use of the photoaffinity label described here, ^{125}I-[Phe^8(pBz)]SP, and other photoaffinity analogues in which the photoreactive group is incorporated at different positions on the SP molecule, it should be possible to define in detail the amino residues comprising the three-dimensional SP binding pocket of the receptor. Information obtained by this approach will complement the results of studies on receptors subjected to mutagenesis, for example, site-directed or chimeric mutants.

In an effort to obtain a photolabeled peptide fragment that can be sequenced, photolabeled SP receptors were (i) solubilized, (ii) partially purified, and (iii) digested with different concentrations of trypsin. Incubation with low concentrations

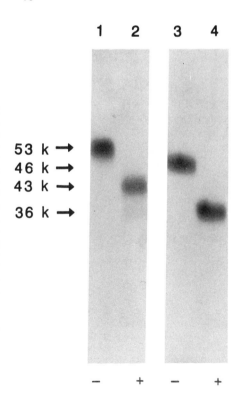

FIGURE 6. Endoglycosidase F treatment of the resolved 53-kDa and 46-kDa photo-labeled SP receptor polypeptides. The 53-kDa and 46-kDa photolabeled SP recep-tor polypeptides were obtained by preparative SDS-PAGE and electroelu-tion. The resolved photolabeled polypep-tides were incubated at 37 °C for 12 h in 50 mM sodium phosphate buffer (pH 6.0) containing 1% (wt/vol) Nonidet P-40 in the presence (+) and absence (−) of en-doglycosidase F (5 units/mL). Following the incubation period, samples were re-solved by SDS-PAGE and visualized by autoradiography. Lanes 1 and 2: the 53-kDa photolabeled polypeptide incubated without and with endoglycosidase F, re-spectively. Lanes 3 and 4: the 46-kDa pho-tolabeled polypeptide incubated without and with endoglycosidase F, respectively.

of trypsin produced in almost quantitative yield a single radiolabeled fragment of M_r = 28 kDa. Under these conditions of low enzyme concentration, dibasic residues are the most susceptible to tryptic cleavage. Cleavage at the dibasic residues $Lys_{61}Arg_{62}$ and $Lys_{280}Lys_{281}$ on the first intracellular (C_1) and third extracellular (E_3) domains yields a tryptic fragment with a calculated molecular weight of 26,200, which is in excellent agreement with the observed M_r, particularly when the molecular weight of the covalently attached photoaffinity label is taken into account. These results suggest that the site of covalent attachment of the photolabel is contained within the internal hydrophobic core of the SP receptor. This assignment for the location of the photolabeled fragment obtained by limited tryptic digestion is further supported by the lack of endoglycosidase F sensitivity of this fragment. Incubation with higher concentrations of trypsin produced progressively smaller photolabeled fragments. However, at the concentration of trypsin required for complete digestion, the photolabel itself was susceptible to proteolytic cleavage, resulting in the minimal photolabeled tryptic fragment being obtained in low (<20%) yield. To further restrict the location of the covalent attachment site, the 28-kDa tryptic fragment was subcleaved with cyanogen bromide, a reagent that cleaves at the C-terminal side of methionine. A CNBr cleavage product of M_r = 6.2 kDa was obtained in high yield and was subjected to HPLC analysis on a reversed-phase C_4 column. A single radioactive peptide fraction was found, indicating that only one of the CNBr cleavage products contains the photolabel. Experiments are currently in progress to obtain this photolabeled fragment in sufficient purity and quantity for sequence analysis.

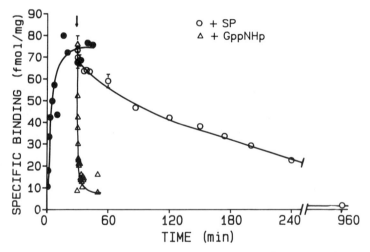

FIGURE 7. The effect of GppNHp on the rate of dissociation of ^{125}I-SP from rat submaxillary gland membranes. Membranes were incubated with 1.5 nM ^{125}I-SP (●) until the binding reached equilibrium (30 min). The membranes were divided and either 100 × concentrated SP (○) or 100 × concentrated GppNHp (△) was added in sufficient volume to bring the final concentration to 10 μM. The amount of ^{125}I-SP bound was measured at increasing time intervals following these additions. The arrow indicates the time of SP or GppNHp addition. For the +SP curve, all points are triplicate determinations. Error bars are shown, except where smaller than the symbol, and they represent the mean ± SD. Points of the +GppNHp curve represent single sample determinations. The data shown are representative of the results of ten experiments.

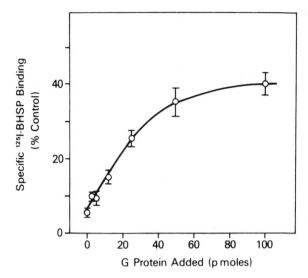

FIGURE 8. Dependence of ^{125}I-SP binding on the amount of G proteins added to pH 11.5–treated membranes. Purified G proteins (G_o/G_i) were incorporated into pH 11.5–treated membranes using the cholate dilution procedure. Specific ^{125}I-SP binding to reconstituted membranes (~ 100 µg of membrane protein plus specified amounts of G_o/G_i) was determined in triplicate. Data are the mean ± SD values expressed as percentages of the specific binding to control membranes measured under the same experimental conditions.

SP Receptor–G Protein Coupling

The initial suggestion that the SP receptor is coupled to a G protein was a consequence of the observation that the binding of SP to receptors in brain and salivary gland is inhibited in the presence of guanine nucleotides.[5,24–26] Typically, receptors linked to G proteins have decreased affinity (increased K_D) in response to guanine nucleotides; however, the observed effect in these studies was a decrease in the number of binding sites (decrease in B_{max}). A possible reason for this apparent loss of binding sites was that the affinity was decreased to such a great extent that low-affinity binding could not be detected by standard filtration assays.

To see if we could find evidence for conversion of high-affinity binding to low-affinity binding in the presence of guanine nucleotides, we modified the binding assay in order to detect low-affinity, rapidly dissociating ^{125}I-SP binding.[27] Using this assay, we were able to show that the effect of guanine nucleotides is to markedly decrease the binding affinity. Thus, in the presence of 5'-guanylyl imidodiphosphate (GppNHp), there was a >20-fold increase in the K_D as determined by Scatchard analysis and the concentration of SP required to inhibit half of the ^{125}I-SP binding (IC$_{50}$) increased ~ 30-fold. Consistent with a marked decrease in affinity, there was an ~ 100-fold increase in the rate of dissociation of ^{125}I-SP following the addition of GppNHp (FIGURE 7).

In a separate study,[8] we provided the first direct evidence that these effects of guanine nucleotides are mediated by a G protein that is required for the expression of high-affinity binding of SP to its receptor. This conclusion was based on the observation that treatment of rat submaxillary gland membranes with alkaline buffer (pH 11.5) caused a loss of high-affinity, guanine nucleotide–sensitive binding of ^{125}I-SP and a parallel loss of [^{35}S]-GTPγS binding activity. Reconstitution of the alkaline-treated membranes with purified G proteins (G$_o$ and G$_i$) from bovine brain restored high-affinity ^{125}I-SP binding. Recovery of high-affinity binding was dependent on the amount of G protein added and was maximal when the G proteins were incorporated at a 30-fold stoichiometric excess of [^{35}S]-GTPγS binding sites over SP binding sites (FIGURE 8).

The high-affinity binding of ^{125}I-SP to native and reconstituted membranes was inhibited competitively by adding SP with the same IC$_{50}$ = 1 nM (FIGURE 9). Because, under the experimental conditions used, the IC$_{50}$ is a measure of the K_D for SP, this result indicates that SP binds with the same affinity to receptor in native and reconstituted membranes. The reconstituted high-affinity binding was abolished by addition of GppNHp or GTPγS, confirming the role of G proteins in the reconstituted binding. Interestingly, the concentration dependencies for inhibition by these two guanine nucleotides were the same in reconstituted and native membranes (FIGURE 10), suggesting that the SP receptor in salivary gland membranes is coupled to an endogenous G protein that possesses a nucleotide specificity similar to G$_o$ and G$_i$. In contrast, only the binding to reconstituted membranes was affected by pertussis toxin (PTX), an enzyme that catalyzes the ADP-ribosylation of G$_i$ and G$_o$ and prevents their interaction with receptors. The lack of a PTX effect on SP binding to native membranes suggests that the endogenous G protein that couples to SP receptors in salivary gland is not a PTX substrate and is consistent with functional studies that have suggested a role for a PTX-insensitive G protein in SP stimulation of PLC activity in submaxillary gland cells.[28]

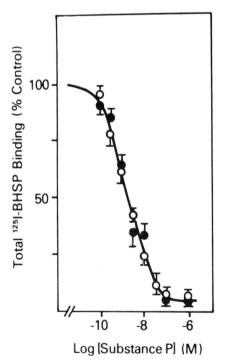

FIGURE 9. Inhibition by SP of ^{125}I-SP binding to untreated and reconstituted pH 11.5–treated membranes. ^{125}I-SP binding to untreated membranes (○) and to pH 11.5–treated membranes reconstituted with G$_o$/G$_i$ at a 333-fold molar ratio of GTPγS binding sites to SP binding sites (●) was determined following a 30-min incubation with 0.2 nM ^{125}I-SP and the specified concentrations of SP. Data are the mean ± SD values expressed as percentages of the specific binding measured in the absence of added SP.

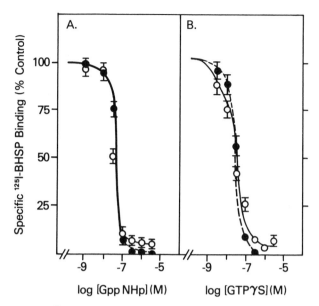

FIGURE 10. Specific ^{125}I-SP binding to untreated and reconstituted pH 11.5–treated membranes in the presence of guanyl nucleotides. ^{125}I-SP binding to untreated membranes (○) and to pH 11.5–treated membranes reconstituted with G_o/G_i (●) was determined following equilibration with 0.2 nM ^{125}I-SP in the presence of the specified concentrations of GppNHp (A) and GTPγS (B). Data are the means of triplicate determinations of the specific component of ^{125}I-SP binding expressed as percentages of the binding observed in the absence of added guanine nucleotide. The data in A are from a single experiment, which was repeated three times with similar results. The data in B are from a representative experiment, which was performed twice.

Purification of the G protein associated with the SP receptor in salivary gland will be an important next step leading to the eventual elucidation of its amino acid sequence. The reconstitution procedure we developed should also be useful in achieving this goal because it can serve during chromatographic fractionation as a convenient functional and sensitive assay (see FIGURE 8) to identify active G proteins and to distinguish those with PTX-insensitive activity.

ACKNOWLEDGMENTS

We wish to express our gratitude to Janet Hoogasian and Carl White for technical assistance and to Gaile Arcouette-Curtis for preparation of the manuscript.

REFERENCES

1. HANLEY, M. R., C. M. LEE, L. M. JONES & R. H. MITCHELL. 1980. Similar effects of substance P and related peptides on salivation and on phosphatidylinositol turnover in rat salivary glands. Mol. Pharmacol. **18:** 78–83.

2. WATSON, S. P. & C. P. DOWNES. 1983. Substance P induced hydrolysis of inositol phospholipids in guinea-pig ileum and rat hypothalamus. Eur. J. Pharmacol. **93:** 245–253.

3. BERRIDGE, M. J. & R. F. IRVINE. 1984. Inositol trisphosphate, a novel second messenger in cellular signal transduction. Nature **312:** 315–321.

4. MANTYH, P. W., R. D. PINNOCK, C. P. DOWNES, M. GOEDERT & S. P. HUNT. 1984. Correlation between inositol phospholipid hydrolysis and substance P receptors in rat CNS. Nature **309:** 795–797.

5. LEE, C-M., J. A. JAVITCH & S. H. SNYDER. 1983. ^{3}H–Substance P binding to salivary gland membranes. Mol. Pharmacol. **23:** 563–569.

6. TAYLOR, C. W., J. E. MERRITT, J. W. PUTNEY & R. P. RUBIN. 1986. A guanine nucleotide–dependent regulatory protein couples substance P receptors to phospholipase C in rat parotid gland. Biochem. Biophys. Res. Commun. **136:** 362–368.

7. NAKAJIMA, Y., S. NAKAJIMA & N. INOUE. 1988. Pertussis toxin–insensitive G protein mediates substance P–induced inhibition of potassium channels in brain neurons. Proc. Natl. Acad. Sci. U.S.A. **85:** 3643–3647.

8. MACDONALD, S. G. & N. D. BOYD. 1989. Regulation of substance P receptor affinity by guanine nucleotide binding proteins. J. Neurochem. **53:** 264–271.

9. YOKOTA, Y., Y. SASAI, K. TANAKA, T. FUJIWARA, K. TSUCHIDA, R. SHIGEMOTO, A. KAKIZUKA, H. OHKUBO & S. NAKANISHI. 1989. Molecular characterization of a functional cDNA for rat substance P receptor. J. Biol. Chem. **264:** 17649–17652.

10. HERSHEY, A. D. & J. E. KRAUSE. 1990. Molecular characterization of a functional cDNA encoding the rat substance P receptor. Science **247:** 958–962.

11. BOYD, N. D., C. F. WHITE, R. CERPA, E. T. KAISER & S. E. LEEMAN. 1991. Photoaffinity labeling with substance P receptor using a derivative or substance P containing p-benzoyl phenylalanine. Biochemistry **30:** 336–342.

12. STERNWEIS, P. C. & J. D. ROBISHAW. 1984. Isolation of two proteins with high affinity for guanine nucleotides from membranes of bovine brain. J. Biol. Chem. **259:** 13806–13813.

13. LAEMMLI, U. K. 1970. Nature **227:** 680–685.

14. BRESLOW, R. 1980. Acc. Chem. Res. **13:** 170–177.

15. MAGGIO, J. E. 1988. Tachykinins. Annu. Rev. Neurosci. **11:** 13–28.

16. VIGER, A., J. C. BEAUJOUAN, Y. TORRENS & J. GLOWINSKI. 1983. Specific binding of a ^{125}I–substance P derivative to rat brain synaptosomes. J. Neurochem. **40:** 1030–1038.

17. LIANG, T. & M. A. CASCIERI. 1981. Substance P on parotid cell membranes. J. Neurosci. **10:** 1133–1140.

18. CASCIERI, M. A., G. G. CHICCHI & T. LIANG. 1985. Substance P receptor on parotid cell membranes. J. Biol. Chem. **260:** 1501–1507.

19. BUCK, S. H., E. BURCHER, C. W. SHULTS, W. LOVENBERG & T. L. O'DONOHUE. 1984. Novel pharmacology of substance K–binding sites: a third type of tachykinin receptor. Science **226:** 987–989.

20. REGOLI, D., G. DRAPEAU, S. DION & R. COUTURE. 1988. New selective agonists for neurokinin receptors: pharmacological tools for receptor characterization. Trends Pharmacol. Sci. **9:** 290–295.

21. HELENE, C. 1972. Photochem. Photobiol. **16:** 519–522.

22. BENOVIC, J. L., G. L. STILES, R. J. LEFKOWITZ & M. G. CARON. 1984. Biochem. Biophys. Res. Commun. **110:** 504–511.

23. AMLAIKY, N. & M. G. CARON. 1986. J. Neurochem. **47:** 196–204.

24. CASCIERI, M. A. & T. LIANG. 1983. Characterization of the substance P receptor in rat brain cortex membranes and the inhibition of radioligand binding by guanine nucleotides. J. Biol. Chem. **258:** 5158.

25. BAHOUTH, S. W. & J. M. MUSACCHIO. 1985. Specific binding of [^{3}H]–substance P to the rat submaxillary gland: the effects of ions and guanine nucleotides. J. Pharmacol. Exp. Ther. **234:** 326.

26. SHARMA, P. M. & J. M. MUSACCHIO. 1987. N-Ethylmaleimide blocks the modulatory effects of divalent cations and guanine nucleotides on the brain substance P receptor. Eur. J. Pharmacol. **138:** 9.

27. LUBER-NAROD, J., N. D. BOYD & S. E. LEEMAN. 1990. Guanine nucleotides decrease the affinity of substance P binding to its receptor. Eur. J. Pharmacol. (Mol. Pharmacol. Sect.) **188:** 185–191.

28. LANIYONU, A., E. SLIWINSKI-LIS & N. FLEMING. 1988. Different tachykinin receptor subtypes are coupled to the phosphoinositide and cyclic AMP signal transduction pathways in rat submaxillary glands. FEBS Lett. **240:** 186–190.

Role of Inositol Phosphates in the Actions of Substance P on NK$_1$ Receptors in Exocrine Gland Cells

JAMES W. PUTNEY, JR., GARY ST. J. BIRD,
DEBRA A. HORSTMAN, ARLENE R. HUGHES,
FRANK S. MENNITI, KATSUMI NOGIMORI,
JOHNNY OBIE, KERRY G. OLIVER, HIROSHI SUGIYA,
AND HARUO TAKEMURA

Calcium Regulation Section
Laboratory of Cellular and Molecular Pharmacology
National Institute of Environmental Health Sciences
Research Triangle Park, North Carolina 27709

INTRODUCTION

A wide variety of peptide hormones and neurotransmitters are known to stimulate the turnover of membrane phosphoinositides.[1] Our understanding of the significance of this phenomenon began with the 1975 review by Michell.[2] Michell noted that the receptors that stimulated phosphoinositide turnover also activated Ca^{2+}-dependent processes in the cell and thus proposed that receptor-stimulated phosphoinositide turnover serves as the link between these receptors and cellular Ca^{2+} signaling.[2] Today, we know that the stimulated turnover of inositol lipids results from the phospholipase C–catalyzed hydrolysis of a quantitatively minor phosphoinositide, phosphatidylinositol 4,5-bisphosphate (PIP$_2$), resulting in the formation of water-soluble inositol 1,4,5-trisphosphate [(1,4,5)IP$_3$] and lipid-soluble diacylglycerol. In 1983, Berridge proposed that (1,4,5)IP$_3$ was the likely intracellular messenger that stimulated release of Ca^{2+} from intracellular stores.[3] Soon thereafter, the effects of (1,4,5)IP$_3$ on Ca^{2+} mobilization were demonstrated in permeabilized pancreatic acinar cells,[4] where it was found that micromolar concentrations of (1,4,5)IP$_3$ rapidly released Ca^{2+} from a nonmitochondrial store. These results were quickly confirmed for other cell types in other laboratories.[3,5] At present, the evidence is compelling that (1,4,5)IP$_3$, generated upon the activation of Ca^{2+}-mobilizing receptors, releases Ca^{2+} from intracellular stores.

This review briefly summarizes some of the current issues regarding the regulation of cellular Ca^{2+} metabolism by inositol phosphates. The emphasis will be on examples from studies of the actions of substance P on NK$_1$ receptors in exocrine gland cells.

INOSITOL PHOSPHATES AND THE ACTIONS OF SUBSTANCE P

Nonexcitable exocrine gland cells have served as excellent models for investigating the roles of inositol phosphates and Ca^{2+} signaling in the actions of substance P. Indeed, it was the potent sialagogic action of substance P that provided the basis for its isolation by Chang and Leeman.[6] In rat parotid gland, substance P was found to stimulate breakdown[7] and turnover[8] of inositol lipids and this was subsequently shown to involve degradation of PIP_2,[9] and generation of $(1,4,5)IP_3$.[10,11] Substance P methyl ester activates $(1,4,5)IP_3$ formation in parotid cells with a potency and efficacy approaching that of substance P,[12] indicating that the receptor type in these cells is the SP-P type or, in the modern nomenclature, NK_1.[13] The activation of phospholipase C in parotid gland by substance P appears to involve a guanine nucleotide–dependent regulatory protein,[14] as has been shown for a variety of phospholipase C–linked receptors.[15] Associated with this hydrolysis of polyphosphoinositides, substance P causes a rapid increase in cytosolic Ca^{2+} ($[Ca^{2+}]_i$) in parotid acinar cells, attributable to a release of intracellular Ca^{2+}, followed by an influx of Ca^{2+} from the extracellular space.[16–19] $(1,4,5)IP_3$ rapidly releases Ca^{2+} from an intracellular store in permeabilized parotid acinar cells[20–22] and, thus, it is likely that this action of $(1,4,5)IP_3$ is responsible for the initial intracellular release of Ca^{2+} seen in intact cells stimulated with substance P. The mechanism by which substance P and other agonists of this class regulate Ca^{2+} entry is less well understood and is discussed herein in more detail.

AR4-2J is a cell line derived from a rat exocrine pancreatoma.[23] Unlike the nontransformed rat exocrine pancreatic acinar cells, AR4-2J cells express functional receptors for substance P and Womack *et al.*[23] have pointed out their potential utility for investigations into substance P receptor mechanisms. As shown in FIGURE 1, these cells respond to substance P methyl ester with increases in $[Ca^{2+}]_i$ along with increases in $(1,4,5)IP_3$, indicating the presence of an NK_1-type receptor. In AR4-2J cells, it was possible to devise experimental conditions for labeling cellular inositol lipids with $[^3H]$-inositol to demonstrate isotopic equilibrium.[24] This has permitted estimation of the mass of the inositol phosphates formed on activation of substance P receptors in these cells without the necessity of assumptions regarding homogeneity of labeling of cellular lipid pools. Thus, it has been demonstrated that, in AR4-2J cells, the basal level of $(1,4,5)IP_3$ appeared to be around 2 μM and was increased by substance P activation to around 20 μM.[24] This finding was surprising in light of the observation that, in permeable AR4-2J cells, $(1,4,5)IP_3$ released intracellular Ca^{2+} with an apparent K_D of around 100 nM.[25] Whereas the identity of the material as $(1,4,5)IP_3$ in these studies was based solely on the chromatographic mobility of the $[^3H]$-labeled material, qualitative analysis of the apparent $(1,4,5)IP_3$ formed in these cells revealed in a subsequent report that this material, in both basal and stimulated cells, was essentially pure $(1,4,5)IP_3$.[26] Furthermore, subcellular fractionation and cell permeabilization studies failed to detect substantial compartmentalization of $(1,4,5)IP_3$ in these cells.[25] Thus, it is possible that the sensitivity of $(1,4,5)IP_3$ receptors is regulated by an unknown mechanism in AR4-2J cells as well as in other cell types.

METABOLISM OF INOSITOL PHOSPHATES

Initially, the metabolism of inositol polyphosphates generated in response to the activation of surface membrane receptors was thought to be a rather simple process. It was believed that $(1,4,5)IP_3$ was dephosphorylated to $(1,4)IP_2$, to $(1)IP$, and finally to free inositol by a lithium-sensitive inositol 1-phosphatase. More recently, the pathways of inositol phosphate metabolism have become much more complex.[27,28] This is attributable largely to the development of HPLC analytical procedures that can resolve inositol phosphates with only subtle differences in structure. $(1,4,5)IP_3$ is dephosphorylated by a 5-phosphatase to $(1,4)IP_2$,[29] and $(1,4)IP_2$ is believed to be dephosphorylated almost exclusively to $(4)IP$ by $(1,3,4)IP_3/(1,4)IP_2$-1-phosphatase.[30]

In addition to the dephosphorylation of $(1,4,5)IP_3$ by the 5-phosphatase, most tissues contain a 3-kinase, which transfers a phosphate from ATP to the 3-position of $(1,4,5)IP_3$ to form $(1,3,4,5)IP_4$.[31] This molecule is then dephosphorylated by the same 5-phosphatase that degrades $(1,4,5)IP_3$ to form an isomeric inositol trisphosphate, $(1,3,4)IP_3$. $(1,3,4)IP_3$ is then dephosphorylated by the $(1,3,4)IP_3/(1,4)IP_2$-1-phos-

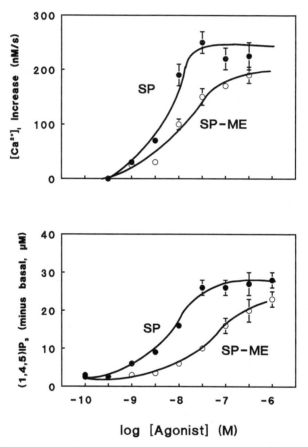

FIGURE 1. Concentration-effect curves for the rate of increase in $[Ca^{2+}]_i$ (top) and the net increase in $[^3H](1,4,5)IP_3$ (bottom) in AR4-2J cells in response to substance P (●) or substance P methyl ester (○). The methods for loading cells with fura-2 for measurement of $[Ca^{2+}]_i$ and for loading cells with $[^3H]$-inositol for measurements of $[^3H](1,4,5)IP_3$ formation were as described previously.[24] Means ± SEM from 4–5 determinations.

phatase to $(3,4)IP_2$[30] and to $(1,3)IP_2$[32] by an enzyme that is not well characterized. These bisphosphates are then dephosphorylated primarily to a mixture of $(1)IP$ and $(3)IP$, which are stereoisomers, and they are not resolved by conventional HPLC.

The complexity of the metabolic pathway for metabolism of $(1,4,5)IP_3$ suggests that other biological functions in addition to the Ca^{2+}-mobilizing actions of $(1,4,5)IP_3$

may be regulated by one or more of these metabolites. For example, there is substantial evidence for biological activity of $(1,3,4,5)IP_4$ either in potentiating the action of $(1,4,5)IP_3$ or in modulating Ca^{2+} entry in a variety of cell types.[33-36] However, studies on the effects of substance P on inositol phosphate metabolism and on Ca^{2+} signaling in AR4-2J pancreatoma cells cast doubt on an obligatory role for $(1,3,4,5)IP_4$ in this instance. One notable difference between these cells and the acinar cells from which they are presumably derived is a deficiency in the 3-kinase enzyme responsible for formation of $(1,3,4,5)IP_4$. Therefore, when AR4-2J cells were stimulated with substance P, there was a substantial increase in the cellular level of $(1,4,5)IP_3$, but no detectable increase in the level of $(1,3,4,5)IP_4$.[24] In addition, metabolites of $(1,3,4,5)IP_4$ were not increased, even in the presence of the inositol monophosphatase inhibitor, LiCl. This is in part due to the low level of the 3-kinase enzyme and in part due to the rapid and complete desensitization of the substance P response in these cells (see discussion later).[37] Thus, AR4-2J cells, under these specific culture conditions, make no detectable $(1,3,4,5)IP_4$ upon stimulation.[24] However, in studies with the intracellular Ca^{2+} indicator, fura-2, substance P caused a substantial mobilization of cellular Ca^{2+}. This rise in cytosolic $[Ca^{2+}]$ was partially dependent on external Ca^{2+} and was partially, but not completely, inhibited by the Ca^{2+} antagonist, La^{3+}.[24] Hence, these cells appear capable of responding to agonist activation by release of intracellular Ca^{2+} and by entry of Ca^{2+} across the plasma membrane, despite the inability to phosphorylate substantial quantities of $(1,4,5)IP_3$ to $(1,3,4,5)IP_4$.[24]

Interestingly, with agonists capable of causing sustained activation of phospholipase C, low levels of $(1,3,4,5)IP_4$ accumulate.[38] This provides precursors for the synthesis of $(1,3,4,5,6)IP_5$ in these cells, which, in turn, is hydrolyzed to $(3,4,5,6)IP_4$ in response to agonist activation.[38] The significance of this latter inositol tetrakisphosphate isomer in cellular signaling in the AR4-2J cells is not known.

CALCIUM ENTRY

Whereas the role of $(1,4,5)IP_3$ as the primary signal for the intracellular release phase of Ca^{2+} mobilization is now firmly established, the regulation of calcium entry, or the second phase of calcium mobilization, is poorly understood.[39,40] In at least one instance, the direct regulation of a plasma membrane Ca^{2+} channel by an activated receptor has been convincingly demonstrated.[41] On the other hand, in many systems, intracellular Ca^{2+} release and Ca^{2+} entry appear to be coordinately regulated by $(1,4,5)IP_3$. For example, injection of $(1,4,5)IP_3$ into sea urchin eggs, lacrimal gland cells, and mast cells produces a response pattern suggestive of an activation of both intracellular calcium release and entry of calcium from the extracellular space.[33-35,42-45] These findings suggest that $(1,4,5)IP_3$, alone or perhaps together with one of its metabolites, can activate both phases of cellular Ca^{2+} mobilization. As discussed previously, the presence of $(1,3,4,5)IP_4$ was necessary in some,[33-35,43] but not all[42,44,45] cases for full expression of the response, especially the second, Ca^{2+} entry phase. In most studies, $(1,4,5)IP_3$ applied directly to plasma membranes did not increase their Ca^{2+} permeability.[46-48] However, $(1,4,5)IP_3$ appeared to increase the permeability of plasma membrane vesicles to Ca^{2+} in one study[49] and, in B-lymphocytes, $(1,4,5)IP_3$ was reported to increase a Ca^{2+} current in excised membrane patches.[50] In mast cells, injection of $(1,4,5)IP_3$ increased Ca^{2+} entry by a conductive (but not voltage-activated) pathway, but a $(1,4,5)IP_3$-regulated Ca^{2+} channel was not identified.[45] These observations suggest that Ca^{2+} entry may be regulated by a variety of different mechanisms. There is considerable evidence that $(1,4,5)IP_3$ may be responsible for the activation of calcium entry in many cell types, but not by acting directly on a plasma membrane channel.

One mechanism by which this could be accomplished would involve a coupling between the internal release of Ca^{2+} and the entry of extracellular Ca^{2+}. An early version of this idea appeared in a report in 1977, in which a model was proposed to explain the rapid replenishment of agonist-sensitive Ca^{2+} stores from the extracellular space following their discharge by a muscarinic-cholinergic agonist in parotid acinar cells.[51] Although this model depicted the surface membrane Ca^{2+} channels and the agonist-regulated intracellular Ca^{2+} stores connected in series, its major flaw was the placement of the intracellular pool in the plasma membrane rather than as a discrete organelle within the cell. Subsequently, a model for the relationship between Ca^{2+} entry and internal release was proposed by Casteels and Droogmans[52] according to which Ca^{2+} flows into the cytoplasm of smooth muscle cells through a process of constant refilling and discharging of the internal pools. In this model and in a subsequent one that encompassed the role of $(1,4,5)IP_3$ in this process,[40] the flow of Ca^{2+} into the pool was proposed to occur by a pathway that did not traverse the major cytoplasmic compartment. Today, the view of regulated Ca^{2+} entry by agonists such as substance P in nonexcitable cells involves not only a mechanism of regulation of Ca^{2+} entry by the state of the intracellular Ca^{2+} pool, but it is also now believed that the pathway for entry of Ca^{2+} is a direct one into the cytoplasm rather than a cycle of filling and emptying of the regulated Ca^{2+} pool.[53,54] A critical tool in investigating this process has been the nonphorbol ester tumor promoter, thapsigargin, which has been shown to discharge the agonist-sensitive intracellular Ca^{2+} pool by inhibiting the ATP-dependent Ca^{2+} uptake process necessary for maintaining this intracellular store.[55] The depletion of the agonist-sensitive intracellular Ca^{2+} pool by thapsigargin results in quantitative and qualitative mimicry of the actions of phosphoinositide-linked agonists in activating Ca^{2+} entry[53,56] and thus provides an experimental paradigm for investigating the mechanisms underlying this poorly understood, but elegantly coordinated signaling system.

REGULATION OF SUBSTANCE P RECEPTORS

The increase in cellular $(1,4,5)IP_3$ in parotid acinar cells as well as in AR4-2J cells following application of a supramaximal concentration of substance P is largely a transient phenomenon, lasting on average from 1 to 2 minutes.[11,37] Thus, as for many peptide receptors, the substance P receptor on exocrine gland cells undergoes rapid and substantial desensitization. Although the onset of this desensitization is rapid, occurring over an interval of from 5 to 30 seconds after agonist addition, the desensitization is quite persistent, requiring 1 or 2 hours after removal of agonist to restore full responsiveness.[11] Interestingly, in parotid cells in the continued presence of substance P, a residual steady-state increased level of $(1,4,5)IP_3$ is maintained for long periods after the initial transient response, whereas the response returns to baseline in AR4-2J cells. Thus, although desensitization is equally rapid in onset and equally persistent in the two cell types, it appears that the desensitization process is a complete one in AR4-2J cells and a partial one in parotid cells. The simplest explanation for this discrepancy is that the residual response in parotid cells results from a population of substance P receptors that are not susceptible to desensitization and that this subpopulation of receptors is missing from the AR4-2J cells. However, there is as yet no direct evidence for such heterogeneity of substance P receptors in parotid cells.

The desensitization of the substance P response appears to be homologous because activation of other phospholipase C–linked receptors does not produce persistent desensitization of the substance P response and, following the induction of persistent desensitization of the substance P response, subsequent responses to agonists acting on other phospholipase C–linked receptors are not attenuated.[11] Associated with the development of desensitization in parotid cells is a loss of surface binding sites for substance P, indicating that desensitization may reflect sequestration and down-regulation of the substance P receptors.

There are numerous documented instances of desensitization of the phospholipase C–coupled receptor that are believed to be mediated through activation of protein kinase C.[57-65] The primary evidence for such a mechanism comes from the observation that phorbol esters, potent activators of protein kinase C, inhibit cellular responses to agonists of this class. This mechanism is believed to represent a negative feedback mechanism because activation of phospholipase C would increase cellular levels of diacylglycerol, the physiological activator of protein kinase C. However, the findings with the NK_1 substance P receptor in exocrine gland cells suggest that it may be incorrect, or at least premature, to conclude that such a mechanism contributes to regulation of these signaling pathways during agonist stimulation. Whereas phorbol esters in parotid acinar cells inhibit substance P–induced $(1,4,5)IP_3$ formation,[66] the activation of protein kinase C does not appear to be involved in the persistent desensitization seen in these cells for the following reasons: (i) the desensitization is homologous in nature,[11] whereas inhibitory mechanisms attributed to second messengers should be equally activated by other phospholipase C–linked agonists; (ii) it is possible to dissociate activation of phospholipase C from desensitization by addition of antimycin, which completely blocks substance P–induced $(1,4,5)IP_3$ formation without inhibiting the development of persistent desensitization;[12] (iii) unlike the agonist-induced persistent desensitization, the inhibitory effects of phorbol esters are rapidly reversed upon removal of the drug, and phorbol esters do not cause a loss of surface membrane binding sites for substance P;[66] and (iv) drugs that inhibit protein kinase C completely prevent the inhibitory effects of phorbol esters on the substance P response, but do not affect either the time course of $(1,4,5)IP_3$ generation due to substance P receptor activation nor the development of persistent desensitization.[67]

For the case of homologous desensitization of NK_1 as well as other phospholipase C–linked receptors, a mechanism may operate that is similar to that for the more extensively studied adenylyl cyclase–coupled β-adrenergic receptor.[68] For this receptor, homologous desensitization also results in receptor sequestration and down-regulation and is believed to be signaled by the phosphorylation of the receptor by a specific β-adrenergic receptor kinase.[69] This mechanism provides a reasonable working hypothesis for future studies on the regulation of the phospholipase C–linked NK_1 substance P receptor in exocrine gland cells and other substance P–responsive systems.

CONCLUSIONS

This review has attempted to summarize some of our current knowledge about the mechanisms by which cellular Ca^{2+} is regulated by phospholipase C–linked NK_1 substance P receptors in exocrine gland cells (FIGURE 2). It is well established that the initial, agonist-induced $[Ca^{2+}]_i$ signal in many cells is derived from the Ca^{2+}-releasing actions of $(1,4,5)IP_3$ on at least one specific intracellular Ca^{2+}-sequestering organelle and there is substantial evidence that this mechanism applies to the substance P receptor in exocrine gland cells as well. The metabolism of $(1,4,5)IP_3$ formed in activated cells is exceedingly complex and the significance of this complexity to cellular signaling mechanisms is not yet fully understood. In virtually all cells that utilize the phosphoinositide-linked Ca^{2+} signaling system, the initial release of intracellular Ca^{2+} due to agonist activation is followed or accompanied by an accelerated entry of Ca^{2+} into the cytoplasm across the plasma membrane. The mechanism by which this process is regulated has been somewhat more elusive and may vary in different cellular systems. Yet, there is strong evidence in many cell

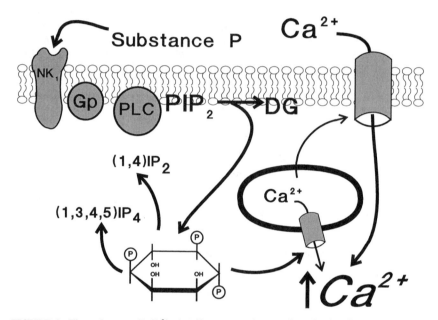

FIGURE 2. The substance P–Ca^{2+} signaling system in exocrine gland cells. In these cells, substance P acts primarily through NK_1 receptors to activate a polyphosphoinositide-specific phospholipase C (PLC) via an intermediary guanine nucleotide–dependent regulatory protein (Gp). This phospholipase C cleaves phosphatidylinositol 4,5-bisphosphate (PIP_2) into diacylglycerol (DG) and inositol 1,4,5-trisphosphate. The latter is metabolized either by dephosphorylation to inositol 1,4-bisphosphate [$(1,4)IP_2$] or by phosphorylation to inositol 1,3,4,5-tetrakisphosphate [$(1,3,4,5)IP_4$]. Inositol 1,4,5-trisphosphate acts to cause the discharge of Ca^{2+} from an intracellular organelle and the depletion of Ca^{2+} from this organelle may secondarily signal Ca^{2+} entry across the plasma membrane.

types, including exocrine gland cells, that depletion of agonist-sensitive intracellular Ca^{2+} stores by $(1,4,5)IP_3$ generates a secondary signal of unknown nature that activates Ca^{2+} entry. The relationship between the levels of $(1,4,5)IP_3$ generated in AR4-2J cells stimulated with substance P and the ensuing Ca^{2+} signals has been investigated in some detail. A paradox exists in that the basal and stimulated levels of $(1,4,5)IP_3$ are considerably above the concentration range over which mobilization of Ca^{2+} is observed in permeabilized cells; this may indicate that mechanisms exist for dynamic regulation of the sensitivity of the $(1,4,5)IP_3$ signaling system in intact cells.

Clearly, there are rapid mechanisms for regulating the substance P signaling system in exocrine cells at the level of the receptor. A rapid loss of surface membrane binding sites is observed in substance P–stimulated cells, representing a mechanism for homologous desensitization of this pathway. The continued investigation of these and other interesting aspects of the phospholipase C–linked NK_1 substance P receptor pathway in exocrine gland cells should provide us with many additional insights into the complex control mechanisms underlying this intriguing peptide signaling system.

REFERENCES

1. PUTNEY, J. W., JR. 1986. Phosphoinositides and Receptor Mechanisms. Alan R. Liss. New York.
2. MICHELL, R. H. 1975. Biochim. Biophys. Acta **415**: 81–147.
3. BERRIDGE, M. J. 1983. Biochem. J. **212**: 849–858.
4. STREB, H., R. F. IRVINE, M. J. BERRIDGE & I. SCHULZ. 1983. Nature **306**: 67–68.
5. JOSEPH, S. K., A. P. THOMAS, R. J. WILLIAMS, R. F. IRVINE & J. R. WILLIAMSON. 1984. J. Biol. Chem. **259**: 3077–3081.
6. CHANG, M. M. & S. E. LEEMAN. 1970. J. Biol. Chem. **245**: 4784–4790.
7. JONES, L. M. & R. H. MICHELL. 1978. Biochem. Soc. Trans. **6**: 1035–1037.
8. HANLEY, M. R., C. M. LEE, L. M. JONES & R. H. MICHELL. 1980. Mol. Pharmacol. **18**: 78–83.
9. WEISS, S. J., J. S. McKINNEY & J. W. PUTNEY, JR. 1982. Biochem. J. **206**: 555–560.
10. AUB, D. L. & J. W. PUTNEY, JR. 1985. Biochem. J. **225**: 263–266.
11. SUGIYA, H., K. A. TENNES & J. W. PUTNEY, JR. 1987. Biochem. J. **244**: 647–653.
12. SUGIYA, H. & J. W. PUTNEY, JR. 1988. Am. J. Physiol. **255**: C149–C154.
13. WATSON, S. P. & A. ABBOTT. 1990. Trends Pharmacol. Sci. **11**(suppl.): 25–26.
14. TAYLOR, C. W., J. E. MERRITT, J. W. PUTNEY, JR. & R. P. RUBIN. 1986. Biochem. Biophys. Res. Commun. **136**: 362–368.
15. TAYLOR, C. W. & J. E. MERRITT. 1986. Trends Pharmacol. Sci. **7**: 238–242.
16. RUDICH, L. & F. R. BUTCHER. 1976. Biochim. Biophys. Acta **444**: 704–711.
17. MARIER, S. H., J. W. PUTNEY, JR. & C. M. VAN DE WALLE. 1978. J. Physiol. (London) **279**: 141–151.
18. MERRITT, J. E. & T. J. RINK. 1987. J. Biol. Chem. **262**: 14912–14916.
19. MERRITT, J. E. & T. J. RINK. 1987. J. Biol. Chem. **262**: 17362–17369.
20. SCHULZ, I., H. STREB, E. BAYERDORFFER & F. THEVENOD. 1985. Curr. Eye Res. **4**: 467–473.
21. THEVENOD, F. & I. SCHULZ. 1988. Am. J. Physiol. **255**: G429–G440.
22. PUTNEY, J. W., JR., D. L. AUB, C. W. TAYLOR & J. E. MERRITT. 1986. Fed. Proc. Fed. Am. Soc. Exp. Biol. **45**: 2634–2638.
23. WOMACK, M. D., M. R. HANLEY & T. M. JESSEL. 1985. J. Neurosci. **5**: 3370–3378.
24. HORSTMAN, D. A., H. TAKEMURA & J. W. PUTNEY, JR. 1988. J. Biol. Chem. **263**: 15297–15303.
25. BIRD, G. ST. J., K. G. OLIVER, D. A. HORSTMAN, J. OBIE & J. W. PUTNEY, JR. 1991. Biochem. J. **273**: 541–546.
26. NOGIMORI, K., F. S. MENNITI & J. W. PUTNEY, JR. 1990. Biochem. J. **269**: 195–200.
27. MAJERUS, P. W., T. M. CONNOLLY, V. S. BANSAL, R. C. INHORN, T. S. ROSS & D. L. LIPS. 1988. J. Biol. Chem. **263**: 3051–3054.
28. PUTNEY, J. W., JR. 1987. Trends Pharmacol. Sci. **8**: 481–486.
29. DOWNES, C. P., M. C. MUSSAT & R. H. MICHELL. 1982. Biochem. J. **203**: 169–177.
30. INHORN, R. C., V. S. BANSAL & P. W. MAJERUS. 1987. Proc. Natl. Acad. Sci. U.S.A. **84**: 2170–2174.
31. IRVINE, R. F., A. J. LETCHER, J. P. HESLOP & M. J. BERRIDGE. 1986. Nature **320**: 631–634.
32. BANSAL, V. S., R. C. INHORN & P. W. MAJERUS. 1987. J. Biol. Chem. **262**: 9444–9447.
33. IRVINE, R. F. & R. M. MOOR. 1986. Biochem. J. **240**: 917–920.

34. MORRIS, A. P., D. V. GALLACHER, R. F. IRVINE & O. H. PETERSEN. 1987. Nature **330:** 653–655.
35. CHANGYA, L., D. V. GALLACHER, R. F. IRVINE, B. V. L. POTTER & O. H. PETERSEN. 1989. J. Membr. Biol. **109:** 85–93.
36. CHANGYA, L., D. V. GALLACHER, R. F. IRVINE & O. H. PETERSEN. 1989. FEBS Lett. **251:** 43–48.
37. MENNITI, F. S., H. TAKEMURA, K. G. OLIVER & J. W. PUTNEY, JR. 1991. Mol. Pharmacol. Submitted.
38. MENNITI, F. S., K. G. OLIVER, K. NOGIMORI, J. F. OBIE, S. B. SHEARS & J. W. PUTNEY, JR. 1990. J. Biol. Chem. **265:** 11167–11176.
39. PUTNEY, J. W., JR. 1990. *In* Current Topics in Cellular Regulation. A. Levitzki, Ed. Academic Press. New York.
40. PUTNEY, J. W., JR. 1986. Cell Calcium **7:** 1–12.
41. BENHAM, C. D. & R. W. TSIEN. 1987. Nature **328:** 275–278.
42. SLACK, B. E., J. E. BELL & D. J. BENOS. 1986. Am. J. Physiol. **250:** C340–C344.
43. IRVINE, R. F. & R. M. MOOR. 1987. Biochem. Biophys. Res. Commun. **146:** 284–290.
44. LLANO, I., A. MARTY & J. TANGUY. 1987. Pflügers Arch. **409:** 499–506.
45. PENNER, R., G. MATTHEWS & E. NEHER. 1988. Nature **334:** 499–504.
46. DELFERT, D. M., S. HILL, H. A. PERSHADSINGH & W. R. SHERMAN. 1986. Biochem. J. **236:** 37–44.
47. UEDA, T., S. H. CHURCH, M. W. NOEL & D. L. GILL. 1986. J. Biol. Chem. **261:** 3184–3192.
48. DARGEMONT, C., M. HILLY, M. CLARET & J-P. MAUGER. 1988. Biochem. J. **256:** 117–124.
49. RENGASAMY, A. & H. FEINBERG. 1988. Biochem. Biophys. Res. Commun. **150:** 1021–1026.
50. KUNO, M. & P. GARDNER. 1987. Nature **326:** 301–304.
51. PUTNEY, J. W., JR. 1977. J. Physiol. (London) **268:** 139–149.
52. CASTEELS, R. & G. DROOGMANS. 1981. J. Physiol. (London) **317:** 263–279.
53. TAKEMURA, H., A. R. HUGHES, O. THASTRUP & J. W. PUTNEY, JR. 1989. J. Biol. Chem. **264:** 12266–12271.
54. KWAN, C. Y. & J. W. PUTNEY, JR. 1990. J. Biol. Chem. **265:** 678–684.
55. THASTRUP, O. 1990. Agents Actions **29:** 8–15.
56. THASTRUP, O., A. P. DAWSON, O. SCHARFF, B. FODER, P. J. CULLEN, B. K. DROBAK, P. J. BJERRUM, S. B. CHRISTENSEN & M. R. HANLEY. 1989. Agents Actions **27:** 17–23.
57. JOHNSON, R. M., P. A. CONNELLY, R. B. SISK, B. F. POBINER, E. L. HEWLETT & J. C. GARRISON. 1986. Proc. Natl. Acad. Sci. U.S.A. **83:** 2032–2036.
58. HEPLER, J. R., H. S. EARP & T. K. HARDEN. 1988. J. Biol. Chem. **263:** 7610–7619.
59. CROUCH, M. F. & E. G. LAPETINA. 1989. J. Biol. Chem. **264:** 584–588.
60. WILLEMS, P. H. G. M., I. G. P. VAN NOOIJ, H. E. M. G. HAENEN & J. J. H. H. M. DE PONT. 1987. Biochim. Biophys. Acta **930:** 230–236.
61. ORELLANA, S., P. A. SOLSKI & J. H. BROWN. 1987. J. Biol. Chem. **262:** 1638–1643.
62. LABARCA, R., A. JANOWSKY, J. PATEL & S. M. PAUL. 1984. Biochem. Biophys. Res. Commun. **123:** 703–709.
63. MULDOON, L. L., G. A. JAMIESON, JR. & M. L. VILLEREAL. 1987. J. Cell Physiol. **130:** 29–36.
64. OSUGI, T., T. IMAIZUMI, A. MIZUSHIMA, S. UCHIDA & H. YOSHIDA. 1987. J. Pharmacol. Exp. Ther. **240:** 617–622.
65. LILES, W. C., D. D. HUNTER, K. E. MEIER & N. M. NATHANSON. 1986. J. Biol. Chem. **261:** 5307–5313.
66. SUGIYA, H., J. F. OBIE & J. W. PUTNEY, JR. 1988. Biochem. J. **253:** 459–466.
67. SUGIYA, H. & J. W. PUTNEY, JR. 1988. Biochem. J. **256:** 677–680.
68. BENOVIC, J. L., M. BOUVIER, M. G. CARON & R. J. LEFKOWITZ. 1988. Annu. Rev. Cell Biol. **4:** 405–428.
69. STRASSER, R. H., J. L. BENOVIC, M. G. CARON & R. J. LEFKOWITZ. 1986. Proc. Natl. Acad. Sci. U.S.A. **83:** 6362–6366.

Substance P Induced Inhibition of Potassium Channels via a Pertussis Toxin–insensitive G Protein[a]

YASUKO NAKAJIMA,[b] SHIGEHIRO NAKAJIMA,[c] AND
MASUMI INOUE[d]

[b]Department of Anatomy and Cell Biology
[c]Department of Pharmacology
University of Illinois
College of Medicine at Chicago
Chicago, Illinois 60612

[d]Department of Physiology
Fukuoka University School of Medicine
Fukuoka 814-01, Japan

INTRODUCTION

Substance P, an undecapeptide, is distributed widely, but in a specific fashion in the nervous system.[1,2] It is considered to be a putative neurotransmitter substance.[3] Its main effect is to exert a slow excitatory influence.[4-6] Cholinergic neurons in the nucleus basalis of Meynert receive nerve endings containing substance P–like immunoreactivity[7] and they are also rich in substance P receptors.[8] In humans, these cholinergic neurons seem to play important roles in the etiology of Alzheimer's disease. As for the mode of action of substance P, Adams et al.[9] showed that substance P produces an excitatory action by inhibiting the M-current in sympathetic neurons.

In 1985, we succeeded in making primary dissociated cholinergic neuron cultures from the nucleus basalis of Meynert of the rat.[10] In these cultured cholinergic neurons, we observed that substance P produced a long-lasting depolarization.[10] Subsequently, Stanfield et al.[11] found that this effect of substance P was produced by suppression of the inwardly rectifying K-conductance (also see Yamaguchi et al.[12]).

We have extended our investigation of the substance P effect to the mechanism of the intracellular signal transduction. Although it is known that G proteins mediate the actions of certain inhibitory neurotransmitters,[13-21] it is not clear whether G proteins also play a role in the signal transduction of excitatory neurotransmitters that modulate K-conductance. We have found that the effect of substance P on inward rectification channels is mediated through a G protein that is resistant to pertussis toxin.[22]

MATERIALS AND METHODS

First, brain slices of newborn rats were made and then, by visualizing the basal forebrain region under the dissecting microscope, tissue fragments from the nucleus

[a]This work was supported by NIH Grant No. AG06093 and by an Alzheimer's Disease and Related Disorders Association Grant.

103

basalis were dissected out, dissociated, and cultured.[10] Recently, we have improved our previously reported method[10] by using papain instead of trypsin and by supplementing the culture medium with 5% rat serum and 10% horse serum instead of 10% fetal bovine serum and 10% horse serum.

Electrophysiological experiments were conducted by using the whole-cell patch clamp method.[23] During the experiments, cultures were superfused with an oxygenated Krebs solution containing 1 μM tetrodotoxin. The patch pipette (internal) solution contained 2 mM Na_2ATP and usually 100 μM Na_2GTP. When GTP analogues or GDP analogues were added to the internal solution, GTP was omitted from the internal solution. Substance P was applied by puffing from a glass pipette placed about 40 μm from the cell body. The bath temperature was 33–36 °C.

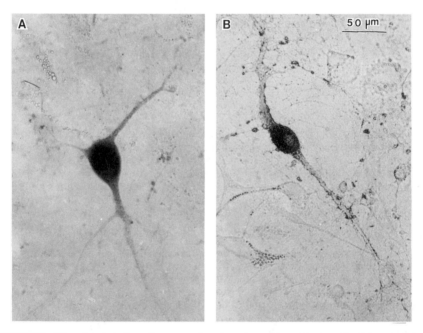

FIGURE 1. Dissociated cholinergic neurons in culture from the nucleus basalis of the rat. (A) A neuron showing immunoreactivity to choline acetyltransferase. Cultured for 21 days. (B) A neuron showing histochemical reaction to acetylcholinesterase. Cultured for 23 days.

RESULTS

The cultured cholinergic neurons from the nucleus basalis were identified with choline acetyltransferase immunocytochemistry. The neurons were large with a mean soma diameter of 23 μm.[10] If we counted only large neurons (20 μm or larger in diameter), about 75% were cholinergic;[10] therefore, we used such large neurons for our experiments. FIGURE 1A shows a large cholinergic neuron having choline acetyltransferase immunoreactivity and FIGURE 1B shows a neuron having a strongly positive acetylcholinesterase histochemical reaction. Levey et al.[24] showed that neurons that are strongly positive to acetylcholinesterase in the basal forebrain nuclei are all cholinergic.

Signal Transduction Mechanisms of Substance P Effects

Brief application of substance P caused a long-lasting depolarization in our cholinergic neurons.[10–12] With the whole-cell voltage clamp method, substance P produced an inward current accompanied by a decline of membrane conductance, which recovered slowly (FIGURE 2A). Analysis of this phenomenon revealed that the substance P effect consisted of suppressing the inwardly rectifying K-conductance.[11,12]

Nonhydrolyzable Analogues of GTP Maintain the Substance P Effect

If substance P binds to its receptors that interact with a G protein, GDP will be dissociated from the G protein and GTP will bind to the G protein. This process activates the G protein. The activation is terminated when GTP is hydrolyzed by the G protein. If hydrolysis-resistant GTP is present, the G protein will be activated almost irreversibly.[25] Thus, we did experiments in which we preloaded neurons with a nonhydrolyzable analogue of GTP such as GTPγS (guanosine 5'-[γ-thio]triphosphate) through a patch pipette.

FIGURE 2A shows a control neuron in which the patch pipette contained the standard internal solution with 100 μM GTP. We waited for five minutes after breaking the patch in order for the GTP in the pipette to equilibrate with the cytosol and then substance P (300 nM) was applied from outside. This produced a decrease in conductance and a slow inward current (corresponding to depolarization) that slowly recovered to the original level. A second application of substance P induced a similar response, but the magnitude of the response was slightly less than the first one, probably due to desensitization. In contrast, when the cell was preloaded with 100 μM GTPγS for five minutes, application of substance P produced an almost irreversible reduction in membrane conductance and an almost irreversible inward current (FIGURE 2B). The second application of substance P failed to produce any further change in membrane conductance. We have computed substance P–sensitive currents by subtracting the current under the substance P influence from the current before the application of substance P. In both control neurons and GTPγS-loaded neurons, the substance P–sensitive currents showed inward rectification and changed polarity at the K-equilibrium potential. These results suggest that a G protein is involved in the substance P–produced suppression of the inward rectification channels. It should be noted that merely loading the cell with GTPγS in the absence of agonists did not seem to produce any effect on the K-channels during the five-minute equilibrating time; this is different from the situation in heart muscle, in which the application of GTPγS alone produced spontaneous effects on K-channels.[16,20]

Gpp(NH)p (5'-guanylyl imidodiphosphate), another hydrolysis-resistant GTP analogue, had an effect similar to GTPγS, but the effect was weaker than that of GTPγS. This is probably due to the fact that the affinity of Gpp(NH)p to G proteins (G_s or G_i) is smaller than that of GTPγS.[25,26] We also intracellularly applied a GDP derivative, GDPβS (guanosine 5'-O-[β-thio]diphosphate), which inhibits the G protein reaction with GTP.[27] However, application of GDPβS even at 500 μM did not significantly decrease the substance P–sensitive conductance. This result may be related to the fact that the affinity of GDPβS to G proteins is less than that of GDP or GTP.[28]

The Substance P Effect Is Pertussis Toxin–insensitive

Pertussis toxin inhibits the action of several G proteins such as G_i, G_o, and G_t by ADP-ribosylation.[29–32] In our study of somatostatin effects on cultured noradrenergic neurons from the locus coeruleus,[21] pretreatment of neurons with pertussis toxin[17] abolished the somatostatin-induced response completely. The somatostatin-induced hyperpolarization is therefore mediated through a pertussis toxin–sensitive G protein, G_i (an inhibitory G protein) or G_o.

In contrast, when the same procedure of pertussis toxin pretreatment (500 ng/mL toxin for 15–22 hours) was applied to cultured cholinergic neurons, the substance P

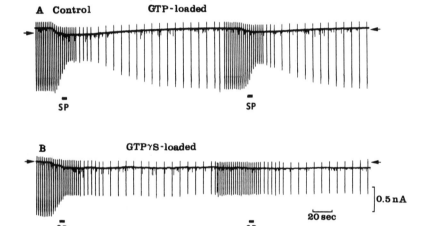

FIGURE 2. The substance P effect on cultured nucleus basalis neurons loaded with GTPγS. Records were obtained five minutes after breaking the patch. Hyperpolarizing square-wave pulses (50 mV, 100 ms) were intermittently imposed. (A) Control neuron loaded with 100 μM GTP: Application of 300 nM substance P (SP) produced a decrease in membrane conductance. This reduction in membrane conductance recovered to the original level in about two minutes and the second application of substance P produced a response similar to the first one. Holding potential, −74 mV. (B) Neuron loaded with 100 μM GTPγS: Application of 300 nM substance P (SP) produced an almost irreversible reduction in membrane conductance and the second application of substance P failed to produce any further change in membrane conductance. Holding potential, −74 mV. (Modified from reference 22.)

effect was not significantly influenced (FIGURE 3), indicating that the G protein that mediates the substance P effect is pertussis toxin–resistant.[22] (Our pertussis toxin pretreatment was appropriate; see reference 22 for details.)

Application of Cyclic AMP and IBMX or SQ22,536 Does Not Influence the Substance P Effect

G_s (a stimulatory G protein) is pertussis toxin–insensitive. Thus, G_s could be the G protein that mediates the substance P effect. G_s is known to stimulate adenylate cyclase and thereby to enhance the production of cyclic AMP. Therefore, we tested

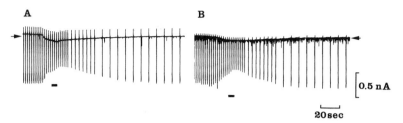

FIGURE 3. Pertussis toxin pretreatment on cultured nucleus basalis neurons. Current records under whole-cell clamp. Hyperpolarizing pulses (50 mV, 100 ms) were intermittently imposed. (A) Control neuron: Application of 300 nM substance P produced a reduction in conductance and an inward shift of the baseline current. Holding potential, -74 mV. (B) Neuron pretreated with pertussis toxin (500 ng/mL) for 18 hours: Application of substance P produced a response similar to that of the control neuron. Holding potential, -74 mV. (Reproduced from reference 22.)

the possible involvement of cyclic AMP in the substance P effect by intracellularly loading neurons with 100 μM cyclic AMP and 1 mM IBMX (3-isobutyl-1-methylxanthine)[18] or by extracellularly applying 100 μM SQ22,536 [9-(tetrahydro-2-furyl)adenine, a gift of the Squibb Institute], which is an inhibitor of adenylate cyclase.[33,34] After these treatments, though, the substance P response was almost normal (FIGURE 4), indicating that the substance P response that we have described is not mediated through the cyclic AMP system.[22] We have recently applied cholera toxin, which ribosylates and activates G_s,[35] and have found that the substance P

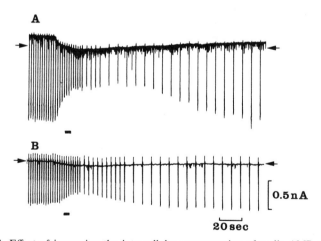

FIGURE 4. Effect of increasing the intracellular concentration of cyclic AMP on cultured nucleus basalis neurons. Hyperpolarizing square pulses were intermittently imposed. (A) Neuron loaded with 100 μM cyclic AMP and 1 mM IBMX. Holding potential, -74 mV. Each hyperpolarizing pulse was 50 mV, 100 ms. (Reproduced from reference 22.) (B) Neuron on which 100 μM SQ22,536 was applied externally. Holding potential, -74 mV. Each pulse consisted of two hyperpolarizing square pulses—one with 20 mV, 100 ms, and the other with 50 mV, 100 ms—with an interval of 200 ms between these two. In both neurons, substance P (300 nM) produced normal responses (inward currents and a decrease in membrane conductance).

response was still normal, suggesting that a direct involvement of α_s does not occur (Kozasa, Nakajima, and Nakajima, unpublished data).

DISCUSSION

We found in basal forebrain cholinergic neurons that a pertussis toxin–insensitive G protein mediates the suppression of inward rectifying potassium channels by substance P, suggesting that G_i, G_o, or G_t does not mediate this effect of substance P. We also obtained data suggesting that G_s does not mediate this effect. Thus, it is likely that this G protein is an unidentified G protein. Almost simultaneously with our report,[22] Pfaffinger[36] reported that a pertussis toxin–insensitive G protein was involved in the modulation of the M-current by muscarine or by t-LHRH in sympathetic neurons.

In a recent review, Gilman and his co-workers[37] suggested that the G protein implicated in our experiments with substance P[22] could correspond to a new G

K-channel

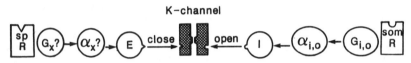

FIGURE 5. Hypothetical scheme based on our results of substance P and somatostatin experiments.[21,22] The same inward rectification channel (K-channel) is modulated by substance P through a pertussis toxin–insensitive G protein and by somatostatin through a pertussis toxin–sensitive G protein. When substance P binds to a substance P receptor (SP R), a pertussis toxin–insensitive G protein ($G_{x?}$) is activated and its α subunit ($\alpha_{x?}$) is released. Whether this α subunit opens K-channels directly or through another messenger (E) is not clear. The somatostatin part of this figure is almost the mirror image of the substance P part. However, the G protein involved in the somatostatin effect is pertussis toxin–sensitive and probably represents G_i or G_o ($G_{i,o}$). The α subunits of these G proteins ($\alpha_{i,o}$) may close the K-channel directly or indirectly through another messenger (I). This scheme represents a cell, such as a locus coeruleus neuron, that has both substance P receptors and somatostatin receptors.

protein, $G_{(x\ or\ z)}$ (G_x and G_z are the same G protein, but named differently), whose cDNA was recently isolated.[38,39] The amino acid sequence of this G protein suggests insensitivity to pertussis toxin because the cysteine residue at the critical position for the toxin sensitivity is replaced by isoleucine. In addition to $G_{(x\ or\ z)}$, there are other pertussis toxin–insensitive G proteins including low molecular weight GTP-binding proteins such as rap 1-b[40] and p21ras. We plan to investigate whether these pertussis toxin–insensitive G proteins modulate the substance P effect. Applying these G proteins (or their α subunits) to the cell membrane or using antibodies against them may give us an answer.

FIGURE 5 shows our hypothetical scheme of the modulation of the inward rectification channel based on our substance P and somatostatin experiments.[12,21,22] It shows that the same inward rectification channel is modulated by substance P and somatostatin in the opposite way. Substance P suppresses the channel through a pertussis toxin–insensitive G protein, whereas somatostatin activates the channel through a pertussis toxin–sensitive G protein (G_i or G_o). Whether α subunits of the G proteins modulate the channel directly or through excitatory or inhibitory messengers (E and I in FIGURE 5) is still an open question. However, recent work by Yatani *et al.*[20] suggests that the α subunit of an inhibitory G protein directly modulates the inward rectification channel in heart muscle. In the experiments described in this report, we used locus coeruleus for studying the somatostatin effect and nucleus basalis for the substance P effect. However, we know that substance P also produces long-lasting excitation in locus coeruleus neurons: this substance P effect on locus coeruleus neurons seems to be derived at least partly from the inhibition of potassium channels.[22,41] Thus, FIGURE 5 is regarded as expressing the situation in locus coeruleus neurons. It is noted that FIGURE 5 is our hypothesis, not a conclusion. Future experiments will test the validity of this hypothesis.

CONCLUSIONS

Inhibition of inward rectification channels by substance P in cultured cholinergic neurons from the nucleus basalis of Meynert of the rat is mediated through a G protein, but not through the cyclic AMP system. The G protein that mediates the substance P effect is insensitive to pertussis toxin and is, as yet, an unidentified G protein.

REFERENCES

1. NILSSON, G., T. HÖKFELT & B. PERNOW. 1974. Distribution of substance P–like immunoreactivity in the rat central nervous system as revealed by immunohistochemistry. Med. Biol. **52:** 424–427.
2. BROWNSTEIN, M. J., E. A. MROZ, J. S. KIZER, M. PALKOVITS & S. E. LEEMAN. 1976. Regional distribution of substance P in the brain of the rat. Brain Res. **116:** 299–305.
3. NICOLL, R. A., C. SCHENKER & S. E. LEEMAN. 1980. Substance P as a transmitter candidate. Annu. Rev. Neurosci. **3:** 227–268.
4. DUN, N. J. & A. G. KARCZMAR. 1979. Action of substance P on sympathetic neurons. Neuropharmacology **18:** 215–218.
5. DUN, N. J. & S. MINOTA. 1981. Effects of substance P on neurons of the inferior mesenteric ganglia of the guinea-pig. J. Physiol. (London) **321:** 259–271.
6. OTSUKA, M., S. KONISHI, M. YANAGISAWA, A. TSUNOO & H. AKAGI. 1982. Role of substance P as a sensory transmitter in spinal cord and sympathetic ganglia. *In* Substance P in the Nervous System: Ciba Foundation Symposium. Vol. 91: 13–34. Pitman. London.
7. BOLAM, J. P., C. A. INGHAM, P. N. IZZO, A. I. LEVEY, D. B. RYE, A. D. SMITH & B. H. WAINER. 1986. Substance P–containing terminals in synaptic contact with cholinergic neurons in the neostriatum and basal forebrain: a double immunocytochemical study in the rat. Brain Res. **397:** 279–289.
8. DIETL, M., A. PROBST & J. M. PALACIOS. 1986. Mapping of substance P receptor sites in the human brain: high densities in the substantia innominata and effect of senile dementia. Soc. Neurosci. Abstr. **12:** 831.
9. ADAMS, P. R., D. A. BROWN & S. W. JONES. 1983. Substance P inhibits the M-current in bullfrog sympathetic neurones. Br. J. Pharmacol. **79:** 330–333.
10. NAKAJIMA, Y., S. NAKAJIMA, K. OBATA, C. G. CARLSON & K. YAMAGUCHI. 1985. Dissociated cell culture of cholinergic neurons from nucleus basalis of Meynert and other basal forebrain nuclei. Proc. Natl. Acad. Sci. U.S.A. **82:** 6325–6329.
11. STANFIELD, P. R., Y. NAKAJIMA & K. YAMAGUCHI. 1985. Substance P raises neuronal membrane excitability by reducing inward rectification. Nature **315:** 498–501.
12. YAMAGUCHI, K., Y. NAKAJIMA, S. NAKAJIMA & P. R. STANFIELD. 1990. Modulation of inwardly rectifying channels by substance P in cholinergic neurones from rat brain in culture. J. Physiol. (London) **426:** 499–520.

13. BREITWIESER, G. E. & G. SZABO. 1985. Uncoupling of cardiac muscarinic and β-adrenergic receptors from ion channels by a guanine nucleotide analogue. Nature **317**: 538–540.

14. PFAFFINGER, P. J., J. M. MARTIN, D. D. HUNTER, N. M. NATHANSON & B. HILLE. 1985. GTP-binding proteins couple cardiac muscarinic receptors to a K channel. Nature **317**: 536–538.

15. ANDRADE, R., R. C. MALENKA & R. A. NICOLL. 1986. A G protein couples serotonin and GABA_B receptors to the same channels in hippocampus. Science **234**: 1261–1265.

16. KURACHI, Y., T. NAKAJIMA & T. SUGIMOTO. 1986. On the mechanism of activation of muscarinic K^+ channels by adenosine in isolated atrial cells: involvement of GTP-binding proteins. Pflügers Arch. **407**: 264–274.

17. HOLZ, G. G., IV, S. G. RANE & K. DUNLAP. 1986. GTP-binding proteins mediate transmitter inhibition of voltage-dependent calcium channels. Nature **319**: 670–672.

18. LEWIS, D. L., F. F. WEIGHT & A. LUINI. 1986. A guanine nucleotide–binding protein mediates the inhibition of voltage-dependent calcium current by somatostatin in a pituitary cell line. Proc. Natl. Acad. Sci. U.S.A. **83**: 9035–9039.

19. MIHARA, S., R. A. NORTH & A. SURPRENANT. 1987. Somatostatin increases an inwardly rectifying potassium conductance in guinea-pig submucous plexus neurones. J. Physiol. (London) **390**: 335–355.

20. YATANI, A., J. CODINA, A. M. BROWN & L. BIRNBAUMER. 1987. Direct activation of mammalian atrial muscarinic potassium channels by GTP regulatory protein G_K. Science **235**: 207–211.

21. INOUE, M., S. NAKAJIMA & Y. NAKAJIMA. 1988. Somatostatin induces an inward rectification in rat locus coeruleus neurones through a pertussis toxin–sensitive mechanism. J. Physiol. (London) **407**: 177–198.

22. NAKAJIMA, Y., S. NAKAJIMA & M. INOUE. 1988. Pertussis toxin–insensitive G protein mediates substance P–induced inhibition of potassium channels in brain neurons. Proc. Natl. Acad. Sci. U.S.A. **85**: 3643–3647.

23. HAMILL, O. P., A. MARTY, E. NEHER, B. SAKMANN & F. J. SIGWORTH. 1981. Improved patch-clamp techniques for high-resolution current recording from cell and cell-free membrane patches. Pflügers Arch. **391**: 85–100.

24. LEVEY, A. I., B. H. WAINER, E. J. MUFSON & M-M. MESULAM. 1983. Co-localization of acetylcholinesterase and choline acetyltransferase in the rat cerebrum. Neuroscience **9**: 9–22.

25. BOKOCH, G. M., T. KATADA, J. K. NORTHUP, M. UI & A. G. GILMAN. 1984. Purification and properties of the inhibitory guanine nucleotide–binding regulatory component of adenylate cyclase. J. Biol. Chem. **259**: 3560–3567.

26. CASSEL, D. & Z. SELINGER. 1977. Activation of turkey erythrocyte adenylate cyclase and blocking of the catecholamine-stimulated GTPase by guanosine 5′-(γ-thio)triphosphate. Biochem. Biophys. Res. Commun. **77**: 868–873.

27. ECKSTEIN, F., D. CASSEL, H. LEVKOVITZ, M. LOWE & Z. SELINGER. 1979. Guanosine 5′-O-(2-thiodiphosphate): an inhibitor of adenylate cyclase stimulation by guanine nucleotides and fluoride ions. J. Biol. Chem. **254**: 9829–9834.

28. YAMANAKA, G., F. ECKSTEIN & L. STRYER. 1985. Stereochemistry of the guanyl nucleotide binding site of transducin probed by phosphorothioate analogues of GTP and GDP. Biochemistry **24**: 8094–8101.

29. KATADA, T., M. OINUMA, K. KUSAKABE & M. UI. 1987. A new GTP-binding protein in brain tissues serving as the specific substrate of islet-activating protein, pertussis toxin. FEBS Lett. **213**: 353–358.

30. TOUTANT, M., D. AUNIS, J. BOCKAERT, V. HOMBURGER & B. ROUOT. 1987. Presence of three pertussis toxin substrates and $G_{oα}$ immunoreactivity in both plasma and granule membranes of chromaffin cells. FEBS Lett. **215**: 339–344.

31. IYENGAR, R., K. A. RICH, J. T. HERBERG, D. GRENET, S. MUMBY & J. CODINA. 1987. Identification of a new GTP-binding protein. J. Biol. Chem. **262**: 9239–9245.

32. ROSS, E. M. & A. G. GILMAN. 1980. Biochemical properties of hormone-sensitive adenylate cyclase. Annu. Rev. Biochem. **49**: 533–564.

33. HARRIS, D. N., M. M. ASAAD, M. B. PHILLIPS, H. J. GOLDENBERG & M. J. ANTONACCIO. 1979. Inhibition of adenylate cyclase in human blood platelets by 9-substituted adenine derivatives. J. Cyclic Nucleotide Res. **5:** 125–134.

34. BROWN, D. A. & P. M. DUNN. 1983. Cyclic adenosine 3′,5′-monophosphate and β-effects in rat isolated superior cervical ganglia. Br. J. Pharmacol. **79:** 441–449.

35. CASSEL, D. & Z. SELINGER. 1977. Mechanism of adenylate cyclase activation by cholera toxin: inhibition of GTP hydrolysis at the regulatory site. Proc. Natl. Acad. Sci. U.S.A. **74:** 3307–3311.

36. PFAFFINGER, P. 1988. Muscarine and t-LHRH suppress M-current by activating an IAP-insensitive G-protein. J. Neurosci. **8:** 3343–3353.

37. FREISSMUTH, M., P. J. CASEY & A. G. GILMAN. 1989. G proteins control diverse pathways of transmembrane signaling. FASEB J. **3:** 2125–2131.

38. MATSUOKA, M., H. ITOH, T. KOZASA & Y. KAZIRO. 1988. Sequence analysis of cDNA and genomic DNA for a putative pertussis toxin–insensitive guanine nucleotide–binding regulatory protein α subunit. Proc. Natl. Acad. Sci. U.S.A. **85:** 5384–5388.

39. FONG, H. K. W., K. K. YOSHIMOTO, P. EVERSOLE-CIRE & M. I. SIMON. 1988. Identification of a GTP-binding protein α subunit that lacks an apparent ADP-ribosylation site for pertussis toxin. Proc. Natl. Acad. Sci. U.S.A. **85:** 3066–3070.

40. SIESS, W., D. A. WINEGAR & E. G. LAPETINA. 1990. Rap 1-b is phosphorylated by protein kinase A in intact human platelets. Biochem. Biophys. Res. Commun. **170:** 944–950.

41. MASUKO, S., Y. NAKAJIMA, S. NAKAJIMA & K. YAMAGUCHI. 1986. Noradrenergic neurons from the locus coeruleus in dissociated cell culture: culture methods, morphology, and electrophysiology. J. Neurosci. **6:** 3229–3241.

Pharmacological and Biochemical Evidence for Multiple Types of Tachykinin NK₂ Receptors

STEPHEN H. BUCK,[a] BRADFORD O. FANGER,[a] AND
PAUL L. M. VAN GIERSBERGEN[a,b]

[a]Marion Merrell Dow Research Institute
Cincinnati, Ohio 45215

[b]Department of Pharmacology and Cell Biophysics
University of Cincinnati College of Medicine
Cincinnati, Ohio 45267

INTRODUCTION

The mammalian tachykinin peptides—substance P (SP), neurokinin A (NKA), and neurokinin B (NKB)—have been postulated to preferentially bind to and activate distinct types of tachykinin receptors. For SP, these receptors are NK₁; for NKA, they are NK₂; and for NKB, they are NK₃.[1-5] All three receptors have now been cloned and their primary sequences have been deduced.[6-8] They all appear to be closely related, G protein–linked receptors, each with multiple, membrane-spanning, hydrophobic domains; an N-terminal extracellular tail; and a C-terminal intracellular tail. These three receptors may all be linked to phosphatidylinositol (PI) turnover.[5] Some investigators have speculated that there may be different types of SP receptors (NK₁).[9,10] The evidence for this, though, is far from compelling. Very recently, convincing evidence for the existence of different types of NK₂ receptors has begun to appear. This latter evidence is highlighted in this report.

RESULTS AND DISCUSSION

The tachykinin NK₂ (NKA) receptor was first postulated in 1984 (see reference 11). Based on this early receptor binding study and on many subsequent pharmacological, physiological, and biochemical investigations, it is clear that biological response patterns exist wherein tachykinin peptide agonists display the potency rank order of NKA > NKB > SP ≫ senktide (senktide = a highly NK₃-selective agonist[12]). This potency rank order has become a primary means of identifying NK₂-receptor-mediated events.[1-5] Tissues that display this pharmacological rank order and that have been classified as containing relatively pure populations of NK₂ receptors include rat vas deferens (RVD), rat duodenum, rabbit pulmonary artery (RPA), hamster urinary bladder (HUB), hamster trachea (HT), guinea pig gall bladder, guinea pig trachea (GPT), human bronchus, human urinary bladder, and others.[1-5,13-16]

McKnight and co-workers reported in 1987 that the NK₁-selective agonist, septide,[17,18] was a potent contractile agent in GPT (NK₂ tissue).[19] SP (NK₁-selective) and senktide (NK₃-selective) were 100 times and 1500 times less potent than septide, respectively, suggesting that NK$_1$ or NK$_3$ receptors were not prominently involved in GPT contraction.[19] In contrast to the high potency of septide in GPT, this peptide was more than 1000 times less potent in RVD.[20] NKA itself had EC$_{50}$ values of 10 nM in GPT and 100 nM in RVD.[3] These results suggested that the NK$_2$ receptor in GPT was different from the NK$_2$ receptor in RVD.

The Merck Neuroscience group has reported NKA antagonists that differentiate two types of NK$_2$ receptors. The cyclic hexapeptide, L-659,877 [cyclo(Gln-Trp-Phe-Gly-Leu-Met)], and its linear version, L-659,874 (Ac-Leu-Met-Gln-Trp-Phe-Gly-NH$_2$), exhibit pA$_2$ values that are 1000 times greater in RVD than in GPT. Neither peptide has appreciable antagonist activity at NK$_1$ or NK$_3$ receptors.[21] In addition, we have observed in receptor binding assays that L-659,877 and L-659,874 have at least 20 times higher affinity for the HUB NK$_2$ receptor than for the NK$_2$ receptor in bovine stomach or bovine bladder smooth muscle or in murine fibroblast cells transfected with the bovine stomach cDNA, pSKR56S.[22] RVD, rat duodenum, and rat urinary bladder membranes appeared to have an NK$_2$ receptor with L-659,877 and L-659,874 affinities similar to those in HUB.[23] Furthermore, binding of iodinated NKA to the NK$_2$ receptor in bovine stomach and in the transfected cell line was more effectively stimulated by Mn^{++} and was more effectively inhibited by guanine nucleotide analogues than binding to the HUB NK$_2$ receptor.[23] Thus, it appears that these different types of NK$_2$ receptors differ both in their binding requirements for some antagonists and in their coupling mechanisms to G protein.

A reduced bond analogue of NKA that we have investigated also markedly differentiated between the NK$_2$ receptor types in different tissues. MDL 28,564 ([Leu$^9\Psi$(CH$_2$NH)Leu^{10}]-NKA(4-10)) was a full agonist (relative to NKA) for contraction and for PI turnover in GPT, but produced no sustained contraction and only 10% maximum activation (relative to NKA) of PI turnover in HUB. In the latter tissue, MDL 28,564 was a competitive antagonist (up to 30 μM) of NKA-induced PI turnover with a pA$_2$ of 6.7 and was a competitive antagonist (up to 10 μM) of NKA-induced contraction with a pA$_2$ of 5.4. At 50 μM in HUB, though, MDL 28,564 depressed the maximum NKA-induced contraction in a manner consistent with antagonism by a partial agonist. MDL 28,564 up to high μM concentrations did not bind to rat salivary gland NK$_1$ receptors nor to rat cerebral cortex NK$_3$ receptors.[24] This peptide should be invaluable as an agonist that clearly differentiates two types of NK$_2$ receptors.

Another interesting NKA antagonist containing three DTrp residues, MEN 10207 (Asp-Tyr-DTrp-Val-DTrp-DTrp-Arg-NH$_2$), has been reported by Maggi *et al.*[25] MEN 10207 was a competitive antagonist of NKA and an NKA analogue ([βAla^8]-NKA(4-10)) on contractile responses in RPA and HT, which are two "pure" NK$_2$ tissues. However, the pA$_2$ values for MEN 10207 were 7.6 in RPA and 5.8 in HT. The peptide had pA$_2$ values of 5.2 against SP in a dog carotid artery relaxation assay (NK$_1$) and of 4.9 against NKB in a rat portal vein contraction assay (NK$_3$).[25] We have also observed that MEN 10207 binds with low affinity ($K_r \simeq 3$ μM) to HUB NK$_2$ receptors (unpublished observations). In contrast to the aforementioned NK$_2$ antagonists, MEN 10207 seems to be fairly selective for the NK$_2$ receptor in RPA. The hexapeptide antagonists are somewhat selective for the HUB, RVD, and (presumably) HT NK$_2$ receptors. It will be extremely interesting to see how these differentially selective NK$_2$ antagonists are used in the future to classify the numerous other tissues and responses that have been classified until now as uniformly NK$_2$.

We have used the technique of covalent cross-linking of radioligand and subsequent SDS-PAGE electrophoresis to examine the binding proteins for iodinated NKA in several tissues.[26] Using a centrifugation binding assay and bis(sulfosuccinimidyl) suberate (5 mM) as the cross-linker, we observed that specifically bound, iodinated NKA was covalently cross-linked to a protein of M_r 43,000 and to a protein of M_r 86,000 in membranes prepared from HUB. However, in membranes prepared from the transfected fibroblast cell line mentioned earlier, the iodinated NKA was cross-linked to proteins of M_r 70,000 and M_r 140,000 (FIGURE 1). Under reducing conditions (i.e., the presence of 100 mM dithiothreitol), both the HUB M_r 86,000 band and the fibroblast M_r 140,000 band completely disappeared, indicating that these bands were composed of protein subunits linked by disulfide bonds.

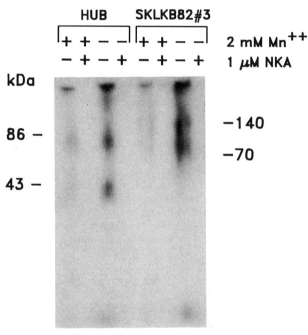

FIGURE 1. Affinity cross-linking of ^{125}I-NKA to membranes from HUB and SKLKB82#3 cells. Autoradiogram of SDS-PAGE gel (without DTT). The binding to both bands in both tissues was completely inhibited by 1 μM unlabeled NKA and was markedly enhanced by 2 mM Mn^{++}.

CONCLUSIONS

At present, there are peptide agonists and antagonists available that clearly indicate that there is more than one type of tachykinin receptor that preferentially binds NKA over SP and NKB. The cross-linking experiments also suggest that there are differences in NKA binding proteins among different tissues. Additional research will be required to clarify whether these multiple types of receptors are due simply to species differences, to the existence of true NK$_2$ receptor subtypes, or to the existence of a novel tachykinin peptide receptor (e.g., neuropeptide K or neuropeptide γ receptor[27]) that coincidentally has a similar affinity for NKA at the NK$_2$ receptor.

REFERENCES

1. BUCK, S. H., R. M. PRUSS, J. L. KRSTENANSKY, P. J. ROBINSON & K. A. STAUDERMAN. 1988. Trends Pharmacol. Sci. **9**: 3–5.
2. BURCHER, E. 1989. Clin. Exp. Pharmacol. Physiol. **16**: 539–543.
3. REGOLI, D., G. DRAPEAU, S. DION & P. D'ORLEANS-JUSTE. 1989. Pharmacology **38**: 1–15.
4. HELKE, C. J., J. E. KRAUSE, P. W. MANTYH, R. COUTURE & M. J. BANNON. 1990. FASEB J. **4**: 1606–1615.
5. GUARD, S. & S. P. WATSON. 1991. Neurochem. Int. **18**: 149–165.
6. MASU, Y., K. NAKAYAMA, H. TAMAKI, Y. HARADA, M. KUNO & S. NAKANISHI. 1987. Nature **329**: 836–838.
7. YOKOTA, Y., Y. SASAI, K. TANAKA, T. FUJIWARA, K. TSUCHIDA, R. SHIGEMOTO, A. KAKIZUKA, H. OHKUBO & S. NAKANISHI. 1989. J. Biol. Chem. **264**: 17649–17652.
8. SHIGEMOTO, R., Y. YOKOTA, K. TSUCHIDA & S. NAKANISHI. 1990. J. Biol. Chem. **265**: 623–628.
9. HALL, M. E., F. MILEY & J. M. STEWART. 1989. Peptides **10**: 895–901.
10. LEW, R., D. P. GERAGHTY, G. DRAPEAU, D. REGOLI & E. BURCHER. 1990. Eur. J. Pharmacol. In press.
11. BUCK, S. H., E. BURCHER, C. W. SHULTS, W. LOVENBERG & T. L. O'DONOHUE. 1984. Science **226**: 987–989.
12. LAUFER, R., U. WORMSER, Z. Y. FRIEDMAN, C. GILON, M. CHOREV & Z. SELINGER. 1985. Proc. Natl. Acad. Sci. U.S.A. **82**: 7444–7448.
13. MAGGI, C. A., R. PATACCHINI, P. ROVERO & A. MELI. 1989. Eur. J. Pharmacol. **166**: 435–440.
14. SHOOK, J. E. & T. F. BURKS. 1986. Life Sci. **39**: 2533–2539.
15. ADVENIER, C., E. NALINE, G. DRAPEAU & D. REGOLI. 1987. Eur. J. Pharmacol. **139**: 133–137.
16. DION, S., J. CORCOS, M. CARMEL, G. DRAPEAU & D. REGOLI. 1988. Neuropeptides **11**: 83–87.
17. WORMSER, U., R. LAUFER, Y. HART, M. CHOREV, C. GILON & Z. SELINGER. 1986. EMBO J. **5**: 2805–2808.
18. BUCK, S. H. & J. L. KRSTENANSKY. 1987. Eur. J. Pharmacol. **144**: 109–111.
19. MCKNIGHT, A. T., J. J. MAGUIRE & M. A. VARNEY. 1987. Br. J. Pharmacol. **91**: 360 (abstract).
20. FLETCHER, A. E., A. T. MCKNIGHT & J. J. MAGUIRE. 1987. Br. J. Pharmacol. **90**: 266 (abstract).
21. MCKNIGHT, A. T., J. J. MAGUIRE, B. J. WILLIAMS, A. C. FOSTER, R. TRIDGETT & L. L. IVERSEN. 1988. Regulat. Peptides **22**: 127 (abstract).
22. VAN GIERSBERGEN, P. L. M., S. A. SHATZER, A. K. HENDERSON, J. LAI, S. NAKANISHI, H. I. YAMAMURA & S. H. BUCK. 1991. Proc. Natl. Acad. Sci. U.S.A. **88**: 1661–1665.
23. VAN GIERSBERGEN, P. L. M., S. A. SHATZER, S. L. HARBESON, N. ROUISSI, F. NANTEL & S. H. BUCK. 1991. This volume.
24. BUCK, S. H., S. L. HARBESON, C. F. HASSMAN, S. A. SHATZER, N. ROUISSI, F. NANTEL & P. L. M. VAN GIERSBERGEN. 1990. Life Sci. **47**: PL-37–PL-41.
25. MAGGI, C. A., R. PATACCHINI, S. GIULIANI, P. ROVERO, S. DION, D. REGOLI, A. GIACHETTI & A. MELI. 1990. Br. J. Pharmacol. **100**: 588–592.
26. BUCK, S. H., S. A. SHATZER, P. L. M. VAN GIERSBERGEN & B. O. FANGER. 1991. This volume.
27. TAKEDA, Y. & J. E. KRAUSE. 1989. Soc. Neurosci. Abstr. **15**: 346.

Strategies to Detect Heterologously Expressed Tachykinin Receptors in *Xenopus* Oocytes

CLAES WAHLESTEDT

Division of Neurobiology
Department of Neurology and Neuroscience
Cornell University Medical College
New York, New York 10021

INTRODUCTION

Oocytes from *Xenopus laevis* have been extensively used in biological research both for developmental studies and for efficient mRNA translation and posttranslational processing of a variety of proteins including G protein–coupled receptors for neurotransmitters/hormones.[1-3] The latter feature of the oocyte allowed the pioneering expression cloning of the bovine substance K receptor (SKR) from a stomach cDNA library by Nakanishi and colleagues; their approach depended critically on electrophysiological recordings.[4,5] Oocytes have also played a vital role in the cloning and characterization of a number of other G protein–coupled receptors. For example, in the case of the substance P receptor (SPR), a rat brain cDNA mixture containing functional SPR was first identified by oocyte electrophysiology and a single SPR clone was then isolated by cross-hybridization to SKR cDNA.[5,6] Functional cDNA clones for rat SKR[7] and neuromedin K receptors (NKR)[8] were subsequently identified in stomach and brain cDNA libraries, respectively, by cross-hybridization to bovine SKR.

The molecular cloning of the three tachykinin receptors and their heterologous expression have lent further support to the proposal that they all, upon agonist stimulation, have the capacity to mobilize intracellular calcium ions (Ca^{++}) as a result of phospholipase C–mediated inositol triphosphate (IP_3) generation.[5,9] This phenomenon has been studied in some detail by using *Xenopus* oocytes. Indeed, the oocyte is a widely used model to study mechanisms in Ca^{++} signaling. Like *de novo* expressed tachykinin receptors, native muscarinic receptors will cause release of Ca^{++} from intracellular stores (e.g., see reference 1), possibly accompanied by Ca^{++} influx from the extracellular medium.[10] Elevation of Ca^{++} concentration in the oocyte in turn induces the opening of Ca^{++}-activated Cl^- channels, resulting in fast and slow Cl^- conductances (e.g., see reference 11).

In this report, published and previously unpublished data on the expression of the cloned bovine SKR and rat SPR in defolliculated *Xenopus* oocytes will be briefly reviewed. Contrary to the biological sequence of events following receptor activation, five methods will be presented in the following order: (1) increased Cl^- conductance (electrophysiology); (2a) Ca^{++} mobilization (Ca^{++} imaging); (2b) Ca^{++} mobilization ($^{45}Ca^{++}$ efflux); (3) phosphatidyl inositide (PI) hydrolysis (inositol monophosphate accumulation); and (4) ligand binding (^{125}I-SK). Although it will be argued that all methods (except binding) can be used to detect *de novo* tachykinin receptor expression, a comparative analysis of the respective value of the methods will be presented.

ELECTROPHYSIOLOGY

The perhaps most widely employed technique for functional detection of stimulated G protein–coupled and PI-coupled receptors in *Xenopus* oocytes is inward (Cl⁻ carried) current recording. This approach is facilitated by the shear size of the cell (approximately 1 mm in diameter), making it possible to quickly impale it with two electrodes and to perform conventional voltage clamping. This method was introduced by Miledi and co-workers for the study of endogenous muscarinic receptors (for a review, see reference 2). Miledi's group also first demonstrated that, in the

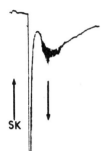

SK

FIGURE 1. Electrophysiological recording of the substance K (SK)–sensitive current under voltage clamp. Current is inward (and corresponds to efflux of Cl⁻ from the cell) and is shown as a downward deflection of the current trace. Holding potential was −50 mV. SK (Bachem) was superfused at a concentration of 1 μM. Two days prior to the experiment, the oocyte was defolliculated and injected with 350 pg of *in vitro* transcribed bovine SK receptor mRNA. See text for further information.

50nA

1 min

oocyte, rat brain mRNA encodes functional SPRs by use of the voltage clamp technique.[12] Similarly, Nakanishi and colleagues[13] expressed SPR and SKR (encoded by brain and stomach mRNAs, respectively) and argued that the observed inward currents were a result of Cl⁻ efflux.

Typical electrophysiological recording of inward currents induced by stimulation of the *de novo* expressed cloned SKR in a voltage-clamped oocyte is shown in FIGURE 1. In experiments, SPR and SKR mRNAs have been transcribed *in vitro* as described[14] and have been microinjected into defolliculated oocytes. At the earliest, tachykinin responsiveness is detected about 30 hours after receptor mRNA injection and maximum responsiveness is generally developed by 60–80 hours. Responses are concentration-dependent and typically biphasic.

Interestingly, it seems that the cloned SPR and SKR differ in their desensitization patterns when *de novo* expressed in *Xenopus* oocytes (FIGURE 2); this phenomenon has been previously observed in, for example, iris[15] and blood vessels[16] and following tissue-derived mRNA expression in oocytes.[5,13] Thus, repeated stimulation of the cloned SPR results in more pronounced desensitization than the corresponding stimulation of the cloned SKR; as could be expected, this difference is clearly affected by varying receptor and agonist concentrations. The tracing shown in FIGURE 2 was obtained after injection of the oocyte with a moderate amount (approximately 35 pg) of receptor mRNA. Presently, the favored view is the one

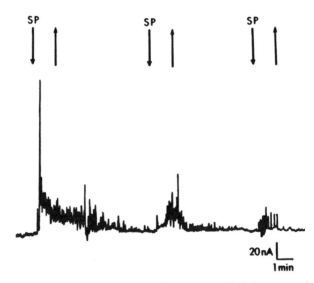

FIGURE 2. Electrophysiological recordings of currents evoked by repeated exposure to substance P (SP) in a voltage-clamped (holding potential, −50 mV) oocyte injected with *in vitro* transcribed SP receptor mRNA (approximately 35 pg). SP (Bachem) was perfused as indicated at a concentration of 30 nM. Upward deflection represents inward current. See text for further information.

where the difference in the desensitization pattern relates to the fact that SPR contains many more Ser/Thr residues as potential phosphorylation sites in the third cytoplasmic loop and in the C-terminus than does SKR (cf. reference 5).

CA++ MOBILIZATION

Ca++ Imaging

In their studies on angiotensin II receptors, Catt and co-workers found that oocytes preloaded with the photoprotein aequorin responded to the agonist by displaying an increase in light emission, reflecting an increase in cytosolic Ca^{++}.[17] The latter study stimulated the drive to pursue imaging of oocytes using the Ca^{++}-sensitive dyes, fura-2[18] and fluo-3.[19] By use of a digital imaging fluorescence microscopy system, individual defolliculated oocytes were studied 1–4 days after injection of *in vitro* transcribed bovine SKR mRNA as described.[14] Fura-2 or fluo-3 was injected at 1 mM (35 nL, pH 7.4) 1–3 hours before imaging. As reported,[14] application of SK caused a concentration-dependent wave of Ca^{++} mobilization to spread from a focus in the animal pole and to thereby elevate the Ca^{++} concentration throughout the oocyte. There never was a response in vehicle-injected cells. The rise in Ca^{++} induced by SK was due to internal Ca^{++} mobilization and was independent of external Ca^{++}. By use of fura-2 and its calibration with Ca^{++}/EGTA standards, it was found that the basal Ca^{++} concentration in oocytes varied between 50 and 90 nM. Application of SK at a maximally effective concentration caused the Ca^{++} to rise above 200 μM (cf. reference 14).

The dye, fluo-3, appears to be more sensitive than fura-2,[14,19] allowing detection of smaller changes in Ca^{++}. Another slight advantage of fluo-3 is that this dye can be imaged by using excitation energy in the visible region of the spectrum, making screening in plastic or other ultraviolet-light-opaque dishes possible. (This feature may be particularly advantageous when studying cultured cells, but applies also for oocyte work.)

$^{45}Ca^{++}$ *Efflux*

One of the most frequently studied sequelae of Ca^{++} mobilization is the accelerated efflux of the ion as monitored after preloading cells with $^{45}Ca^{++}$. As pointed out by Williams *et al.* in 1988, the fact that the $^{45}Ca^{++}$ efflux is somewhat of an indirect measure of receptor activation is compensated for by its ease and lack of requirement of any specialized equipment other than a liquid scintillation counter. The present work confirms that the $^{45}Ca^{++}$ efflux assay has an excellent signal-to-noise ratio and suggests that it is well suited for the study of tachykinin receptors. Obviously, however, this method does not allow spatial localization of Ca^{++} release as does the imaging system.

Briefly, for the study of *de novo* expressed (cloned) SPR and SKR, their respective *in vitro* transcribed mRNAs were injected at a concentration of 100 ng/μL in 35 nL of H_2O into defolliculated oocytes. Approximately 48 hours later, the cells (and H_2O-injected controls) were incubated with $^{45}Ca^{++}$ (the standard modified Barth's medium was fortified to 60 μCi/mL with $^{45}Ca^{++}$ from Amersham, 2.14 mCi/mL). On the next day (20–24 hours after starting the $^{45}Ca^{++}$ incubation), oocytes were washed five times and placed in groups of five into 220 μL of medium in the wells of 96-well flat-bottomed plates. Media (200 μL) were initially discarded and replaced every 5 min. Starting at 90 min, samples were collected for subsequent measurement by liquid scintillation counting. The agonists, that is, the tachykinins SP, SK, and NK (Bachem), were added in various concentrations (FIGURES 3 and 4) at the sixth-collected 5-min sample, resulting in an increased $^{45}Ca^{++}$ efflux of considerable duration lasting 20–30 min after agonist application.

FIGURES 3 and 4 illustrate the usefulness of the $^{45}Ca^{++}$ efflux technique for the study of bovine SKR and rat SPR, respectively. For bovine SKR, the order of potency was SK > NK > SP (FIGURE 3); for rat SPR, it was SP > SK > NK. This order of potency is identical to that found by Nakanishi and co-workers in their displacement binding studies on transfected COS cells (see, for example, reference 5). However, the tachykinin concentrations required to elicit accelerated $^{45}Ca^{++}$ efflux in oocytes were significantly higher than in Nakanishi's binding studies.

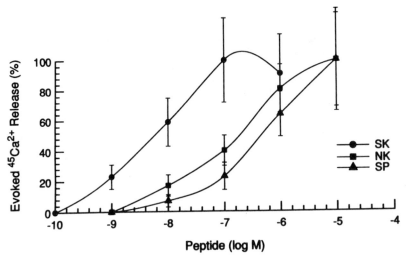

FIGURE 3. Accelerated $^{45}Ca^{++}$ efflux induced by substance K (SK), neuromedin K (NK), and substance P (SP) from defolliculated oocytes injected with *in vitro* transcribed bovine SK receptor mRNA (approximately 100 pg/cell) 65–75 hours earlier. Oocytes were prelabeled with $^{45}Ca^{++}$ (see text) and were studied in groups of five. Accelerated $^{45}Ca^{++}$ efflux was determined by calculating the ratio between four intervals of 5 min after and before peptide application. E_{max} values corresponded to increases in $^{45}Ca^{++}$ efflux by 800% to 1400% and were not significantly different between the three peptides. The H_2O-injected (control) cells did not respond to any tachykinin. Means ± SEM. See text for further information.

INOSITOL MONOPHOSPHATE ACCUMULATION

It was shown that stimulation of certain Ca^{++}-mobilizing receptors results in phosphatidyl inositide (PI) hydrolysis in *Xenopus* oocytes.[20] Because this should conceivably be the case also for tachykinin receptors, preliminary experiments were performed using standard techniques[21] to assay for inositol monophosphate accumulation in oocytes microinjected with bovine SKR mRNA (100 ng/μL, 35 nL) as described earlier. Inositol phospholipids were labeled by 24-h incubation with 40 μCi of *myo*-[^{3}H]inositol (17.1 Ci/mmol; New England Nuclear) followed by washing and treatment with 10 mM LiCl (10 min) and then they were challenged by 1 μM SK for 30 min. Oocytes were studied in groups of 12 and showed a 55 ± 12% ($n = 6$; mean ± SEM) increase in inositol monophosphate accumulation (SKR mRNA versus H_2O-injection) after SK treatment (basal rate of ^{3}H-inositol monophosphate formation was 146 ± 31 cpm/1000 cpm of total inositol phospholipids).

LIGAND BINDING

Finally, attempts to study the binding of (2-[^{125}I]iodohistidyl)SK (Amersham) to membranes of SKR mRNA-injected oocytes were undertaken. These membranes were prepared as described by Kobilka *et al.*[22] in their studies on β_2-adrenoreceptors, and iodinated SK binding was performed essentially as described by Quirion and co-workers (e.g., reference 23). However, hitherto, it has been impossible to detect specific iodinated SK binding to such membranes; the most extensive experiment involved some 500 mRNA-injected oocytes.

CONCLUSIONS

The *Xenopus* oocyte is an excellent expression system for Ca^{++}-mobilizing receptors such as tachykinin receptors. Whereas electrophysiological recordings after voltage clamping have been the most commonly applied approach to detect *de novo* expression of such receptors, direct measures of Ca^{++} may offer certain advantages. Thus, Ca^{++} imaging by use of fura-2 or, better, fluo-3 was about as sensitive as electrophysiology for detection of SKR expression and, in addition, imaging proved much faster for screening. Moreover, Ca^{++} imaging obviously provided means to determine spatial aspects of Ca^{++} mobilization mechanisms in the oocyte.

This report demonstrates the usefulness of studying accelerated $^{45}Ca^{++}$ efflux as an index of stimulation of the *de novo* expressed cloned (rat) SPR and (bovine) SKR. Hence, when intracellular Ca^{++} stores of the mRNA-injected oocytes were pre-loaded with $^{45}Ca^{++}$, subsequent application of tachykinins resulted in prolonged $^{45}Ca^{++}$ efflux displaying the appropriate agonist orders of potency. The $^{45}Ca^{++}$ efflux technique was simple, reliable, and sensitive (good signal/noise ratio).

Finally, it was possible to detect tachykinin-induced PI hydrolysis and it was argued that oocytes are not very useful as a source of membranes for tachykinin radioreceptor binding.

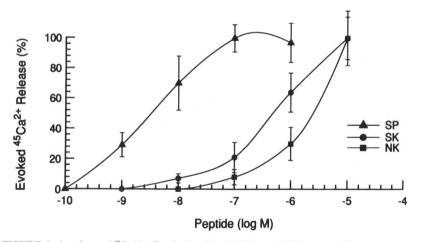

FIGURE 4. Accelerated $^{45}Ca^{++}$ efflux induced by SP, NK, and SK from defolliculated oocytes injected with *in vitro* transcribed rat SP receptor mRNA (approximately 100 pg/cell) 50–60 hours earlier. Oocytes were prelabeled (see text) and were studied in groups of five. Accelerated $^{45}Ca^{++}$ efflux was determined by calculating the ratio between four intervals of 5 min after and before peptide application. E_{max} values corresponded to increases in $^{45}Ca^{++}$ efflux by 600% to 1100% and were not significantly different between the three peptides. The H_2O-injected (control) cells did not respond to any tachykinin. Means ± SEM. See text for further information.

ACKNOWLEDGMENTS

S. Nakanishi is acknowledged for extensive scientific support and for generously supplying tachykinin receptor clones. I also wish to express my gratitude to G. Brooker and D. J. Reis for fruitful collaboration and discussion.

REFERENCES

1. DASCAL, N. 1987. CRC Crit. Rev. Biochem. **22:** 317–387.
2. MILEDI, R., I. PARKER & K. SUMIKAWA. 1989. *In* Fidia Award Lectures. Vol. 3. E. Costa, Ed.: 57–90. Raven Press. New York.
3. SOREQ, H. 1985. CRC Crit. Rev. Biochem. **18:** 199–238.
4. MASU, Y., K. NAKAYAMA, H. TAMAKI, Y. HARADA, M. KUNO & S. NAKANISHI. 1987. Nature (London) **329:** 836–838.
5. OHKUBO, H. & S. NAKANISHI. 1991. This volume.
6. YOKOTA, Y., Y. SASAI, K. TANAKA, T. FUJIWARA, K. TSUCHIDA, R. SHIGEMOTO, A. KAKIZUKA, H. OHKUBO & S. NAKANISHI. 1989. J. Biol. Chem. **264:** 17649–17652.
7. SASAI, Y. & S. NAKANISHI. 1989. Biochem. Biophys. Res. Commun. **165:** 695–702.
8. SHIGEMOTO, R., Y. YOKOTA, K. TSUCHIDA & S. NAKANISHI. 1990. J. Biol. Chem. **265:** 623–628.
9. PUTNEY, J. W., JR., *et al.* 1991. This volume.
10. SNYDER, P. M., K-H. KRAUSE & M. J. WELSH. 1988. J. Biol. Chem. **263:** 11048–11051.
11. BOTON, R., B. GILLO, N. DASCAL & Y. LASS. 1989. J. Physiol. (London) **408:** 511–534.
12. PARKER, I., K. SUMIKAWA & R. MILEDI. 1986. Proc. R. Soc. London **B229:** 151–159.
13. HARADA, Y., T. TAKAHASHI, M. KUNO, K. NAKAYAMA, Y. MASU & S. NAKANISHI. 1987. J. Neurosci. **7:** 3265–3273.
14. BROOKER, G., T. SEKI, D. CROLL & C. WAHLESTEDT. 1990. Proc. Natl. Acad. Sci. U.S.A. **87:** 2813–2817.
15. BEDING, B., R. HAKANSON, F. SUNDLER & C. WAHLESTEDT. 1985. *In* Tachykinin Antagonists. R. Håkanson & F. Sundler, Eds.: 103–108. Elsevier. Amsterdam/New York.
16. MOSKOWITZ, M. A., C. KUO, S. E. LEE, M. E. JESSEN & C. K. DERIAN. 1987. J. Neurosci. **7:** 2344–2351.
17. SANDBERG, K., A. J. MARKWICK, D. P. TRINH & K. J. CATT. 1988. FEBS Lett. **241:** 177–180.
18. GRYNKIEWICZ, G., M. POENIE & R. Y. TSIEN. 1985. J. Biol. Chem. **260:** 3440–3450.
19. MINTA, A., J. P. KAO & R. Y. TSIEN. 1989. J. Biol. Chem. **264:** 8171–8178.
20. MCINTOSH, R. P. & K. J. CATT. 1987. Proc. Natl. Acad. Sci. U.S.A. **84:** 9045–9048.
21. BERRIDGE, M. J., C. P. DOWNES & M. R. HANLEY. 1982. Biochem. J. **206:** 587–595.
22. KOBILKA, B. K., C. MACGREGOR, K. DANIEL, T. S. KOBILKA, M. G. CARON & R. J. LEFKOWITZ. 1987. J. Biol. Chem. **262:** 15796–15802.
23. DAM, T-V., Y. TAKEDA, J. E. KRAUSE, E. ESCHER & R. QUIRION. 1990. Proc. Natl. Acad. Sci. U.S.A. **87:** 246–250.

PART III

Concepts in Characterization of Tachykinin Receptors[a]

ELIZABETH BURCHER,[b] CHRISTIAN J. MUSSAP,[b]

DOMINIC P. GERAGHTY,[c]

JILLIANNE M. McCLURE-SHARP,[c] AND

DIANNE J. WATKINS[c,d]

b School of Physiology and Pharmacology
University of New South Wales
Sydney, N.S.W. 2033, Australia

c Department of Biological Sciences
Deakin University
Victoria 3217, Australia

INTRODUCTION

The tachykinins are a group of structurally related peptides found in many regions of the nervous system including brain and spinal cord, intrinsic neurons of the intestine, and primary afferent sensory nerves in various organs such as the respiratory system.[1-3] Several preprotachykinins (PPTs) are derived from differential processing of cDNA. αPPT-I gives rise to SP; βPPT-I gives rise to SP, NKA, NKA(3–10), and NPK, which is an extended form of NKA; and γPPT-I gives rise to SP, NKA, NKA(3–10), and another extended form of NKA, NPγ[4-6] (for structures, refer to TABLE 1). Another mammalian tachykinin, NKB, is derived from PPT-II via a different gene.[6]

It is generally accepted that three tachykinin receptors exist (NK_1, NK_2, and NK_3), whose endogenous ligands have been assumed to be substance P (SP), neurokinin A (NKA), and neurokinin B (NKB), respectively.[7-9] This hypothesis, although convenient, may require modification in the future. In the absence of selective antagonists, classification was based on the relative potency orders—that is, at the NK_1 receptor, SP > NKA > NKB; at the NK_2 receptor, NKA > NKB > SP; at the NK_3 receptor, NKB > NKA > SP.[7-9] With the advent of selective antagonists, receptor subtypes are being revealed. NK_1, NK_2, and NK_3 receptors are now sequenced,[10-13] although their three-dimensional structures remain unknown.

Considerable homology in receptor structure may explain the lack of receptor selectivity of the endogenous tachykinins. All three receptors (NK_1, NK_2, and NK_3) recognize the common C-terminus of the tachykinins. Virtually all actions of the tachykinins can be produced in nanomolar concentrations at any of the three receptors; therefore, the absence of an appropriate receptor does not preclude an action by the corresponding "endogenous ligand". Paradoxically, in both functional and binding studies, SP is active in the high picomolar range at NK_1 receptors, but NKA and NKB are much less potent at their respective receptors.[14] Thus, not only

[a] This study was supported by grants to E. Burcher by the National Health and Medical Research Council of Australia and by the Australian Tobacco Research Foundation.

[d] Present address: Department of Medicine, Austin Hospital, Heidelberg, Victoria 3084, Australia.

TABLE 1. Structures of Tachykinins, Selective Agonists, and Antagonists

Mammalian

Substance P   Arg-Pro-Lys-Pro-Gln-Gln-Phe-Phe-Gly-Leu-Met-NH$_2$

Neurokinin A   His-Lys-Thr-Asp-Ser-Phe-Val-Gly-Leu-Met-NH$_2$

Neurokinin B   Asp-Met-His-Asp-Phe-Phe-Val-Gly-Leu-Met-NH$_2$

Neuropeptide K   Asp-Ala-Asp-Ser-Ser-Ile-Glu-Lys-Gln-Val-Ala-Leu-
                    Leu-Lys-Ala-Leu-Tyr-Gly-His-Gly-Gln-Ile-Ser-His-
                    Lys-Arg-His-Lys-Thr-Asp-Ser-Phe-Val-Gly-Leu-Met-NH$_2$

Neuropeptide γ   Asp-Ala-Gly-His-Gly-Gln-Ile-Ser-His-Lys-Arg-
                    His-Lys-Thr-Asp-Ser-Phe-Val-Gly-Leu-Met-NH$_2$

Nonmammalian

Physalaemin   pGlu-Ala-Asp-Pro-Asn-Lys-Phe-Tyr-Gly-Leu-Met-NH$_2$

Kassinin   Asp-Val-Pro-Lys-Ser-Asp-Gln-Phe-Val-Gly-Leu-Met-NH$_2$

Eledoisin   pGlu-Pro-Ser-Lys-Asp-Ala-Phe-Ile-Gly-Leu-Met-NH$_2$

Scyliorhinin I   Ala-Lys-Phe-Asp-Lys-Phe-Tyr-Gly-Leu-Met-NH$_2$

Scyliorhinin II   ⌐Pro-Asp-Cys-Phe-Val-Gly-Leu-Met-NH$_2$
                    Gly   │
                                  └Asp-Pro-Cys-Lys-Ser-Asn-Ser-Pro-Ser

Selective NK1 agonist

[Sar^9,Met(O$_2$)^{11}]-SP

                    Arg-Pro-Lys-Pro-Gln-Gln-Phe-Phe-Sar-Leu-Met(O$_2$)-NH$_2$

Selective NK2 agonists

[Nle^{10}]-NKA(4-10)   Asp-Ser-Phe-Val-Gly-Leu-Nle-NH$_2$

[Lys^5,MeLeu^{9}Nle^{10}]NKA(4-10)   Asp-Lys-Phe-Val-Gly-MePhe-Nle-NH$_2$

Selective NK3 agonists

senktide   succinyl-Asp-Phe-MePhe-Gly-Leu-Met-NH$_2$

[MePhe^7]-NKB(4-10)   Asp-Phe-Phe-MePhe-Gly-Leu-Met-NH$_2$

Selective NK2 antagonists

L-659877   cyclo(Gln-Trp-Phe-Gly-Leu-Met)

MDL 29,913   cyclo(Gln-Trp-Phe-Gly-Leuψ(CH$_2$NCH$_3$)Leu)

MEN 10,207   Asp-Tyr-DTrp-Val-DTrp-DTrp-Arg-NH$_2$

potency order, but also absolute potency is of importance in receptor characterization. Current receptor characterization studies use synthetic analogues of greater receptor selectivity (TABLE 1) and, as new selective antagonists become available, the current receptor classification may be modified and refined. If and when new tachykinins are discovered that are more potent than those presently described, current concepts regarding the nature of endogenous ligands may also be revised.

Other factors to be taken into consideration for receptor characterization include the effects of various tissue-specific peptidases. One example here is the effect of endopeptidase 3.4.24.11 inhibitors, such as phosphoramidon and thiorphan, on bronchoconstriction and mucus secretion in the lung. In the presence of these peptidase inhibitors, the absolute potencies of the tachykinins were substantially increased. However, rank potency orders were also changed, with responses to NKB even more enhanced than responses to other tachykinins.[15]

SUBSTANCE P–PREFERRING RECEPTORS

NK_1 receptors are widely distributed[9] and have been extensively investigated using both functional and radioreceptor techniques. A number of radioligands [many based on $[^{125}I]$-Bolton-Hunter (BH) reagent] used for the study of NK_1 and other receptors are listed in TABLE 2. NK_1 receptors are differentially localized from other tachykinin receptors in many areas of the brain and spinal cord.[16–18] They also exist on smooth muscle layers of the intestine,[19] on bladder[20] (several species), on submandibular and parotid glands, on lymphocytes, on mucus glands, and on smooth muscle[21] in the airways. They occur on the endothelium of some major arteries[14,22] (where they mediate endothelium-dependent vasodilation), on renal blood vessels,[23] and on other vascular smooth muscle (where they mediate vasoconstriction).[14,24] NK_1 receptors on postcapillary venules in the skin,[25] bladder, ureter, and other organs also cause plasma extravasation. In addition, NK_1 receptors occur on ganglia of the intestine,[26] where they influence secretion. [**Note added in proof:** Recently, a potent, nonpeptide selective NK_1 antagonist, CP-96,345, has been described by Snider and co-workers (*Science* **251:** 435–437).]

Do NK_1 Receptor Subtypes Exist?

We have recently speculated that subtypes of the NK_1 receptor may exist.[27] This was based on a radioligand binding study in rat brain and submandibular gland that showed differences in affinity for a number of fragments and tachykinins when competing for binding of the NK_1 selective BH-$[Sar^9,Met(O_2)^{11}]$-SP. Although SP, $[Sar^9,Met(O_2)^{11}]$-SP, and SP(3–11) had similar affinity for the brain and submandibular site, SP(5–11), kassinin, NKB, and SP methyl ester, in particular, had 8-fold to 50-fold lower affinity for the brain compared with the submandibular site.[27] Other evidence supporting the hypothesis that binding sites in these two tissues may differ includes the poor affinity of the unselective radioligand BH-eledoisin (BHELE) for

TABLE 2. Some Radioligands Currently Employed in the Characterization of Tachykinin Receptors

Radioligand	Selectivity	Specific Binding
BHSP	$NK_1 \gg NK_2 > NK_3$	80–95%
BH-$[Sar^9,Met(O_2)^{11}]$-SP	NK_1	90+%
$[^3H]$-SP	$NK_1 > NK_2 > NK_3$ all SP-preferring receptors	65%
BHELE	NK_3 in CNS NK_1, NK_2, NK_3 in periphery	70% 55–80%
INKA	$NK_2 > NK_1$ (does not bind to lung NK_2 sites)	95%
BHSCYII	NK_3 in CNS NK_1 in submandibular gland	85%
$[^3H]$-senktide	NK_3 in CNS NK_3 in myenteric plexus	40–50%

brain compared with peripheral NK_1 sites.[19,20] Against this hypothesis is the finding that identical clones of the two receptors are found in these two sites.[13] Possibly, differences in receptor glycosylation may explain such anomalies.

OTHER SUBSTANCE P RECEPTORS

The C-terminus of SP is important for many peripheral actions of SP mediated by the NK_1 receptor, with pD_2 approximately 8–10. However, the N-terminus is essential for a number of other actions requiring higher doses of SP. These include modulation of catecholamine release,[28] algesia, centrally mediated decreases in blood pressure,[29] stimulation of dorsal horn neurons,[30] and histamine release.[31] N-Terminal fragments formed by proteolytic cleavage, for example, by endopeptidase 3.4.24.11 or by angiotensin-converting enzyme, may also be the endogenous ligands for these receptors. Recent evidence has demonstrated that SP(1–7), but not SP injected together with phosphoramidon, lowers blood pressure after injection into the nucleus tractus solitarius.[32]

A Novel Substance P Binding Site in Bovine Adrenal Medulla

Capsaicin-sensitive SP-containing sensory nerves are present in the adrenal medulla of several species. SP inhibits nicotinic-receptor-mediated catecholamine release and also protects against the nicotinic desensitization of catecholamine release.[28] We attempted to characterize the receptor(s) responsible for these events using radioligand binding techniques. Our initial attempts to characterize binding using the C-terminally directed BHSP were unsuccessful; however, by using the less selective [³H]-SP, saturable, specific binding was obtained, with a K_D of 1.5 nM.[33] It is clear that this binding site is not the NK_1 receptor: BHSP showed no specific binding, the K_D was approximately 10-fold higher than values typically obtained at the NK_1 receptor, and the rank potency order of competitors was different from that seen at the NK_1 receptor. Specific binding of [³H]-SP was displaced by SP > SP(3–11) = NKA > SP(1–9) > SP(1–6) $\gg$ NKB[33] (TABLE 3). The presence of Lys at position 3 may be critical for binding, probably interacting with an anionic binding site. The possibility exists that the [³H]-SP binding site may represent part of the nicotinic receptor.[34]

SP Receptors in Rat Brain

Lower affinity SP receptors exist in other organs. In our laboratory, preliminary studies in rat cortex membranes have shown the presence of two distinct binding sites for [³H]-SP.[35] This is in contrast to BHSP and BH-[Sar⁹,Met(O₂)¹¹]-SP, which label only a single class of high affinity sites in rat brain.[27] High affinity sites with an approximate K_D of 0.02 nM represent about 20% of the [³H-SP] sites and probably correspond to NK_1 receptors; low affinity sites (approximate K_D of 2.6 nM) represent 80% of the sites (FIGURE 1). Binding of [³H]-SP was displaced by SP $\approx$ [Sar⁹,Met(O₂)¹¹]-SP $\gg$ SP(4–11) $\approx$ SP(3–11) > NPγ $\geq$ NKA = NKB > physalaemin.[35] Senktide and SP(1–9) amide had low affinity and SP(7–11), SP(1–6), and SP(1–4) had negligible affinity. The low affinity site is not the NK_3 receptor, which is present in large numbers in rat CNS:[18] not only was the NK_3-selective senktide an ineffective competitor for binding, but preliminary saturation studies repeated in the presence of senktide were no different from studies without senktide.

TABLE 3. Competition by Tachykinins and Fragments for Specific [³H]-SP Binding in Bovine Adrenal Medulla[a]

Peptide	K_D (nM)	Potency relative to SP
Substance P	2.14 ± 1.28	100
Neurokinin A	32 ± 12	6.7
Neurokinin B	≈ 4000	< 0.50
SP(3–11)	54 ± 15	4.0
SP(5–11)	> 10,000	< 0.05
SP(7–11)	> 10,000	< 0.05
SP(9–11)	> 10,000	< 0.05
SP(1–3)	3570 ± 703	0.06
SP(1–4)	411 ± 98	0.52
SP(1–6)	438 ± 89	0.49
SP(1–7)	383 ± 78	0.56
SP(1–9)	58 ± 19	3.7
Tuftsin	12,800 ± 2120	0.02

[a]Inhibition K_D values were derived using the nonlinear curve fitting program LIGAND and are the geometric mean ± SE (approximate) of 3–5 determinations. Data are from reference 33.

It is possible that SP itself is not the endogenous ligand for this N-terminally directed SP receptor. Both higher molecular weight forms of SP and SP fragments have been reported in cerebrospinal fluid. It remains to be established whether the SP binding site in the bovine adrenal medulla is similar to either of our cortical

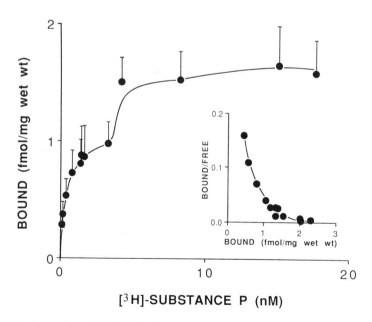

FIGURE 1. Saturation of [³H]-SP binding to rat cerebral cortex membranes. Inset: Biphasic Scatchard plot from a representative experiment indicating binding to more than one class of sites.

binding sites or to the functionally described, N-terminally directed SP CNS receptors[29,30] and the [³H]-SP(1–7) binding site described recently in mouse brain.[36]

Mast Cell SP "Receptors"

Micromolar concentrations of SP and SP(1–4) release histamine and other mediators from mast cells.[31] However, in autoradiographic studies, we have shown that BHSP does not label mast cells in rat footpad skin[25] or in rat mesentery whole mounts (E. Burcher and C. Taylor, unpublished data), indicating a lack of NK_1 receptors on these mast cells. The mast cell SP "receptor" may be an anionic binding site on G proteins, able to interact directly and unselectively with basic molecules.[31]

NEUROKININ A–PREFERRING RECEPTORS

In contrast to NK_1 receptors, which are found on neurons, glands, endothelial cells, and smooth muscle, NK_2 receptors appear to be found mainly on smooth muscle of the gastrointestinal, urinary, and respiratory tracts.[19-21] NKA-preferring receptors ("substance K receptors") have been isolated from bovine[10] and rat stomach and human trachea.[11]

In a number of tissues considered to contain NK_2 receptors, such as rat duodenum and rabbit pulmonary artery, NKA is a more potent contractile agent than either NKB or the nonmammalian kassinin, with SP being the least potent;[14] however, in dog and hamster urinary bladder, kassinin is more potent than NKA, with SP again being least potent.[37] Puzzlingly, NKA and NKB are greater than one order of magnitude more potent as agonists on the dog carotid artery (NK_1 system) than they are on (presumably) their own receptors in the rabbit pulmonary artery (NK_2) and the rat portal vein (NK_3).[14] Such findings suggest that the hypothesis of three endogenous ligands for three receptors may be oversimplistic and may need reassessment. Recently, two new tachykinins, neuropeptide K (NPK) and neuropeptide γ (NPγ), have been described, both of which possess the NKA structure at their C-terminus. Either of these may be an endogenous ligand at the NK_2 receptors in some tissues.

Evidence is growing that NK_2 receptors may be heterogenous. Recently, new selective analogues and antagonists have been developed that appear to divide peripheral tissues into two groups.[38,39] One group, in which MDL 29,913 and L-659,877 are potent antagonists, MDL 28,564 is a weak agonist, and MEN 10,207 is a weak antagonist, includes the hamster urinary bladder. Another group, in which MEN 10,207 is a potent antagonist, MDL 29,913 and L-659,877 are weak antagonists, and MDL 28,564 is a weak partial agonist/antagonist, includes the guinea pig trachea and a cell line[38] expressing the "substance K receptor" cloned by Masu, Nakanishi, and co-workers.[10] These data are discussed in detail elsewhere.[38,39] Our recent binding and functional studies (reported later) suggest that NPγ may be equipotent with NKA in the first group of tissues just described and may be substantially more potent than NKA in the second group.

Characterization of NK₂ Receptors in Dog Bladder

We have employed the technique of radioligand binding to characterize the tachykinin receptors present in homogenates of dog urinary bladder, using the

NK$_2$-preferring [^{125}I]-iodohistidyl-NKA (INKA). INKA was found to bind to a single class of sites with moderate affinity (K_D, 3.6 ± 0.3 nM). NPγ was an extremely potent competitor, followed by the nonmammalian kassinin, NPK, and NKA. The NK$_1$-preferring [Sar^9,Met(O$_2$)^{11}]-SP, SP, and physalaemin and the NK$_3$-preferring [Me-Phe^7]-NKB, [Pro^7]-NKB, and senktide were weak or ineffective competitors (TABLE 4), suggesting an absence of any significant numbers of NK$_1$ or NK$_3$ receptors in the dog bladder. The NK$_2$ subtype–selective antagonist MDL 29,913 was also a weak competitor.[38]

Although INKA has been considered to be a reasonably selective radioligand for the NK$_2$ receptor,[9] the rank potency order of competitors against this radioligand is clearly not consistent with inhibition from previously described "classical" NK$_2$ sites. In particular, in the dog bladder, NPγ was a much more potent inhibitor than either NKA or NPK. Excluding these new tachykinins (NPγ and NPK), the potency order for inhibition of INKA binding appears similar to the contractile potency of

TABLE 4. Competition by Tachykinins and Analogues for INKA Binding in Dog Bladder Homogenates[a]

Competitor	K_D (nM)	Potency relative to NPγ
Neuropeptide γ	0.20 ± 0.05	100
Kassinin	2.49 ± 0.84	8.0
Neuropeptide K	2.21 ± 0.28	9.1
Neurokinin A	3.65 ± 0.35	7.4
Neurokinin B	27.7 ± 3.2	0.7
Eledoisin	29.2 ± 6.08	0.7
[Sar^9,Met(O$_2$)^{11}]-SP	41.2 ± 4.3	0.5
Substance P	60.5 ± 7.4	0.3
Physalaemin	104 ± 38	0.2
L-659,877	174 ± 14	0.1
MDL 29,913	H: 34.3 ± 27.9	0.6
	L: 415 ± 452	0.05
Senktide	NE	

[a]Inhibition K_D values were derived using the computer program LIGAND and are the mean ± SEM of 4–6 determinations. Terms: H, high affinity; L, low affinity; NE, not effective at 10 µM.

tachykinins in the isolated bladder, with kassinin more potent than NKA.[37] This study suggests that NPγ could be the endogenous ligand at the "NK$_2$-like" receptor that we have characterized in dog urinary bladder. This receptor may represent one subtype of the NK$_2$ receptor.

Characterization of Tachykinin Receptors in Isolated Guinea Pig Hilus Bronchus

The actions of tachykinins in the respiratory system mimic in many ways the symptoms of asthma, for example, bronchoconstriction, mucus secretion, plasma extravasation, and airway edema.[40] Hence, much interest has centered on the characterization of the tachykinin receptor mediating bronchoconstriction. Initial studies showed that NKA was the most potent tachykinin bronchoconstrictor, suggesting an action through NK$_2$ receptors.[41] However, it is now clear that the tachykinin receptor on respiratory smooth muscle has unusual characteristics and interpretation of earlier data is complicated by some metabolism of tachykinins by endopeptidase 3.4.24.11.[15] Suggestions have been made that tachykinin-mediated bronchoconstriction is mediated by a novel "NK$_4$" receptor[42] or by a combination of NK$_1$ and NK$_2$ receptors. In our concurrent radioligand binding studies using INKA, we failed to detect NK$_2$ binding sites on respiratory smooth muscle in sections[21] or in lung homogenates[43] (see discussion later). In this study, we investigated the potencies of some tachykinins and analogues in contracting respiratory smooth muscle of the guinea pig hilus bronchus in the presence of the peptidase inhibitors, phosphoramidon and enalapril (both 10 μM). We included NPK and NPγ in order to investigate the hypothesis that one or both of these peptides may have a greater importance/potency in respiratory smooth muscle compared with NKA.

In normal animals, the order of potency in contracting the hilus was NPγ > NPK > NKB ≥ NKA > SP ≈ [Sar^9,Met(O$_2$)^{11}]-SP (FIGURE 2).[44] The NK$_3$ receptor–selective analogue, senktide, was inactive. The concentration response curves to NPγ, NPK, NKA, and NKB were shallow and suggest that bronchoconstriction may be mediated by more than one receptor. In the presence of 2 μM MDL 29,913, concentration response curves to these four peptides were substantially steepened and responses to NPγ, NKA, and NKB were significantly antagonized (TABLE 5). Responses to SP and [Sar^9,Met(O$_2$)^{11}]-SP were unaffected by MDL 29,913, showing that these two peptides are not acting through NK$_2$ receptors, but are probably acting through NK$_1$ receptors. Unfortunately, a selective NK$_1$ antagonist was not available to us for this study.

Our data show that NPγ and NPK are more potent in contracting the guinea pig

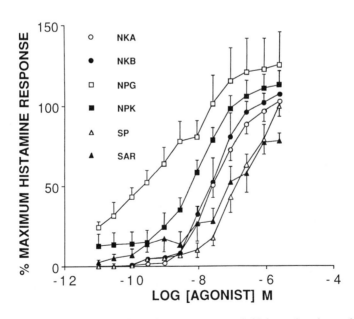

FIGURE 2. Cumulative concentration response curves to tachykinins and analogues from 4–8 experiments. Terms: NPG, NPγ; SAR, [Sar^9,Met(O$_2$)^{11}]-SP.

TABLE 5. pD$_2$ Values for the Potency of Tachykinins in Contracting the Guinea Pig Hilus Bronchus[a]

Peptide	Without Antagonist	With Antagonist
Neuropeptide γ	8.76 ± 0.26	7.72 ± 0.02[b]
Neuropeptide K	7.64 ± 0.25	7.16 ± 0.11
Neurokinin A	7.63 ± 0.22	6.63 ± 0.10[b]
Neurokinin B	7.88 ± 0.46	6.78 ± 0.06[b]
Substance P	6.58 ± 0.15	6.33 ± 0.09
[Sar^9,Met(O$_2$)^{11}]-SP	7.63 ± 0.44	7.15 ± 0.13

[a]For each animal, paired data were obtained in the absence (one hilus) and the presence (second hilus) of 2 μM MDL 29,913.
[b]$P < 0.05$, two-tailed t test.

hilus bronchus than other tachykinins. This appears to be the first report of the excellent bronchoconstrictor potency of NPγ. Current work indicates that NPγ is also 10-fold more potent than NKA in the isolated human bronchus.[45] NPK was previously demonstrated to have bronchoconstrictor potency,[46] although reports suggest that NPK may be more important as an NKA precursor than in its own right.[47]

Studies Comparing [^{125}I]-Bolton-Hunter SP (BHSP) with [^{125}I]-Neurokinin A in Guinea Pig Lung

Following reports that NKA was a potent bronchoconstrictor and that NK$_2$ receptors might exist on respiratory smooth muscle, we carried out a number of studies comparing receptor localization using BHSP and INKA. In our autoradiographic studies with phosphoramidon present, dense numbers of binding sites for BHSP were seen over the smooth muscle of the trachealis muscle and over bronchi and bronchioles.[21] In adjacent sections, labeling of smooth muscle by INKA was very much weaker. Characterization in sections showed that INKA binding was displaced by SP > NKA > NKB, demonstrating binding to the NK$_1$ rather than to the NK$_2$ receptor.[21]

We have recently characterized binding in homogenates of guinea pig lung using BHSP and INKA in the presence of phosphoramidon and other peptidase inhibitors.[43] Binding of both radioligands was displaced by SP > [Sar^9,Met(O$_2$)^{11}]-SP > SP methyl ester ≥ NPγ > NKA ≈ NKB ≈ kassinin > eledoisin, suggesting binding to the NK$_1$ receptor (TABLE 6). However, competition curves to SP and [Sar^9,Met(O$_2$)^{11}]-SP could be resolved into two components. One component, of very high affinity, probably represents the NK$_1$ receptor, but the nature of the other binding site remains to be established. This lower affinity component is not the NK$_3$ receptor because senktide was an extremely weak competitor.

As discussed earlier, evidence presented at this meeting[37,38] has suggested that distinct NK$_2$ receptor subtypes may exist. One possible explanation of these data is that, although both subtypes recognize NKA, the respiratory smooth muscle binding site cannot recognize INKA due to steric hindrance by the large iodine molecule on His^1. This might suggest that the receptor on guinea pig respiratory smooth muscle

TABLE 6. Competition by Tachykinins and Analogues for Specific BHSP and INKA Binding in Guinea Pig Lung Homogenates[a]

	K_D (nM)	
Competitor	BHSP	INKA
Substance P	0.30 ± 0.07	0.007 ± 0.002
[Sar^9,Met(O$_2$)^{11}]-SP	1.16 ± 0.16	0.12 ± 0.02
SP methyl ester	3.69 ± 0.62	0.93 ± 0.17
Neuropeptide γ	6.07 ± 1.8	0.90 ± 0.08
Neurokinin A	17.9 ± 4.6	1.19 ± 0.11
Neurokinin B	20.9 ± 3.4	1.81 ± 0.33
Kassinin	21.3 ± 0.79	3.22 ± 0.70
Eledoisin	27.6 ± 1.02	4.06 ± 1.00
Senktide	NE	NE

[a]Inhibition K_D values were derived using the computer program LIGAND and are the geometric mean ± SE (approximate) of 3–5 determinations; NE, not effective at 10 μM.

requires the N-terminal region of NKA for full recognition, whereas the NK$_2$ receptor on the hamster bladder, etc., recognizes primarily the C-terminus of the molecule. It is not clear whether NKA is the endogenous ligand at both of these NK$_2$ receptor subtypes. Other possible candidates known at this time include NPγ, NPK, NKA(3–10), and possibly an eledoisin-like peptide reportedly present in lung extracts and yet to be sequenced.

NEUROKININ B–PREFERRING RECEPTORS

NK$_3$ binding sites have been demonstrated autoradiographically in several areas of the CNS, where they appear to outnumber NK$_1$ sites approximately 10-fold.[18] Fewer populations of NK$_3$ receptors exist in the periphery, where they have been reported in areas including guinea pig myenteric plexus[19,48,49] and rat portal vein.[24]

The dogfish peptide scyliorhinin II (SCYII), which is the first naturally occurring cyclic tachykinin isolated, is NK$_3$-selective.[50] We have successfully prepared a novel radioligand BHSCYII and have purified it by using reverse phase HPLC.[51] Comparisons with BHELE show a very similar distribution of binding sites in rat brain.[51] In rat brain homogenates, specific binding of BHSCYII was of higher affinity than that of BHELE, although both radioligands labeled a similar number of binding sites.[51]

Virtually identical competition profiles were seen for both BHSCYII and BHELE and demonstrated binding to the NK$_3$ receptor. The rank order of potency of the compounds was SCYII ≥ [MePhe^7]-NKB ≥ senktide > NKB ≥ kassinin ≥ eledoisin > [Pro^7]-NKB > NKA > NPK ≥ SP > [Sar^9,Met(O$_2$)^{11}]-SP.[51] It is interesting that the fish peptide SCYII shows a higher affinity for the brain NK$_3$ site than the putative endogenous mammalian ligand, NKB. Factors important in the binding of SCYII to the brain NK$_3$ site may include possession of aspartic acid at position 4 (relative to NKB; refer to TABLE 1) and the disulfide bridge. Conformation changes resulting from such bridging may enhance the interaction of the N-terminal aspartic acids (refer to TABLE 1) with complementary cationic binding sites. The recent cloning of the NK$_3$ receptor[12] should stimulate future development of new selective ligands.

In rat brain, specific binding of BHSCYII was high. In contrast, the unselective BHELE showed high affinity binding and BHSCYII showed very weak binding in homogenates of several peripheral tissues containing NK_1 and NK_2 receptors (TABLE 7). The only tissues where characterization of binding was possible were the rat submandibular gland, where BHSCYII bound to both NK_1 and NK_3 sites,[52] and the guinea pig ileum, where binding was weak. These data suggest an absence of appreciable numbers of NK_3 receptors in peripheral tissues. This is in accordance with the paucity of NKB-like immunoreactivity in the periphery.[53]

In the guinea pig ileum, NK_3 receptors mediate acetylcholine release from myenteric plexus neurons.[48] With some difficulty, NK_3 binding sites have been demonstrated in myenteric plexus/longitudinal muscle homogenates using BHELE[19] and [^{3}H]-senktide.[49] In this tissue, both the affinity and the density of NK_3 sites are considerably lower than in the brain.[49] In preliminary autoradiographic studies, we have shown binding of BHSCYII over myenteric plexus neurons in the guinea pig ileum (FIGURE 3), although further studies will be required to delineate the type of binding sites present.

CONCLUSIONS

The present classification of tachykinin receptors will probably require revision as new, selective, and peptidase-resistant antagonists are developed, which may reveal possible subtypes of receptors. Advances in molecular biological techniques will help to define the active site within the receptors. In addition, new tachykinins may be found in extracts from mammalian tissues, which may alter our concepts of the nature of the "endogenous ligands" at these receptors. Although the NK_1, NK_2, and NK_3 receptors recognize the C-terminus of the molecule, other subtypes may interact with the N-terminus or with extended forms of tachykinins. Newly developed radioligands are considerably more selective than older versions based on the endogenous mammalian tachykinins, but there is room for considerable improvement. Monoclonal antibodies raised against receptor fragments may replace radioligands in the future.

TABLE 7. Representative dpm Values for Total Binding, Nonspecific Binding (NSB), and Percent Specific Binding (%SB) for BHSCYII (50 pM) and BHELE (80 pM) in a Range of Mammalian Peripheral Tissue Homogenates[a]

	BHSCYII			BHELE		
Tissue	Total	NSB	%SB	Total	NSB	%SB
Rat brain	10,100	1396	86	5735	1345	76
Rat fundus	945	765	19	4758	793	83
Dog urinary bladder	826	778	6	2108	242	88
Rat duodenum[b]	1259	890	29	2118	720	66
Guinea pig ileum[b]	1500	910	39	1972	638	68
Guinea pig lung	3015	2846	6	5189	733	86
Rat submandibular gland	2300	550	76	2880	221	92

[a]NSB is defined by 1 μM SCYII or eledoisin. The table includes data from reference 51.
[b]Mucosa removed.

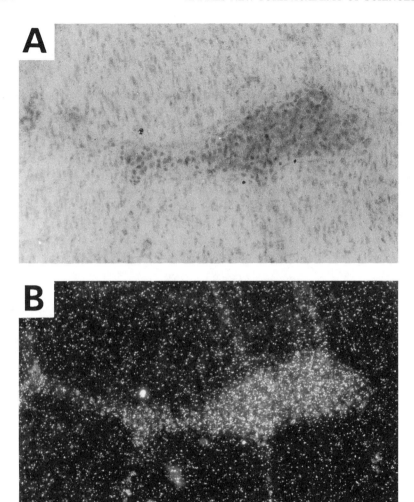

FIGURE 3. Light-field (A) and dark-field (B) photomicrographs of a whole mount of guinea pig ileum longitudinal muscle/myenteric plexus labeled with 50 pM BHSCYII. Nonspecific binding was defined with 1 μM SCYII. Labeled sections were dipped in photographic emulsion and were exposed for 14 days before developing and staining with pyronin Y. Moderate specific binding of BHSCYII was seen over ganglia and nerve trunks with only marginal binding to the longitudinal muscle. Magnification: ×280.

ACKNOWLEDGMENTS

We thank Claire Taylor for technical assistance, J. A. Angus (Baker Medical Research Institute, Melbourne, Australia) and T. J. Campbell (University of New South Wales) for donation of dog tissues, and S. H. Buck (Marion Merrell Dow Research Institute, Cincinnati, Ohio) for the kind gift of peptides and analogues.

REFERENCES

1. NICOLL, R. A., C. SCHENKER & S. E. LEEMAN. 1980. Annu. Rev. Neurosci. **3:** 227–268.
2. ERSPAMER, V. 1981. Trends Neurosci. **4:** 267–269.
3. PERNOW, B. 1983. Pharmacol. Rev. **35:** 85–141.
4. NAWA, H., H. KOTANI & S. NAKANISHI. 1984. Nature **321:** 729–734.
5. KOTANI, H., M. HOSHIMARU, H. NAWA & S. NAKANISHI. 1986. Proc. Natl. Acad. Sci. U.S.A. **83:** 7074–7148.
6. KRAUSE, J. E., J. M. CHIRGWIN, M. S. CARTER, Z. S. XU & A. D. HERSHEY. 1987. Proc. Natl. Acad. Sci. U.S.A. **84:** 881–885.
7. BUCK, S. H. & E. BURCHER. 1986. Trends Pharmacol. Sci. **7:** 65–68.
8. GUARD, S. & S. P. WATSON. 1990. Neurochem. Int. **18:** 149–165.
9. BURCHER, E. 1989. Clin. Exp. Pharmacol. Physiol. **16:** 539–543.
10. MASU, Y., K. NAKAYAMA, H. TAMAKI, Y. HARADA, M. KUNO & S. NAKANISHI. 1987. Nature **329:** 836–838.
11. GERARD, N. P., R. L. EDDY, T. B. SHOWS & C. GERARD. 1990. J. Biol. Chem. **265:** 20455–20462.
12. SHIGEMOTO, R., Y. YOKOTA, K. TSUCHIDA & S. NAKANISHI. 1990. J. Biol. Chem. **265:** 623–628.
13. HERSHEY, A. D. & J. E. KRAUSE. 1990. Science **247:** 958–962.
14. REGOLI, D., G. DRAPEAU, S. DION & R. COUTURE. 1988. Trends Pharmacol. Sci. **9:** 290–295.
15. SEKIZAWA, K., J. TAMAOKI, P. D. GRAF, C. B. BASBAUM, D. B. BORSON & J. A. NADEL. 1987. J. Pharmacol. Exp. Ther. **243:** 1211–1217.
16. BUCK, S. H., C. J. HELKE, E. BURCHER, C. W. SHULTS & T. L. O'DONOHUE. 1986. Peptides **7:** 1109–1120.
17. SAFFROY, M., J-C. BEAUJOUAN, Y. TORRENS, J. BESSEYRE, L. BERGSTROM & J. GLOWINSKI. 1988. Peptides **9:** 227–241.
18. DAM, T-V., E. ESCHER & R. QUIRION. 1988. Brain Res. **453:** 372–376.
19. BURCHER, E., S. H. BUCK, W. LOVENBERG & T. L. O'DONOHUE. 1986. J. Pharmacol. Exp. Ther. **236:** 819–831.
20. BURCHER, E. & S. H. BUCK. 1986. Eur. J. Pharmacol. **128:** 165–177.
21. BURCHER, E., D. J. WATKINS & N. M. O'FLYNN. 1989. Pulmon. Pharmacol. **1:** 201–203.
22. STEPHENSON, J. A., E. BURCHER & R. J. SUMMERS. 1986. Eur. J. Pharmacol. **124:** 377–378.
23. STEPHENSON, J. A., R. J. SUMMERS & E. BURCHER. 1986. Eur. J. Pharmacol. **142:** 391–402.
24. MASTRANGELO, D., R. MATHISON, H. G. HUGGEL, S. DION, P. D'ORLEANS-JUSTE, N. E. RHALEB, G. DRAPEAU, P. ROVERO & D. REGOLI. 1986. Eur. J. Pharmacol. **134:** 321–326.
25. O'FLYNN, N. M., R. D. HELME, D. J. WATKINS & E. BURCHER. 1989. Neurosci. Lett. **106:** 43–48.
26. BURCHER, E. & J. C. BORNSTEIN. 1988. Synapse **2:** 232–239.
27. LEW, R., D. P. GERAGHTY, G. DRAPEAU, D. REGOLI & E. BURCHER. 1990. Eur. J. Pharmacol. **184:** 97–108.
28. BOKSA, P. & B. G. LIVETT. 1985. Brain Res. **332:** 29–38.
29. HALL, M. E., P. GRANTHAM, J. LIMOLI & J. M. STEWART. 1987. Brain Res. **420:** 82–94.
30. PIERCEY, M. F., P. J. K. DOBREY, F. J. EINSPAHR, L. A. SCHROEDER & N. MASIQUES. 1982. Regulat. Peptides **3:** 337–349.
31. MOUSLI, M., J-L. BUEB, C. BRONNER, B. ROUOT & Y. LANDRY. 1990. Trends Pharmacol. Sci. **11:** 358–362.
32. HALL, M. E., F. MILEY & J. M. STEWART. 1989. Peptides **10:** 895–901.
33. GERAGHTY, D. P., B. G. LIVETT, F. M. ROGERSON & E. BURCHER. 1990. Neurosci. Lett. **112:** 276–281.
34. WEILAND, G. A., J. A. DURKIN, J. M. HENLEY & S. M. SIMASKO. 1988. Mol. Pharmacol. **32:** 625–632.
35. GERAGHTY, D. P. & E. BURCHER. 1990. Clin. Exp. Pharmacol. Physiol. Suppl. **17:** 25.
36. IGWE, O. J., D. C. KIM, V. S. SEYBOLD & A. A. LARSON. 1990. J. Neurosci. **10:** 3653–3663.

37. MIZRAHI, J., S. DION, P. D'ORLEANS-JUSTE, E. ESCHER, G. DRAPEAU & D. REGOLI. 1985. Eur. J. Pharmacol. **118:** 25–36.
38. VAN GIERSBERGEN, P. L. M., S. A. SHATZER, S. L. HARBESON, N. ROUISSI, F. NANTEL & S. H. BUCK. 1991. This volume.
39. MAGGI, C. A., R. PATACCHINI, S. GIULIANI, P. ROVERO, S. DION, D. REGOLI, A. GIACHETTI & A. MELI. 1990. Br. J. Pharmacol. **100:** 588–592.
40. BARNES, P. J. 1987. J. Allergy Clin. Immunol. **79:** 285–295.
41. HUA, X., J. M. LUNDBERG, E. THEODORSSON-NORHEIM & E. BRODIN. 1984. Naunyn-Schmiedeberg's Arch. Pharmacol. **328:** 196–201.
42. MCKNIGHT, A. T., J. J. MAGUIRE, B. J. WILLIAMS, A. C. FOSTER, R. TRIDGETT & L. L. IVERSEN. 1988. Regulat. Peptides **22:** 127 (abstract).
43. GERAGHTY, D. P. & E. BURCHER. 1990. Clin. Exp. Pharmacol. Physiol. Suppl. **16:** 27.
44. MCCLURE-SHARP, J. M. & E. BURCHER. 1990. Proc. Aust. Physiol. Pharmacol. Soc. **21:** 172P.
45. BURCHER, E., L. A. ALOUAN, P. R. A. JOHNSON & J. L. BLACK. 1991. Neuropeptides. In press.
46. TATEMOTO, K., J. M. LUNDBERG, H. JORNVALL & V. MUTT. 1985. Biochem. Biophys. Res. Commun. **128:** 947–953.
47. MARTLING, C-R., E. THEODORSSON-NORHEIM, I. NORHEIM & J. M. LUNDBERG. 1987. Naunyn-Schmiedeberg's Arch. Pharmacol. **336:** 183–189.
48. LAUFER, R., U. WORMSER, Z. Y. FRIEDMAN, C. GILON, M. CHOREV & Z. SELINGER. 1985. Proc. Natl. Acad. Sci. U.S.A. **82:** 7444–7448.
49. GUARD, S., S. P. WATSON, J. E. MAGGIO, H-P. TOO & K. J. WATLING. 1990. Br. J. Pharmacol. **99:** 767–773.
50. BUCK, S. H. & J. L. KRSTENANSKY. 1987. Eur. J. Pharmacol. **144:** 109–111.
51. MUSSAP, C. J. & E. BURCHER. 1990. Peptides **11:** 827–836.
52. MUSSAP, C. J. & E. BURCHER. 1991. This volume.
53. TOO, H-P., J. L. CORDOVA & J. E. MAGGIO. 1989. Regulat. Peptides **26:** 93–105.

Selective Neurokinin Receptor Radioligands[a]

RÉMI QUIRION,[b] THAN-VINH DAM,
AND STEVE GUARD[c]

Department of Psychiatry
and
Douglas Hospital Research Center
McGill University
Verdun, Québec, Canada H4H 1R3

INTRODUCTION

The existence of at least three major classes of neurokinin (NK) receptors is now well established.[1-5] Following their characterizations using a variety of pharmacological and biological assays (for recent reviews, see references 1–5), the NK-1,[6,7] NK-2,[8] and NK-3[9] receptors have been cloned and sequenced. All three receptors are G protein–coupled and are members of the rhodopsin–seven transmembrane domain receptor family.[6-9]

The NK-1 receptor is composed of 407 (rat) amino acid residues having a molecular weight of 46 kDa,[6,7] whereas the NK-2 receptor possesses an apparent molecular weight of 43 kDa and is composed of 384 (bovine) amino acid residues. The NK-3 receptor is similarly constituted with 452 (rat) amino acid residues and has a molecular weight of 51 kDa.[9] The mammalian NKs, substance P (SP), neurokinin A (NKA), and neurokinin B (NKB), preferentially act through the NK-1, NK-2, and NK-3 receptor classes, respectively.[1-5] However, none of these endogenous NKs are highly selective for a given receptor class and all can act on all three major NK receptors under certain conditions.[3,4] This can create major problems because most biological preparations are enriched with more than one class of NK receptors.[3,4] It even complicates the characterization of cloned NK receptors expressed in oocytes or stable cell lines because radioligands used in their characterization were not selective for a given receptor type, being similar to naturally occurring NKs. Moreover, it is well known that radiolabeled probes derived from endogenous ligands lack appropriate selectivity (e.g., acetylcholine for nicotinic and muscarinic receptors; dopamine for D_1–D_3 sites; serotonin for 5-HT$_1$, 5-HT$_2$, and 5-HT$_3$ receptors; etc.).

Thus, it is evident that the development of new radioligands based on the characterization of highly selective NK receptor subtype agonists and antagonists is required. Such tools are usually most helpful in clarifying receptor classification as exemplified by opiate,[10] serotonergic,[11] and cholinergic[12] receptors, among others. In that regard, the development of selective and potent agonists[13-16] and, more recently, antagonists[16-19] for each NK receptor class is promising and we briefly summarize

[a]This research project was supported by the Medical Research Council of Canada and by the Douglas Hospital Research Center.
[b]R. Quirion is a "Chercheur-Boursier" of the "Fonds de la Recherche en Santé du Québec".
[c]Present address: Parke-Davis Research Unit, Addenbrookes Hospital Site, Cambridge, United Kingdom.

137

here recent progress in that field. The future use of highly selective radioligands for each receptor subtype should facilitate further characterization of the structural requirements and biochemical features of each receptor type and, in addition, may clarify issues regarding the existence of given receptor classes in certain preparations.

NK-1 RECEPTORS

Thus far, [³H]SP and [¹²⁵I]Bolton-Hunter (BH)–SP have been used in most NK-1 receptor binding studies (e.g., see references 20–30). In addition, [³H]physalaemin[31] and [¹²⁵I]physalaemin,[32] two radiolabeled analogues of the amphibian tachykinin physalaemin, have been characterized as NK-1 receptor ligands (TABLE 1). Whereas these radioligands demonstrate high affinity (pM–nM range) and a high percentage of specific labeling (especially for iodinated ligands), they lack appropriate selectivity

TABLE 1. Neurokinin-1 Receptor Radioligands

	Advantages	Inconveniences
Nonselectives [¹²⁵I]BH-SP [³H]SP [¹²⁵I]physalaemin [³H]physalaemin	High specific binding especially with iodinated ligands Easily available	Lack of selectivity for the NK-1 sites
Selectives [¹²⁵I]BH-[Sar⁹,Met(O₂)¹¹]-SP	High specific binding Good selectivity	Possible alterations of binding properties by BH derivative
[³H]-[Sar⁹,Met(O₂)¹¹]-SP	Good selectivity Highly similar to unlabeled analogue	Lower % of specific binding
Needs selective radiolabeled antagonists SP-methyl ester for possible subtype recognition		

for the NK-1 receptor, being able to bind to other NK receptors under certain assay conditions.[3,4] This could be especially problematic in tissues or preparations highly enriched with NK-2 or NK-3 sites because a certain proportion of these sites could certainly be labeled by radiolabeled SP. This can now be avoided by the use of highly selective NK-1 receptor radioligands such as [³H]-[Sar⁹,Met(O₂)¹¹]-SP and [¹²⁵I]BH-[Sar⁹,Met(O₂)¹¹]-SP.

In a series of recent studies, we observed that [³H]-[Sar⁹,Met(O₂)¹¹]-SP apparently highly selectively binds to NK-1 receptors in rat brain.[33,34] The apparent affinity (K_d) of this radioligand is in the low nM range (1.4 ± 0.5 nM)[34] as reported for less selective NK-1 ligands like [³H]SP, [³H]physalaemin, [¹²⁵I]physalaemin, and [¹²⁵I]BH-SP (lower affinity sites).[20–32] Using an iodinated form of this selective analogue, Lew *et al.*[35] have recently reported a K_d value of 261 pM in rat brain membrane preparations. It is likely that the difference in K_d values observed between the tritiated and iodinated probes is related to the recognition of a high affinity state of the NK-1 receptor by the iodinated ligand. Similar findings have been reported for a variety of receptors, with the higher affinity states hardly being recognized by tritiated ligands due to technical difficulties.[36]

The selectivity of $[^3H]$-$[Sar^9,Met(O_2)^{11}]$-SP for the NK-1 receptor is revealed by its ligand competition profile. Whereas SP (IC_{50} = 5.6 nM) and nonradioactive $[Sar^9,Met(O_2)^{11}]$-SP (IC_{50} = 0.6 nM) are potent competitors of $[^3H]$-$[Sar^9,Met(O_2)^{11}]$-SP binding, NKB and eledoisin are only weakly active (IC_{50} > 100 nM). Selective NK-2 ($[Nle^{10}]$-$NKA_{(4-10)}$[13]) and NK-3 (senktide[14]) receptor agonists are mostly devoid of activity (IC_{50} > 1000 nM) at those sites. Interestingly, SP-methyl ester, a purported selective NK-1 agonist,[37] is only weakly active (IC_{50} > 500 nM) on $[^3H]$-$[Sar^9,Met(O_2)^{11}]$-SP binding in rat brain membrane preparations. Similar results have recently been reported using the iodinated ligand $[^{125}I]BH$-$[Sar^9,Met(O_2)^{11}]$-SP. Moreover, the results of this research demonstrated that SP-methyl ester was more potent (50-fold) on salivary gland $[^{125}I]BH$-$[Sar^9,Met(O_2)^{11}]$-SP binding sites as compared to sites present in a CNS preparation.[35] This may suggest that NK-1 receptors in brain and salivary gland possess slightly different structural requirements that can be detected by radiolabeled $[Sar^9,Met(O_2)^{11}]$-SP, but not by SP.

Autoradiographic studies also suggest the possible existence of NK-1 receptor subtypes, with one being especially well recognized by the selective radioligand, $[^3H]$-$[Sar^9,Met(O_2)^{11}]$-SP. Whereas the general distribution of $[^3H]$-$[Sar^9,Met(O_2)^{11}]$-SP binding is similar to those previously reported for nonselective ligands such as $[^3H]SP$[20] and $[^{125}I]BH$-SP,[27-30] differences are observed in certain brain regions such as the hippocampal formation and the ventral horn of the spinal cord.[34] For example, we found that $[^3H]$-$[Sar^9,Met(O_2)^{11}]$-SP binding sites are almost exclusively located in the granular cell layer of the dentate gyrus,[34] whereas $[^3H]SP$[20] and $[^{125}I]BH$-SP[27-30] sites are more broadly distributed, being concentrated in this same cell group as well as in other fields and laminae (just above the pyramidal cell layer and in the stratum lacunosum moleculare). Hence, the more restricted distribution of $[^3H]$-$[Sar^9,Met(O_2)^{11}]$-SP labeling in certain brain regions and its relative resistance to SP-methyl ester may suggest the existence of NK-1 receptor subtypes.[34,35] On the other hand, it is also possible that the additional population of sites visualized using less selective ligands ($[^3H]SP$ and $[^{125}I]BH$-SP) could reflect binding of these probes to other receptor classes (NK-2, NK-3).

In brief, the usefulness of selective NK-1 receptor ligands is evident because they may eventually permit the recognition of receptor subtypes. In that regard, the use of $[^{125}I]/[^3H]$-$[Sar^9,Met(O_2)^{11}]$-SP and hopefully $[^3H]SP$-methyl ester could prove most relevant, as well as the development of selective NK-1 radiolabeled antagonists (possibly GR71251[17]). Similar strategies have been most important for the characterization of subtypes of a given receptor class (e.g., 5-HT_1,[11] opioid,[10] muscarinic[12]), with endogenous ligands not being able, by definition, to differentiate between putative subtypes.

NK-2 RECEPTORS

Selective radioligands still remain to be developed for the NK-2 receptor class. Thus far, $[^3H]NKA$[38] and (2-$[^{125}I]iodohistidyl^1$)-NKA[3,29,30] have been used as radioligands (TABLE 2). However, these probes are not selective, labeling all NK receptor classes depending on the assay conditions and the respective densities of each receptor.[3,33] Moreover, their poor stability and solubility render them less than ideal radioligands. Therefore, it is not surprising that confusion still exists regarding NK-2 receptor binding characteristics and distribution, especially in the CNS[3,33] where they are expressed in limited amounts.[39]

TABLE 2. Neurokinin-2 Receptor Radioligands

	Advantages	Inconveniences
Nonselectives		
[³H]NKA	—	Poor % of specific binding
(2-[¹²⁵I]iodohistidyl¹)-NKA	High specific binding	Lack of selectivity and instability
[¹²⁵I]neuropeptide γ	High specific binding	⎰ Poor selectivity for NK-2 versus
[¹²⁵I]-γ-PPT₍₇₂₋₉₂₎-peptide amide	High affinity	⎱ NK-1 sites

Selective
  none available

Needs
  selective radiolabeled agonists ([β-Ala⁸]NKA₍₄₋₁₀₎) and antagonists (MEN 10,207,
    L-659,877)

Recently, we have used $[^{125}I]$-γ-preprotachykinin$_{(72-92)}$-peptide amide or neuropeptide γ (NPγ) as a putative ligand for the characterization of NK-2 receptors.[40] Although it is evident that this peptide possesses high affinity for NK-2 receptors in a variety of preparations,[40–42] it also binds to NK-1 receptors, especially in tissues or brain areas heavily enriched with NK-1 sites such as the locus coeruleus and the amygdalo-hippocampal area (Guard *et al.*, unpublished results). For example, we observed that $[^{125}I]$NPγ binding in the dentate gyrus and amygdalo-hippocampal area is highly sensitive to the selective NK-1 agonist $[Sar^9,Met(O_2)^{11}]$-SP,[13] whereas an NK-2 agonist such as $[β-Ala^8]NKA_{(4-10)}$[15] is able to compete for specific labeling only in certain thalamic nuclei and hippocampal laminae. Consequently, the need for the development of selective NK-2 receptor radioligands remains. In that regard, the characterization of highly potent and selective NK-2 receptor antagonists such as L-659,877 and L-659,874[18] is promising, as well as the recent development of analogues that may permit the recognition of NK-2 receptor subtypes (MEN 10,207[16] or MDL 28,564[43]).

NK-3 RECEPTORS

As for the other NK receptor classes, naturally occurring tachykinins were first used as radioligands, especially $[^3H]$NKB[44] and $[^{125}I]$BH-eledoisin[29,30,45–50] (TABLE 3). However, these probes lack appropriate selectivity even though the specificity of the binding was very good, especially for $[^{125}I]$BH-eledoisin.[29,30,45–50] Thus, care must be taken when using this latter ligand because it is now apparent that it may label NK-1 sites in regions highly enriched with this receptor class such as the locus coeruleus and the amygdalo-hippocampal area.

In 1986, senktide was developed as a highly selective NK-3 receptor agonist.[14] Whereas iodinated forms of this analogue did not prove useful in binding assays, $[^3H]$senktide has recently been characterized as a selective NK-3 receptor probe.[33,51,52] $[^3H]$Senktide apparently labels a single class of high affinity (nM range), low capacity sites in both CNS and peripheral tissue membrane preparations.[51,52] The ligand selectivity profile clearly demonstrates that $[^3H]$senktide labels NK-3 receptor sites in brain and periphery. For example, whereas NKB and eledoisin are potent competitors, other naturally occurring tachykinins such as physalaemin, SP, and NKA are much weaker.[52] Selective NK-3 receptor agonists (senktide[14] and [MePhe⁷]NKB[13]) are potent competitors (IC_{50} in the nM range) of [³H]senktide binding, whereas NK-2 ([Nle[10]]NKA$_{(4-10)}$)[13] and NK-1 agonists (SP-methyl ester[37] and [Sar⁹,Met(O₂)[11]]-SP[13]) are virtually inactive. Similarly, various NK-1/NK-2 receptor antagonists ([D-Pro⁴,D-Trp[7,9,10]]-SP$_{(4-11)}$,[4] L-659,877,[18] and L-659,874[18]) are inactive on [³H]senktide binding at concentrations up to 10 μM.

The autoradiographic distribution of [³H]senktide binding sites in the rat brain[51] is similar to that reported for [¹²⁵I]BH-eledoisin,[29,30,47,48,50] with high densities of labeling seen in the midcortical layers, the supraoptic nucleus, the basolateral nucleus of the amygdala, and the interpeduncular nucleus. However, [¹²⁵I]BH-eledoisin apparently labels more sites than [³H]senktide in regions such as the caudate-putamen, amygdalo-hippocampal area, and locus coeruleus.[51] Because these regions are highly enriched (high densities) with NK-1 sites, it is likely that [¹²⁵I]BH-eledoisin, in contrast to [³H]senktide, binds to both NK-1 and NK-3 sites in these areas.[34,51] This further demonstrates the need for the use of selective radioligands, especially in tissues enriched with multiple classes of NK receptors. We would argue that selective radioligands should always be used, even if their signal-to-noise ratio may not be as optimal (as for [³H]senktide[51,52]) in certain preparations.

Recently, Mussap and Burcher[53] have proposed the use of [¹²⁵I]BH-scyliorhinin II as a novel, selective radioligand for the NK-3 receptor. However, it now appears that this ligand also labels a substantial proportion of NK-1 sites, at least in the CNS.[54] Thus, it may not prove as useful as expected at first (as in the case of [¹²⁵I]NPγ for the NK-2 sites; see earlier discussion) and it would appear that [³H]senktide remains the only selective NK-3 radioligand currently available. The potential development of radiolabeled NK-3 receptor antagonists[19] would also certainly be of interest.

CONCLUSIONS

In summary, fairly selective radioligands are now available for the NK-1 and NK-3 receptor classes, whereas the development of selective NK-2 probes is awaited with great interest. It is also likely that more selective NK-1 and NK-3 radioligands will be developed in the near future. Hopefully, these will include both agonists and

TABLE 3. Neurokinin-3 Receptor Radioligands

	Advantages	Inconveniences
Nonselectives		
[³H]NKB		Poor % of specific binding
[³H]eledoisin	—	Poor selectivity and stability
[¹²⁵I]BH-eledoisin	High specific binding	Poor selectivity
[¹²⁵I]BH-scyliorhinin II	High specific binding / High affinity	Poor selectivity for NK-3 versus NK-1 sites
Selective		
[³H]senktide	High selectivity / Similar to unlabeled analogue	Lower % of specific binding
Needs		
selective radiolabeled antagonists		
iodinated, highly selective agonists		

antagonists. This should permit a more precise characterization of the possible existence of multiple NK receptor subtypes and affinity states.

Finally, it must be recognized that future progress in the field of NK receptor binding studies depends on the development and uses of highly selective radioligands. This is well exemplified by most other receptor families (e.g., see references 10–13), with endogenously occurring ligands rarely being useful for the characterization of different receptor classes or subtypes.

ACKNOWLEDGMENT

The expert secretarial assistance of J. Currie is acknowledged.

REFERENCES

1. BUCK, S. H. & E. BURCHER. 1986. The tachykinins: a family of peptides with a brood of "receptors". Trends Pharmacol. Sci. **7:** 65–68.
2. MAGGIO, J. E. 1988. Tachykinins. Annu. Rev. Neurosci. **11:** 13–28.
3. QUIRION, R. & T-V. DAM. 1988. Multiple neurokinin receptors: recent developments. Regulat. Peptides **22:** 18–25.
4. REGOLI, D., G. DRAPEAU, S. DION & P. D'ORLÉANS-JUSTE. 1987. Recent developments in neurokinin pharmacology. Life Sci. **40:** 100–117.
5. GUARD, S. & S. P. WATSON. 1990. Tachykinin receptor subtypes: classification and membrane signaling mechanisms. Neurochem. Int. **17.**
6. YOKOTA, Y., Y. SASAI, K. TANAKA, T. FUJIWARA, K. TSUCHIDA, R. SHIGEMOTO, A. KAKIZUKA, H. OHKUBO & S. NAKANISHI. 1989. Molecular characterization of a functional cDNA for rat substance P receptor. J. Biol. Chem. **264:** 17649–17652.
7. HERSHEY, A. D. & J. E. KRAUSE. 1990. Molecular characterization of a functional cDNA encoding the rat substance P receptor. Science **247:** 958–962.
8. MASU, Y., K. NAKAYAMA, H. TAMAKI, Y. HARADA, M. KUNO & S. NAKANISHI. 1987. cDNA cloning of bovine substance-K receptor through oocyte expression system. Nature (London) **328:** 836–838.
9. SHIGEMOTO, R., Y. YOKOTA, K. TSUCHIDA & S. NAKANISHI. 1990. Cloning and expression of a rat neuromedin K receptor cDNA. J. Biol. Chem. **265:** 623–628.
10. QUIRION, R., J. M. ZAJAC, J. L. MORGAT & B. P. ROQUES. 1983. Autoradiographic distribution of mu and delta opiate receptors in rat brain using highly selective ligands. Life Sci. **33**(1): 227–230.
11. PEROUTKA, S. 1988. 5-Hydroxytryptamine receptor subtypes: molecular, biochemical, and physiological characterization. Trends Neurosci. **11:** 496–500.
12. QUIRION, R., I. AUBERT, P. A. LAPCHAK, R. P. SCHAUM, S. TEOLIS, S. GAUTHIER & D. M. ARAUJO. 1989. Muscarinic receptor sub-types in human neurodegenerative diseases: focus on Alzheimer's disease. Trends Pharmacol. Sci. (Suppl. Dec.) **IV:** 80–84.
13. DRAPEAU, G., P. D'ORLÉANS-JUSTE, S. DION, N. E. RHALEB & D. REGOLI. 1987. Selective agonists for substance P and neurokinin receptors. Neuropeptides **10:** 43–54.
14. WORMSER, U., R. LAUFER, Y. HART, M. CHOREV, C. GILON & Z. SELINGER. 1986. Highly selective agonists for substance P receptor subtypes. EMBO J. **5:** 2805–2808.
15. MAGGI, C. A., S. GIULIANI, L. BALLATI, P. ROVERO, L. ABELLI, S. MANZINI, A. GIACHETTI & A. MELI. 1990. *In vivo* pharmacology of [β-Ala⁸]neurokinin A$_{(4-10)}$, a selective NK-2 tachykinin receptor agonist. Eur. J. Pharmacol. **177:** 81–86.
16. MAGGI, C. A., R. PATACCHINI, M. ASTOLFI, P. ROVERO, S. GIULIANI & A. GIACHETTI. 1991. NK-2 receptor agonists and antagonists. This volume.
17. HALL, J. M. & I. K. M. MORTON. 1991. Novel ligands confirm NK-1 receptor–mediated modulation of neurotransmission in the guinea pig vas deferens preparation. This volume.

18. McKnight, A. T., J. J. Maguire, B. J. Williams, A. C. Foster, R. Tridgett & L. L. Iversen. 1988. Pharmacological specificity of synthetic peptides as antagonists at tachykinin receptors. Regulat. Peptides **22**: 127.

19. Rouissi, N., F. Nantel, N. E. Rhaleb, D. Jukic, G. Drapeau & D. Regoli. 1990. New potent and selective antagonists for the NK-3 receptor. This conference.

20. Quirion, R., C. W. Shults, T. W. Moody, C. B. Pert, T. N. Chase & T. L. O'Donohue. 1983. Autoradiographic distribution of substance P receptors in rat central nervous system. Nature (London) **303**: 714–716.

21. Park, C. H., V. J. Massari, R. Quirion, Y. Tizabi, C. W. Shults & T. L. O'Donohue. 1984. Characteristics of ^{3}H–substance P binding sites in rat brain membranes. Peptides **5**: 833–836.

22. Lee, C. M., N. J. Campbell, B. J. Williams & L. L. Iversen. 1986. Multiple tachykinin binding sites in peripheral tissues and brain. Eur. J. Pharmacol. **130**: 209–217.

23. Nakata, Y., H. Tanaka, Y. Morishima & T. Segawa. 1988. Solubilization and characterization of substance P binding protein from bovine brain stem. J. Neurochem. **50**: 522–527.

24. Beaujouan, J-C., Y. Torrens, A. Herbert, M. C. Daguet, J. Glowinski & A. Prochiantz. 1982. Specific binding of an immunoreactive and biologically active ^{125}I-labeled substance P derivative to mouse mesencephalic cells in primary culture. Mol. Pharmacol. **22**: 48–55.

25. Torrens, Y., J-C. Beaujouan, A. Viger & J. Glowinski. 1983. Properties of a ^{125}I–substance P derivative binding to synaptosomes from various brain structures and the spinal cord of the rat. Naunyn-Schmiedeberg's Arch. Pharmacol. **324**: 134–139.

26. Cascieri, M. A. & T. Liang. 1983. Characterization of the substance P receptor in rat brain cortex membranes and the inhibition of radioligand binding by guanine nucleotides. J. Biol. Chem. **258**: 5158–5164.

27. Shults, C. W., R. Quirion, B. Chronwall, T. N. Chase & T. L. O'Donohue. 1984. A comparison of the anatomical distribution of substance P and substance P receptors in the rat central nervous system. Peptides **5**: 1097–1128.

28. Quirion, R. & T-V. Dam. 1986. Ontogeny of substance P receptor binding sites in rat brain. J. Neurosci. **6**: 2187–2199.

29. Saffroy, M., J-C. Beaujouan, Y. Torrens, J. Besseyre, L. Bergstrom & J. Glowinski. 1988. Localization of tachykinin binding sites (NK$_1$, NK$_2$, NK$_3$ ligands) in the rat brain. Peptides **9**: 227–241.

30. Mantyh, P. W., T. Gates, C. R. Mantyh & J. E. Maggio. 1989. Autoradiographic localization and characterization of tachykinin receptor binding sites in the rat brain and peripheral tissues. J. Neurosci. **9**: 258–279.

31. Mohini, P., S. W. Bahouth, D. E. Brundish & J. M. Musacchio. 1985. Specific labeling of rat brain substance P receptor with [^{3}H]physalaemin. J. Neurosci. **5**: 2079–2085.

32. Wolf, S. S., T. W. Moody, R. Quirion & T. L. O'Donohue. 1985. Biochemical characterization and autoradiographic localization of central substance P receptors using [^{125}I]physalaemin. Brain Res. **332**: 299–307.

33. Guard, S., T-V. Dam, S. P. Watson, B. Martinelli, K. J. Watling & R. Quirion. 1991. [^{3}H]-[Sar^9,Met(O$_2$)^{11}]-SP and [^{3}H]-succinyl-[Asp^6,MePhe^8]-SP$_{(6-11)}$ senktide: new selective radioligands for NK-1 and NK-3 tachykinin receptors. Biotechnol. Update **6**: 4–8.

34. Dam, T-V., B. Martinelli & R. Quirion. 1990. Autoradiographic distribution of brain neurokinin-1/substance P receptors using a highly selective ligand [^{3}H]-[Sar^9, Met(O$_2$)^{11}]–substance P. Brain Res. **531**: 333–337.

35. Lew, R., D. P. Geraghty, G. Drapeau, D. Regoli & E. Burcher. 1990. Binding characteristics of [^{125}I]Bolton-Hunter [Sar^9,Met(O$_2$)^{11}]–substance P, a new selective radioligand for the NK-1 receptor. Eur. J. Pharmacol. **184**: 97–108.

36. Quirion, R. & P. Gaudreau. 1985. Strategies in neuropeptide receptor binding research. Neurosci. Biobehav. Rev. **9**: 413–420.

37. Watson, S. P., B. E. B. Sandberg, M. R. Hanley & L. L. Iversen. 1983. Tissue selectivity of substance P alkyl esters: suggesting multiple receptors. Eur. J. Pharmacol. **87**: 77–84.

38. Bergstrom, L., J-C. Beaujouan, Y. Torrens, M. Saffroy, J. Glowinski, S. Lavielle,

G. CHASSAING, A. MARQUET, P. D'ORLÉANS-JUSTE, S. DION & D. REGOLI. 1987. [³H]Neurokinin A labels a specific tachykinin binding site in the rat duodenal smooth muscle. Mol. Pharmacol. **32:** 764–771.

39. HERSHEY, A. D., L. POLENZANI, R. M. WOODWARD, R. MILEDI & J. E. KRAUSE. 1991. Molecular and genetic characterization, functional expression, and mRNA expression patterns of a rat substance P receptor. This volume.

40. DAM, T-V., Y. TAKADA, J. E. KRAUSE, E. ESCHER & R. QUIRION. 1990. γ-Preprotachy-kinin (72–92) peptide amide: an endogenous preprotachykinin-I-gene derived peptide that preferentially binds to neurokinin-2 receptor. Proc. Natl. Acad. Sci. U.S.A. **87:** 246–250.

41. DAM, T-V., Y. TAKADA, J. E. KRAUSE & R. QUIRION. 1991. Comparative autoradiographic distribution of [^{125}I]neuropeptide γ and [^{125}I]neurokinin A binding sites in guinea pig brain. This volume.

42. VAN GIERSBERGEN, P. L. M., S. A. SHATZER, H. C. CHENG, E. BURCHER & S. H. BUCK. 1990. Are neuropeptide K and neuropeptide γ endogenous NK-2 receptor agonists? This conference.

43. BUCK, S. H., S. L. HARBESON, C. F. HASSMANN III, S. A. SHATZER, N. ROUISSI, F. NANTEL & P. L. M. VAN GIERSBERGEN. 1990. [Leu^9(CH$_2$NH)Leu^{10}]–Neurokinin A (4–10) (MDL 28,564) distinguishes tissue tachykinin peptide NK-2 receptors. Life Sci. **47:** 37–41.

44. BERGSTROM, L., Y. TORRENS, M. SAFFROY, J-C. BEAUJOUAN, S. LAVIELLE, G. CHASSAING, J. L. MORGAT, J. GLOWINSKI & A. MARQUET. 1987. ³H–Neurokinin B and ^{125}I–Bolton Hunter eledoisin label identical tachykinin binding sites in the rat brain. J. Neurochem. **48:** 125–133.

45. CASCIERI, M. A. & T. LIANG. 1984. Binding of [^{125}I]–Bolton Hunter conjugated eledoisin to rat brain cortex membranes—evidence for two classes of tachykinin receptors in the mammalian central nervous system. Life Sci. **35:** 179–184.

46. BEAUJOUAN, J-C., Y. TORRENS, A. VIGER & J. GLOWINSKI. 1984. A new type of tachykinin binding site in the rat brain characterized by the specific binding of a labeled eledoisin derivative. Mol. Pharmacol. **26:** 248–254.

47. BEAUJOUAN, J-C., Y. TORRENS, M. SAFFROY & J. GLOWINSKI. 1986. Quantitative autora-diographic analysis of the distribution of binding sites for [^{125}I]Bolton-Hunter deriva-tives of eledoisin and substance P in the rat brain. Neuroscience **18:** 857–875.

48. DANKS, J. A., R. B. ROTHMAN, M. A. CASCIERI, G. G. CHICCHI, T. LIANG & M. HERKENHAM. 1986. A comparative autoradiographic study of the distributions of substance P and eledoisin binding sites in rat brain. Brain Res. **385:** 273–291.

49. BURCHER, E., S. H. BUCK, W. LOVENBERG & T. L. O'DONOHUE. 1986. Characterization and autoradiographic localization of multiple tachykinin binding sites in gastrointesti-nal tract and bladder. J. Pharmacol. Exp. Ther. **236:** 819–830.

50. DAM, T-V., E. ESCHER & R. QUIRION. 1988. Evidence for the existence of three classes of neurokinin receptors in brain: differential ontogeny of neurokinin-1, neurokinin-2, and neurokinin-3 binding sites in rat cerebral cortex. Brain Res. **453:** 372–376.

51. DAM, T-V., E. ESCHER & R. QUIRION. 1990. Visualization of neurokinin-3 receptor sites in rat brain using the highly selective ligand [³H]senktide. Brain Res. **506:** 175–178.

52. GUARD, S., S. P. WATSON, J. E. MAGGIO, H. P. TOO & K. J. WATLING. 1990. Pharmacolog-ical analysis of [³H]senktide binding to NK$_3$ tachykinin receptors in guinea pig ileum longitudinal muscle myenteric plexus and cerebral cortex membranes. Br. J. Pharmacol. **99:** 767–773.

53. MUSSAP, C. J. & E. BURCHER. 1990. [^{125}I]-Bolton-Hunter scyliorhinin II: a novel, selective radioligand for the tachykinin NK-3 receptor in rat brain. Peptides **11:** 827–836.

54. BURCHER, E., C. J. MUSSAP, D. P. GERAGHTY, J. M. MCCLURE-SHARP & D. J. WATKINS. 1991. Concepts in characterization of tachykinin receptors. This volume.

Myoinositol Uptake in Rat Parotid Gland

A Selective Bioassay for NK$_1$ Receptors

Y. TORRENS, M. M. DIETL, J-C. BEAUJOUAN, AND
J. GLOWINSKI

Département de Neuropharmacologie
Collège de France
75231 Paris Cedex 05, France

INTRODUCTION

Three types of receptors of tachykinins have been described in the central or peripheral nervous systems, namely, NK$_1$, NK$_2$, and NK$_3$ receptors, whose main endogenous ligands are, respectively, substance P (SP), neurokinin A (NKA), and neurokinin B (NKB).[1] These receptors were first characterized in binding studies made with appropriate ligands in either central or peripheral tissues.[2-7] NK$_1$ and NK$_3$ binding sites have exhibited a distinct distribution in the brain.[8-10] However, although NKA and longer peptides containing NKA, such as neuropeptide K (NPK) and neuropeptide γ (NPγ), are present in the brain[11] and specific central biological responses mediated by NKA have been demonstrated,[12,13] the presence of NKA binding sites in brain tissues is still a matter of controversy.[6,9,10,14] More recently, thanks to the development of molecular biology approaches, these three tachykinin receptors have been cloned using central or peripheral tissues and they have been shown to possess seven transmembrane-spanning regions representing the general structure of receptors coupled to G proteins.[15-17] In parallel, several efforts were made by chemists to synthesize selective agonists of NK$_1$, NK$_2$, and NK$_3$ receptors because the selectivity of endogenous peptides for their receptors was not very high.[18-20] Several analogues of tachykinins were also shown to exert antagonistic properties and a few of them possessed some selectivity. Nevertheless, further research is required to obtain powerful antagonists acting on the three types of tachykinin receptors.[21,22]

Binding studies have been of particular help in demonstrating that tachykinin analogues recognize tachykinin receptors, but the agonist or antagonist properties of these compounds have been shown in general by using biological assays on peripheral isolated organs. Thus, it has been claimed that the dog carotid artery, the rabbit pulmonary artery, and the rat portal vein allow for the distinguishing of the respective responses mediated by NK$_1$, NK$_2$, and NK$_3$ receptors.[23] Nevertheless, there is not always a perfect correlation between the relative potencies of tachykinins or their analogues in binding studies and in assays made on these peripheral organs. This could be related to a partial peptidasic inactivation of some of the tested peptides in the assays or to the presence of low densities of other subtypes of tachykinin receptors (in addition to the main tachykinin receptor examined). In spite of these difficulties, biological assays on isolated organs are of great importance for the pharmacological characterization of specific agonists and antagonists. However, biological assays on more simplified systems are absolutely necessary.

Attempts have been made to examine the effects of tachykinins at a cellular level, particularly by measuring the second messengers that are formed in response to the stimulation of tachykinin receptors. Several authors have shown that tachykinins stimulate the turnover of phosphoinositides either in the brain or in some peripheral tissues.[24-29] However, in most cases, responses were of relatively low amplitude, the type of tachykinin receptor involved was not fully characterized, and tachykinins were used in rather high concentrations. Nevertheless, two preparations seem to be of great interest. Indeed, using the hamster urinary bladder, a tissue that seems to possess exclusively NK_2 receptors, Bristow et al.[28] have demonstrated that NKA stimulates markedly the activity of phospholipase C. A very nice correlation was also found between the potencies of several tachykinins and their analogues in displacing the labeled ligand from NK_2 binding sites and in stimulating IP_3 formation. Furthermore, we have shown that cortical astrocytes in primary culture from a newborn

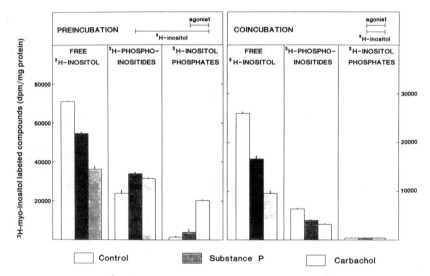

FIGURE 1. Substance P–induced and carbachol-induced reduction of ^{3}H-myoinositol uptake into rat parotid slices. On the left side, parotid gland slices are preincubated for 60 min with ^{3}H-myoinositol and agonists are added for a further 15 min. On the right side, parotid gland slices are exposed simultaneously to ^{3}H-myoinositol and the agonists. Free cytosolic ^{3}H-myoinositol, its incorporation into phospholipids, and ^{3}H-myoinositol phosphate formation were determined. Note in both protocols that a reduction in the initial accumulation of cytosolic ^{3}H-myoinositol is observed.

mouse possess only NK_1 binding sites and that the stimulation of NK_1 receptors evokes a very pronounced activation of phospholipase C.[29] Here again, the examination of the potencies of a large number of tachykinin analogues in binding assays and on the activation of phospholipase C has revealed a perfect correlation and, in addition, IC_{50} and EC_{50} values have been found identical. More recently, we have compared results found with astrocytes with those obtained in the parotid gland of the adult rat, a tissue that predominantly possesses NK_1 receptors.[30,31] In agreement with previous reports, the activation of phospholipase C by SP was of much lower amplitude than that observed on astrocytes (FIGURE 1). Interestingly, in this study, we observed that SP inhibits the transport of ^{3}H-myoinositol into parotid acinar cells.[32,33] In the present review, we summarize a series of recent results indicating that this effect is specifically mediated by NK_1 receptors and that the measurement of this response provides a valid index for the characterization of specific agonists or antagonists of this tachykinin receptor type.

SOME CHARACTERISTICS OF ³H-MYOINOSITOL TRANSPORT IN RAT PAROTID ACINAR CELLS

It has been shown in several tissues that myoinositol penetrates into cells by an Na^+-dependent uptake process or by a facilitated diffusion.[34-38] Using parotid gland prisms, we could show that this is also the case in this tissue. Indeed, two components could be demonstrated for the transport of ³H-myoinositol—a predominant one that was sodium-dependent and saturable and a minor one that was sodium-independent and nonsaturable, representing a facilitated diffusion process. In addition, the initial accumulation of ³H-myoinositol was found to be temperature-dependent.

Confirming the implication of an Na^+-dependent transport of ³H-myoinositol, several compounds known to affect the sodium gradient were found to alter ³H-myoinositol transport. For example, pharmacological agents leading to an increase (by different mechanisms) of intracellular sodium such as ouabain, monensin, and veratridine reduced ³H-myoinositol uptake. However, inhibitors of ATP synthesis were ineffective, revealing that ³H-myoinositol transport in salivary glands was not directly dependent on mitochondrial activity as found by others in different tissues. On the other hand, in competition experiments made with increasing concentrations of D-glucose, a noncompetitive inhibition was observed, indicating that two distinct carriers were responsible for the transport of ³H-myoinositol and D-glucose.

EVIDENCE FOR AN INHIBITORY EFFECT OF SUBSTANCE P ON THE SODIUM-DEPENDENT TRANSPORT OF ³H-MYOINOSITOL

Using a single high concentration of SP (10^{-6} M), it was found that this tachykinin reduces rapidly the initial accumulation of ³H-myoinositol into parotid acinar cells because a 40% reduction of this accumulation was observed as soon as 5 min after the beginning of the incubation (FIGURE 2). This reduced accumulation corresponds to an inhibition of ³H-myoinositol uptake. Indeed, no acceleration in the rate of ³H-myoinositol efflux from the cells was seen when SP (10^{-6} M) was added into the incubation medium of parotid prisms prelabeled with ³H-myoinositol. On the other hand, a similar SP-induced reduction in tissue levels of ³H-myoinositol was found in the presence of lithium, indicating that rapid alteration in phosphoinositide metabolism had no significant contribution in the observed phenomenon. Of particular interest, we could then show that the effect of SP on ³H-myoinositol transport was solely due to an inhibitory action of this peptide on the sodium-dependent process, with the sodium-dependent uptake of ³H-myoinositol being reduced by 50% after a 15-min incubation. This SP-evoked inhibition of the sodium-dependent transport of ³H-myoinositol was linked both to a markedly reduced V_{max} (8.2 and 4.0 pmol/mg protein/min, respectively) and to a slight decrease in the K_m (99 and 74 μM, respectively). As expected, the decrease in ³H-myoinositol transport induced by SP was associated with a parallel reduction in the incorporation of ³H-myoinositol into membrane phospholipids because both cytosolic levels of ³H-myoinositol and lipidic concentrations of ³H-phosphoinositides were similarly decreased.

CHARACTERIZATION OF THE SUBSTANCE P–EVOKED INHIBITORY RESPONSE ON ³H-MYOINOSITOL TRANSPORT

Several tachykinins including SP and their analogues were used in increasing concentrations in order to characterize the receptor involved in the SP-evoked inhibitory effect on ³H-myoinositol transport. For this purpose, prisms from the parotid gland were incubated for 15 min with both ³H-myoinositol and the tested compounds. This analysis led to several conclusions: (1) the rank order of potency of mammalian tachykinins was SP > NKA > NKB; (2) short C-terminal fragments of SP were much less potent than SP, whereas N-terminal fragments were ineffective;

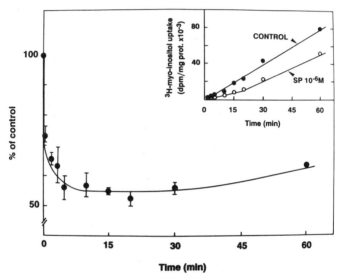

FIGURE 2. Time course of substance P–induced reduction of ³H-myoinositol uptake into rat parotid gland slices. Parotid gland slices were coincubated for various times with ³H-myoinositol (2 μCi/250 μL) and substance P (10⁻⁶ M) (○) or incubated with ³H-myoinositol alone for controls (●) at 37 °C. Results are represented as percentages of the control value for each time considered. In the inset, data obtained in the same experiments are expressed in dpm/mg protein.

(3) selective agonists of NK₁ receptors such as [Pro⁹]SP and SP methyl ester were active, with [Pro⁹]SP exhibiting a potency identical to that found for SP, whereas selective agonists of NK₂ ([Lys⁵]NKA(4–10), etc.) or NK₃ ([Pro⁷]NKB or senktide) receptors were without effect (TABLE 1); (4) spantide, a weak antagonist of NK₁ receptors, shifted in a competitive manner the dose-response curve of SP. Other observations should also be underlined: (1) the IC₅₀ and EC₅₀ values of SP in competing for [¹²⁵I]BHSP binding on isolated acinar cells and in inhibiting ³H-myoinositol transport in parotid gland prisms, respectively, were found to be identical; (2) excellent correlations were found when comparing the rank orders of potency of several tachykinins and their analogues for inhibiting ³H-myoinositol transport with either their inhibitory effect on [¹²⁵I]BHSP binding on rat brain

TABLE 1. Effect of Tachykinins and Selective Agonists on ^{3}H-Myoinositol Total Uptake in Rat Parotid Gland

Compound	EC_{50} (nM)[a]
SP(1–11)	5.8
[L-Pro^9]SP	2.3
Septide	320.0
NKA	160.0
[Lys^5]NKA(4–10)	310.0
[Lys^5,MeLeu^9,Nle^{10}]NKA(4–10)	1600.0
NKB	830.0
[Pro^7]NKB	> 10,000
Senktide	> 10,000

[a]EC_{50} values (nM) of tachykinins and their analogues for inhibiting ^{3}H-myoinositol uptake were calculated from data obtained in at least three distinct experiments.

synaptosomes or their stimulatory effect on inositol phosphate formation on cortical mouse astrocytes in primary culture (FIGURE 3).

Altogether, these results demonstrate that the tachykinin receptors involved in the SP-inhibitory response exhibit the pharmacological pattern of NK_1 receptors.

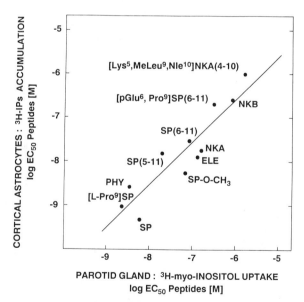

FIGURE 3. Correlation between two biological assays for receptors of the NK_1 type: correlation between EC_{50} values for tachykinin-induced ^{3}H-inositol phosphate formation in mouse cortical astrocytes and for tachykinin-induced reduction in ^{3}H-myoinositol uptake into rat parotid gland slices.

SPECIFICITY OF THE SUBSTANCE P–INHIBITORY EFFECT ON ^{3}H-MYOINOSITOL TRANSPORT IN RAT PAROTID ACINAR CELLS

Two types of specificity were analyzed. First, the effect of SP was compared to those of other transmitters and their agonists and, second, attempts were made to demonstrate the existence or not of this SP-evoked response in other tissues.

Besides sensory fibers, which are rich in peptides such as SP, NKA, and calcitonin gene–related peptide, salivary glands are also innervated by sympathetic neurons containing both noradrenaline and neuropeptide Y (NPY) and by parasympathetic neurons in which acetylcholine is colocalized with vasoactive intestinal peptide (VIP).[39] Interestingly enough, SP, noradrenaline, and carbachol (an agonist of muscarinic receptors) inhibited the transport of ^{3}H-myoinositol in our preparation. When these agonists were used at their maximal effective concentration (10^{-4} M), their effects were not additive with that of SP used at 10^{-6} M. This indicates that a common mechanism intervenes in the observed responses. In addition, further studies performed with carbachol indicated that its inhibitory effect was completely prevented by atropine, whereas the muscarinic antagonist did not alter the SP-evoked response. Therefore, the inhibitory effects of both SP and carbachol were mediated through different types of receptors. Neuropeptides such as VIP, NPY, calcitonin gene–related peptide, cholecystokinin, neurotensin, and somatostatin were without effect when used at 10^{-6} M.

As already indicated, another aspect of specificity in the inhibitory effect of SP on ^{3}H-myoinositol transport mediated through NK_1 receptors concerns the tissue specificity. SP inhibited ^{3}H-myoinositol transport into the rat submaxillary glands, but not into the rat pancreas, which also possesses NK_1 receptors,[40,41] suggesting further that the phenomenon observed is a peculiar property of salivary glands. In addition, SP-induced modification of ^{3}H-myoinositol transport was observed neither on slices from the rat prefrontal cortex or striatum nor on mouse cortical astrocytes, which are preparations rich in NK_1 receptors and in which SP stimulates phospholipase C activity.[42]

CONCLUSIONS

It can be proposed tentatively that the end result of the cascade of events intervening between the stimulation of NK_1, muscarinic, or adrenergic receptors and the modification of ^{3}H-myoinositol transport into salivary glands is due to a reduced sodium gradient. Such a statement is reinforced by the absolute requirement of sodium for the carrier-mediated transport of ^{3}H-myoinositol. One hypothesis, which is not exclusive, is that the increase in intracellular calcium levels due to the concomitant activation of phospholipase C and the formation of IP_3 results in the opening of calcium-sensitive potassium channels, leading to a massive influx of sodium and thus to a reduced driving force in the ^{3}H-myoinositol transport. In fact, it has been elegantly demonstrated that SP stimulates sodium influx into parotid cells.[43]

By its accuracy and rapidity, the estimation of the sodium-dependent transport of ^{3}H-myoinositol into salivary glands represents a new performable biological assay for the screening of potent agonists and antagonists of NK_1 receptors. In addition, recent results indicate that both the uptake of ^{3}H-myoinositol and the amplitude of the inhibitory effect of SP are more important when salivary glands of young rats are used. Incidentally, we have also observed that the stimulatory effect of SP on phospholipase C activity is much more pronounced in the salivary gland of newborn than adult rats and that a very marked SP-evoked stimulation of inositol phosphate formation can be demonstrated in the brain stem of a newborn rat, that is, when numerous NK_1 receptors may still be present on astrocytes.[44]

Presently, several peripheral or central biological tests are now available for the characterization of compounds acting on NK_1 receptors. Although more extensive pharmacological studies with different tachykinins and analogues should be made, there is clearly some indication in the literature that SP exerts other interesting effects. For instance, SP has been shown to stimulate calcium influx in spinal interneurons,[45] to activate the incorporation of $[^{14}C]$-uridine into RNA[46] and the formation of arachidonic acid and its metabolites in astrocytes,[47] and to inhibit the β-adrenergic-evoked release of taurine in astrocytes.[48] Showing further the peculiar interest of astrocytes that solely possess NK_1 receptors, we have recently observed that SP and an SP-specific agonist such as $[Pro^9]SP$ increased markedly the cytosolic concentration of calcium in these cells.[49] Curiously, besides the hamster urinary bladder in which the stimulation of NK_2 receptors induces a pronounced formation of inositol phosphates,[28] no other selective cellular effects of NKA mediated by NK_2 receptors have been described to our knowledge. It should be recalled, however, that NKA stimulates the release of dopamine from dendrites and nerve terminals in the rat when applied locally into the substantia nigra and that these effects can be distinguished from those evoked by SP.[12,50] The situation is even worse in the case of NK_3 receptors because, besides the reported effect of NKB on acetylcholine release in the guinea pig ileum,[20] no convincing pharmacological study of NK_3 receptor–mediated cellular responses has been reported to our knowledge. Therefore, as done for NK_1 receptors, the discovery of specific cellular biological responses of large amplitude mediated by NK_2 or NK_3 receptors in both peripheral and central tissues is one of the prerequisites for progress in the tachykinin field.

REFERENCES

1. MAGGIO, J. E. 1988. Tachykinins. Annu. Rev. Neurosci. **11:** 13–28.
2. VIGER, A., J-C. BEAUJOUAN, Y. TORRENS & J. GLOWINSKI. 1983. Specific binding of a ^{125}I-substance P derivative to rat brain synaptosomes. J. Neurochem. **40:** 1030–1039.
3. BERGSTRÖM, L., J-C. BEAUJOUAN, Y. TORRENS, M. SAFFROY, J. GLOWINSKI, S. LAVIELLE, G. CHASSAING, A. MARQUET, P. D'ORLEANS-JUSTE, S. DION & D. REGOLI. 1987. ^3H–Neurokinin A labels a specific tachykinin-binding site in the rat duodenal smooth muscle. Mol. Pharmacol. **32:** 764–771.
4. BERGSTRÖM, L., Y. TORRENS, M. SAFFROY, J-C. BEAUJOUAN, S. LAVIELLE, G. CHASSAING, J. L. MORGAT, J. GLOWINSKI & A. MARQUET. 1987. ^3H–Neurokinin B and ^{125}I–Bolton Hunter eledoisin label identical tachykinin binding sites in the rat brain. J. Neurochem. **48:** 125–133.
5. CASCIERI, M. A., G. G. CHICCHI & T. LIANG. 1985. Demonstration of two distinct tachykinin receptors in rat brain cortex. J. Biol. Chem. **260:** 1501–1507.
6. BUCK, S. H., C. J. HELKE, E. BURCHER, C. W. SHULTS & T. L. O'DONOHUE. 1986. Pharmacologic characterization and autoradiographic distribution of binding sites for iodinated tachykinins in the rat central nervous system. Peptides **7:** 1109–1120.
7. BURCHER, E., S. H. BUCK, W. LOVENBERG & T. L. O'DONOHUE. 1986. Characterization and autoradiographic localization of multiple binding sites in gastrointestinal tract and bladder. J. Pharmacol. Exp. Ther. **236:** 819–831.
8. BEAUJOUAN, J-C., Y. TORRENS, A. VIGER & J. GLOWINSKI. 1984. A new type of tachykinin binding site in the rat brain characterized by specific binding of a labeled eledoisin derivative. Mol. Pharmacol. **26:** 248–256.
9. SAFFROY, M., J-C. BEAUJOUAN, Y. TORRENS, J. BESSEYRE, L. BERGSTRÖM & J. GLOWINSKI. 1988. Localization of tachykinin binding sites (NK_1, NK_2, NK_3 ligands) in the rat brain. Peptides **9:** 227–241.
10. MANTYH, P. W., T. GATES, C. R. MANTYH & J. E. MAGGIO. 1989. Autoradiographic

localization and characterization of tachykinin receptor binding sites in the rat brain and peripheral tissues. J. Neurosci. **9:** 258–279.

11. ARAI, H. & P. C. EMSON. 1986. Regional distribution of neuropeptide K and other tachykinins (neurokinin A, neurokinin B, and substance P) in rat central nervous system. Brain Res. **399:** 240–249.

12. BARUCH, P., F. ARTAUD, G. GODEHEU, L. BARBEITO, J. GLOWINSKI & A. CHERAMY. 1988. Substance P and neurokinin A regulate by different mechanisms dopamine release from dendrites and nerve terminals of the nigrostriatal dopaminergic neurons. Neuroscience **25:** 889–898.

13. KALIVAS, P. W., A. Y. DEUTCH, J. E. MAGGIO, P. W. MANTYH & R. H. ROTH. 1985. Substance K and substance P in the ventral tegmental area. Neurosci. Lett. **57:** 241–246.

14. DAM, T-V., Y. TAKEDA, J. KRAUSE, E. ESCHER & R. QUIRION. 1990. γ-Preprotachykinin-(72–92)-peptide amide: an endogenous preprotachykinin I gene–derived peptide that preferentially binds to neurokinin-2 receptors. Proc. Natl. Acad. Sci. U.S.A. **87:** 246–250.

15. SHIGEMOTO, R., Y. YOKOTA, K. TSUCHIDA & S. NAKANISHI. 1990. Cloning and expression of a rat neuromedin K receptor cDNA. J. Biol. Chem. **265:** 623–628.

16. MASU, Y., K. NAKAYAMA, H. TAMAKI, Y. HARADA, M. KUNO & S. NAKANISHI. 1987. cDNA cloning of bovine substance K receptor through oocyte expression system. Nature **329:** 836–838.

17. YOKOTA, Y., Y. SASAI, K. TANAKA, T. FUJIWARA, K. TSUCHIDA, R. SHIGEMOTO, A. KAKIZUKA, H. OHKUBO & S. NAKANISHI. 1989. Molecular characterization of a functional cDNA for rat substance P receptor. J. Biol. Chem. **264:** 17649–17652.

18. LAVIELLE, S., G. CHASSAING, O. PLOUX, D. LOEUILLET, J. BESSEYRE, S. JULIEN, A. MARQUET, O. CONVERT, J-C. BEAUJOUAN, Y. TORRENS, L. BERGSTRÖM, M. SAFFROY & J. GLOWINSKI. 1988. Analysis of tachykinin binding site interactions using constrained analogues of tachykinins. Biochem. Pharmacol. **37:** 41–49.

19. REGOLI, D., G. DRAPEAU, S. DION & P. D'ORLEANS-JUSTE. 1989. Receptors for substance P and related neurokinins. Pharmacology **38:** 1–15.

20. WORMSER, U., R. LAUFER, Y. HART, M. CHOREV, C. GILON & Z. SELINGER. 1986. Highly selective agonists for substance P receptor subtypes. EMBO J. **5:** 2805–2808.

21. FOLKERS, K., R. HÅKANSON, X. HÖRIG, X. JIE-CHENG & S. LEANDER. 1984. Biological evaluation of substance P antagonists. Br. J. Pharmacol. **83:** 449–456.

22. MCKNIGHT, A. T., J. J. MAGUIRE, B. J. WILLIAMS, A. C. FOSTER, R. TRIDGETT & L. L. IVERSEN. 1988. Pharmacological specificity of synthetic peptides as antagonists at tachykinin receptors. Regulat. Peptides **22:** 127.

23. DRAPEAU, G., P. D'ORLEANS-JUSTE, S. DION, N. E. RHALEB, N. E. ROUISSI & D. REGOLI. 1987. Selective agonists for substance P and neurokinin receptors. Neuropeptides **10:** 43–54.

24. WATSON, S. P. & C. P. DOWNES. 1983. Substance P induced hydrolysis of inositol phospholipids in guinea-pig ileum and rat hypothalamus. Eur. J. Pharmacol. **93:** 245–253.

25. AUB, D. L. & J. PUTNEY. 1985. Properties of receptor-controlled inositol triphosphate formation in parotid acinar cells. Biochem. J. **225:** 263–266.

26. MANTYH, P. W., R. D. PINNOCK, C. P. DOWNES, M. GOEDERT & S. P. HUNT. 1984. Correlation between inositol phospholipid hydrolysis and substance P receptors in rat CNS. Nature **309:** 795–797.

27. HUNTER, J. C., M. GOEDERT & R. D. PINNOCK. 1985. Mammalian tachykinin-induced hydrolysis of inositol phospholipids in rat brain slices. Biochem. Biophys. Res. Commun. **127:** 616–622.

28. BRISTOW, D. R., N. R. CURTIS, N. SUMAN-CHAUHAN, K. J. WATLING & B. J. WILLIAMS. 1987. Effects of tachykinins on inositol phospholipid hydrolysis in slices of hamster urinary bladder. Br. J. Pharmacol. **90:** 211–217.

29. TORRENS, Y., M. C. DAGUET DE MONTETY, M. EL ETR, J-C. BEAUJOUAN & J. GLOWINSKI. 1989. Tachykinin receptors of the NK$_1$ type (substance P) coupled positively to phospholipase C on cortical astrocytes from the newborn mouse in primary culture. J. Neurochem. **52:** 1913–1918.

30. LIANG, T. & M. A. CASCIERI. 1981. Substance P receptor on parotid cell membranes. J. Neurosci. **1:** 1133–1141.

31. GIULIANI, S., C. A. MAGGI, D. REGOLI, G. DRAPEAU, P. ROVERO & A. MELI. 1988. NK-1 receptors mediate the tachykinin stimulation of salivary secretion: selective agonists provide further evidence. Eur. J. Pharmacol. **150:** 377–379.
32. TORRENS, Y., M. DIETL, J-C. BEAUJOUAN & J. GLOWINSKI. 1989. Réduction par la substance P de l'accumulation initiale du *myo*-[³H]inositol dans les cellules acineuses de la glande parotide de rat. C. R. Acad. Sci. Paris **309:** 295–300.
33. DIETL, M., Y. TORRENS, J-C. BEAUJOUAN & J. GLOWINSKI. 1989. Substance P–induced reduction in the initial accumulation of cytosolic myo-[³H]inositol in rat parotid acinar cells mediated by the NK₁ tachykinin receptor. J. Neurochem. **53:** 1640–1643.
34. CASPARY, W. F. & R. K. CRANE. 1970. Active transport of myo-inositol and its relation to the sugar transport system in hamster small intestine. Biochim. Biophys. Acta **203:** 308–316.
35. HAMMERMAN, M., B. SACKTOR & W. DAUGHADAY. 1980. Myo-inositol transport in renal brush border vesicles and its inhibition by D-glucose. Am. J. Physiol. **239:** F113–F120.
36. WADA, E., T. TAKENAWA & T. TSUMITA. 1979. A defect of the myo-inositol maintenance mechanism in the lens of hereditary cataract mice. Biochim. Biophys. Acta **554:** 148–155.
37. MOLITORIS, B. A., I. E. KARL & W. DAUGHADAY. 1980. Concentration of myo-inositol in skeletal muscle of the rat occurs without active transport. J. Clin. Invest. **65:** 783–788.
38. SPECTOR, R. 1976. Inositol accumulation by brain slices *in vitro*. J. Neurochem. **27:** 1273–1276.
39. LUNDBERG, J. M., C. R. MARTLING & T. HÖKFELT. 1988. Airways, oral cavity, and salivary glands: classical transmitters and peptides in sensory and autonomic motor neurons. *In* Handbook of Chemical Neuroanatomy. Vol. 6. The Peripheral Nervous System. A. Bjorklund, T. Hökfelt & C. Owman, Eds.: 391–444. Elsevier. Amsterdam/New York.
40. JENSEN, R. T. & J. D. GARDNER. 1979. Interaction of physalaemin, substance P, and eledoisin with specific membrane receptors on pancreatic acinar cells. Proc. Natl. Acad. Sci. U.S.A. **76:** 5679–5683.
41. SJÖDIN, L., T. P. CONLON, C. GUSTAVSON & K. UDDHOLM. 1980. Interaction of substance P with dispersed pancreatic acinar cells from the guinea-pig: stimulation of calcium outflux, accumulation of cyclic GMP, and amylase release. Acta Physiol. Scand. **109:** 107–110.
42. TORRENS, Y., J-C. BEAUJOUAN, M. SAFFROY, M. C. DAGUET DE MONTETY, L. BERGSTRÖM & J. GLOWINSKI. 1986. Substance P receptors in primary cultures of cortical astrocytes from the mouse. Proc. Natl. Acad. Sci. U.S.A. **83:** 9216–9220.
43. SOLTOFF, S., M. MCMILLIAN, L. CANTLEY, E. CRAGOE, JR. & B. TALAMO. 1989. Effects of muscarinic, alpha-adrenergic, and substance P agonists and ionomycin on ion transport mechanisms in the rat parotid acinar cell. J. Gen. Physiol. **93:** 285–319.
44. BEAUJOUAN, J-C., M. C. DAGUET DE MONTETY, Y. TORRENS, M. SAFFROY, M. DIETL & J. GLOWINSKI. 1990. Marked regional heterogeneity of ¹²⁵I–Bolton Hunter substance P binding and substance P–induced activation of phospholipase C in astrocyte cultures from the embryonic or newborn rat. J. Neurochem. **54:** 669–675.
45. WOMACK, M. D., A. B. MACDERMOTT & T. M. JESSELL. 1988. Sensory transmitters regulate intracellular calcium in dorsal horn neurons. Nature **334:** 351–353.
46. LEE, C. M., W. KUM, C. S. COCKRAM, R. TEOH & J. D. YOUNG. 1988. Substance P receptors on a human astrocytoma cell line. Regulat. Peptides **22:** 111.
47. HARTUNG, M. P., K. HEININGER, B. SCHÄFER & K. TOYKA. 1988. Substance P and astrocytes: stimulation of the cyclooxygenase pathway of arachidonic acid metabolism. FASEB J. **2:** 48–51.
48. PERRONE, M. H., R. D. LEPORE & W. SHAIN. 1986. Identification and characterization of substance P receptors on LRM55 glial cells. J. Pharmacol. Exp. Ther. **238:** 389–395.
49. DELUMEAU, C., F. PETITET, J-C. BEAUJOUAN, J. PRÉMONT & J. GLOWINSKI. 1990. Increased cytosolic calcium by activation of NK₁ receptors on mouse cortical astrocytes in primary culture: potentiation by 2-chloro-adenosine. This conference.
50. CHERAMY, A., A. NIEOULLON, R. MICHELOT & J. GLOWINSKI. 1977. Effects of intranigral application of dopamine and substance P on the *in vivo* release of newly synthesized ³H-dopamine in the ipsilateral caudate nucleus of the cat. Neurosci. Lett. **4:** 105–109.

Tachykinins in Autonomic Control Systems

The Company They Keep[a]

C. J. HELKE,[b] C. A. SASEK,[b] A. J. NIEDERER,[b] AND
J. E. KRAUSE[c]

[b]Department of Pharmacology
Uniformed Services University of the Health Sciences
Bethesda, Maryland 20814

[c]Department of Anatomy and Neurobiology
Washington University School of Medicine
St. Louis, Missouri 63110

Multiple neurochemicals coexist in individual neurons and may play a role in chemical communication.[1] Tachykinins were in the forefront of putative transmitters studied for transmitter coexistence. The earliest demonstration of coexistence in CNS neurons involved substance P (SP) and serotonin (5-HT) in medullary neurons.[2] Additional studies showed that somatic sensory neurons colocalize SP and other putative transmitters.[3,4] The multiplicity and diversity of combinations of colocalized chemical messengers within a neuronal system are potential substrates for refinements of function.[1] This concept is likely to be important in the function of autonomic control systems producing subtle alterations of autonomic outflow to specific organs as well as massive discharges of the entire system.

Neural regulation of autonomic functions involves multiple peripheral and CNS pathways and neurotransmitters. Substance P is present in both central and peripheral components of autonomic control systems. In the afferent limb of autonomic reflexes, visceral sensory neurons of the vagus and glossopharyngeal nerves initiate many visceral reflexes. Their sensory receptors detect such diverse stimuli as elevations in blood pressure; inhaled irritants; changes in blood oxygenation; and distension of the heart, stomach, and lungs.[5] Visceral sensory neurons of the vagus and glossopharyngeal nerves located in the nodose and petrosal ganglia, respectively, contain SP.[6,7] Sympathetic preganglionic neurons in the intermediolateral cell column (IML) of the thoracic spinal cord receive many direct inputs from premotor neurons largely located in the medulla. Medullary SP-immunoreactive neurons provide a robust input to the IML.[8,9] SP-containing sensory nerves that send processes to the sympathetic ganglia[10] may also influence autonomic functions.

[a]This work was supported by NIH Grant Nos. NS20991 and NS24876 and USUHS Grant No. R075AS to C. J. Helke and by NIH Grant No. NS21937 and a grant from the Pew Memorial Trust to J. E. Krause.

COEXISTENCE WITH NONTACHYKININ TRANSMITTERS IN AUTONOMIC CONTROL SYSTEMS

Visceral Afferent Neurons

Visceral afferent neurons of the nodose and petrosal ganglia are immunoreactive (ir) for tachykinins and other putative neurotransmitters [e.g., SP, calcitonin gene–related peptide (CGRP), and dopamine (tyrosine hydroxylase–ir; TH)].[7,11–13] We studied the coexistence of SP-ir with CGRP-ir or TH-ir in individual neurons of the rat ganglia using fluorescence immunocytochemistry (FIGURE 1, panels C–F).[14] SP-ir and CGRP-ir were similarly distributed in scattered cells, concentrated mostly in the rostral pole of the nodose ganglion and in the petrosal ganglion. SP-ir completely coexisted with CGRP-ir. However, there was at least twice the number of CGRP-ir neurons as SP-ir neurons. Thus, CGRP-ir neurons that did not contain SP-ir were also present. In contrast, SP-ir and TH-ir had different distributions in both the nodose and petrosal ganglia. SP-ir was located in the more rostral regions of both the nodose and petrosal ganglia. TH-ir was detected throughout the nodose ganglion and only in the most caudal region of the petrosal ganglion. There was no coexistence of SP-ir and TH-ir.

These data provide evidence for the differential coexistence of SP-ir with other putative transmitters in visceral afferent neurons of the nodose and petrosal ganglia as SP-ir is contained only in a subpopulation of CGRP-ir neurons and does not coexist with TH-ir. The presence of SP-ir in some, but not all CGRP-ir neurons of these visceral afferent ganglia suggests the presence of at least two populations of CGRP-ir neurons. Whether these neurochemically defined subpopulations of CGRP-ir neurons are correlated with morphologic subpopulations (i.e., myelinated and unmyelinated) of CGRP-ir visceral afferent neurons is unknown.

Sympathetic Premotor Neurons

Our initial work on tachykinins and the coexistence in medullary projections to the IML focused on SP and 5-HT. We employed the approaches of serotonin neurotoxin–induced lesions and radioimmunoassay (RIA) of microdissected IML.[8,15] Whereas the serotonin neurotoxin, 5,7-dihydroxytryptamine (5,7-DHT), depleted the serotonin content of the spinal cord and reduced the thyrotropin-releasing hormone (TRH) content of the IML by 45%, it did not significantly alter the SP content of the IML (FIGURE 2). However, the ventral horn content of both TRH and SP was reduced by 92% and 42%, respectively, in 5,7-DHT-treated rats (FIGURE 2).[15] Although indirect, these data suggest that TRH coexists with 5-HT in IML projections, whereas SP does not. The question of TRH coexistence with SP could not be addressed by this approach.

More recently, we studied SP coexistence in IML projections with dual color immunohistochemistry combined with retrograde tracing.[16] Multiple antigens were viewed in individual IML-projecting cells (i.e., containing rhodamine beads retrogradely transported from T_{3-4} IML) by dual color immunofluorescence. Using primary antibodies from different species and secondary antisera coupled with either FITC (green) or 7-amino-4-methyl-coumarin-3-acetic acid (AMCA, blue), two antigens could be seen in a single projection-specific neuron. In some studies, a third antigen was identified in a single neuron by comparing adjacent 4-μm sections.

Several coexistences were found in IML-projecting neurons, that is, SP and

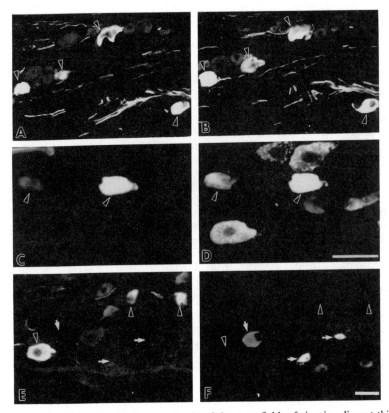

FIGURE 1. (A & B) Paired photomicrographs of the same fields of view in adjacent thin (6 μm) sections of petrosal ganglion immunostained for SP-ir (A) and NKA-ir (B). Arrowheads indicate selected neurons that were immunoreactive for both SP and NKA. (C & D) Paired photomicrographs of the same fields of view in a single section of the petrosal ganglion stained for SP-ir (C) and CGRP-ir (D). Arrowheads indicate selected neurons that were immunoreactive for both SP and CGRP. (E & F) Paired photomicrographs of the same fields of view in a single section of the petrosal ganglion stained for SP-ir (E) and TH-ir (F). Arrowheads indicate the location of SP-ir neurons, whereas white arrows indicate the location of TH-ir neurons. Note the absence of SP-ir and TH-ir coexistence in these neurons. Calibration bars = 50 μm. Panels A, B, E, and F and C and D are of equal magnification. Data are adapted with permission from reference 14.

TRH; SP and 5-HT; SP, TRH, and 5-HT (FIGURE 3).[16] These cells were found in the midline raphe and the parapyramidal region. Of the ventral medullary IML-projecting cells, most of the SP-ir neurons contained TRH-ir and many were also serotonergic. In addition, immunocytochemical studies of SP and TRH colocalization in the IML clearly showed the presence of both in serotonergic and nonserotonergic terminals.[17,18]

The finding of colocalized SP and 5-HT in IML-projecting neurons and in terminals in the IML contrasts with our previous interpretation of studies in which the content of SP (and TRH) was assayed in the IML after the destruction of serotonin nerve terminals with 5,7-DHT.[8,15] Whereas these studies suggested the coexistence of TRH-ir and 5-HT-ir in the IML, the finding that the IML content of SP did not significantly decline following destruction of serotonin nerve terminals suggested the absence of coexistence of SP and 5-HT in the IML.[8,15] However, our more recent immunocytochemical data clearly show that SP and 5-HT are colocalized in IML projections. The failure of RIA to detect a decline of SP content following neurotoxin treatment probably occurs because the IML content of SP also arises from nonserotonergic SP-ir terminals of intraspinal neurons[19] and from SP-ir cell bodies in the IML[20,21] that would not be affected by the serotonin neurotoxin. Sprouting of the remaining bulbospinal SP-ir terminals may further maintain the SP content of the nucleus.[19] In contrast, the TRH content of the IML and both the SP and TRH contents of the ventral horn arose largely from serotonergic medullary sources and thus were significantly reduced after serotonin neurotoxin treatment.[8,15]

Because of the similar localization of SP and enkephalin (ENK) cells in ventral medullary sites, we also studied the coexistence of these peptides. Although IML-projecting ENK-ir neurons were intermingled with those containing SP-ir, the two peptides rarely coexisted.[22] This suggests the presence of at least two separate

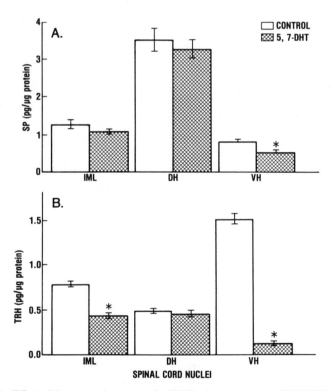

FIGURE 2. Effect of the serotonin neurotoxin, 5,7-dihydroxytryptamine (5,7-DHT), on the SP (A) and TRH (B) content of microdissected thoracic spinal cord nuclei. Peptide content was measured with specific radioimmunoassays. Asterisk: $p < 0.05$ for grouped comparisons with vehicle control values. Terms: IML, intermediolateral cell column; DH, dorsal horn; VH, ventral horn. Adapted with permission from reference 15.

transmitter-specific ventral medullary projections to the IML—one that contains SP/5-HT/TRH and one that contains ENK.

COEXISTENCE OF MULTIPLE TACHYKININS IN AUTONOMIC CONTROL SYSTEMS

Differential splicing of the SP gene primary transcript results in three different preprotachykinin (PPT) mRNAs.[23,24] SP is encoded by all three (α, β, γ) PPT

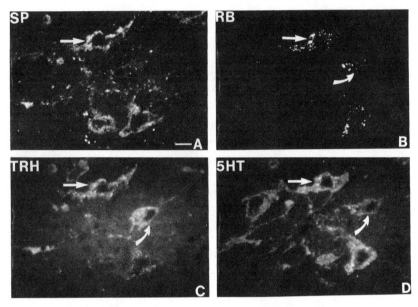

FIGURE 3. Photomicrographs of two adjacent 4-μm sections through the ventral medulla of the rat. (A & C) The same field of view in a section that was immunostained for SP and TRH. (B & D) The same field of view as panels A and C from an adjacent section that was immunostained for 5-HT and SP (SP immunostaining not shown). Rhodamine-labeled latex microspheres (RB) that were retrogradely transported from the T_{3-4} intermediolateral cell column are shown in panel B. Straight arrows point to a single neuron that contains SP-ir, TRH-ir, and 5-HT-ir. This same neuron contains RB (panel B) and is therefore an IML-projecting neuron. Curved arrows in panels B and D point to a single neuron that contains TRH-ir and 5-HT-ir, but no SP-ir. This same neuron contains RB (panel B), indicating a projection to the IML. Scale bar = 10 μm. All micrographs are of equal magnification. Reprinted by permission from reference 16.

mRNAs. Another tachykinin peptide, neurokinin A (NKA, formerly called substance K), is produced by both β and γ preprotachykinin mRNA, but not by α PPT mRNA.[23,25] The predominance of β and γ PPT mRNA in rat brain tissue suggests similar regional distributions for SP and NKA-related peptides. However, this assumes that the production of each of the peptide products is similar in all systems. In addition, the previous studies were largely done with dissection and RIA techniques in which cellular resolution was lost and, thus, the direct demonstration of coexistence of tachykinins was not possible. For example, although RIA demonstrated the presence of NKA-ir in the medulla,[26] it was not known if ventral medullary SP-ir cells actually expressed the NKA peptide.

Another tachykinin, neurokinin B (NKB), is produced from a separate preprotachykinin gene[27,28] and the distributions of PPT mRNA are frequently different than for NKB precursor mRNA.[20] However, colocalization of these mRNAs is found in neurons of the medial habenula.[29] Hence, it was unknown whether NKB coexisted with SP or NKA in neurons of autonomic control systems.

Because of the carboxy-terminal homology among the tachykinins, many antisera raised against one peptide cross-react with other tachykinins.[14,30] Whereas radioimmunoassay combined with chromatographic procedures permits the detection of specific tachykinin peptides, immunocytochemical studies are not afforded the chemical resolution of chromatographic studies. Thus, lack of specificity is a common problem in immunocytochemical studies attempting to view specific tachykinin peptides. In order to study tachykinins at the cellular level with immunocytochemistry, it was necessary to identify specific antibodies. We screened SP, NKA, and NKB antibodies for recognition of the desired tachykinin and for specificity using an immunoblot procedure[31] and standard preabsorption controls in tissue sections. One rabbit polyclonal SP antiserum (Incstar, Stillwater, Minnesota) recognized SP, but not NKA (FIGURE 4), whereas other antibodies (monoclonal SP antibody from Sera Labs, polyclonal SP antisera from S. Leeman) also recognized NKA to varying extents (not shown). The rabbit NKA antibody recognized all concentrations of NKA tested in the immunoblot studies (FIGURE 4). To a lesser extent, the NKA antibody also recognized SP (not shown). However, when it was preabsorbed with 100 μg/mL of SP, SP immunostaining was largely abolished, whereas NKA immunostaining remained intact both in the immunoblot procedure (FIGURE 4) and in tissue processed for immunocytochemistry. Thus, the NKA antibody was routinely preabsorbed with 100 μg/mL of SP. A rabbit polyclonal NKB antibody (J. Krause) recognized NKB, not SP or NKA, in the immunoblot procedure (FIGURE 4). Tissue preabsorption controls were consistent with the immunoblot data. Therefore, Incstar's SP, S. Leeman's NKA (preabsorbed with SP), and J. Krause's NKB antibodies were used in these studies.

In the visceral afferent system, SP-ir and NKA-ir neurons were similarly distributed in scattered cells, concentrated mostly in the rostral pole of the nodose ganglion and in many neurons throughout the petrosal ganglion.[7] The coexistence of SP-ir and NKA-ir was studied in adjacent thin sections of ganglia (FIGURE 1, panels A and B). There was extensive coexistence ($> 94\%$) between the two peptides in both the nodose and petrosal ganglia. The near complete coexistence of SP-ir with NKA-ir suggests that, as in the brain and other sensory ganglia, the predominant forms of PPT mRNA in the nodose and petrosal ganglia are the β and/or γ PPT mRNAs that encode both SP and NKA.[23] NKB-ir cell bodies were not apparent in either the nodose or petrosal ganglion. The absence of NKB-ir in these visceral sensory ganglia is consistent with the absence of NKB mRNA in other sensory ganglia.[20]

In preliminary studies of the ventral medullary bulbospinal system, NKA-ir neurons were found in the midline raphe and parapyramidal regions of the ventral medulla, where extensive coexistence with SP-ir was demonstrated (FIGURE 5).[32] Moreover, the distribution patterns of SP-ir and NKA-ir terminals in the spinal cord were found to be the same, for example, very dense labeling of terminals in the dorsal horn, dense labeling in the intermediolateral cell column (FIGURE 5B), and moderate labeling in the ventral horn. Whether NKA-ir is present in IML-projecting cells

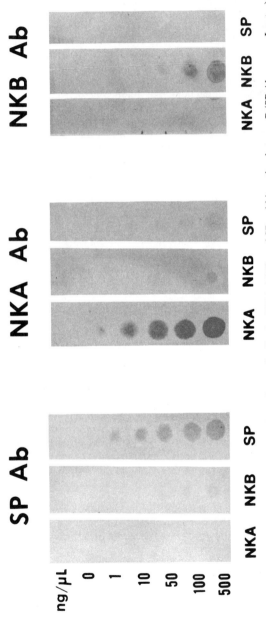

FIGURE 4. Immunoblots of the reactivities of the following antibodies for NKA, NKB, and SP: rabbit anti–substance P (SP Ab; source, Incstar); rabbit anti–neurokinin A that was preabsorbed with 100 µg/mL of SP (NKA Ab; source, S. Leeman); and rabbit anti–neurokinin B (NKB Ab; source, J. Krause). Peptides were spotted at varying concentrations (2 µL/spot; 0–500 ng/µL) onto Whatman no. 1 filter paper and were fixed *in vacuo* with paraformaldehyde vapors at 80 °C using Larsson's[31] immunoblotting technique. The papers were then processed using a Vectastain ABC Kit (Vector Laboratories, Burlingame, California).

that contain all three of the other neurochemicals of interest (SP/5-HT/TRH) remains to be determined.

NKB-ir terminals were present in the thoracic spinal cord, but their distribution was different than that of SP-ir and NKA-ir (FIGURE 6). Whereas NKB-ir terminals were moderately dense in lamina 2, there were no apparent NKB-ir terminals in the

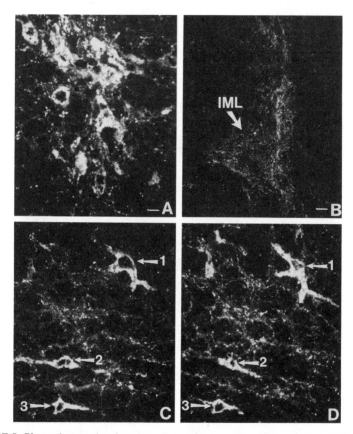

FIGURE 5. Photomicrographs of sections through the ventral medulla (A, C, and D) and the IML (B). (A) NKA-ir cells and fibers in the midline raphe pallidus. (B) NKA-ir fibers and terminals in a horizontal section of the T_{3-4} IML. Medial is to the left. (C & D) Same field of view in two adjacent 4-μm sections of the ventral medulla (lateral to midline) stained for SP-ir (C) and NKA-ir (D). Numbered arrows point to three neurons that contained both SP-ir and NKA-ir. Bars = 10 μm. Panels A, C, and D are of equal magnification.

IML. These data are consistent with the finding that NKB precursor mRNA is prominent in spinal cord dorsal horn and is absent from the intermediolateral cell column.[20] Additionally, NKB precursor mRNA is not found in medullary raphe neurons that are known to project to the spinal cord.[20] Thus, it is unlikely that NKB neurons innervate sympathetic preganglionic neurons.

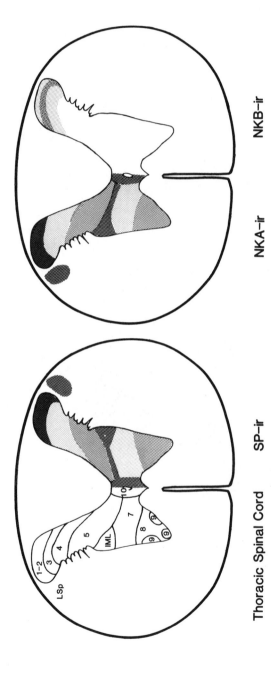

FIGURE 6. Schematic illustrations of the laminar divisions of the thoracic spinal cord in the rat (far left) and the distributions and relative intensities of SP-ir, NKA-ir, and NKB-ir in fibers and terminals of the rat thoracic spinal cord. Abbreviations: IML = intermediolateral cell column; ir = immunoreactivity; LSp = lateral spinal nucleus; NKA = neurokinin A; NKB = neurokinin B; PPT = preprotachykinin.

DISCUSSION

It now appears that SP is one member of a family of mammalian tachykinin peptides, which, in addition to NKA and NKB, includes neuropeptide K (NPK), neuropeptide γ (NPγ), and the neurokinin A fragment [NKA(3–10)].[33–35] Because the discovery of some of these mammalian tachykinins [e.g., especially NPγ and NKA(3–10)] has been very recent, earlier radioimmunoassay and immunocytochemical studies could not have accounted for the potential antibody cross-reactivities with these previously undiscovered NKA-related peptides. Hence, the distinct cellular and nuclear distributions of each of the multiple tachykinin peptides could not be completely delineated. For example, NPK-ir neurons are also detected in the medullary raphe;[36] however, the currently published immunocytochemical studies of NPK-ir must be interpreted conservatively. NPK antibodies may cross-react with the intervening sequences between SP and NKA in β-PPT [e.g., β-PPT(72–96)-OH] that are liberated from NPK when NKA is processed out; thus, the NPK antisera may merely show the presence of β-PPT. Furthermore, immunocytochemical studies of tachykinins suffer from the lack of knowledge of the reactivities of the antibodies used with the more recently discovered NKA-related peptides [e.g., NPγ and NKA(3–10)].

Specific information on the distribution of each of the SP/NKA (PPT I) gene–derived tachykinin peptides [SP, NKA, NPK, NPγ, and NKA(3–10)] is now available only from studies of homogenized grossly dissected tissue. Each of the tachykinin products of the SP/NKA gene is present in brain tissue and the total molar amounts of NKA, NPK, NPγ, and NKA(3–10) are about equal to those of SP.[37] Additional information on the cellular localization of each of these specific tachykinins is currently unavailable, but is necessary to more completely understand the cell biology of tachykinin peptide-receptor interactions.

Our studies described herein are a start at understanding the distribution and colocalization of the tachykinin peptides, SP, NKB, and NKA, in specific neuronal pathways. Whereas we have used selective antibodies in these studies, we cannot rule out the possibility that the NKA-ir may reflect the presence of NKA or other NKA-related peptides [NPK, NPγ, NKA(3–10)]. Nevertheless, these studies do clearly demonstrate the coexistence of SP with both nontachykinin and NKA-related peptides in autonomic control systems.

The significance of multiple tachykinins and other neurochemicals in visceral afferent neurons and in ventral medullary projections to the IML is unknown. It will be important to show whether the individual agents are involved in chemical communication, whether they are trophic factors, or perhaps whether they are vestigial agents that have no significant role in the mature organism.

In the visceral afferent system, each of the coexisting agents (SP, NKA, CGRP) is released in the CNS projection nucleus (e.g., nucleus of the solitary tract).[26,38–40] Moreover, receptor binding sites for each peptide are present in the nucleus of the solitary tract.[41–43] Hence, it is likely that each agent plays a role in visceral afferent communication. The coexistence of tachykinins and other putative transmitters in individual visceral afferent neurons may provide for the refinement of transmission at both the peripheral and central ends of the sensory axons. Depending on factors such as the amount of each agent and the characteristics of its release, neurons that contain distinct combinations of transmitters could potentially convey distinct information. In addition, because differential regulation of SP and CGRP content has been demonstrated in the cultured nodose ganglion,[44] it is possible that physiologic or pathophysiologic conditions may alter the relative abundance of individual coexisting putative transmitters and thus the resulting neurochemical signal acting upon the nucleus of the solitary tract.

IML-projecting ventral medullary neurons contain various putative neurotransmitters (e.g., SP, TRH, 5-HT, ENK) that can each alter preganglionic neuronal activity in the IML[45–48] and, subsequently, cardiovascular function.[49–52] SP, TRH, and

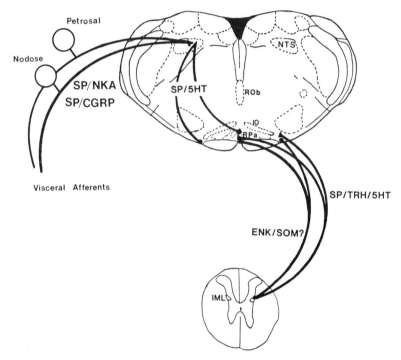

FIGURE 7. Schematic of the rat thoracic spinal cord, medulla oblongata, and visceral afferent input from the nodose and petrosal ganglia. The left side of the medulla shows (1) the neuronal projections from the visceral sensory ganglia of the vagus and glossopharyngeal nerves to the NTS that colocalize the tachykinins SP and NKA (but not NKB)[66] and CGRP and (2) the projections to the NTS from the ventral medulla that colocalize SP and 5-HT (actual projection was demonstrated to more caudal regions of the NTS).[67] The right side of the medulla shows the neuronal projections to the IML that colocalize SP, TRH, and 5-HT or that contain enkephalin (and perhaps somatostatin, based on the demonstration of such a coexistence in spinal projections).[68] NKA is present in SP neurons of the ventral medulla; however, the projection sites of these neurons are not yet determined. Abbreviations: ENK = enkephalin; 5HT = 5-hydroxytryptamine (serotonin); IO = inferior olive; NTS = nucleus of the solitary tract; ROb = raphe obscurus; RPa = raphe pallidus; SOM = somatostatin; TRH = thyrotropin-releasing hormone.

5-HT each excited preganglionic sympathetic neurons in the IML.[45–48,53] Intrathecal (i.t.) administration of SP or TRH agonists increased the mean arterial pressure (MAP) by activating sympathetic outflow to the adrenals and to the vasculature.[49,50,51,54] Intrathecal administration of NKA analogues did not alter MAP,[54] a finding that is consistent with the apparent absence of selective (NK-2) binding sites for NKA in the IML.[41,55]

Much remains to be learned about the functional roles of each of the colocalized putative transmitters in ventral medullary projections to the IML. Whereas the release of SP, 5-HT, TRH, and NKA was separately demonstrated for each agent in the CNS,[56] their release from the IML has not been directly demonstrated. Because certain coexisting putative transmitters are differentially released and mediate specific effects,[57] the condition under which individual agents are released is also of interest. However, this has not yet been studied in the IML. Moreover, the relationship of neurochemically specific projections from the ventral medulla to the IML to the functional heterogeneity seen in sympathetic outflow elicited from the same region[58] remains to be determined. However, because the putative transmitters of at least one projection (SP/TRH/5-HT) to the IML are excitatory, whereas those of another projection to the IML (ENK) are inhibitory,[46,53,59] it is likely that sympathoexcitatory and sympathoinhibitory influences elicited from the midline raphe and the parapyramidal region result from activation of neurochemically distinct neurons. Whereas 5-HT neurons are important in mediating the pressor effects elicited from the ventral medulla,[60] it is unclear which of the multiple neurochemicals associated with 5-HT neurons is/are responsible.

The possibility of transmitting several different signals lends new dimensions and complexity to the function of a neuronal system. Differential actions of each of the agents may result in differential effects, for example, depending on cellular localization of binding sites (presynaptic versus postsynaptic, specific target of postsynaptic neuron affected), time course of action, etc. In addition, neurochemical interactions between the coexisting neurochemicals could alter the functional state of the neuronal system. Although the interactions of colocalized tachykinin and nontachykinin putative transmitters in visceral afferent neurons or in bulbospinal projections to the IML have not yet been studied, other studies with spinal cord show that interactions between SP, 5-HT, and TRH can occur. For example, 5-HT evokes the release of SP,[61] whereas SP modulates the inhibition of 5-HT release resulting from 5-HT-induced activation of its autoreceptor.[62] Other types of interactions between coexisting neurochemicals include alterations in receptor binding,[63,64] neuronal excitability,[65] and transmitter metabolism.[1]

When the numerous putative neurotransmitters and combinations of colocalized putative transmitters in visceral afferent neurons projecting to the nucleus of the solitary tract or in medullary neurons projecting to the IML are considered, it becomes apparent that the modulation of sympathetic activity may be quite complex. A very sophisticated level of modulation of sympathetic activity could also be provided for by frequency-dependent differential release of colocalized transmitters[57] and by differences in afferent or efferent connections of specific ventral medullary neurons. Considering the subtle differences found between the cardiovascular and regional hemodynamic effects of SP and TRH when each is administered intrathecally,[50,51] the chance of intricate and selective modulatory influences becomes likely.

In summary, tachykinin-containing neurons in both the afferent and efferent limbs of autonomic control systems are neurochemically complex groups of cells (FIGURE 7) that affect autonomic activity. The importance of this neurochemical complexity in either discrete regulation or refinement of autonomic activity (e.g., in regard to specific vascular beds or the heart) remains to be determined.

REFERENCES

1. HÖKFELT, T., V. R. HOLETS, W. STAINES, B. MEISTER, T. MELANDER, M. SCHALLING, M. SCHULTZBERG, J. FREEDMAN, H. BJORKLUND, L. OLSON, B. LINDH, L-G. ELFVIN, J. M.

LUNDBERG, J. A. LINDGREN, B. SAMUELSSON, B. PERNOW, L. TERENIUS, C. POST, B. EVERITT & M. GOLDSTEIN. 1986. Co-existence of neuronal messengers—an overview. Prog. Brain Res. **68:** 33–70.

2. HÖKFELT, T., A. LJUNGDAHL, H. STEINBUSCH, A. VERHOFSTAD, G. NILSSON, E. BRODIN, B. PERNOW & M. GOLDSTEIN. 1978. Immunohistochemical evidence of substance P–like immunoreactivity in some 5-hydroxytryptamine-containing neurons in the rat central nervous system. Neuroscience **3:** 517–538.

3. TUCHSCHERER, M. M. & V. S. SEYBOLD. 1985. Immunohistochemical studies of substance P, cholecystokinin-octapeptide, and somatostatin in dorsal root ganglia of the rat. Neuroscience **14:** 593–605.

4. JU, G., T. HÖKFELT, E. BRODIN, J. FAHRENKRUG, J. A. FISCHER, P. FREY, R. P. ELDE & J. C. BROWN. 1987. Primary sensory neurons of the rat showing calcitonin gene–related peptide immunoreactivity and their relation to substance P–, somatostatin-, galanin-, vasoactive intestinal polypeptide–, and cholecystokinin-immunoreactive ganglion cells. Cell Tissue Res. **247:** 417–431.

5. PAINTAL, A. S. 1973. Vagal sensory receptors and their reflex effects. Physiol. Rev. **53:** 159–227.

6. HELKE, C. J., T. L. O'DONOHUE & D. M. JACOBOWITZ. 1980. Substance P as a baro- and chemo-receptor afferent neurotransmitter: immunocytochemical and neurochemical evidence in the rat. Peptides **1:** 1–9.

7. HELKE, C. J. & K. M. HILL. 1988. Immunohistochemical study of neuropeptides in vagal and glossopharyngeal afferent neurons in the rat. Neuroscience **26:** 539–551.

8. HELKE, C. J., J. J. NEIL, J. MASSARI & A. D. LOEWY. 1982. Substance P neurons project from the ventral medulla to the intermediolateral cell column and ventral horn in the rat. Brain Res. **243:** 147–152.

9. CHARLTON, C. G. & C. J. HELKE. 1987. Substance P–containing medullary projections to the intermediolateral cell column: identification with retrogradely transported rhodamine-labeled latex microspheres and immunohistochemistry. Brain Res. **418:** 245–254.

10. DALSGAARD, C-J., T. HÖKFELT, L-G. ELFVIN, L. SKIRBOLL & P. EMSON. 1982. Substance P–containing primary sensory neurons projecting to the inferior mesenteric ganglion: evidence from combined retrograde tracing and immunohistochemistry. Neuroscience **7:** 647–654.

11. KATZ, D. M., K. A. MARKEY, M. GOLDSTEIN & I. B. BLACK. 1983. Expression of catecholaminergic characteristics by primary sensory neurons in the normal adult rat *in vivo.* Proc. Natl. Acad. Sci. U.S.A. **80:** 3526–3530.

12. LUNDBERG, J. M., T. HÖKFELT, G. NILSSON, L. TERENIUS, J. REHFELD, R. ELDE & S. SAID. 1978. Peptide neurons in the vagus, splanchnic, and sciatic nerves. Acta Physiol. Scand. **104:** 499–501.

13. MANTYH, P. W. & S. P. HUNT. 1984. Neuropeptides are present in projection neurones at all levels in visceral and taste pathways: from periphery to sensory cortex. Brain Res. **299:** 297–311.

14. HELKE, C. J. & A. J. NIEDERER. 1990. Studies on the coexistence of substance P with other putative transmitters in the nodose and petrosal ganglia. Synapse **5:** 144–151.

15. HELKE, C. J., S. C. SAYSON, J. R. KEELER & C. G. CHARLTON. 1986. Thyrotropin-releasing hormone neurons project from the ventral medulla to the intermediolateral cell column: partial coexistence with serotonin. Brain Res. **381:** 1–7.

16. SASEK, C. A., M. W. WESSENDORF & C. J. HELKE. 1990. Evidence for coexistence of thyrotropin releasing hormone, substance P, and serotonin in ventral medullary neurons that project to the intermediolateral cell column in the rat. Neuroscience **35:** 105–119.

17. APPEL, N. M., M. W. WESSENDORF & R. P. ELDE. 1986. Coexistence of serotonin- and substance P–like immunoreactivity in nerve fibers apposing identified sympathoadrenal preganglionic neurons in rat intermediolateral cell column. Neurosci. Lett. **65:** 241–246.

18. STAINES, W. A., B. MEISTER, T. MELANDER, J. I. NAGY & T. HÖKFELT. 1988. Three-color immunofluorescence histochemistry allowing triple labeling within a single section. J. Histochem. Cytochem. **36:** 145–151.

19. DAVIS, B. M., J. E. KRAUSE, J. F. MCKELVY & J. B. CABOT. 1984. Effects of spinal lesions on substance P levels in the rat sympathetic preganglionic cell column: evidence for local spinal regulation. Neuroscience **13**: 1311–1316.

20. WARDEN, M. K. & W. S. YOUNG III. 1988. Distribution of cells containing mRNAs encoding substance P and neurokinin B in the rat central nervous system. J. Comp. Neurol. **272**: 90–113.

21. KRUKOFF, T. L., J. CIRIELLO & F. R. CALARESU. 1985. Segmental distribution of peptide-like immunoreactivity in cell bodies of the thoracolumbar sympathetic nucleus of the cat. J. Comp. Neurol. **240**: 90–102.

22. SASEK, C. A. & C. J. HELKE. 1989. Enkephalin-immunoreactive neuronal projections from the medulla oblongata to the intermediolateral cell column: relationship to substance P–immunoreactive neurons. J. Comp. Neurol. **287**: 484–494.

23. KRAUSE, J. E., J. M. CHIRGWIN, M. S. CARTER, Z. S. XU & A. D. HERSHEY. 1987. Three rat preprotachykinin mRNAs encode the neuropeptides substance P and neurokinin A. Proc. Natl. Acad. Sci. U.S.A. **84**: 881–885.

24. NAWA, H., H. KOTANI & S. NAKANISHI. 1984. Tissue-specific generation of two preprotachy-kinin mRNAs from one gene by alternative RNA splicing. Nature **312**: 729–734.

25. KRAUSE, J. E., J. D. CREMENS, M. S. CARTER, E. R. BROWN & M. R. MACDONALD. 1989. Solution hybridization–nuclease protection assays for sensitive detection of differentially spliced substance P– and neurokinin A–encoding messenger ribonucleic acids. Methods Enzymol. **168**: 634–652.

26. LINDEFORS, N., E. BRODIN, E. THEODORSSON-NORHEIM & U. UNGERSTEDT. 1985. Calcium-dependent potassium-stimulated release of neurokinin A and neurokinin B from rat brain regions *in vitro*. Neuropeptides **6**: 453–461.

27. KOTANI, H., M. HOSHIMARU, H. NAWA & S. NAKANISHI. 1986. Structure and gene organization of bovine neuromedin K precursor. Proc. Natl. Acad. Sci. U.S.A. **83**: 7074–7078.

28. BONNER, T. I., H-U. AFFOLTER, A. C. YOUNG & W. S. YOUNG III. 1987. A cDNA encoding the precursor of the rat neuropeptide, neurokinin B. Mol. Brain Res. **2**: 243–249.

29. BURGUNDER, J-M. & W. S. YOUNG III. 1989. Neurokinin B and substance P genes are co-expressed in a subset of neurons in the rat habenula. Neuropeptides **13**: 165–169.

30. MILNER, T. A., V. M. PICKEL, C. ABATE, T. H. JOH & D. J. REIS. 1988. Ultrastructural characterization of substance P–like immunoreactive neurons in the rostral ventrolateral medulla in relation to neurons containing catecholamine-synthesizing enzymes. J. Comp. Neurol. **270**: 427–445.

31. LARSSON, L. I. 1981. A novel immunocytochemical model system for specificity and sensitivity screening of antisera against multiple antigens. J. Histochem. Cytochem. **29**: 408–410.

32. SASEK, C., M. HAXHIU & C. HELKE. 1990. Relationship of immunoreactive neurokinin A and substance P in ventral medullary neurons that project to the intermediolateral cell column and in IML fibers. Soc. Neurosci. Abstr. **16**: 519.

33. TATEMOTO, K., J. M. LUNDBERG, H. JORNVALL & V. MUTT. 1985. Neuropeptide K: isolation, structure, and biological activities of a novel brain tachykinin. Biochem. Biophys. Res. Commun. **128**: 947–953.

34. KAGE, R., G. P. MCGREGOR, L. THIM & J. M. CONLON. 1988. Neuropeptide gamma: a peptide isolated from rabbit intestine that is derived from gamma-preprotachykinin. J. Neurochem. **50**: 1412–1417.

35. MACDONALD, M. R., J. TAKEDA, C. M. RICE & J. E. KRAUSE. 1989. Multiple tachykinins are produced and secreted upon posttranslational processing of the three substance P precursor proteins, alpha-, beta-, and gamma-preprotachykinin. J. Biol. Chem. **264**: 15578–15592.

36. VALENTINO, K. L., K. TATEMOTO, J. HUNTER & J. D. BARCHAS. 1986. Distribution of neuropeptide K–immunoreactivity in the rat central nervous system. Peptides **7**: 1043–1059.

37. TAKEDA, Y., J. TAKEDA, B. M. SMART & J. E. KRAUSE. 1990. Regional distribution of substance P, neurokinin A, neuropeptide K, and neuropeptide gamma in the rat. Regulat. Peptides **28**: 323–333.

38. FRANCO CERECEDA, A., H. HENKE, J. M. LUNDBERG, J. B. PETERMANN, T. HÖKFELT & J. A. FISCHER. 1987. Calcitonin gene–related peptide (CGRP) in capsaicin-sensitive substance P–immunoreactive sensory neurons in animals and man: distribution and release by capsaicin. Peptides **8:** 399–410.
39. HELKE, C. J., D. M. JACOBOWITZ & N. B. THOA. 1981. Capsaicin and potassium evoked substance P release from the nucleus tractus solitarius and spinal trigeminal nucleus *in vitro.* Life Sci. **29:** 1779–1785.
40. LANE, J. D. & M. H. APRISON. 1977. Calcium-dependent release of endogenous serotonin, dopamine, and norepinephrine from nerve endings. Life Sci. **20:** 665–672.
41. BUCK, S. H., C. J. HELKE, E. BURCHER, C. W. SHULTS & T. L. O'DONOHUE. 1986. Pharmacologic characterization and autoradiographic distribution of binding sites for iodinated tachykinins in the rat central nervous system. Peptides **7:** 1109–1120.
42. HELKE, C. J., C. W. SHULTS, T. N. CHASE & T. L. O'DONOHUE. 1984. Autoradiographic localization of substance P receptors in rat medulla: effect of vagotomy and nodose ganglionectomy. Neuroscience **12:** 215–223.
43. SKOFITSCH, G. & D. M. JACOBOWITZ. 1985. Autoradiographic distribution of ^{125}I calcitonin gene–related peptide binding sites in the rat central nervous system. Peptides **4:** 975–986.
44. MACLEAN, D. B., B. BENNETT, M. MORRIS & F. B. WHEELER. 1989. Differential regulation of calcitonin gene–related peptide and substance P in cultured neonatal rat vagal sensory neurons. Brain Res. **478:** 349–355.
45. GILBEY, M. P., K. E. MCKENNA & L. P. SCHRAMM. 1983. Effects of substance P on sympathetic preganglionic neurones. Neurosci. Lett. **41:** 157–159.
46. MCCALL, R. B. 1983. Serotonergic excitation of sympathetic preganglionic neurons: a microiontophoretic study. Brain Res. **289:** 121–127.
47. MA, R. C. & N. J. DUN. 1986. Excitation of lateral horn neurons of the neonatal rat spinal cord by 5-hydroxytryptamine. Dev. Brain Res. **24:** 89–98.
48. DUN, N. J. & N. MO. 1988. *In vitro* effects of substance P on neonatal rat sympathetic preganglionic neurones. J. Physiol. (London) **399:** 321–333.
49. KEELER, J. R., C. G. CHARLTON & C. J. HELKE. 1985. Cardiovascular effects of spinal cord substance P: studies with a stable receptor agonist. J. Pharmacol. Exp. Ther. **233:** 755–760.
50. HELKE, C. J., E. T. PHILLIPS & J. T. O'NEILL. 1987. Regional peripheral and CNS hemodynamic effects of intrathecal administration of a substance P receptor agonist. J. Autonomic Nerv. Syst. **21:** 1–7.
51. HELKE, C. J. & E. T. PHILLIPS. 1988. Thyrotropin-releasing hormone receptor activation in the spinal cord increases blood pressure and sympathetic tone to the vasculature and the adrenals. J. Pharmacol. Exp. Ther. **245:** 41–46.
52. LI, S-J., X. ZHANG & A. J. INGENITO. 1988. Depressor and bradycardic effects induced by spinal subarachnoid injection of D-Ala^2-D-Leu^5-enkephalin in rats. Neuropeptides **12:** 81–88.
53. BACKMAN, S. B. & J. L. HENRY. 1984. Effects of substance P and thyrotropin-releasing hormone on sympathetic preganglionic neurones in the upper thoracic intermediolateral nucleus of the cat. Can. J. Physiol. Pharmacol. **62:** 248–251.
54. HASSESSIAN, H., G. DRAPEAU & R. COUTURE. 1988. Spinal actions of neurokinins producing cardiovascular responses in the conscious freely moving rat: evidence for a NK-1 receptor mechanism. Naunyn-Schmiedeberg's Arch. Pharmacol. **338:** 649–654.
55. MANTYH, P. W., T. S. GATES, C. R. MANTYH & J. E. MAGGIO. 1989. Autoradiographic localization and characterization of tachykinin receptor binding sites in the rat brain and peripheral tissues. J. Neurosci. **9:** 258–279.
56. BARTFAI, T., K. IVERFELDT, G. FISONE & P. SERFOZO. 1988. Regulation of the release of coexisting neurotransmitters. Annu. Rev. Pharmacol. Toxicol. **28:** 285–310.
57. LUNDBERG, J. M. & T. HÖKFELT. 1983. Coexistence of peptides and classical neurotransmitters. Trends Neurosci. (TINS) **6:** 325–333.
58. MCCALL, R. B. & M. E. CLEMENT. 1989. Identification of serotonergic and sympathetic neurons in medullary raphe nuclei. Brain Res. **477:** 172–182.

59. FRANZ, D. N., B. D. HARE & K. L. MCCLOSKEY. 1982. Spinal sympathetic neurons: possible sites of opiate-withdrawal suppression by clonidine. Science **215:** 1643–1645.

60. MINSON, J. B., J. P. CHALMERS, A. C. CAON & B. RENAUD. 1987. Separate areas of rat medulla oblongata with populations of serotonin- and adrenalin-containing neurons alter blood pressure after L-glutamate stimulation. J. Autonomic Nerv. Syst. **19:** 39–50.

61. IVERFELDT, K., L-L. PETERSON, E. BRODIN, S. OGREN & T. BARTFAI. 1986. Serotonin type-2 receptor mediated regulation of substance P release in the ventral spinal cord and the effects of chronic antidepressant treatment. Naunyn-Schmiedeberg's Arch. Pharmacol. **333:** 1–6.

62. MITCHELL, R. & S. FLEETWOOD-WALKER. 1981. Substance P, but not TRH, modulates the 5-HT autoreceptor in ventral lumbar spinal cord. Eur. J. Pharmacol. **76:** 119–120.

63. SHARIF, N. A. & D. R. BURT. 1983. Micromolar substance P reduces spinal receptor binding for thyrotropin-releasing hormone—possible relevance to neuropeptide coexistence? Neurosci. Lett. **43:** 245–251.

64. AGNATI, L. F., K. FUXE, F. BENEFANATI, I. ZINI & T. HÖKFELT. 1983. On the functional role of coexistence of 5-HT and substance P in bulbospinal 5-HT neurons: substance P reduces affinity and increases density of ^{3}H-5-HT binding sites. Acta Physiol. Scand. **117:** 299–301.

65. CLARKE, K. A., A. J. PARKER & G. C. STIRK. 1985. Potentiation of motoneurone excitability by combined administration of 5-HT agonist and TRH analogue. Neuropeptides **6:** 269–282.

66. HELKE, C. J., C. G. CHARLTON & R. G. WILEY. 1986. Studies on the cellular localization of spinal cord substance P receptors. Neuroscience **19:** 523–533.

67. THOR, K. B. & C. J. HELKE. 1989. Serotonin and substance P colocalization in medullary projections to the nucleus tractus solitarius: dual-color immunohistochemistry combined with retrograde tracing. J. Chem. Neuroanat. **2:** 139–148.

68. MILLHORN, D. E., K. SEROOGY, T. HÖKFELT, L. C. SCHMUED, L. TERENIUS, A. BUCHAN & J. C. BROWN. 1987. Neurons of the ventral medulla oblongata that contain both somatostatin and enkephalin immunoreactivities project to nucleus tractus solitarius and spinal cord. Brain Res. **424:** 99–108.

Neurokinin Agonists and Antagonists

D. REGOLI,[a] F. NANTEL,[b] C. TOUSIGNANT,[c] D. JUKIC,

N. ROUISSI, N-E. RHALEB,[d] S. TÉLÉMAQUE,

G. DRAPEAU,[e] AND P. D'ORLÉANS-JUSTE

Department of Pharmacology
School of Medicine
University of Sherbrooke
Sherbrooke, Canada J1H 5N4

INTRODUCTION

Substance P (SP), neurokinin A (NKA), and neurokinin B (NKB) are mammalian peptides characterized by the C-terminal sequence, Phe-X-Gly-Leu-Met-NH$_2$. The primary structures of these peptides are presented in TABLE 1 along with those of physalaemin (PHY), eledoisin (ELE), and kassinin (KAS), which are three tachykinins of nonmammalian origins. Neurokinins are present in the brain and in peripheral organs where they are known to mediate transmission of pain,[1] motility of smooth muscle,[2] distribution of peripheral blood flow,[3] and hormone and neurotransmitter secretion.[4,5] The neurokinins act through activation of three receptor types named NK-1 for SP, NK-2 for NKA, and NK-3 for NKB.[6]

The characterization of these receptors was made with pharmacological,[7] biochemical,[8] and histochemical[9] approaches. The pharmacological characterization required (a) the use of isolated smooth muscle preparations known to contain single or multiple receptor types and (b) the development of agonists selective for a single receptor type.

In this report, we analyze five vascular preparations that have been found to be useful for the study of neurokinin receptors and focus on two rabbit veins, the jugular[10] and vena cava (Nantel *et al.*, unpublished), which contain only the NK-1 type. The identification and the development of selective neurokinin receptor agonists are also described along with the use of selective NK-1 agonists for biochemical studies.

Another important step in receptor characterization is the utilization of selective antagonists. The search of such compounds is performed in various research centers and we are able to include here some recent data on new NK-3 receptor antagonists obtained in our laboratory.

PHARMACOLOGICAL PREPARATIONS

Sensitive pharmacological preparations are essential tools for receptor characterization. This is also the case for the three neurokinin receptor types that have been

[a] D. Regoli is a career investigator at the Medical Research Council of Canada (M.R.C.C.).
[b] F. Nantel was supported by the Georges Phénix Foundation.
[c] C. Tousignant was supported by the M.R.C.C.
[d] N-E. Rhaleb was supported by the Canadian Heart and Stroke Foundation.
[e] G. Drapeau is a fellow of the Fonds de la Recherche en Santé du Québec.

TABLE 1. Primary Structure of Neurokinins and Tachykinins

Name	0	1	2	3	4	5	6	7	8	9	10	11
							Structure					
Substance P		Arg-	Pro-	Lys-	Pro-	Gln-	Gln-	Phe-	Phe-	Gly-	Leu-	Met-NH$_2$
Neurokinin A		His-	Lys-	Thr-	Asp-	Ser-	Phe-	Val-	Gly-	Leu-	Met-NH$_2$	
Neurokinin B		Asp-	Met-	His-	Asp-	Phe-	Phe-	Val-	Gly-	Leu-	Met-NH$_2$	
Physalaemin		pGlu-	Ala-	Asp-	Pro-	Asn-	Lys-	Phe-	Tyr-	Gly-	Leu-	Met-NH$_2$
Eledoisin		pGlu-	Pro-	Ser-	Lys-	Asp-	Ala-	Phe-	Ile-	Gly-	Leu-	Met-NH$_2$
Kassinin	Asp-	Val-	Pro-	Lys-	Ser-	Asp-	Gly-	Phe-	Val-	Gly-	Leu-	Met-NH$_2$

studied on various isolated organs including the dog carotid artery (DCA),[11] the rabbit jugular vein (RJV),[10] and the rabbit vena cava (RVC), which contain only the NK-1 receptor; the rabbit pulmonary artery (RPA), which has only the NK-2 receptor type;[12] and the rat portal vein (RPV), which has only the NK-3 receptor type.[13] The pharmacological activities of neurokinins, tachykinins, and some neurokinin fragments on these preparations are presented in TABLE 2.

The data in TABLE 2 indicate that SP is the most active neurokinin on the DCA, the RJV, and the RVC, where it shows a pD_2 value higher than 8.6. On the DCA, NKA is more active than NKB, whereas NKA and NKB show similar affinities on the rabbit veins. The order of potency of the tachykinins is PHY > ELE > KAS on the DCA and PHY > ELE = KAS on the RJV and the RVC. All the fragments analyzed in TABLE 2 were found to have affinities lower than SP in the three NK-1 preparations.

For several years, the NK-1 receptor has been studied on the DCA despite some limitations; in fact, SP exerts an indirect inhibitory effect on this tissue because the DCA responds to neurokinins with an endothelium-dependent relaxation. The NK-1 receptor is present on endothelial cells and its activation brings about the release of the endothelium-derived relaxing factor (EDRF),[11] a potent relaxant of smooth muscle fibers believed to be nitric oxide.[14] The effect of SP on the DCA is therefore the result of two processes, namely, the stimulus-secretion (release of EDRF) and a subsequent stimulus-relaxation process (inhibition of vascular tonus). When suspended in vitro, the artery has no intrinsic tension and it must first be precontracted with noradrenaline (NA) (2.8×10^{-8} M). SP then acts as a physiological antagonist of the NA-elicited contraction. Because the tissue may be not contracted to its maximum, it is then possible that the affinities of agonists may be overestimated. This is suggested by the results shown in FIGURE 1, where maximal contraction of the DCA obtained with a high dose of NA (1.2×10^{-5} M) causes a rightward shift in the SP relaxation curve and a drop in the relative affinity from a pD_2 value of 10.0 to 9.53. There is also a decrease of the maximal effect, as if SP could not completely eliminate the contraction induced by the high dose of NA. Furthermore, because the DCA cannot be relaxed by 100%, the evaluation of agonist intrinsic activities (α^E) is extremely difficult, if not impossible, if we also consider that the maximal relaxation of a given tissue may depend more on the state of its endothelium than on the nature or concentration of the agonist used.

On the other hand, the two rabbit veins respond to neurokinins with concentration-dependent contractions that are evoked by the stimulation of smooth muscle receptors because they occur equally well in the absence or in the presence of the endothelium. The observed effect is thus direct and results from a stimulus-contraction process in which the endothelium may play no role. The two veins then permit a precise evaluation of the apparent affinity (pD_2) and the intrinsic activity (α^E),[10] according to the classical receptor theory.[15]

On the RPA (TABLE 2), NKA is the most active neurokinin, followed by NKB and SP. The order of affinity of the tachykinins is ELE > KAS > PHY. NKA(4–10) is the most active fragment with an affinity even higher than that of NKA or ELE. The heptapeptide and hexapeptide fragments of SP have also been found to be more active than SP.

The RPV shows a high sensitivity to NKB, which is the neurokinin that shows the highest affinity ($pD_2 = 7.68$) on this tissue, whereas NKA is over 10 times less active than NKB and SP is almost inactive ($pD_2 = 5.82$). The tachykinins have the following order of affinity: KAS > ELE > PHY. Among the fragments, both SP(6–11) and NKA(4–10) are more active than their corresponding peptides.

TABLE 2. Pharmacological Activities of Neurokinins, Tachykinins, and Fragments on Vascular Smooth Muscle Preparations[a]

	DCA		RJV			RVC			RPA			RPV		
	pD_2	RA	pD_2	RA	α^E	pD_2	RA	α^E	pD_2	RA	α^E	pD_2	RA	α^E
Substance P	10.00	100	8.83	100	1.0	8.63	100	1.0	6.13	100	1.0	5.82	100	1.0
Neurokinin A	9.40	25	7.65	7	0.9	7.31	5	1.0	8.22	12,303	1.4	6.45	427	3.0
Neurokinin B	8.90	8	7.84	10	0.7	7.20	4	1.0	7.45	2089	1.4	7.68	7244	2.5
Physalaemin	10.00	100	8.88	112	1.1	8.88	162	1.1	6.02	78	1.0	6.18	229	2.0
Eledoisin	9.50	32	8.43	43	1.0	7.72	12	1.0	8.22	12,303	1.4	7.11	1950	3.5
Kassinin	9.20	16	8.48	45	0.9	7.78	14	1.0	7.66	3388	1.4	7.20	2399	3.5
SP(4–11)	9.67	47	8.62	61	1.0	8.52	78	1.0	6.23	126	0.7	5.87	112	2.5
SP(5–11)	9.30	20	8.20	26	0.9	8.08	24	1.0	6.53	251	0.9	5.54	52	2.0
SP(6–11)	8.64	4	8.41	38	0.9	7.57	9	1.0	5.71	38	0.9	6.30	281	2.3
NKA(4–10)	8.62	4	7.40	4	0.9	6.75	1	1.0	8.52	24,547	1.1	6.79	933	2.5

[a]Terms—pD_2: $-$log of the molar concentration of agonist causing 50% of the maximal response; RA: relative affinity expressed in percentage of that of SP; α^E: intrinsic activity expressed as a fraction of that of SP.

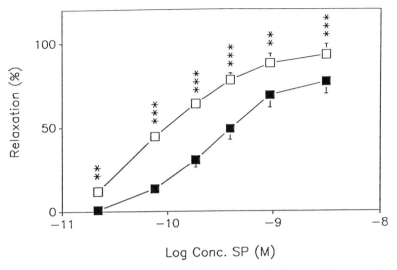

FIGURE 1. Concentration-response curve of substance P on the dog carotid artery previously contracted with noradrenaline—2.8×10^{-8} M ($\square$) or 1.2×10^{-5} M ($\blacksquare$). Ordinate: Relaxation expressed in percentage. Abscissa: Log of the molar concentration of SP. Each point represents the average from seven determinations and the vertical bars represent the standard error; **: $p < 0.01$; ***: $p < 0.001$.

DEVELOPMENT OF SELECTIVE AGONISTS

Even though the neurokinins and tachykinins were useful in the characterization of their respective receptors, it was found that they were not selective enough for biochemical or physiological studies. Among the natural neurokinins, SP is the most selective, having 100 to 1000 times more activity on the NK-1 than on the NK-2 or NK-3 systems (TABLE 2). NKA is at most 10 times more active on the RPA (NK-2) than on the two rabbit veins (NK-1), but it has a lower affinity than on the DCA, the other NK-1 preparation. The affinity of NKB on the NK-3 system of the rat portal vein ($pD_2 = 7.68$) is lower than its affinity on the DCA ($pD_2 = 8.90$) or on the RJV ($pD_2 = 7.84$) and it is almost equal to that of the RPA ($pD_2 = 7.45$). This has prompted the search for more selective agonists that are active on only one neurokinin receptor type.

NK-1 Selective Agonists

Results obtained with the selective compounds as well as with other analogues of the three neurokinins that led to the identification of selective agonists are summarized in TABLE 3. Early work on neurokinin selective agonists was purely empirical and centered on the SP molecule. It was first reported that the methylation of SP led to NK-1 receptor selectivity: SP-OMe was found to be active on the DCA and inactive on the RPA and the RPV.[16] However, SP-OMe was metabolically unstable: to improve the stability and affinity for the NK-1 receptor, Gly[9] was replaced by Sar.[17] The compound, [Sar[9]]SP, has a high affinity on the DCA, is inactive on the RPA, and has a low activity on the RPV. The oxidation of Met[11] to Met(O_2) increased the selectivity without decreasing the affinity for the NK-1 receptor of the DCA. Indeed, [Sar[9],Met(O_2)[11]]SP is selective for the NK-1 receptor, being very active on the DCA and inactive on the other two preparations (TABLE 3). The size of the selective agonist was then decreased to that of a hexapeptide, [Arg[6],Sar[9],Met(O_2)[11]]SP(6–11), without a major loss of affinity.[18] Acetylation of the N-terminal amine of this hexapeptide to prevent histamine release from mast cells[19] kept its affinity and selectivity for the NK-1 receptor.

NK-2 Selective Agonists

As shown earlier in TABLE 2, it was found that NKA(4–10) was much more active than NKA on the NK-2 receptor system of the RPA. Replacement of the Met[10] with Nle lowered the peptide affinity on the NK-2 receptor by 40%, but almost abolished the activity on NK-1 and NK-3 receptor systems.[17] Also, elongation of the peptide chain at the level of Gly[8] by one carbon gave a compound, [βAla[8]]NKA(4–10), that was more active than NKA on the RPA (pD_2 = 8.60), but that showed little activity on the DCA[20] and some decrease on the RPV (TABLE 3).

NK-3 Selective Agonists

The search for an NK-3 selective agonist started with the observation that DiMeC7 shows low activity on NK-1 and NK-2 systems.[21] The chemical features of DiMeC7 were reproduced in the sequence NKB(4–10) and its activity on the NK-3 receptor was found to be fairly good, whereas activity on NK-1 did not change. Activity on the NK-3 receptor was further improved by the elimination of Sar[8]: the

TABLE 3. Pharmacological Activities of Neurokinin Receptor Selective Agonists[a]

	DCA		RPA		RPV	
	pD_2	RA	pD_2	RA	pD_2	RA
Substance P	10.0	100	6.13	100	5.82	100
SP-OMe	9.60	40	inactive		inactive	
[Sar[9]]SP	10.4	240		0.1	5.80	98
[Sar[9],Met(O_2)[11]]SP	10.5	282	inactive		inactive	
[Arg[6],Sar[9],Met(O_2)[11]]SP(6–11)	10.1	126	inactive		inactive	
Ac-[Arg[6],Sar[9],Met(O_2)[11]]SP(6–11)	10.2	174	inactive		inactive	
Neurokinin A	9.40	100	8.22	100	6.45	100
NKA(4–10)	8.62	17	8.52	200	6.77	219
[Nle[10]]NKA	7.64	4.4	8.01	62	6.49	110
[Nle[10]]NKA(4–10)	7.00	0.1	7.64	26		<0.1
[βAla[8]]NKA(4–10)	6.71	0.5	8.60	240	6.13	48
Neurokinin B	8.90	100	7.45	100	7.68	100
NKB(4–10)	8.70	63	7.95	316	6.67	10
[pGlu[6],MePhe[8],Sar[9]]SP(5–11)(DiMeC7)	7.50	4	inactive		6.35	5
[MePhe[7],Sar[8]]NKB(4–10)	7.61	5	inactive		7.03	22
[MePhe[7]]NKB(4–10)	7.09	2	inactive		7.58	79
[MePhe[7]]NKB	7.15	2	5.24	1	8.30	417

[a]Terms are defined in the footnote to TABLE 2.

hexapeptide [MePhe^7]NKB(4–10) was one of the first NK-3 selective agonists to be identified,[22] together with senktide.[23] Activity on NK-3 and selectivity were further improved by replacing Val^7 with MePhe on the full NKB molecule: [MePhe^7]NKB is a compound with an activity 4 times higher than NKB on the RPV and with a low affinity for the NK-1 and NK-2 receptor sites,[17] as shown in TABLE 3.

Uses of Selective Agonists

Selective agonists have been used first to identify other tissues that contain only one neurokinin receptor type (TABLE 4). This has been the case for the two rabbit veins presented earlier and also for some human tissues. Indeed, the RJV and the RVC respond to the NK-1 selective agonist [Sar^9,Met(O$_2$)^{11}]SP, but show little sensitivity to [Nle^{10}]NKA(4–10) and [MePhe^7]NKB. On the other hand, human bronchus (HB) and human urinary bladder (HmUB) are 10 times more sensitive to NKA than to other neurokinins. In fact, the NK-2 selective agonist [Nle^{10}]NKA(4–10) is active in both preparations, whereas the NK-1 and NK-3 selective agonists have no or very little effects (TABLE 4). These findings suggest that both HB and HmUB contain only NK-2 receptors.[24] The human ileum was also characterized by Maggi et al.[25] using different selective agonists and it was shown to be a pure NK-2 receptor preparation.

Other organs currently used in pharmacological studies of neurokinin receptors include, for instance, the guinea pig ileum (GPI), which is considered an NK-1 preparation when treated with atropine;[26] the rat duodenum (RD), which is used as an NK-2 system;[27] and the hamster urinary bladder (HUB), which was initially used for identification of the NK-3 site.[8] As shown in TABLE 4, the GPI responds to all three selective agonists and therefore possesses NK-1, NK-2, and NK-3 receptor sites. As to the NK-3 sites, these were shown by Laufer et al.[26] to promote the release of acetylcholine from intramural nerves: in fact, treatment of the tissue with atropine abolishes the response of the GPI to [MePhe^7]NKB (not shown), but not to NK-1 and NK-2 selective agonists. The rat duodenum, which has been used as an NK-2 preparation, responds to both [Nle^{10}]NKA(4–10) and [MePhe^7]NKB, indicating that both NK-2 and NK-3 receptors may be present. The same is true for the HUB, which has both NK-2 and NK-3 functional sites, because it responds to NK-2 and NK-3 selective agonists. In conclusion, three of the preparations analyzed in TABLE 4 (GPI, RD, and HUB) contain more than one receptor type and are not suited for pharmacologic studies directed to characterization of neurokinin receptors or of new neurokinin-related peptides, both agonists and antagonists. For further discussion on this point, see references 2 and 28.

USE OF NK-1 SELECTIVE AGONISTS AS LABELS

Biochemical characterization of NK-1 receptors in rat brain homogenates has been carried out with radiolabeled ^{125}I-Bolton-Hunter-SP.[29,30] However, results obtained in pharmacological studies on isolated organs have suggested that SP may not be a very selective compound because it acts (although weakly) on NK-2 and NK-3 functional sites.[2,7,28] After the identification of NK-1 selective agonists, some of those compounds were labeled with either ^{125}I or ^{3}H to better characterize the NK-1 binding site.

Results obtained in our laboratory with three ligands are presented in TABLE 5 by

TABLE 4. Pharmacological Activities of Neurokinins and Selective Agonists on Rabbit Veins and Human Smooth Muscle Preparations[a]

| | NK-1 | | | | | | NK-2 | | | | | | NK-3 | |
| | RJV | | RVC | | GPI | | HB | | HmUB | | RD | | HUB | |
	pD_2	RA	pD_2	RA	pD_2	RA	pD_2	RA	pD_2	RA	pD_2	RA	pD_2	RA
Substance P	8.83	100	8.63	100	8.78	100	6.30	3	6.00	3	6.50	2	5.57	2
Neurokinin A	7.65	7	7.31	5	8.40	42	7.83	100	7.60	100	8.22	100	7.40	159
Neurokinin B	7.84	10	7.20	4	8.64	72	6.05	2	6.53	9	8.15	85	7.20	100
[Sar^9,Met(O$_2$)^{11}]SP	8.86	107	8.60	93	8.91	135	inactive		5.65	1	6.67	3	inactive	
[Nle^{10}]NKA(4–10)	5.88	0.1	5.37	0.1	7.99	16	6.97	14	6.60	10	8.02	63	7.09	78
[MePhe^7]NKB	6.23	0.3	5.63	0.1	8.76	96	inactive		5.19	0.4	8.66	275	6.14	9

[a]Terms are defined in the footnote to TABLE 2 and in the text.

showing the relative affinity of neurokinins and selective agonists to inhibit three putative NK-1 ligands, mainly, ^{125}I-BH-SP, ^{3}H-[Sar^{9},Met(O$_{2}$)^{11}]SP, and ^{125}I-BH-[Sar^{9},Met(O$_{2}$)^{11}]SP, from rat brain membranes. The three ligands gave very similar results: in fact, the order of the affinity of neurokinins was found to be SP > NKA > NKB and, of the selective agonists, only [Sar^{9},Met(O$_{2}$)^{11}]SP showed high affinity, with the other two being almost inactive. These results are similar to those observed in the dog carotid artery, that is, the NK-1 receptor system. They show that ^{125}I-BH-SP is selective for the NK-1 receptor and is equivalent to the other two selective ligands. Furthermore, ^{125}I and ^{3}H can both be used with success because no differences were observed either in the affinity of the ligand or in the order of the affinity of nonlabeled peptides in competition studies. The iodinated ligands have the advantage of being more suitable for autoradiographic studies, whereas the tritiated ligand (which has the same structure as the natural peptide) shows much lower nonspecific binding (Tousignant *et al.*, unpublished).

NK-1 binding sites were also characterized on guinea pig ileum membranes using ^{3}H-[Sar^{9},Met(O$_{2}$)^{11}]SP as a ligand. A comparison of the affinities of neurokinins and analogues obtained in competition studies performed on rat brain and guinea pig ileum membranes is presented in FIGURE 2. The two sets of data fit a straight line and show a good correlation: indeed, the correlation coefficient is positive and significant ($r = 0.95$, $p < 0.001$), suggesting that the NK-1 binding site that is present on the rat brain is the same as that of the guinea pig ileum.

Furthermore, the biological activities of neurokinins, tachykinins, SP fragments, and selective agonists observed on the rabbit jugular vein are compared with binding affinities of the same compounds evaluated in competition studies on rat brain membranes using as ligand either ^{125}I-BH-SP or ^{125}I-BH-[Sar^{9},Met(O$_{2}$)^{11}]SP. With both ligands, a positive and significant correlation between binding affinities and biological activities is observed (FIGURE 3). Correlation coefficients of 0.91 ($p < 0.001$) and 0.82 ($p < 0.001$) are observed, respectively, with ^{125}I-BH-SP and ^{125}I-BH-[Sar^{9},Met(O$_{2}$)^{11}]SP. These findings strongly support the interpretation that NK-1 binding sites characterized in binding studies are very similar, possibly identical to the functional sites that are responsible for the biological responses of the RJV to substance P and related peptides.

TABLE 5. Relative Affinity of Neurokinins and Selective Agonists to Inhibit Various NK-1 Selective Ligands on Rat Brain Membranes[a]

	Radioactive Ligand					
	^{3}H-[Sar^{9},Met(O$_{2}$)^{11}]SP		^{125}I-BH-[Sar^{9},Met(O$_{2}$)^{11}]SP		^{125}I-BH-SP	
Peptide	$-\text{Log}$ K_i	RA	$-\text{Log}$ K_i	RA	$-\text{Log}$ K_i	RA
Neurokinins						
SP	9.19	100	9.21	100	9.11	100
NKB	5.25	0.01	5.57	0.02	6.35	0.2
NKA	6.95	0.6	7.20	1	7.18	1
Selective Agonists						
[Sar^{9},Met(O$_{2}$)^{11}]SP	8.50	10	9.00	62	8.60	31
[MePhe^{7}]NKB	4.53	0.002	4.40	0.002	4.51	0.002
[βAla^{8}]NKA(4–10)	inactive		4.46	0.002	4.12	0.002

[a]Terms are defined in the footnote to TABLE 2; $-\log K_i$: $-\log$ of the concentration of peptide that inhibits 50% of the bound ligand.

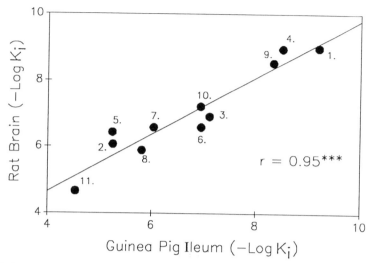

FIGURE 2. Log-log plot of the binding affinities of neurokinins and analogues on rat brain and guinea pig ileum membranes. Key: (1) SP, (2) NKB, (3) NKA, (4) PHY, (5) ELE, (6) SP(4–11), (7) SP(5–11), (8) SP(6–11), (9) [Sar^9,Met(O$_2$)^{11}]SP, (10) Ac-[Arg^6,Sar^9,Met(O$_2$)^{11}]SP(6–11), and (11) [MePhe^7]NKB. Ordinate: −Log K_i of peptides evaluated by their ability to inhibit the ligand ^{3}H-[Sar^9,Met(O$_2$)^{11}]SP on guinea pig ileum membrane. Abscissa: −Log K_i of peptides evaluated by their ability to inhibit the ligand ^{3}H-[Sar^9,Met(O$_2$)^{11}]SP on rat brain membrane. ***:$p < 0.001$.

NK-3 ANTAGONISTS

To obtain new selective NK-2 agonists suitable for labeling, Val^7 of [βAla^8]NKA(4–10) was replaced with a Tyr. [Tyr^7,βAla^8]NKA(4–10), although weak as an agonist on the NK-2 receptor, was found to be an antagonist on the rat portal vein, that is, the NK-3 receptor system.

Until now, only weak and possibly nonselective antagonists for the NK-3 receptor have been reported.[31] The observation in the preceding paragraph therefore prompted a careful analysis of new NK-3 antagonists derived from the sequence of [βAla^8]NKA(4–10) and [βAla^8]NKB(4–10). Several compounds were prepared and tested.[32] The pharmacological activities of six putative NK-3 receptor antagonists, evaluated on four selective monoreceptor systems [mainly, the rat portal vein (NK-3), the rabbit pulmonary artery (NK-2), the dog carotid artery, and the rabbit jugular vein (NK-1)], are presented in TABLE 6.

For comparison, data obtained with NKA(4–10) and NKB(4–10) have also been shown. The two natural fragments act as full agonists in the four preparations (see pD$_2$ values in TABLE 6): their activities are very similar because the two compounds differ only by the residue in position 5, which is Ser in NKA(4–10) and Phe in NKB(4–10). Replacement of Gly^8 by βAla and of Val^7 by an aromatic residue—Tyr, Phe, MePhe, or Trp—leads to fairly active NK-3 antagonists. In fact, a pA$_2$ value of 6.93 is observed with [Tyr^7,βAla^8]NKA(4–10) on the NK-3 system (RPV), whereas the compound is an agonist on the other three tissues and, when applied at high concentrations, also on the RPV. Elimination of the Met in position 10 as in [Tyr^7,βAla^8]NKA(4–9) leads to a marked decrease in all activities. When Phe is used instead of Tyr in position 7 as in [Phe^7,βAla^8]NKA(4–10), the compound maintains a good antagonist affinity (pA$_2$ = 6.92) and loses some of its agonistic effect on the RPV. However, [Phe^7,βAla^8]NKA(4–10) is not selective because it also acts as an antagonist on the RPA (NK-2) with a pA$_2$ of 7.04. Replacement of Val^7 with Trp^7 leads to an increase of antagonist affinity on the RPV (pA$_2$ value of 7.46) and to a weak agonistic effect on the other preparations. [Trp^7,βAla^8]NKA(4–10) also stimulates the RPV, but only at concentrations 50 times or higher than those needed for antagonism.

Some analogues of [βAla^8]NKB(4–10) were also prepared and the results are shown in TABLE 6. Both [Tyr^7,βAla^8]NKB(4–10) and [MePhe^7,βAla^8]NKB(4–10) act as antagonists on the RPV with a residual agonistic activity and they act as full

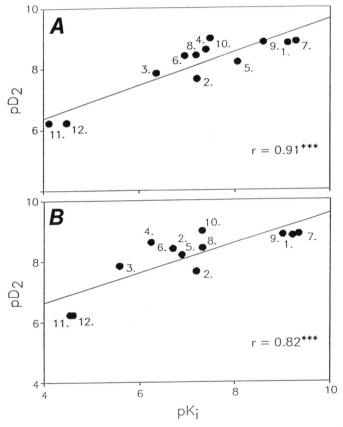

FIGURE 3. Log-log plot of the biological activities and binding affinities of neurokinins and analogues on the rabbit jugular vein and rat brain membranes. Key: (1) SP, (2) NKA, (3) NKB, (4) SP(4–11), (5) SP(5–11), (6) SP(6–11), (7) PHY, (8) ELE, (9) [Sar^9,Met(O$_2$)^{11}]SP, (10) Ac-[Arg^6,Sar^9,Met(O$_2$)^{11}]SP(6–11), (11) [βAla^8]NKA(4–10), and (12) [MePhe^7]NKB. Ordinate: −Log of the molar concentration of peptide at the ED$_{50}$ (pD$_2$) in the biological assay. Abscissa: −Log of K_i (pK_i) of peptides evaluated by their ability to inhibit ^{125}I-Bolton-Hunter-SP (in *A*) or ^{125}I-Bolton-Hunter-[Sar^9,Met(O$_2$)^{11}]SP (in *B*) from rat brain membranes. ***: p < 0.001.

TABLE 6. Pharmacological Evaluation of Putative NK-3 Receptor Antagonists on Four Isolated Vessels[a]

	RPV			RPA			DCA		RJV		
	pA_2	pD_2	α^E	pA_2	pD_2	α^E	pA_2	pD_2	pA_2	pD_2	α^E
NKA(4–10)	In.	6.79	1.0	In.	8.52	1.0	In.	8.62	In.	7.40	0.9
NKB(4–10)	In.	6.67	1.0	In.	7.95	1.0	In.	8.70	In.	6.07	0.8
[Tyr⁷,βAla⁸]NKA(4–10)	6.93	5.66	1.0	In.	6.75	1.0	In.	7.12	In.	6.70	0.9
[Tyr⁷,βAla⁸]NKA(4–9)	5.46	4.89	0.4	5.85	4.90	0.6	In.	6.50	In.	6.28	0.8
[Phe⁷,βAla⁸]NKA(4–10)	6.92	ND	0.5	7.04	6.29	1.0	In.	7.25	In.	6.99	1.1
[Trp⁷,βAla⁸]NKA(4–10)	7.46	5.73	1.0	In.	6.31	1.0	In.	6.50	In.	6.86	0.5
[Tyr⁷,βAla⁸]NKB(4–10)	6.96	5.41	0.6	In.	5.40	0.8	In.	7.35	In.	7.75	0.8
[MePhe⁷,βAla⁸]NKB(4–10)	7.26	5.41	0.5	In.	5.97	1.1	In.	6.18	In.	6.24	0.7

[a] Terms are defined in the footnote to TABLE 2 and in the text; pA_2: −log of the concentration of antagonist that reduces the effect of a double dose of agonist to that of a single one; In. = inactive; ND = not determined.

agonists on the other three preparations. The antagonist affinity of [MePhe⁷,βAla⁸]NKB(4–10) is fairly good (pA_2 value of 7.26) and the compound is less active as an agonist than [Trp⁷,βAla⁸]NKA(4–10) on the RPA, DCA, and RJV. Further studies are needed to improve antagonist affinity, eliminate residual agonistic effects, and improve selectivity for the NK-3 receptor.

CONCLUSIONS

The neurokinins exert a wide variety of central and peripheral effects including transmission of pain, vasodilation, plasma extravasation, and contraction of smooth muscle cells of the cardiovascular (arteries, veins), pulmonary, urinary, and gastrointestinal systems. The neurokinins act on three receptors, NK-1, NK-2, and NK-3. Each receptor has been characterized pharmacologically on isolated vascular smooth muscle preparations by the use of neurokinins, tachykinins, and fragments. The dog carotid artery, the rabbit jugular vein, and the rabbit vena cava have been found to contain only receptors of the NK-1 type. The responses of both rabbit veins to neurokinins are direct and result in contractions elicited by the activation of receptors that may be localized on smooth muscle cells. The relaxation of the dog carotid artery in response to neurokinins is indirect because the NK-1 receptor is present on the endothelium, where it mediates the release of the endothelium-derived relaxing factor. The rabbit pulmonary artery and the rat portal vein have, respectively, NK-2 and NK-3 receptor type.

Because the naturally occurring neurokinins were not selective for one receptor only, selective agonists for a single receptor type were developed and tested on the isolated organ preparations. Selective agonists also permitted the characterization of neurokinin receptors on human tissues. The human bronchus, urinary bladder, and ileum were found to contain only NK-2 receptors.

Biochemical studies with radiolabeled NK-1 selective agonists suggest that the NK-1 binding site in the central nervous system and in peripheral organs is the same entity. In addition, a positive correlation was found between the binding affinities and the biological activities of neurokinins and their analogues when measured on the NK-1 receptor on the rat brain and rabbit jugular vein. These findings support the interpretation that the biological effects of substance P are the result of the coupling of the peptide with the NK-1 receptor type.

NK-3 receptor antagonists were developed by substituting the Val^7 of [βAla^8]NKA(4–10) or of [βAla^8]NKB(4–10) with aromatic amino acids (Phe, Me-Phe, Tyr, or Trp). [$Trp^7,\beta Ala^8$]NKA(4–10) and [$MePhe^7,\beta Ala^8$]NKB(4–10) were found to exert fairly good antagonist activities on the NK-3 system of the rat portal vein (pA_2 values > 7.0) and weak agonistic activities on NK-1 and NK-2 preparations.

ACKNOWLEDGMENTS

We gratefully acknowledge the technical assistance of M. Battistini, M. Boussougou, and R. Laprise.

REFERENCES

1. COUTURE, R., K. YASHPAL, J. L. HENRY, E. ESCHER & D. REGOLI. 1985. Characterization of spinal actions of four substance P analogues. Eur. J. Pharmacol. **110:** 63–69.
2. REGOLI, D., G. DRAPEAU, S. DION & P. D'ORLÉANS-JUSTE. 1989. Receptors for substance P and neurokinins. Pharmacology **38:** 1–15.
3. COUTURE, R. & D. REGOLI. 1982. Mini-review: smooth muscle pharmacology of substance P. Pharmacology **24:** 1–25.
4. LUNDBERG, J. M. & T. HÖKFELT. 1983. Coexistence of peptides and classical neurotransmitters. Trends Neurosci. **6:** 325–333.
5. LIANG, T. & M. A. CASCIERI. 1981. Substance P receptor on parotid cell membranes. J. Neurosci. **1:** 1133–1141.
6. HENRY, J. L. 1987. Discussion of nomenclature for tachykinins and tachykinin receptors. *In* Substance P and Neurokinins. J. L. Henry, R. Couture, A. C. Cuello, G. Pelletier, R. Quirion & D. Regoli, Eds.: 17–18. Springer-Verlag. New York/Berlin.
7. REGOLI, D., G. DRAPEAU, S. DION & P. D'ORLÉANS-JUSTE. 1987. Pharmacological receptors for substance P and neurokinins. Life Sci. **40:** 109–117.
8. BUCK, S. H., E. BURCHER, C. W. SHULTS, W. LOVENBERG & T. L. O'DONOHUE. 1984. Novel pharmacology of substance K binding sites: a third type of neurokinin receptor. Science **226:** 987–989.
9. QUIRION, R. & T-V. DAM. 1985. Multiple tachykinin receptors in guinea pig brain: high density of substance K binding sites in the substantia nigra. Neuropeptides **6:** 191–204.
10. NANTEL, F., N. ROUISSI, N-E. RHALEB, S. DION, G. DRAPEAU & D. REGOLI. 1990. The rabbit jugular vein is a contractile NK-1 monoreceptor system. Eur. J. Pharmacol. **179:** 457–462.
11. D'ORLÉANS-JUSTE, P., S. DION, J. MIZRAHI & D. REGOLI. 1985. Effects of peptides and nonpeptides on isolated arterial smooth muscles: role of endothelium. Eur. J. Pharmacol. **114:** 9–21.
12. D'ORLÉANS-JUSTE, P., S. DION, G. DRAPEAU & D. REGOLI. 1986. Different receptors are involved in the endothelium mediated relaxation and the smooth muscle contraction of the rabbit pulmonary artery in response to substance P and related neurokinins. Eur. J. Pharmacol. **125:** 37–44.
13. MASTRANGELO, D., H. J. MATHISON, H. J. HUGGEL, S. DION, P. D'ORLÉANS-JUSTE, N-E. RHALEB, G. DRAPEAU, P. ROVERO & D. REGOLI. 1986. The rat isolated portal vein: a preparation sensitive to neurokinins, particularly neurokinin B. Eur. J. Pharmacol. **134:** 321–326.
14. PALMER, R. M. J., A. G. FERRIGE & S. MONCADA. 1987. Nitric oxide release accounts for the biological activity of endothelium-derived relaxing factor. Nature **327:** 524–526.

15. ARIENS, E. J., J. M. VAN ROSSUM & A. M. SIMONIS. 1957. Intrinsic activity and drug interactions. Pharmacol. Rev. **9:** 218–236.
16. WATSON, S. P., B. E. B. SANDBERG, M. R. HANLEY & L. L. IVERSEN. 1983. Tissue selectivity of substance P alkyl esters: suggesting multiple receptors. Eur. J. Pharmacol. **87:** 77–84.
17. DRAPEAU, G., P. D'ORLÉANS-JUSTE, S. DION, N-E. RHALEB, N. ROUISSI & D. REGOLI. 1987. Selective agonists for substance P and neurokinins. Neuropeptides **10:** 43–54.
18. DRAPEAU, G., S. DION, P. D'ORLÉANS-JUSTE, N-E. RHALEB & D. REGOLI. 1988. Development of selective agonists for substance P and neurokinin receptors. *In* Peptides—Chemistry and Biology. Proceedings of the Tenth American Peptide Symposium. G. R. Marshall, Ed.: 497–499.
19. DEVILLIER, P., G. DRAPEAU, M. RENOUX & D. REGOLI. 1989. Role of the N-terminal arginine in the histamine-releasing activity of substance P, bradykinin, and related peptides. Eur. J. Pharmacol. **168:** 53–60.
20. ROVERO, P., V. PESTELLINI, N-E. RHALEB, S. DION, N. ROUISSI, C. TOUSIGNANT, S. TÉLÉMAQUE, G. DRAPEAU & D. REGOLI. 1989. Structure-activity studies of neurokinin A. Neuropeptides **13:** 263–270.
21. SANDBERG, B. E. B., C. M. LEE, M. R. HANLEY & L. L. IVERSEN. 1981. Synthesis and biological properties of enzyme-resistant analogues of substance P. Eur. J. Biochem. **114:** 329–337.
22. DRAPEAU, G., P. D'ORLÉANS-JUSTE, S. DION, N-E. RHALEB & D. REGOLI. 1987. Specific agonists for neurokinin B receptors. Eur. J. Pharmacol. **136:** 401–403.
23. LAUFER, R., C. GILON, M. CHOREV & Z. SELINGER. 1986. Characterization of a neurokinin B receptor site in the rat brain using a highly selective radioligand. J. Biol. Chem. **261:** 10257–10263.
24. DION, S., N. ROUISSI, F. NANTEL, G. DRAPEAU, D. REGOLI, E. NALINE & C. ADVENIER. 1990. Receptors for neurokinins in human bronchus and urinary bladder are of the NK-2 type. Eur. J. Pharmacol. **178:** 215–219.
25. MAGGI, C. A., R. PATACCHINI, P. SANTICIOLI, S. GIULIANI, D. TURINI, G. BARBANTI, P. BENEFORTI, D. MISURI & A. MELI. 1989. Human isolated small intestine: motor responses of the longitudinal muscle to field stimulation and exogenous neuropeptides. Naunyn-Schmiedeberg's Arch. Pharmacol. **339:** 415–423.
26. LAUFER, R., U. WORMSER, Z. Y. FRIEDMAN, C. GILON, M. CHOREV & Z. SELINGER. 1985. Neurokinin B is a preferred agonist for a neuronal substance P receptor and its action is antagonized by enkephalin. Proc. Natl. Acad. Sci. U.S.A. **82:** 7444–7448.
27. ERSPAMER, V. & G. FACONIERI-ERSPAMER. 1962. Pharmacological actions of eledoisin on extravascular smooth muscle. Br. J. Pharmacol. **19:** 337–354.
28. REGOLI, D., G. DRAPEAU, S. DION & R. COUTURE. 1988. New selective agonists for neurokinin receptors: pharmacological tools for receptor characterization. Trends Pharmacol. Sci. **9:** 290–295.
29. CASCIERI, M. A. & T. LIANG. 1983. Characterization of substance P receptor in rat brain cortex membranes and the inhibition of radioligand binding by guanine nucleotides. J. Biol. Chem. **258:** 5158–5164.
30. QUIRION, R. & T-V. DAM. 1986. Ontogeny of substance P receptor binding sites in rat brain. J. Neurosci. **6:** 131–133.
31. VAUGHT, J. L., J. L. SCOTT, D. WRIGHT & H. JACOBY. 1987. [D-Pro^2,D-Trp^{6,8},Nle^{10}]-Neurokinin B: pharmacological profile of a novel neurokinin antagonist. *In* Substance P and Neurokinins. J. L. Henry, R. Couture, A. C. Cuello, G. Pelletier, R. Quirion & D. Regoli, Eds.: 122–124. Springer-Verlag. New York/Berlin.
32. DRAPEAU, G., N. ROUISSI, F. NANTEL, N-E. RHALEB, C. TOUSIGNANT & D. REGOLI. 1991. Antagonists for the neurokinin NK-3 receptor evaluated in selective monoreceptor systems. Regulat. Peptides. In press.

NK-2 Receptor Agonists and Antagonists

CARLO ALBERTO MAGGI,[a] RICCARDO PATACCHINI,[a]
MARA ASTOLFI,[b] PAOLO ROVERO,[c]
SANDRO GIULIANI,[a] AND ANTONIO GIACHETTI[a]

[a] *Department of Pharmacology*
Research Laboratories
A. Menarini Pharmaceuticals
50131 Florence, Italy

[b] *Department of Pharmacology*
Menarini Sud
Pomezia, Rome, Italy

[c] *Department of Chemistry*
Peptide Synthesis Laboratory
A. Menarini Pharmaceuticals
50131 Florence, Italy

INTRODUCTION

Tachykinins are a family of peptides that share the common C-terminal sequence, Phe-X-Gly-Leu-Met-NH$_2$. In mammals, at least three different tachykinins, namely, substance P (SP), neurokinin A (NKA), and neurokinin B (NKB), are the most likely candidates for a transmitter role in the central and peripheral nervous system (see references 1 and 2 for reviews). To date, the available evidence indicates that three distinct tachykinin receptors mediate the biological effects of these peptides in mammalian tissues.[3-6]

These receptors are now termed NK-1, NK-2, and NK-3 and the C-terminal sequence of the tachykinins is critical for their activation. Natural tachykinins possess a different affinity for these three receptors, with SP, NKA, and NKB being more potent at NK-1, NK-2, and NK-3 sites, respectively. However, naturally occurring tachykinins at high concentrations stimulate equally well all the three receptors recognized by their common C-terminal sequence, thus limiting their usefulness as tools to identify the various receptors responsible for their biological effects. In the past few years, we became interested in developing selective agonists and antagonists for the NK-2 tachykinin receptor because of its role in mediating the spasmogenic effect of tachykinins on human smooth muscles. A comparison of the receptors responsible for the contractile response to tachykinins in rat, guinea pig, or human isolated smooth muscles indicates that, in many animal tissues, at least two or, in some instances, even three of the known tachykinin receptors are involved in the spasmogenic response to these peptides, whereas NK-2 receptors are dominant in most human tissues (TABLE 1).[7-11]

[βALA⁸]-NKA(4–10) AS A SELECTIVE NK-2 AGONIST

In searching for NK-2 receptor selective ligands, we used the C-terminal heptapeptide of neurokinin A, NKA(4–10), as a backbone on which amino acid substitutions

TABLE 1. Tachykinin Receptors Mediating Smooth Muscle Contraction in Various Mammalian Species

	NK-1	NK-2	NK-3	Reference
Rat				
urinary bladder	+	+		7
small intestine	+	+	+	7
Guinea pig				
urinary bladder	+	+		7
ileum	+	+	+	7
airways	+	+		7
Human				
urinary bladder		+		8
urethra		+		unpublished results
ileum (longitudinal)		+		9
ileum (circular)	+	+		10
bronchi		+		11

were made (see TABLE 2 for the primary structures of the peptides presented in this study). NKA(4–10) was selected because it maintains full agonist activity and strong affinity for NK-2 receptors, whereas it is less potent than NKA at NK-1 or NK-3 receptors.[4] Thus, NKA(4–10) is a slightly more selective NK-2 agonist than NKA. Methylation of an individual peptide bond, which introduces a limited conformational constraint, has been successfully used to develop the selective agonist at the NK-3 receptor.[12] This approach, when applied to NKA(4–10), was unsuccessful.[13] In contrast, introduction of βAla, which confers conformational freedom to the peptide backbone, favorably affected selectivity. In particular, replacement of Gly in position 8 with βAla yielded a peptide endowed with a remarkable selectivity for NK-2 receptors.[14] An additional advantage of [βAla⁸]-NKA(4–10) is represented by its resistance to degradation by endopeptidase 24.11,[15] possibly originating from the fact that the Gly 8–Leu 9 bond is a major site of cleavage for the natural tachykinins.

NK-2 SELECTIVE ANTAGONISTS

The first generation of SP antagonists, developed at the beginning of the 1980s, was obtained by replacing certain amino acids in the SP sequence with one or more D-Trp residues. These antagonists suffered from many drawbacks[16] including a poor ability to discriminate between NK-1 and NK-2 receptors.[17] Since 1988, a number of

TABLE 2. Amino Acid Sequences of Peptides Used in This Study

NKA	H-His-Lys-Thr-Asp-Ser-Phe-Val-Gly-Leu-Met-NH₂
NKA(4–10)	H-Asp-Ser-Phe-Val-Gly-Leu-Met-NH₂
[βAla⁸]-NKA(4–10)	H-Asp-Ser-Phe-Val-βAla-Leu-Met-NH₂
MEN 10,207	H-Asp-Tyr-DTrp-Val-DTrp-DTrp-Arg-NH₂
MEN 10,282	H-Asp-Tyr-DTrp-Val-DTrp-Trp-Arg-NH₂
L659,877	cyclo(Leu-Met-Gln-Trp-Phe-Gly)
R 396	Ac-Leu-Asp-Gln-Trp-Phe-Gly-NH₂
MDL 28,564	H-Asp-Ser-Phe-Val-Gly-Leuψ(CH₂NH)Leu-NH₂

TABLE 3.　pA$_2$ Values of Three Tachykinin Antagonists in Selected Bioassays for NK-1, NK-2, and NK-3 Receptors[a]

	NK-1 Receptor		NK-2 Receptor		NK-3 Receptor
Antagonist	DCA	GPI	RPA	RVD	RPV
MEN 10,207	5.2 ± 0.4	5.5 ± 0.5	7.9 ± 0.2	6.8 ± 0.1	4.9 ± 0.3
L659,877	NT	5.6 ± 0.6	6.9 ± 0.4	7.9 ± 0.2	5.4 ± 0.3
R 396	<5	<5	5.4 ± 0.1	6.2 ± 0.2	<5

[a]Terms: DCA = dog carotid artery (SP as agonist); GPI = guinea pig ileum (atropine and chlorpheniramine in the bath, SP methyl ester as agonist); RPA = rabbit pulmonary artery (endothelium-denuded, NKA as agonist); RVD = rat vas deferens (NKA as agonist); RPV = rat portal vein (NKB as agonist). Each value is the mean ± SE of at least four determinations; NT = not tested. Data obtained for MEN 10,207 and R 396 in the DCA, RPA, and RPV are from reference 24.

receptor selective antagonists have been synthesized in several laboratories using different approaches. Our approach, along the lines described herein, was to design selective NK-2 receptor antagonists on the backbone of the relatively selective NK-2 ligand, NKA(4–10). A first series of low-affinity antagonists was obtained by introduction of D-Trp in positions 6 and 8.[18] Both a further increase in affinity and a marked increase in selectivity for NK-2 as compared to NK-1 or NK-3 receptors were achieved by insertion of an additional D-Trp in position 9 and by insertion of Tyr and Arg in positions 5 and 10, respectively.[19] The resultant compound, [Tyr^5,D-Trp^{6,8,9},Arg^{10}]-NKA(4–10) (MEN 10,207, TABLE 2), proved to be a potent and selective NK-2 antagonist,[19] although a residual partial agonist activity (about 30% of that of NKA) was still observed at 3 μM or higher concentrations (unpublished observations).

The data in TABLE 3 show the spectrum of activity of MEN 10,207 at NK-1, NK-2, or NK-3 receptors as compared to that of two other NK-2 selective antagonists, namely, the cyclic hexapeptide L659,877[20] and R 396, which is a linear hexapeptide developed by the group of Regoli[21] on the backbone of L659,877 by replacing the Met with Asp (TABLE 2). As can be noted, the three antagonists were invariably more potent in the two classical bioassays for the NK-2 receptors, that is, the endothelium-denuded rabbit pulmonary artery (RPA) and the rat vas deferens (RVD), than in bioassays for the NK-1 or NK-3 receptors. However, quantitative differences in the apparent affinities were observed for each peptide between the RPA and the RVD. As such, these differences might have several explanations, including a different penetration rate of the antagonists in different tissues or a different susceptibility to local metabolism by peptidases. Additional studies, though, described in the next section indicate that at least part of the quantitative differences in antagonist potency observed on different NK-2 receptor bioassays are due to the existence of NK-2 receptor subtypes.

NK-2 RECEPTOR SUBTYPES

As mentioned earlier, the structure-activity studies leading to the development of MEN 10,207 were based on the RPA as a bioassay for NK-2 receptors.[4] Owing to the fact that NK-2 receptors are present in the human airways[11] and to the possible use of tachykinin antagonists to prevent bronchoconstriction in humans, we also developed a new preparation, the hamster isolated trachea (HT), for studying the effect of tachykinin-related peptides on an airway smooth muscle containing only NK-2 receptors.[22] Experiments with natural tachykinins and synthetic receptor-selective tachykinin agonists indicated that the two preparations (RPA and HT) have several common characteristics. In both tissues, the contractile response to tachykinins is (a) mediated chiefly, if not exclusively, by NK-2 receptors; (b) unaffected by the addition of a mixture of peptidase inhibitors (thiorphan, captopril, and bestatin); and (c) unchanged by adrenergic (RPA) or cholinergic (HT) blockers, antihistaminics, or inhibitors of prostanoid synthesis;[23,24] this latter point strongly suggests that, in both tissues, tachykinins induce contraction by directly stimulating smooth muscle cells.

This picture of close symmetry between RPA and HT was dramatically broken when the NK-2 selective antagonists were introduced (see reference 24 and the present findings for L659,877). The data in TABLE 4 show the activity of MEN 10,207, R 396, and L659,877 as antagonists in the RPA and HT under a variety of experimental conditions. The three peptides behaved as competitive antagonists towards NKA in both preparations and the slope of the Schild's plot of each peptide in the two tissues was not significantly different from unity. However, a marked difference in affinity was observed. MEN 10,207 was about 100 times more potent in the RPA than in the HT and the reverse was found for the linear hexapeptide (TABLE 3, data from reference 24). A certain difference was also evident for L659,877, which resulted in 10–30 times more potency in the HT than in the RPA.

Hence, although there is no reason to believe that NK-2 receptors in the RPA are different from those present in the HT on the basis of the activity of natural tachykinins and synthetic receptor-selective agonists,[23,24] there are very important differences in the affinity of the antagonists with the following rank order of potency: MEN 10,207 > L659,877 > R 396 for the RPA and L659,877 ≃ R 396 ≫ MEN 10,207 for the HT. Further experiments were designed to assess the bases for these striking differences. First, neither peptide affected the response to noradrenaline (in the RPA) or carbachol (in the HT), thus ruling out unspecific smooth muscle relaxant properties. Moreover, no change in affinity was found for each individual antagonist when the contact time was extended from 15 to 90 min (data not shown),

TABLE 4. pA_2 Values and 95% CL of Three Tachykinin Antagonists in the Rabbit Pulmonary Artery (RPA) or in Hamster Trachea (HT) against NKA (with or without Peptidase Inhibitors) or against the NK-2 Selective Agonist $[\beta Ala^8]$-NKA(4–10)[a]

	RPA			HT		
	Agonist			Agonist		
Antagonist	NKA	NKA*	$[\beta Ala^8]$-NKA(4–10)	NKA	NKA*	$[\beta Ala^8]$-NKA(4–10)
MEN 10,207	7.89	7.60	7.74	5.95	5.75	6.15
	(7.71–8.06)	(7.45–7.95)	(7.62–8.11)	(5.72–6.18)	(5.50–6.04)	(5.75–6.54)
L659,877	6.92	6.51	6.78	8.05	7.95	8.24
	(6.72–7.15)	(6.22–6.80)	(6.50–7.10)	(7.79–8.31)	(7.74–8.17)	(7.98–8.50)
R 396	5.42	5.47	5.41	7.63	7.53	7.46
	(5.31–5.52)	(5.39–5.60)	(5.28–5.59)	(7.40–7.85)	(7.34–7.77)	(7.27–7.67)

[a]Each pA_2 value is obtained from 6–9 experiments by means of the constrained plot method as described by Tallarida *et al.* (1979). An asterisk indicates values obtained in the presence of a mixture of peptidase inhibitors (1 μM thiorphan, 1 μM captopril, 1 μM bestatin). Data for MEN 10,207 and R 396 are from reference 24.

TABLE 5. pA_2 Values of MEN 10,207 and MEN 10,282 in Various Bioassays for NK-1, NK-2, and NK-3 Receptors[a]

	NK-1 Receptor	NK-2 Receptor		NK-3 Receptor
Antagonist	GPI	RPA	HT	RPV
MEN 10,207	5.5 ± 0.5	7.9 ± 0.2	5.9 ± 0.2	4.9 ± 0.3
MEN 10,282	5.5 ± 0.3	6.6 ± 0.3	6.3 ± 0.3	na

[a]Terms: GPI = guinea pig ileum (atropine and chlorpheniramine in the bath, SP methyl ester as agonist); RPA = rabbit pulmonary artery (endothelium-denuded, NKA as agonist); HT = hamster trachea (NKA as agonist); RPV = rat portal vein (NKB as agonist). Each value is the mean ± SE of at least four determinations; na = inactive up to 10 μM.

when the experiments were repeated in the presence of peptidase inhibitors, nor when the selective NK-2 agonist, [βAla^8]-NKA(4–10), was used instead of NKA[24] (TABLE 4).

Therefore, neither local metabolism by tissue peptidases nor a different penetration rate of the peptides in the two tissues may account for the large differences in affinity observed with the three NK-2 receptor antagonists. The closeness of the pA_2 values obtained in each preparation and for each antagonist when using NKA or [βAla^8]-NKA(4–10) as an agonist indicates that the estimated affinities are agonist-independent and confirms that the differences observed involve recognition of different NK-2 receptors by the antagonists.

We interpreted[24] these data as pharmacological evidence for the existence of NK-2 receptor subtypes indistinguishable by the currently available generation of tachykinin agonists, but having sufficient structural differences to be recognized with very different affinity by certain antagonists. R 396 and L659,877 are clearly more potent in the HT than in the RPA, but the ability to discriminate between NK-2 receptors in the RPA and HT is more favorable for the linear peptide. It is worth noting that, apart from cyclization, replacement of Met with Asp is the only structural difference between these two peptides (TABLE 2). The data in TABLE 5 also indicate that the ability of MEN 10,207 to discriminate between NK-2 receptors in the RPA and HT depends upon stringent structural requirements. In fact, an analogue of MEN 10,207, in which the D-Trp in position 9 was replaced by Trp (MEN 10,282), retains NK-2 selective antagonist properties, but no longer discriminates between the two preparations.

FURTHER EVIDENCE FOR THE EXISTENCE OF NK-2 RECEPTOR SUBTYPES

While our work on NK-2 antagonists was in progress, we became aware that other evidence for the existence of NK-2 receptor subtypes had been obtained by Buck and co-workers (see their presentation in this volume). Their evidence was based on studies with a new ligand, namely, the pseudopeptide MDL 28,564 ([Leu^{9}ψ(CH$_2$NH)Leu^{10}]-NKA(4–10)), which is highly selective for NK-2 receptors.[25] In view of this, it became of the utmost interest to test the activity of this compound in the two paradigms (RPA and HT) that we had identified as bearing different NK-2 receptor subtypes.

The data in TABLE 6 show that MDL 28,564 acts as a full agonist in the RPA, where it produced a contraction that amounted to about 90% of the maximal response to NKA. Additional experiments have shown that the agonist effect of MDL 28,564 in the RPA is competitively antagonized by MEN 10,207 with an affinity comparable to that exerted toward NKA or [βAla⁸]-NKA(4–10) (unpublished data). This latter finding indicates that, in the RPA, MDL 28,564 stimulates the same receptor population activated by the naturally occurring peptide and by the selective NK-2 agonist.

In sharp contrast with the results in the RPA, very little, if any, agonist activity was observed in the HT: only a few preparations responded with a small (<10% of the NKA maximum), nonconcentration-dependent contraction at a high concentration (10 μM). However, in the HT, MDL 28,564 antagonized competitively (slope of Schild's plot, −0.89 ± 0.2) the response to NKA (TABLE 6). It is to be noted that MDL 28,564 displays similar affinities, in the micromolar range, for NK-2 receptors when acting as a full agonist (e.g., RPA: pD_2 of 6.89) or as a competitive antagonist (e.g., HT: pA_2 of 6.21). Therefore, the main difference in the action of MDL 28,564 at NK-2 receptors present in these two preparations involves its inability to exert an agonist effect in the HT in spite of a significant interaction of the peptide with the receptors, as documented by its competitive antagonist activity. A similar behavior of MDL 28,564 has been observed by Buck and co-workers (this volume) in other tissues endowed with NK-2 receptors: thus, the pseudopeptide acts as a full agonist in the guinea pig trachea, whereas it acts as an antagonist in the hamster urinary bladder. Therefore, the peculiar pattern of action of this highly selective NK-2 receptor ligand has been confirmed in different laboratories.

Taken alone, the peculiar behavior of MDL 28,564 might be explained not only by the existence of NK-2 receptor subtypes, but also might involve differences in receptor reserve and/or receptor-effector coupling between different tissues. Studies are in progress to elucidate these points. However, the evidence obtained with competitive antagonists[24] and that obtained with MDL 28,564 converge in indicating the existence of multiple forms of NK-2 receptors.

On these bases, a tentative schematization for NK-2 receptor subtypes can be proposed. A first group, for which the endothelium-denuded RPA is a suitable bioassay, is characterized by the higher affinity for MEN 10,207 relative to R 396 and by the full agonism exerted by MDL 28,564. A second group, for which the HT is a suitable bioassay, presents the converse picture, being characterized by the higher affinity for R 396 (and L659,877) relative to MEN 10,207 and by the competitive

TABLE 6. Comparison of the Activity of NKA, NKA(4–10), and MDL 28,564 in the Rabbit Pulmonary Artery (RPA) and Hamster Trachea (HT)[a]

	RPA		HT		
Peptide	pD_2 (95% CL)	α	pD_2 (95% CL)	α	pA_2 (95% CL)
NKA	8.31 (8.26–8.37)	1	7.62 (7.44–7.77)	1	—
NKA(4–10)	8.52 (8.42–8.66)	1	7.74 (7.64–7.85)	1	—
MDL 28,564	6.89 (6.73–7.14)	0.9	inactive[b]	0	6.21[c] (6.0–6.41)

[a]Each value is the mean ± SE of at least nine determinations.
[b]Inactive up to 30 μM.
[c]Measured using NKA as an agonist.

antagonism exhibited by MDL 28,564. Recent findings from our laboratory indicate that this schematization holds true for at least two other tissues bearing NK-2 receptors, that is, the guinea pig isolated bronchus and the circular muscle of the human ileum (unpublished results). In both cases, MEN 10,207 antagonized competitively the response to NKA or [βAla⁸]-NKA(4–10) and resulted in more potency than R 396. Moreover, in both tissues, MDL 28,564 behaved as a full agonist. Therefore, both tissues appear to contain an NK-2 receptor subtype similar to that found in the RPA.

CONCLUSIONS

In conclusion, replacement of natural amino acids in selected positions on the backbone of NKA(4–10) has allowed for the obtaining of selective NK-2 receptor agonists and antagonists and the latter peptides have been instrumental in delineating a first discrimination between NK-2 receptor subtypes. Further studies are needed to establish the precise molecular basis underlying the differentiation emerging from the use of the new ligands (MEN 10,207, R 396, MDL 28,564), which appear as very promising tools for studying the distribution and function of tachykinin receptors.

ACKNOWLEDGMENTS

We wish to thank D. Regoli (Department of Pharmacology, University of Sherbrooke, Canada) for the kind gift of R 396 and S. H. Buck (Merrell Dow, Cincinnati, Ohio) for the kind gift of MDL 28,564.

REFERENCES

1. MAGGIO, J. E. 1985. Peptides **6:** 237–245.
2. EMSON, P. C., F. J. DIEZ-GUERRA & A. ARAI. 1987. Mammalian tachykinins: neurochemistry and pharmacology. *In* Neuropeptides and Their Peptidases. A. J. Turner, Ed.: 87–106. Ellis Horwood Pub. Chichester, United Kingdom.
3. BUCK, S. H., E. BURCHER, C. W. SHULTS, W. LOVENBERG & T. L. O'DONOHUE. 1984. Science **226:** 987–989.
4. REGOLI, D., G. DRAPEAU, S. DION & P. D'ORLEANS-JUSTE. 1986. Receptors for neurokinins in peripheral organs. *In* Substance P and Neurokinins (Montreal '86, July 10–23, 1986). J. L. Henry, R. Couture, A. C. Cuello, G. Pelletier, R. Quirion & D. Regoli, Eds.: 99–107. Springer-Verlag. New York/Berlin.
5. LAUFER, R., U. WORMSER, Z. FRIEDMAN, C. GILON, M. CHOREV & Z. SELINGER. 1985. Proc. Natl. Acad. Sci. U.S.A. **82:** 7444–7449.
6. LEE, C. M., N. J. CAMPBELL, B. J. WILLIAMS & L. L. IVERSEN. 1986. Eur. J. Pharmacol. **130:** 209–216.
7. DION, S., P. D'ORLEANS-JUSTE, G. DRAPEAU, N-E. RHALEB, N. ROUISSI, C. TOUSIGNANT & D. REGOLI. 1987. Life Sci. **41:** 2269–2278.
8. MAGGI, C. A., P. SANTICIOLI, R. PATACCHINI, M. CELLERINI, D. TURINI, G. BARBANTI, P. BENEFORTI, P. ROVERO & A. MELI. 1988. Eur. J. Pharmacol. **145:** 335–340.
9. MAGGI, C. A., R. PATACCHINI, P. SANTICIOLI, S. GIULIANI, D. TURINI, G. BARBANTI, P. BENEFORTI, D. MISURI & A. MELI. 1989. Naunyn-Schmiedeberg's Arch. Pharmacol. **339:** 415–423.

10. MAGGI, C. A., R. PATACCHINI, P. SANTICIOLI, S. GIULIANI, D. TURINI, G. BARBANTI, A. GIACHETTI & A. MELI. 1990. Naunyn-Schmiedeberg's Arch. Pharmacol. **341**: 256–261.
11. ADVENIER, C., E. NALINE, G. DRAPEAU & D. REGOLI. 1987. Eur. J. Pharmacol. **139**: 133–137.
12. REGOLI, D., G. DRAPEAU, S. DION & R. COUTURE. 1988. Trends Pharmacol. Sci. **9**: 290–295.
13. ROVERO, P., V. PESTELLINI, R. PATACCHINI, P. SANTICIOLI, C. A. MAGGI & A. MELI. 1987. Neuropeptides **10**: 355–359.
14. ROVERO, P., V. PESTELLINI, R. PATACCHINI, S. GIULIANI, P. SANTICIOLI, C. A. MAGGI, A. MELI & A. GIACHETTI. 1989. Peptides **10**: 593–595.
15. PATACCHINI, R., C. A. MAGGI, P. ROVERO, D. REGOLI, G. DRAPEAU & A. MELI. 1989. J. Pharmacol. Exp. Ther. **250**: 678–681.
16. REGOLI, D. 1985. Trends Pharmacol. Sci. **6**: 481–484.
17. BUCK, S. H. & S. A. SHATZER. 1988. Life Sci. **42**: 2701–2708.
18. ROVERO, P., V. PESTELLINI, R. PATACCHINI, S. GIULIANI, C. A. MAGGI, A. MELI & A. GIACHETTI. 1990. Peptides **11**: 619–620.
19. ROVERO, P., V. PESTELLINI, C. A. MAGGI, R. PATACCHINI, D. REGOLI & A. GIACHETTI. 1990. Eur. J. Pharmacol. **175**: 113–115.
20. MCKNIGHT, A. T., J. J. MAGUIRE, A. G. WILLIAMS, A. C. FOSTER, R. TRIDGETT & L. L. IVERSEN. 1988. Regulat. Peptides **22**: 127.
21. DION, S., N. ROUISSI, F. NANTEL, G. DRAPEAU, D. REGOLI, E. NALINE & C. ADVENIER. 1990. Eur. J. Pharmacol. **178**: 215–219.
22. MAGGI, C. A., R. PATACCHINI, P. ROVERO & A. MELI. 1989. Eur. J. Pharmacol. **166**: 435–440.
23. D'ORLEANS-JUSTE, P., S. DION, G. DRAPEAU & D. REGOLI. 1986. Eur. J. Pharmacol. **125**: 37–44.
24. MAGGI, C. A., R. PATACCHINI, S. GIULIANI, P. ROVERO, S. DION, D. REGOLI, A. GIACHETTI & A. MELI. 1990. Br. J. Pharmacol. **100**: 588–592.
25. HARBESON, S. L., S. H. BUCK, C. F. HASSMANN III & S. A. SHATZER. 1990. Synthesis and biological activity of [ψ(CH$_2$NH)] analogs of neurokinin A (4–10). *In* Peptides: Chemistry, Structure, and Biology. J. E. Rivier & G. R. Marshall, Eds.: 180–181. ESCOM. Leiden, the Netherlands.

PART IV

Tachykinins and Related Peptides in the Substantia Nigra and Neostriatum[a]

T. HÖKFELT,[b] M. REID,[c] M. HERRERA-MARSCHITZ,[c]
U. UNGERSTEDT,[c] L. TERENIUS,[d] R. HÅKANSON,[e]
D. M. FENG,[f] AND K. FOLKERS[f]

[b]Department of Histology and Neurobiology
[c]Department of Pharmacology
[d]Drug Dependence Research
Karolinska Institute
S-104 01 Stockholm, Sweden

[e]Department of Pharmacology
Lund University
Lund, Sweden

[f]Institute for Biomedical Research
University of Texas
Austin, Texas 78712

INTRODUCTION

Substance P, discovered by von Euler and Gaddum[1] and chemically characterized years later by Leeman and collaborators,[2] was initially found to be present in very high concentrations in the basal ganglia by Pernow,[3] with particularly high concentrations in the substantia nigra, as first shown by Lembeck and Starke.[4] Subsequent radioimmunoassay and immunohistochemical studies confirmed the high concentrations of this peptide in these areas, especially in the substantia nigra.[5,6] Furthermore, a close morphological interaction between substance P nerve endings and dopamine-containing cell bodies could be directly demonstrated in the substantia nigra of the rat.[7] Using lesion techniques, it could be established that an important component of substance P neurons in the basal ganglia was confined to a striatonigral pathway.[8-11]

During the last years, we have been interested in understanding in some more detail how substance P and other peptides are involved in basal ganglia function and this work has been presented in two dissertations (references 12 and 13). This work focuses not only on substance P and its relation to dopamine neurons, but also includes GABA, dynorphin, and a substance P–related peptide, gastrin-releasing peptide [GRP(1–27)]. In addition, it involves the use of selective tachykinin antagonists. The functional analysis has been done mainly with two experimental models, based on the rotational behavior and the *in vivo* microdialysis techniques, both developed by Ungerstedt and collaborators.[14,15] The early part of this work was reported at the Substance P Symposium in Montreal.[16] In the present article, we would like to summarize the results obtained with *in vivo* microdialysis, where the effects of nigral stimulations with several peptides and with some drugs on striatal dopamine release have been studied.[13]

[a]This work was supported by the Swedish MRC (Grant Nos. 04X-2887, 14X-8669, and 21P-8154) and by the National Institute of Mental Health (Grant No. MH-43230-02).

192

INTRANIGRAL REGULATION OF STRIATAL DOPAMINE RELEASE

As shown in TABLE 1, various transmitters/peptides induce changes in striatal dopamine release after being injected into the ipsilateral substantia nigra, pars reticulata. Tachykinins induced a dose-dependent increase, whereas GABA, dynorphin A, and also GRP(1–27) induced a dose-dependent decrease in striatal dopamine release. These results suggest that GABA, dynorphin A, and perhaps also GRP(1–27) represent inhibitory components, whereas substance P and neurokinin A represent excitatory components of a striatonigral feedback loop regulating the

TABLE 1. Modulation of Striatal Dopamine Release[a] by Nigral Stimulation with Putative Neurotransmitter/Neuromodulator Substances

| Substances | | Maximum Effect[c] |
Doses (nmol/0.2 μL)[b]	N	(%)
Saline (0.2 μL)	9	96 ± 10
Substance P		
0.00007	4	88 ± 2
0.0007	4	123 ± 10*
0.007	8	153 ± 17**
0.07	4	139 ± 23*
0.7	5	120 ± 7*
7.0	4	42 ± 11**
Neurokinin A		
0.009	4	113 ± 3
0.09	5	138 ± 4**
0.9	5	147 ± 10*
9.0	4	135 ± 5*
GRP(1–27)		
0.005	4	95 ± 3
0.05	4	75 ± 2*
0.5	4	67 ± 8*
GABA		
10	4	86 ± 5
100	4	83 ± 3*
300	4	64 ± 9**
Dynorphin A		
0.005	4	90 ± 3
0.05	4	76 ± 6*
0.5	4	64 ± 6**

[a]Striatal dopamine release was monitored by an HPLC-EC assay of 20-min perfusate samples collected with a 4-mm microdialysis probe implanted into the corpus of the striatum. Data summarized from references 13 and 20 and from Herrera-Marshitz *et al.* (in preparation).

[b]Substances were injected into the ipsilateral substantia nigra, pars reticulata, in a 0.2-μL volume.

[c]Maximum change (expressed as the means ± SEM of the percentage of the level detected at the period when the injection cannula was implanted, previous to the drug injection period) detected among six samples collected after the injection of the corresponding dose: (*) $P < 0.05$; (**) $P < 0.01$.

activity of the nigrostriatal dopamine pathway. Furthermore, it was found that the dose-response curve of the substance P effect was biphasic, whereas that of neurokinin A was monophasic, suggesting therefore different mechanisms of action for these two tachykinins.[13,17]

We have recently reported evidence showing that the biphasic dose-response curve observed after substance P injection is due to the formation of substance P fragments that may modulate the action of the complete peptide. Indeed, the N-terminal fragment, substance P(1–7), is formed in significant amounts in the substantia nigra of rats, and the nigral levels of substance P(1–7) increase in parallel with those of substance P after a single injection of a high dose of this peptide into the substantia nigra, pars reticulata.[18] We have also found that substance P(1–7), but not the C-terminal fragment, substance P(6–11), blocked the effects produced by intranigral substance P.[18,19] Furthermore, substance P(1–7) could not modify the stimulation of striatal dopamine release produced by intranigral neurokinin A.[19] Thus, besides metabolic inactivation, regulation of the actions of peptides may occur via enzymatic conversion to fragments with antagonistic properties.

INTERACTION BETWEEN STRIATONIGRAL AND NIGROSTRIATAL PATHWAYS: ROLE OF INTRINSIC NONDOPAMINERGIC NEURONS IN THE SUBSTANTIA NIGRA

In rats with ibotenic acid lesions in the substantia nigra, pars reticulata, intranigral injections of substance P or neurokinin A still increased dopamine release in the ipsilateral striatum, whereas GABA or dynorphin A decreased dopamine release. Immunohistochemical analysis revealed that cell bodies in the pars reticulata—and also a portion of dopamine neurons in the pars compacta—disappeared. Thus, despite the damage to nigrostriatal dopamine neurons, basal and stimulated levels of striatal dopamine release were not affected, suggesting that partial destruction of the nigrostriatal dopamine projection may be compensated by the remaining neurons. These findings suggest that (1) the modulation of striatal dopamine release by these compounds is mediated by a direct action on the nigrostriatal projection and (2) intrinsic neurons in the pars reticulata are not required to produce this effect. For further details, see reference 20.

INTERACTION OF SUBSTANCE P AND NEUROKININ A WITH TACHYKININ ANTAGONISTS

The tachykinin antagonists, (D-Pro^2,D-Trp^{7,9}) substance P and (D-Arg^1,D-Trp^{7,9},Leu^{11}) substance P (Spantide I), were first investigated. Both antagonists produced a dose-dependent decrease in striatal dopamine release. The (D-Pro^2,D-Trp^{7,9}) substance P inhibited both substance P– and neurokinin A–induced dopamine release, whereas Spantide I blocked the substance P–, but not the neurokinin A–induced increase in striatal dopamine. These results suggested that substance P and neurokinin A act by different receptors. However, both (D-Pro^2,D-Trp^{7,9}) substance P and Spantide I caused a loss of tachykinin-like immunoreactivity (LI) in fibers in the pars reticulata as well as a partial loss of tyrosine hydroxylase–LI in neuronal cell bodies and processes in the pars compacta and in dendrites in the pars reticulata. For further details, see reference 21. A recently developed tachykinin antagonist, (D-NicLys^1,3-Pal^3,D-Cl$_2$Phe^5,Asn^6,D-Trp^{7,9},Nle^{11}) substance P (Spantide

II),[22] was also investigated. When injected alone into the substantia nigra, Spantide II produced a short-lasting and reversible decrease in dopamine release and, at the dose of 0.7 nmol, this antagonist prevented the increase in striatal dopamine release induced by 0.07 nmol of substance P, but not that induced by 0.09 nmol of neurokinin A. Furthermore, it was found that, at the doses tested, Spantide II did not cause significant loss of tyrosine hydroxylase–LI or tachykinin–LI in the substantia nigra. These results suggest that (1) Spantide II is a selective antagonist of substance P effects in the substantia nigra, (2) there are different receptors for substance P and neurokinin A in this brain region, and (3) striatonigral substance P neurons exert a tonic stimulatory regulation on nigrostriatal dopamine neurons. For further details, see reference 23.

EFFECT OF GRP ON STRIATAL DOPAMINE RELEASE

GRP has been isolated from the porcine gastrointestinal tract[24] and has been synthesized as a prepro-GRP peptide, which by proteolytic processing is converted into GRP(1–27).[25,26] At its carboxy-terminus, GRP is homologous to the tetradecapeptide, bombesin, isolated from amphibian skin.[27]

A high density of GRP-immunoreactive nerve endings has been observed in the substantia nigra, pars reticulata.[28] These investigators used a specific GRP_{14-27} antiserum and peroxidase immunohistochemical technique and reported that the observed immunoreactivity could be blocked by peptides with a close structural resemblance to GRP_{14-27}, such as GRP_{18-27}, bombesin, and alytesin, but not by substance P nor Met-enkephalin. It has been suggested that the GRP-LI observed in the substantia nigra may provide an anatomical substrate for the locomotor effects seen after intracerebral microinjections of bombesin,[28] which are believed in part to depend upon dopaminergic systems.[29,30] In fact, we found that GRP(1–27) (0.0005–0.5 nmol) (volume of injection = 0.2 μL) injected into the substantia nigra, pars reticulata, produced a long-lasting contralateral rotational behavior. However, it is unlikely that this effect is due to stimulation of dopamine release because, in contrast to substance P and neurokinin A, intranigral GRP(1–27) inhibits dopamine release. The C-terminal fragment, GRP(14–27), also produces inhibition of striatal dopamine release (in preparation). Indeed, the effects produced by GRP(1–27) were similar to those produced by dynorphin A or GABA, which following intranigral administration can induce contralateral rotation, an effect that is still observed in 6-hydroxydopamine-lesioned animals, and can induce a decrease in striatal dopamine release. For further details, see references 12 and 16.

CONCLUSIONS

Neuronal circuitries in the basal ganglia have been studied with in vivo microdialysis and intracerebral administration of putative neurotransmitters and selective drugs. The present results give evidence for a multiplicity of messenger molecules in the striatonigral pathway, which exert differential effects on the nigrostriatal dopamine neurons and, perhaps, on outflow neurons associated with nigrotectal and nigrothalamic pathways. It is suggested that the tachykinins, substance P and neurokinin A, represent excitatory components, whereas GABA, dynorphin A, and perhaps GRP(1–27) represent inhibitory components of a striatonigral feedback loop regulating the activity of the nigrostriatal dopamine pathway.

REFERENCES

1. VON EULER, U. S. & J. H. GADDUM. 1931. An unidentified depressor substance in certain tissue extracts. J. Physiol. **72:** 74–87.
2. CHANG, M. E., S. E. LEEMAN & H. D. NIALL. 1971. Amino acid sequence of substance P. Nature **232:** 86–87.
3. PERNOW, B. 1953. Studies on substance P: purification, occurrence, and biological actions. Acta Physiol. Scand. **105:** 1–90.
4. LEMBECK, F. & K. STARKE. 1963. Substance P content and effect on capillary permeability of extract of various parts of human brain. Nature **199:** 1295–1296.
5. BROWNSTEIN, M., E. A. MROZ, J. S. KIZER, M. PALKOVITS & S. E. LEEMAN. 1976. Regional distribution of substance P in the brain of the rat. Brain Res. **116:** 299–305.
6. HÖKFELT, T., J. O. KELLERTH, G. NILSSON & B. PERNOW. 1975. Substance P: localization in the central nervous system and in some primary sensory neurons. Science **190:** 889–890.
7. LJUNGDAHL, Å., T. HÖKFELT, G. NILSSON & M. GOLDSTEIN. 1978. Distribution of substance P–like immunoreactivity in the central nervous system of the rat. II. Light microscopic localization in relation to catecholamine-containing neurons. Neuroscience **3:** 945–976.
8. GALE, K., J-S. HONG & A. GUIDOTTI. 1977. Presence of substance P and GABA in separate striatonigral neurons. Brain Res. **136:** 371–375.
9. HONG, J-S., H-Y. YANG, G. RACAGNI & E. COSTA. 1977. Projections of substance P containing neurons from neostriatum to substantia nigra. Brain Res. **122:** 541–544.
10. KANAZAWA, I., P. C. EMSON & A. C. CUELLO. 1977. Evidence for the existence of substance P–containing fibers in striato-nigral and pallido-nigral pathways in rat brain. Brain Res. **119:** 447–453.
11. MROZ, E., M. J. BROWNSTEIN & S. E. LEEMAN. 1977. Evidence of substance P in the striatonigral tract. Brain Res. **125:** 305–311.
12. HERRERA-MARSCHITZ, M. 1986. Neuropharmacology and functional anatomy of the basal ganglia. Thesis—Karolinska Institute, Stockholm, Sweden.
13. REID, M. S. 1990. Neuropharmacological circuitry of the basal ganglia studied by *in vivo* microdialysis. Thesis—Karolinska Institute, Stockholm, Sweden.
14. UNGERSTEDT, U. & G. W. ARBUTHNOTT. 1979. Quantitative recording of rotational behavior in rats after 6-hydroxy-dopamine lesions of the nigrostriatal dopamine system. Brain Res. **24:** 485–493.
15. UNGERSTEDT, U., M. HERRERA-MARSCHITZ, U. JUNGNELIUS, L. STÅHLE, U. TOSSMAN & T. ZETTERSTRÖM. 1982. Dopamine synaptic mechanisms reflected in studies combining behavioral recordings and brain dialysis. *In* Advances in Dopamine Research. Advances in Biosciences 37. M. Kohsaka, T. Shomori, Y. Tsukada & G. N. Woodruff, Eds.: 219–231. Pergamon. Elmsford, New York.
16. HERRERA-MARSCHITZ, M., I. NYLANDER, M. REID, M. T. SHARP, T. HÖKFELT, L. TERENIUS & U. UNGERSTEDT. 1987. Different roles for substance P and dynorphin in the striato-nigral pathways of the rat. *In* Substance P and Neurokinin. J. L. Henry, R. Couture, A. C. Cuello, G. Pelletier, R. Quirion & D. Regoli, Eds.: 353–355. Springer Pub. New York.
17. REID, M., M. HERRERA-MARSCHITZ, T. HÖKFELT, L. TERENIUS & U. UNGERSTEDT. 1988. Differential modulation of striatal dopamine release by intranigral injection of gamma-aminobutyric acid (GABA), dynorphin A, and substance P. Eur. J. Pharmacol. **147:** 411–420.
18. HERRERA-MARSCHITZ, M., L. TERENIUS, T. SAKURADA, M. REID & U. UNGERSTEDT. 1990. The substance P(1–7) fragment is a potent modulator of substance P actions in the brain. Brain Res. **521:** 316–320.
19. REID, M. S., M. HERRERA-MARSCHITZ, L. TERENIUS & U. UNGERSTEDT. 1990. Intranigral substance P modulation of striatal dopamine: interaction with N-terminal and C-terminal fragments. Brain Res. **526:** 228–237.
20. REID, M. S., M. HERRERA-MARSCHITZ, T. HÖKFELT, N. LINDEFORS, H. PERSSON & U. UNGERSTEDT. 1990. Striatonigral GABA, dynorphin, substance P, and neurokinin A

modulation of nigrostriatal dopamine release: evidence for direct regulatory mechanisms. Exp. Brain Res. **82:** 293–303.

21. REID, M. S., M. HERRERA-MARSCHITZ, T. HÖKFELT, M. OHLIN, K. L. VALENTINO & U. UNGERSTEDT. 1990. Effects of intranigral substance P and neurokinin A on striatal dopamine release. I. Interactions with substance P antagonists. Neuroscience **36:** 643–658.

22. FOLKERS, K., R. HÅKANSON, Z. WIESENFELD-HALLIN, D. M. FENG, S. LEANDER & N. ASANO. 1990. Spantide II, an effective antagonist without toxicity. Proc. Natl. Acad. Sci. U.S.A. **87:** 4833–4835.

23. REID, M. S., T. HÖKFELT, M. HERRERA-MARSCHITZ, R. HÅKANSON, D. M. FENG, K. FOLKERS, M. GOLDSTEIN & U. UNGERSTEDT. 1990. Intranigral substance P stimulation of striatal dopamine release is inhibited by Spantide II: a new tachykinin antagonist without apparent neurotoxicity. Brain Res. **532:** 175–181.

24. MCDONALD, T. J., H. JÖRNVALL, G. NILSSON, M. VAGNE, M. A. GHATEI, S. R. BLOOM & V. MUTT. 1979. Characterization of a gastrin releasing peptide from porcine non-antral gastric tissue. Biochem. Biophys. Res. Commun. **90:** 7–14.

25. LEBACQ-VERHEYDEN, A-M., G. KRYSTAL, O. SARTOR, J. WAY & J. F. BATTEY. 1988. The rat prepro-gastrin releasing peptide gene is transcribed from two initiation sites in the brain. Mol. Endocrinol. **2:** 556–563.

26. SPINDEL, E. R., W. W. CHIN, J. PRICE, L. H. REES, G. M. BESSER & J. F. HABENER. 1984. Cloning and characterization of cDNAs encoding human gastrin releasing peptide. Proc. Natl. Acad. Sci. U.S.A. **81:** 5699–5703.

27. ANASTASI, A., V. ERSPAMER & M. BUCCI. 1971. Isolation and structure of bombesin and alytesin, two analogous active peptides from the skin of the European amphibians Bombina and Alytes. Experientia **27:** 166–167.

28. LARSEN, P. J., T. SAEMARK & J. D. MIKKELSEN. 1989. An immunohistochemical demonstration of gastrin-releasing peptide (GRP) in the rat substantia nigra. J. Chem. Neuroanat. **2:** 83–93.

29. MERALI, Z., S. JOHNSTON & S. ZALCMAN. 1983. Bombesin-induced behavioral changes: antagonism by neuroleptics. Peptides **4:** 693–697.

30. SCHULZ, D., P-W. KALIVAS, C. B. NEMEROFF & A. J. PRANGE. 1984. Bombesin-induced locomotor hyperactivity: evaluation of the involvement of the mesolimbic dopamine system. Brain Res. **304:** 377–382.

On the Role of Substance P, Galanin, Vasoactive Intestinal Peptide, and Calcitonin Gene–related Peptide in Mediation of Spinal Reflex Excitability in Rats with Intact and Sectioned Peripheral Nerves[a]

Z. WIESENFELD-HALLIN,[b,c] X-J. XU,[c] R. HÅKANSON,[d]
D. M. FENG,[e] K. FOLKERS,[e] K. KRISTENSSON,[f]
M. J. VILLAR,[g] J. FAHRENKRUG,[h]
AND T. HÖKFELT[g]

[c]Department of Clinical Physiology
Section of Clinical Neurophysiology
Karolinska Institute
Huddinge, Sweden

[d]Department of Pharmacology
University of Lund
Lund, Sweden

[e]Institute for Biomedical Research
University of Texas
Austin, Texas

[f]Department of Pathology
Karolinska Institute
Huddinge, Sweden

[g]Department of Histology and Neurobiology
Karolinska Institute
Stockholm, Sweden

[h]Department of Clinical Chemistry
Bispjeberg Hospital
Copenhagen, Denmark

A brief conditioning electrical stimulus train (CS) to unmyelinated afferents causes a prolonged increase in the excitability of the nociceptive flexor reflex in rat.[1] A CS

[a]This study was supported by the following: the Bank of Sweden Tercentenary Foundation, the Swedish MRC (Project No. 07913, 04X-2887), the NIMH (Grant No. MH43230-02), the Marianne och Marcus Wallenbergs Stiftelse, the Konung Gustav V och Drottning Victorias Stiftelse, the Fredrik och Ingrid Thurings Stiftelse, and research funds of the Karolinska Institute. Both X-J. Xu and M. J. Villar were supported by the Wenner-Gren Center Foundation. M. J. Villar was also supported by the Consejo Nacional de Investigaciones Cientificas y Técnicas de la Republica Argentina.
[b]Address for correspondence: Department of Clinical Neurophysiology, Huddinge University Hospital, S-141 86 Huddinge, Sweden.

applied to cutaneous C-fibers facilitates the reflex for 4–5 min and the CS applied to muscle afferents facilitates the reflex for about 1 h. This effect is not seen if only Aβ and Aδ afferents are activated,[1] is independent of changes in the excitability of central afferent terminals and motoneurons,[2] and may be analogous to the "windup" seen in dorsal horn cells after repeated C-fiber stimulation in their receptive fields.[3] The chemical basis of these physiological changes in the dorsal horn is still largely unknown. Because pretreatment of the sciatic nerve with the C-fiber neurotoxin, capsaicin, abolishes the facilitation of the flexor reflex,[4] it appears possible that neuropeptides present in these afferents participate in the process. Stimulation of afferent C-fibers elicits the release of neuropeptides in the dorsal horn[5–7] and it is possible that the C-fiber-mediated facilitation of the flexor reflex reflects the spinal effects of these neuropeptides. In previous studies, we have shown that intrathecal (i.t.) administration of a number of neuropeptides facilitated the flexor reflex in a similar fashion as the C-fiber CS.[8–11] Of special interest as a sensory transmitter through the years has been the undecapeptide, substance P (SP) (for review, see reference 12), originally discovered by von Euler and Gaddum[13] in 1931 and then structurally characterized by Leeman and collaborators 40 years later.[14] However, a direct analysis of the exact role of SP and other peptides has been hampered by the lack of suitable receptor blocking agents for peptides.

We now report that a novel SP analogue, (D-NicLys[1],3-Pal[3],D-Cl$_2$Phe[5],Asn[6],D-Trp[7,9],Nle[11])-SP (Spantide II),[15] antagonizes the facilitation of the flexor reflex induced by i.t. SP as well as by C-fiber CS.[16] Furthermore, a naturally occurring 29-amino-acid neuropeptide, galanin (GAL), similarly blocks the facilitation of the flexor reflex induced by C-fiber CS.[11] This peptide also possesses SP-antagonistic[17,18] and calcitonin gene–related peptide (CGRP)–antagonistic properties.[18] With the use of these agents, we have been able to analyze the role of a number of neuropeptides in mediation of spinal reflex excitability in animals with both intact and sectioned peripheral nerves. The latter was of interest because it has been shown that, after axotomy, the production and the content of some peptides present in primary afferents decrease in dorsal root ganglion cells and in dorsal horn, such as SP,[19,20] CGRP,[21] and somatostatin (SOM),[22] whereas others, notably vasoactive intestinal peptide (VIP)[22–26] and GAL,[27,28] increase. Through the study with Spantide II, GAL, and a VIP-antagonist (VIP-A), (Ac-Try[1],D-Phe[2])-GRF(1–29),[29] we were able to demonstrate that, after axotomy, there is a plasticity in the role of neuropeptides in mediation of spinal cord excitability;[30] namely, the role of tachykinins in mediation of C-fiber activation–induced reflex facilitation in nerve intact rats is taken over by VIP after peripheral nerve section.

THE SP-ANTAGONISTIC EFFECTS OF SPANTIDE II

In a series of behavioral studies, the bioactivity of Spantide II was tested by i.t. application in rats implanted with chronic i.t. catheters with their tip on the lumbar spinal cord.[31] Spantide II over a wide dose range (0.5–10 μg) evoked no behavioral response, but blocked the caudally directed biting/scratching elicited by 1 μg of i.t. SP in a dose-dependent manner. A similar behavioral response induced by i.t. SOM was not influenced by pretreatment with Spantide II. Spantide II had a weak analgesic effect in the hot plate test and did not produce any motor impairment. Histological examination of rats injected repeatedly with high dose (10 μg) of Spantide II revealed no morphological abnormalities (FIGURES 1A and 1B). In contrast, 2–3 μg of Spantide I, (D-Arg[1],D-Trp[7,9],Leu[11])-SP, injected i.t. caused imme-diate and irreversible paralysis and spinal necrosis, especially in the ventral horn

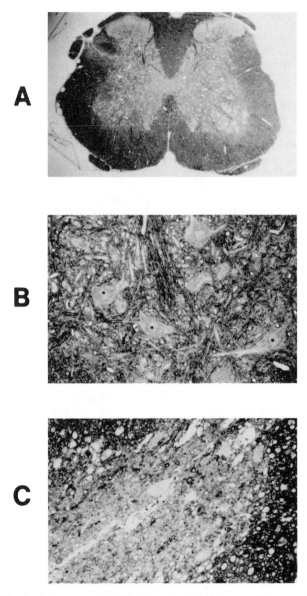

FIGURE 1. Histological appearance of lumbar spinal cord just caudal to the tip of the i.t. catheter in a rat that had been injected with 10 μg of Spantide II six days previously (A,B) and in a rat that had been injected with 3 μg of Spantide I two days previously (C). There are no signs of any damage caused by Spantide II in the whole lumbar cord (A, original magnification ×20) or in the details of the ventral horn (B, ×140). Note the almost total necrosis of the ventral horn after i.t. injection of Spantide I (C, ×140). [The figure, though, has been reduced to 77%.] (Reproduced from reference 31 with permission.)

(FIGURE 1C). These results clearly indicate that, in contrast to previously available SP antagonists (see reference 31 for review), Spantide II appears to be an effective, selective, and safe tachykinin antagonist in the central nervous system.

THE SPECIFIC ANTAGONISTIC EFFECT OF INTRATHECAL SPANTIDE II ON SP-INDUCED AND C-FIBER CS–INDUCED FACILITATION OF THE FLEXOR REFLEX

The effect of i.t. Spantide II on the nociceptive flexor reflex was studied in decerebrate, spinalized, unanesthetized rats over a dose range of 10 ng–10 µg.[16] Intrathecal Spantide II usually caused weak facilitation of the flexor reflex, especially at lower doses (10–100 ng), and it sometimes depressed the reflex at high doses (1–10 µg). The facilitatory effect of Spantide II may reflect a partial agonist action. However, this effect was only about 1% of that of SP. Pretreatment with Spantide II (1–10 µg) effectively antagonized the facilitation of the flexor reflex induced by 10 ng of i.t. SP for about 30 min (FIGURE 2), whereas the facilitation induced by i.t. administration of other neuropeptides present in primary afferents (SOM, VIP, CGRP, and GAL) was not influenced by Spantide II (FIGURE 3).

Because these results further suggest that Spantide II is an effective and specific antagonist for SP in our spinal reflex model, we examined its effect against the increase of excitability after a CS train that activated unmyelinated afferents. It was found that pretreatment with Spantide II effectively blocked the facilitation of the flexor reflex induced by C-fiber CS of the sural nerve with doses and durations of action similar to those blocking the effect of SP (FIGURE 4A).[16] The results therefore suggest that C-fiber CS of cutaneous primary afferents facilitates the nociceptive flexor reflex through a mechanism involving the release of SP or possibly other tachykinins from their central terminals in the dorsal horn.

A CS that activates unmyelinated fibers in a muscle nerve usually facilitates the flexor reflex for a much longer duration than after stimulation of a cutaneous nerve.[1] There has been controversy regarding the level of SP in muscle versus cutaneous afferents. Using immunohistochemistry and radioimmunoassay, it has been reported that the level of SP-like immunoreactivity (LI) in muscle afferents is much lower,[32,33] the same,[34] or higher[35] than that in cutaneous afferents. We conducted experiments to examine whether SP plays a role in reflex facilitation after activation of muscle nerves. As shown in FIGURE 4B, the long-term facilitation of the flexor reflex induced by a CS train applied to the gastrocnemius muscle nerve was strongly depressed by pretreatment with 3 µg of Spantide II, indicating that the increase of spinal cord excitability by activation of unmyelinated fibers in muscle nerve is also mediated by tachykinins.[40] Therefore, the difference in duration of the facilitatory effect of CS to cutaneous and muscle nerve may not be due to the release of different neurotransmitters, but rather to other factors, such as differences in the concentration or relative proportion of coreleased neurotransmitters or the presence of tissue-specific trophic factors that influence the pattern of central responses to sensory inputs of different origins.

THE EFFECT OF GAL ON SPINAL CORD EXCITABILITY AND ITS INTERACTION WITH OTHER NEUROPEPTIDES, MORPHINE, AND C-FIBER CS–INDUCED REFLEX FACILITATION

Intrathecal GAL has a biphasic effect on the spinal nociceptive flexor reflex, including (i) facilitation, (ii) facilitation followed by inhibition, and (iii) pure

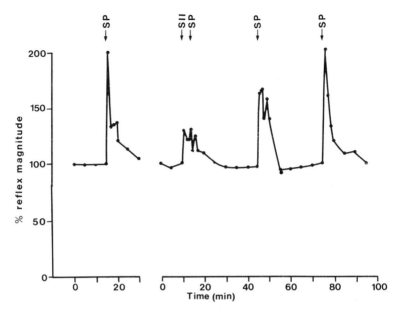

FIGURE 2. The antagonistic effect of i.t. Spantide II (SII) on the facilitation of the flexor reflex by i.t. SP and its time course. The data presented are from a single experiment. The flexor reflex was recorded from the biceps femoris/semitendinosus muscles in decerebrate, spinalized, unanesthetized rats. The reflex was evoked continuously (1/min) by single shocks to the sural nerve and was integrated. Baseline responses, defined as 100% reflex magnitude, were established for at least 20 min. The arrows indicate when the drugs were injected. The effect of a test dose of 10 ng of SP is indicated on the left. Three μg of Spantide II had a weak facilitatory effect and almost totally antagonized the reflex facilitation by SP injected 3 min later. Thirty min after injection of Spantide II, the response to SP was 70% of the control value and, after 55 min, the facilitation by SP returned to the control level. (Reproduced from reference 16 with permission.)

inhibition, in a dose-dependent manner.[11] GAL has no effect on the monosynaptic reflex, indicating that its depressive effect is most likely due to inhibition of dorsal horn neurons.[11] GAL at high doses has a weak analgesic effect.[36] GAL dose-dependently antagonizes C-fiber CS–induced facilitation of the flexor reflex[11] and potentiates the spinal analgesic effect of morphine at doses that by themselves have no analgesic effect.[37] Taken together, these results indicate that GAL may have an inhibitory function on sensory input.

We have recently examined whether the inhibitory function of GAL may be due to a possible interaction with other neuropeptides present in primary afferents. We found that i.t. SP- and CGRP-induced facilitation of the flexor reflex was dose-dependently antagonized by preadministration of GAL.[17,18] This effect of GAL appears not to be due to nonspecific depression because VIP- and SOM-induced reflex facilitations were not blocked by GAL (FIGURE 5).[17,18] It should be noted that GAL-LI has been found to coexist with SP-LI and CGRP-LI, but not with VIP-LI and SOM-LI in dorsal root ganglion cells.[26] These results indicate that GAL selectively antagonizes the excitatory effect of those neuropeptides with which it coexists. This antagonism could explain the inhibitory effect of GAL on C-fiber

CS–induced facilitation of the flexor reflex, which is mediated by neuropeptides, notably SP.[16]

THE EFFECT OF AXOTOMY ON THE ROLE OF NEUROPEPTIDES IN THE TRANSMISSION OF INFORMATION TO THE SPINAL CORD

After peripheral nerve section, there are dramatic and very early changes in the production of neuropeptides in primary sensory neurons that result in changes in the levels of these neuropeptides in primary afferents within 6–12 days. Thus, SP-LI,[19,20] SOM-LI,[22] and CGRP-LI[21] are decreased, whereas VIP-LI[22-26] and GAL-LI[27,28] are increased. One argument against an important role for SP as a neurotransmitter/ modulator in mediation of the increase of spinal excitability after activation of C-afferents has been that no change in the excitability of dorsal horn cells to a C-fiber input could be observed 7–19 days after peripheral nerve section, in spite of the fact that SP was depleted from afferent terminals at this time.[38] The facilitatory effect of the C-fiber CS on the flexor reflex was also unchanged after axotomy.[39] However, a previous study in our laboratory indicated that, although the facilitatory effect of neuropeptides was unchanged, the interaction between i.t. neuropeptides and C-fiber activity on the flexor reflex did change after axotomy.[39] Hence, i.t. SP and C-fiber CS have a strong synergistic facilitatory effect on the flexor reflex in animals with intact peripheral nerves, whereas only a very weak synergism was seen between i.t. VIP and the sural CS. Fourteen days after axotomy, the synergistic effect between SP and C-fiber CS disappeared and, instead, a strong synergism between i.t. VIP and nerve CS emerged. These results indicate that a change in the physiological role of neuropeptides in primary afferents and in the dorsal horn may occur after axotomy.[39]

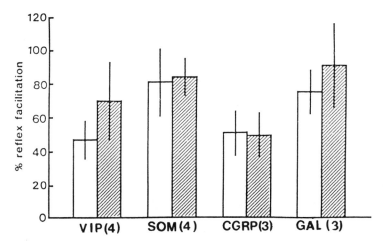

FIGURE 3. The effect of Spantide II on the facilitation of the flexor reflex induced by i.t. VIP (30 ng), SOM (15 ng), CGRP (100 ng), and GAL (30 ng). The change in reflex magnitude is expressed as the percent increase of the response over baseline. Data are from experiments in which the drugs were injected alone (open bars) and 1–3 min after injection of 3 μg of Spantide II (hatched bars). The number of experiments in each group is shown in brackets. (Reproduced from reference 16 with permission.)

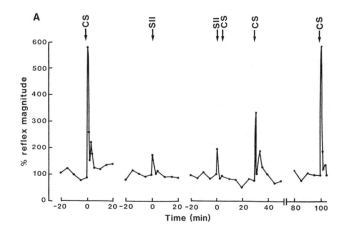

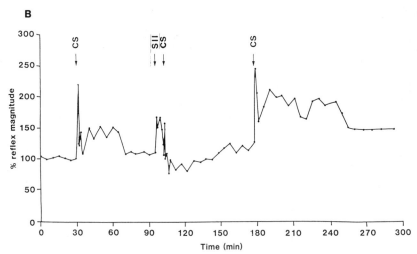

FIGURE 4. The effect of Spantide II (SII) on the facilitation of the flexor reflex by a conditioning stimulus (CS) train (20 s, 1 Hz) that activates unmyelinated afferents in sural (A) and gastrocnemius (B) nerves. In A, the CS initially facilitated the flexor reflex for about 5 min. Three μg of i.t. SP had a weak facilitatory effect on the reflex and totally blocked the sural CS–induced facilitation 5 min after i.t. SII. After 30 min, the CS-induced facilitation was still reduced by about 50%. By 100 min after the SII, the CS-induced facilitation was back to the predrug level. In B, the first and third CS to the gastrocnemius nerve without SII evoked a biphasic response—an intense, brief facilitation followed by a prolonged, weaker facilitation of the flexor reflex for 35 and 70 min, respectively. Three μg of Spantide II was injected i.t. 7 min prior to the second gastrocnemius CS. Note that the reflex amplitude after the i.t. Spantide II returned to baseline before the CS was applied. The CS now facilitated the reflex for only 1 min and the magnitude of the facilitation was reduced by 55% compared to the initial facilitation after the first CS. The last CS, applied after the effect of Spantide II had dissipated, evoked a biphasic response, with the initial effect being similar to that seen after the first CS, but with a longer-lasting late component. (Part A is reproduced from reference 16 and part B is reproduced from reference 40 with permission.)

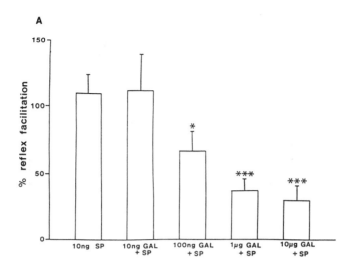

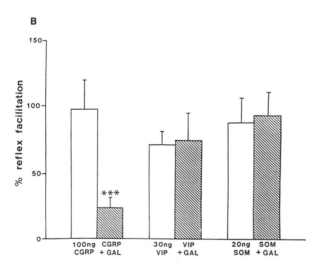

FIGURE 5. Effect of GAL on (A) SP-, (B) CGRP-, VIP-, and SOM-induced facilitation of the flexor reflex in rats with intact sciatic nerves. In A, the effect of 10 ng of SP alone or after various doses of GAL is expressed as the percent increase in reflex magnitude to baseline reflex, which was defined as 100%. Each bar represents 6–19 experiments. ANOVA comparing the five groups was highly significant ($F_{4,39} = 4.986$, $p < 0.005$). Dunnett's test indicated that the response to SP was significantly weaker with 100 ng–10 μg of GAL; * $= p < 0.05$; *** $= p < 0.005$. In B, the effect of each peptide alone (open bars) or after pretreatment with 100 ng of GAL (hatched bars) is shown as the percent increase in reflex magnitude to baseline. Each bar represents 6–8 experiments. Differences were tested with the paired Student's *t* test. Addition of 100 ng of GAL significantly reduced the facilitatory effect of 100 ng of CGRP ($t = 4.405$, $p < 0.005$), but did not influence VIP- or SOM-induced reflex facilitation ($t = 0.313$ and 0.918, respectively; $p > 0.1$). (Reproduced with permission from reference 18.)

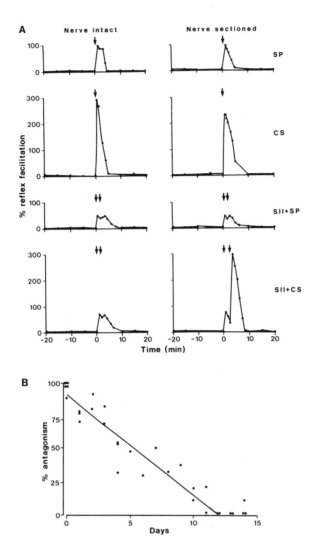

FIGURE 6. (A) The effect of 10 ng of i.t. SP, sural CS (20 s, 1 Hz), and 3 μg of Spantide II (SII) (plus either SP or the CS) in experiments where the sciatic nerve was intact (left) or sectioned 14 days previously (right). The data are expressed as the percent change in the magnitude of the flexor reflex over baseline response. The time of application of the drugs or the sural CS is indicated by the arrows. Note that SII was effective in antagonizing the effect of SP and the sural CS in the experiments where the sciatic nerve was intact, but, after axotomy, SII only antagonized the effect of SP and not the CS. (B) The antagonism of the sural CS–induced facilitation of the flexor reflex by 3 μg of SII in rats with intact nerves (data obtained at day 0) and up to 14 days after sciatic nerve section. Antagonism was calculated according to the following formula: antagonism $(\%) = [(R_0 - R)/R_0] \times 100$, where R_0 is the response to i.t. SP or sural nerve CS without SII and R is the response to i.t. SP or sural CS after administration of SII. For the data from days 0–12, $r^2 = -0.88$ ($p < 0.001$). The regression line is $Y = -7.53X + 90.35$. (Reproduced with permission from reference 30.)

We therefore studied the effect of Spantide II on the flexor reflex in rats with sectioned sciatic nerves to evaluate the possible role for SP in axotomized animals.[30] The facilitation of the flexor reflex induced by 10 ng of i.t. SP and the sural CS was similar in rats with intact and sectioned sciatic nerves (FIGURE 6A). Spantide II (3 µg) effectively antagonized the SP-induced facilitation of the flexor reflex regardless of whether the sciatic nerve was intact (95 ± 10% antagonism) or sectioned (93 ± 10% antagonism). However, although Spantide II was effective in antagonizing the sural CS–induced facilitation of the flexor reflex in rats with intact sciatic nerves (97 ± 5% antagonism), it did not at 11–14 days after sciatic nerve section counteract the facilitation evoked by the sural CS (2 ± 1% antagonism). Further studies revealed a

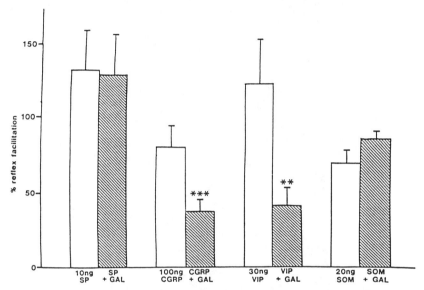

FIGURE 7. Effect of GAL on the facilitation of the flexor reflex induced by various peptides in rats with sectioned sciatic nerves. The effect of each peptide alone (open bars) and after pretreatment with 100 ng of GAL (hatched bars) is shown as the percent increase in reflex magnitude to baseline. Each bar represents 6–7 experiments. Differences were tested with the paired t test. GAL did not affect the facilitation induced by SP ($t = 0.185, p > 0.1$) or SOM ($t = 2.151, p > 0.05$), but significantly antagonized the facilitatory effect of VIP ($t = 3.368$, $p < 0.01$) and CGRP ($t = 4.777, p < 0.005$); ** $= p < 0.01$; *** $= p < 0.005$. (Reproduced with permission from reference 18.)

highly significant negative correlation between the number of days elapsed since nerve section and the effectiveness of the antagonistic effect of Spantide II on the sural CS–induced facilitation of the flexor reflex (FIGURE 6B). These results suggest that, after peripheral nerve section, substances other than SP begin to play a role in the increase of spinal cord excitability responding to C-fiber input.

In contrast to Spantide II, GAL maintained its ability to antagonize the C-fiber CS–induced facilitation of the flexor reflex in rats with sectioned sciatic nerves.[18] This result was somewhat surprising because we have shown that this antagonism is due to the blocking effect of GAL on the excitatory effect of SP and CGRP, which both decline severely after axotomy. A systematic study examining the interaction be-

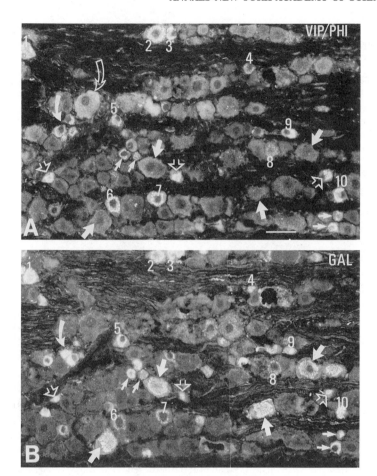

FIGURE 8. Immunofluorescence micrograph of two adjacent, approximately 6-µm-thick sections of L5 ganglia of a rat 14 days after peripheral section of the ipsilateral sciatic nerve and with incubation with a mixture of VIP and PHI antisera (A) and GAL antiserum (B). Numerous VIP/PHI-positive and GAL-positive cells of varying size are seen. Many cells reacting with all three peptides can be distinguished in both sections as indicated by numbers 1–10, as well as by thin straight arrows. Open arrows point to cells, where, in section B, only a very peripheral portion of the cytoplasm can be seen. Curved arrows point to groups of cells likely to be identical. Thick straight arrows point to GAL-positive, VIP/PHI-negative cells. The bar indicates 50 µm. (Reproduced with permission from reference 18.)

tween GAL and other neuropeptides in the mediation of reflex excitability revealed that, 11–24 days after axotomy, GAL was no longer effective in antagonizing the facilitatory effect of SP and its antagonism of CGRP-induced reflex facilitation was decreased. Instead, antagonism by GAL of VIP-induced, but still not of SOM-induced facilitation of the flexor reflex was observed (FIGURE 7). A parallel immunohistochemical study showed that GAL-LI and VIP-LI are increased in the dorsal root ganglia after sciatic nerve section and these two peptides coexist in many cells (FIGURE 8). These results suggest that the interaction between GAL and other neuropeptides is altered by peripheral nerve section, paralleling changes in the levels of these neuropeptides in primary afferents and their pattern of coexistence. The observation that GAL antagonized the sural CS–induced and VIP-induced facilitation of the flexor reflex in axotomized animals indicated that there may be a "switching" of the role of SP and VIP before and after axotomy.

We have recently examined the effect of an analogue of growth hormone releasing factor (GRF), (Ac-Try[1],D-Phe[2])-GRF(1–29), a compound that has been shown to be an antagonist for VIP in the periphery,[29] on the flexor reflex in rats with intact or sectioned sciatic nerves.[30] The facilitation of the flexor reflex induced by i.t. VIP (30 ng) was reduced by pretreatment of the VIP-antagonist under both conditions (77.2 ± 4.3% antagonism in rats with intact nerves, 76.4 ± 5.5% antagonism in axotomized animals). The VIP-antagonist was ineffective in antagonizing the sural CS–induced reflex facilitation in rats with intact sciatic nerves (12.1 ± 8.2%

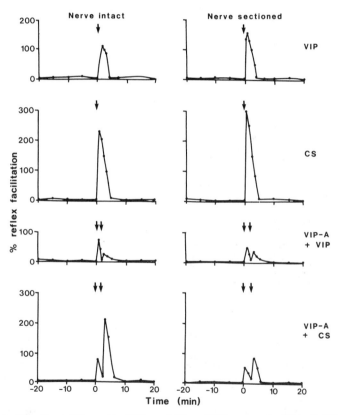

FIGURE 9. The effect of 30 ng of i.t. VIP, sural CS, and VIP-antagonist (VIP-A) (500 ng) plus VIP or CS in experiments where the sciatic nerve was intact (left) or sectioned 14 days previously (right). Data are expressed as in FIGURE 6A. Note that the VIP-antagonist was effective in antagonizing the facilitatory effect of both VIP and the CS in the experiments where the sciatic nerve was previously sectioned. In contrast, in the experiments where the sciatic nerve was intact, the VIP-antagonist was effective against VIP, but not against the sural CS. (Reproduced with permission from reference 30.)

antagonism), but was highly effective in axotomized rats (72.4 ± 4.4% antagonism) (FIGURE 9).

CONCLUSIONS

The present studies, using a variety of methods, suggest an important role for neuropeptides in sensory function and a plasticity of this role after axotomy. We have presented direct evidence using Spantide II, a potent, selective, and nontoxic tachykinin antagonist, that tachykinins, notably SP, play a critical role in the increase of spinal cord excitability after activation of unmyelinated afferents in both cutaneous and muscle nerves when these nerves are intact. This function for tachykinins is taken over by VIP after peripheral nerve section, which is correlated with changes in the levels of these peptides in primary afferents. GAL physiologically antagonizes the excitatory effect of SP and CGRP. All three peptides coexist in primary afferents when peripheral nerves are intact. After axotomy, a switch in the pattern of coexistence occurs and GAL antagonizes the facilitatory effect of VIP. Therefore, GAL seems to be an endogenous neuropeptide that may have an inhibitory action in primary sensory processing.

REFERENCES

1. WALL, P. D. & C. J. WOOLF. 1984. J. Physiol. (London) **356:** 443–458.
2. COOK, A. J., C. J. WOOLF & P. D. WALL. 1986. Neurosci. Lett. **70:** 91–96.
3. MENDELL, L. M. & P. D. WALL. 1965. Nature **206:** 97–99.
4. WOOLF, C. J. & P. D. WALL. 1986. J. Neurosci. **6:** 1433–1442.
5. DUGGAN, A. W. & I. A. HENDRY. 1986. Neurosci. Lett. **68:** 134–140.
6. SARIA, A., R. GAMSE, J. PETERMANN, J. A. FISCHER, E. THEODORSSON-NORHEIM & J. M. LUNDBERG. 1986. Neurosci. Lett. **63:** 310–314.
7. YAKSH, T. L., E. O. IL ABAY & Y. L. W. GO. 1982. Brain Res. **242:** 279–290.
8. WIESENFELD-HALLIN, Z. 1985. Neurosci. Lett. **62:** 69–74.
9. WOOLF, C. J. & Z. WIESENFELD-HALLIN. 1986. Neurosci. Lett. **66:** 226–230.
10. WIESENFELD-HALLIN, Z. 1987. Neurosci. Lett. **80:** 293–297.
11. WIESENFELD-HALLIN, Z., M. J. VILLAR & T. HÖKFELT. 1989. Brain Res. **486:** 205–213.
12. PERNOW, B. 1983. Pharmacol. Rev. **35:** 85–141.
13. VON EULER, U. S. & J. H. GADDUM. 1931. J. Physiol. (London) **72:** 74–87.
14. CHANG, M. M., S. E. LEEMAN & H. D. NIALL. 1971. Nature (London) New Biol. **232:** 86–87.
15. FOLKERS, K., R. HÅKANSON, Z. WIESENFELD-HALLIN, D. M. FENG, S. LEANDER & N. ASANO. 1990. Proc. Natl. Acad. Sci. U.S.A. **87:** 4833–4835.
16. WIESENFELD-HALLIN, Z., X-J. XU, R. HÅKANSON, D. M. FENG & K. FOLKERS. 1990. Brain Res. **526:** 284–290.
17. XU, X-J., Z. WIESENFELD-HALLIN, M. J. VILLAR & T. HÖKFELT. Acta Physiol. Scand. **137:** 463–464.
18. XU, X-J., Z. WIESENFELD-HALLIN, M. J. VILLAR, J. FAHRENKRUG & T. HÖKFELT. 1990. J. Eur. Neurosci. **2:** 733–743.
19. JESSELL, T., A. TSUNNO, I. KANAZAWA & M. OTSUKA. 1979. Brain Res. **168:** 247–259.
20. BARBUT, D., J. M. POLAK & P. D. WALL. 1981. Brain Res. **205:** 289–298.
21. RÉTHELYI, M., A. FÜST & ZS. BARTFAI. 1989. Proc. IUPS **17:** 198.
22. SHEHAB, S. A. S. & M. E. ATKINSON. 1986. Brain Res. **372:** 37–44.
23. MCGREGOR, G. P., S. J. GIBSON, I. M. SABATE, M. A. BLANK, N. D. CHRISTOFIDES, P. D. WALL, J. M. POLAK & S. R. BLOOM. 1984. Neuroscience **13:** 207–216.
24. SHEHAB, S. A. S. & M. E. ATKINSON. 1984. J. Anat. **139:** 725.
25. SHEHAB, S. A. S. & M. E. ATKINSON. 1986. Exp. Brain Res. **62:** 422–430.

26. JU, G., T. HÖKFELT, E. BRODIN, J. FAHRENKRUG, J. A. FISCHER, P. FREY, R. P. ELDE & J. C. BROWN. 1987. Cell Tissue Res. **247**: 417–431.
27. HÖKFELT, T., Z. WIESENFELD-HALLIN, M. J. VILLAR & T. MELANDER. 1987. Neurosci. Lett. **83**: 217–220.
28. VILLAR, M. J., R. CORTÉS, E. THEODORSSON, Z. WIESENFELD-HALLIN, M. SCHALLING, J. FAHRENKRUG, P. C. EMSON & T. HÖKFELT. 1989. Neuroscience **33**: 587–604.
29. WAELBROECK, M., P. ROBBERECHT, D. H. COY, J-C. CAMUS, P. D. DE NEEF & J. CHRISTOPHE. 1985. Endocrinology **116**: 2643–2649.
30. WIESENFELD-HALLIN, Z., X-J. XU, R. HÅKANSON, D. M. FENG & K. FOLKERS. 1990. Neurosci. Lett. **116**: 293–298.
31. WIESENFELD-HALLIN, Z., X-J. XU, K. KRISTENSSON, R. HÅKANSON, D. M. FENG & K. FOLKERS. 1990. Regulat. Peptides **29**: 1–11.
32. MCMAHON, S. B., E. SYKOVA, P. D. WALL, C. J. WOOLF & S. J. GIBSON. 1984. Neurosci. Lett. **52**: 235–240.
33. MCMAHON, S. B., G. R. LEWIN, P. ANAND, M. A. GHATEI & S. R. BLOOM. 1989. Neuroscience **33**: 67–73.
34. MOLANDER, C., J. YGGE & C-J. DALSGAARD. 1987. Neurosci. Lett. **74**: 37–42.
35. O'BRIEN, C., C. J. WOOLF, M. FITZGERALD, R. M. LINDSAY & C. MOLANDER. 1989. Neuroscience **32**: 493–502.
36. POST, C., L. ALARI & T. HÖKFELT. 1988. Acta Physiol. Scand. **132**: 583–584.
37. WIESENFELD-HALLIN, Z., X-J. XU, M. J. VILLAR & T. HÖKFELT. 1990. Neurosci. Lett. **109**: 217–221.
38. WALL, P. D., M. FITZGERALD & S. J. GIBSON. 1981. Neuroscience **6**: 2205–2215.
39. WIESENFELD-HALLIN, Z. 1989. Brain Res. **489**: 129–136.
40. WIESENFELD-HALLIN, Z., X-J. XU, R. HÅKANSON, D. M. FENG & K. FOLKERS. 1991. Acta Physiol. Scand. **141**: 57–61.

Tachykinin-evoked Release of Neurotransmitters from Isolated Spinal Cord of the Newborn Rat

M. OTSUKA, M. SAKUMA, N. KOBAYASHI, Y. ONISHI,
M. YANAGISAWA, H. SUZUKI, AND K. YOSHIOKA

Department of Pharmacology
Faculty of Medicine
Tokyo Medical and Dental University
Bunkyo-ku, Tokyo 113, Japan

INTRODUCTION

Electrophysiological experiments have shown that substance P (SP) and neurokinin A (NKA) exert excitatory actions on neurons in the spinal cord.[1,2] Therefore, it is expected that SP and NKA evoke the release of some neurotransmitters from spinal neurons. There is some evidence suggesting that SP excites cholinergic and GABAergic interneurons in the neonatal rat spinal cord. Bath application of SP to the isolated spinal cord of the newborn rat induced a depolarization of motoneurons, which could be recorded from the ventral root. This SP-induced depolarization of the ventral root was enhanced by an anticholinesterase agent, edrophonium,[3] as well as by a γ-aminobutyric acid (GABA) antagonist, bicuculline.[4] These results suggest that the SP-evoked activations of cholinergic and GABAergic neurons are involved in the SP-induced depolarization of spinal motoneurons in the neonatal rat spinal cord. In the present study, we thus examined by biochemical analyses the effects of SP and NKA on the releases of acetylcholine (ACh) and GABA from the isolated spinal cord of the newborn rat.

METHODS

Under ether anesthesia, spinal cords below thoracic segments were isolated from (2–5)-day-old Wistar rats and were hemisected. One to four hemisected cords were fixed in a perfusion chamber of 1-mL volume and were continuously perfused with artificial cerebrospinal fluid (CSF) (for composition, see reference 5) at a rate of 0.7 mL/min. The medium was thoroughly oxygenated by bubbling with a mixture of 95% O_2 and 5% CO_2 in the reservoir and the perfusion chamber. The temperature of the perfusion chamber was kept at 27 °C. Three-minute fractions were collected through a glass wool filter into test tubes.

ACh Analysis

The collected samples were frozen and lyophilized. Each sample was dissolved in 200 μL of 50 mM sodium phosphate buffer (pH = 8.4) and then was centrifuged at 10,000g for 5 min. Twenty μL of the supernatant was applied to an HPLC (Nihon

Bunko, 800 series). The amount of ACh was measured using an immobilized enzyme column (BAS-Japan) and an electrochemical detection system according to the method of Fujimori and Yamamoto.[6]

GABA Analysis

The samples were frozen, lyophilized, and dissolved in 200 μL of 4 M acetic acid. Then, 100 μL of each sample was injected into an HPLC–amino acid analyzer with an Aminopak (Toso, Japan) column and a fluorescence detector. GABA was assayed by a postcolumn derivatization technique using *o*-phthalaldehyde.

RESULTS

Acetylcholine Release

In order to inhibit enzymatic degradation of ACh, all experiments for examining ACh release were carried out using artificial CSF containing 5 μM eserine. Under such conditions, the basal ACh release was about 0.5 pmol/mg wet weight in each 3-min fraction. Application of SP at 0.1–3 μM resulted in a dose-dependent increase in the ACh release from spinal cords. The effect of SP was significant at 0.1 μM and was close to maximum at 3 μM.[7]

In the experiment illustrated in FIGURE 1A, the effects of low-Ca^{2+}/high-Mg^{2+} medium were examined. When the spinal cords were perfused with a medium containing 0.1 mM Ca^{2+} and 5 mM Mg^{2+}, the basal ACh release was markedly reduced and the SP-evoked ACh release was completely abolished. After perfusing the cords again with normal artificial CSF (containing 1.26 mM Ca^{2+} and 1.15 mM Mg^{2+}), the basal and evoked ACh releases recovered to the original levels.

Tetrodotoxin (TTX) at 0.2 μM similarly depressed both the basal and SP-evoked ACh releases from spinal cords. After washing the cords for 40 min with normal artificial CSF, both the basal and SP-evoked ACh releases recovered partially (FIGURE 2A).

Neurokinin A also evoked an increase in the ACh release from spinal cords. The potency of NKA was comparable to that of SP (FIGURE 3B). Other tachykinin analogues, such as neurokinin B (1 μM), acetyl-Arg^6-septide (1 μM), and SP_{5-11} (1 μM), also evoked a (2–4)-fold increase in the ACh release. By contrast, an N-terminal SP analogue, SP_{1-10} amide, was ineffective at 10 μM.

Moreover, the effects of two tachykinin antagonists, spantide ([D-Arg^1,D-$Trp^{7,9}$, Leu^{11}]SP) and [D-Pro^4,D-$Trp^{7,9,10}$]SP_{4-11}, on the SP- and NKA-evoked ACh releases were examined. Spantide partially blocked the effect of NKA (FIGURE 3B), but had no appreciable effect on the SP-evoked ACh release (FIGURE 3A). [D-Pro^4,D-$Trp^{7,9,10}$]SP_{4-11} was ineffective at 10 μM on both the SP (1 μM)–evoked and NKA (1 μM)–evoked ACh releases.

GABA Release

Basal release of GABA was 0.1–0.5 pmol/mg wet weight in a 3-min fraction. Application of SP at 3–10 μM resulted in a dose-dependent increase in the GABA release from spinal cords. The threshold concentration of SP to evoke a significant

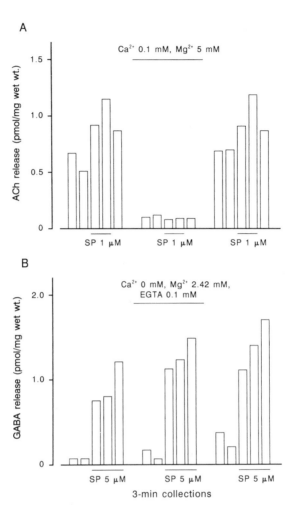

FIGURE 1. Effects of low-Ca^{2+}/high-Mg^{2+} media on the release of ACh (A) and GABA (B). A: Two hemisected spinal cords were perfused with normal artificial CSF containing 5 μM eserine for more than 1 h and then three series of collections were carried out. In each series, five successive 3-min samples were collected. The first two 3-min fractions represented precontrols. Then, the perfusion medium was switched to a solution containing 1 μM SP for 6 min during the period indicated by the horizontal bar under the columns. Immediately after the end of the first series, the perfusion solution was changed to a low-Ca^{2+} (0.1 mM) and high-Mg^{2+} (5 mM) medium until the end of the second series. Then, the spinal cords were again perfused with normal artificial CSF. Each column represents the amount of ACh in pmol/mg wet weight in a 3-min fraction. In each of these and in all the following figures, the results were derived from a single experiment, but similar results were obtained from 2–3 other experiments. B: Effect of Ca^{2+}-free medium on the GABA release. Experimental protocol and other details were similar to those in the ACh release experiment shown in A, except that, during the second collection period, the cords were perfused with a Ca^{2+}-free medium containing 2.42 mM Mg^{2+} and 0.1 mM EGTA and the application periods of SP were 9 min.

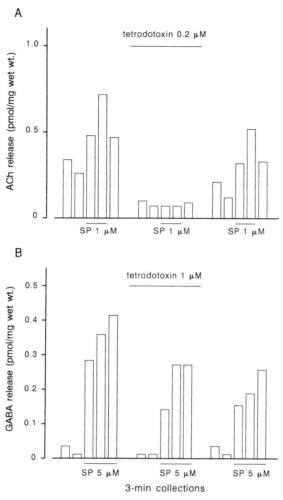

FIGURE 2. Effects of TTX on release of ACh (A) and GABA (B). Experimental protocols were similar to those in FIGURE 1, except a normal artificial CSF containing TTX (0.2 μM in A and 1 μM in B), instead of Ca^{2+}-deficient media, was perfused during the second series of collection.

increase in GABA release was about 3 μM. It was also noted that thorough oxygenation of the spinal cords was necessary to reveal the effect of SP on the GABA release.

In contrast to the SP-evoked ACh release, the SP-evoked GABA release was not appreciably affected by lowering the Ca^{2+} concentration in the medium or by TTX. As shown in FIGURES 1B and 2B, SP at 5 μM evoked an increase in the GABA release in the Ca^{2+}-free medium containing 2.42 mM Mg^{2+} and 0.1 mM EGTA or in the presence of TTX (1 μM) to similar extents as those in normal artificial CSF.[8]

Neurokinin A (10 μM) also evoked a (2–4)-fold increase in the GABA release.

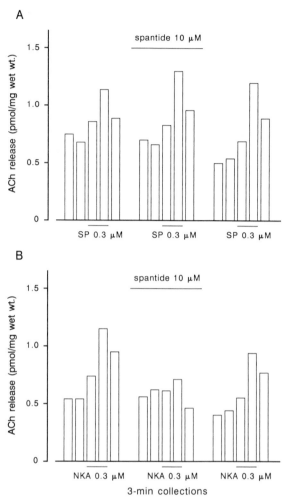

FIGURE 3. Effect of spantide on the ACh release evoked by SP (A) and NKA (B). SP and NKA were applied at 0.3 μM for 6 min during the periods shown by the horizontal bars under the columns. The ACh release was first observed in normal artificial CSF and then, during the second series of collection, the spinal cords were perfused with the solution containing spantide (10 μM) as shown by the horizontal bars above the columns. After finishing the second series of collection, the perfusion medium was returned to normal artificial CSF. After 40–60 min of perfusion, the third series of collection was started.

Furthermore, des-Met[11] SP, that is, SP_{1-10} amide, showed a strong activity to evoke the GABA release. By contrast, SP_{5-11} (10 μM) did not evoke a significant increase in the GABA release.

Spantide in the concentration range of 1–20 μM always induced a marked increase in the GABA release. Therefore, spantide appears to act as an agonist rather than as an antagonist in evoking a GABA release. In contrast, [D-Pro⁴,D-

Trp^{7,9,10}]SP$_{4-11}$ did not significantly increase the GABA release and partially blocked the effect of SP to increase the GABA release (FIGURE 4).

DISCUSSION

The present study showed that SP and NKA at low concentrations evoke a release of ACh from spinal neurons.[7] This is consistent with the results of some physiological experiments. SP-evoked depolarization of the ventral root was enhanced by edrophonium in the isolated spinal cord of the newborn rat (see INTRODUCTION).[3] Furthermore, stimulation of primary afferents at C fiber strength evoked a long-lasting inhibition of monosynaptic reflex in the isolated neonatal rat spinal cord and this inhibition was partially blocked by atropine and a tachykinin antagonist, spantide. The latter results suggest that some primary afferents release SP and NKA, which excite cholinergic interneurons in the spinal cord to produce atropine-sensitive inhibition of the monosynaptic reflex.[9]

The Ca^{2+} sensitivity of ACh release is consistent with the vesicular release of the transmitter. The ACh release is also blocked by TTX, suggesting that tachykinins act on soma-dendrites of cholinergic neurons, which send action potentials to their terminals to evoke release of the transmitter from there. It might be argued that tachykinins activate some excitatory interneurons that activate cholinergic neurons. It is difficult to exclude completely this possibility, but the SP-evoked ACh release was not blocked by an excitatory amino acid antagonist, kynurenic acid (3 mM) (unpublished observation).

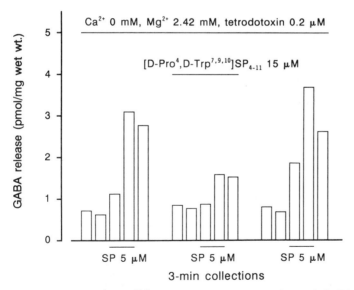

FIGURE 4. Effect of [D-Pro^4,D-Trp^{7,9,10}]SP$_{4-11}$ on the SP-evoked release of GABA. Three consecutive series of collection were performed with intervals of 60 min. The cords were perfused with Ca^{2+}-free artificial CSF containing 2.42 mM Mg^{2+} and 0.2 μM TTX. The tachykinin antagonist was applied during the second series of collection (as shown by a shorter horizontal bar above the columns). Other details were similar to those in FIGURE 3.

A likely source of the tachykinin-evoked ACh release appears to be interneurons in the dorsal horn, although other cholinergic neurons in the lateral or ventral horn may also contribute to the SP-evoked release. Immunohistochemical studies have shown the existence of cholinergic neurons in the superficial dorsal horn.[10] This is the place where tachykinin receptors are densely distributed[11] and where most of the primary afferent C fibers terminate.

It is difficult to characterize the subtypes of tachykinin receptors involved in the tachykinin-evoked ACh release. The NKA-evoked ACh release was blocked by spantide. This is in parallel with our recent observation that the NKA-evoked depolarization of neonatal rat motoneurons in the presence of TTX was competitively antagonized by spantide.[12] In these experiments, the receptors involved appear to be different from either the NK_1 or NK_2 subtype. The SP-evoked ACh release, on the other hand, was not appreciably depressed by spantide, suggesting that another subtype of tachykinin receptor may also be involved in the SP-evoked ACh release. Because SP_{1-10} amide was inactive, whereas SP_{5-11} was active, the receptors involved in the tachykinin-evoked ACh release appear to be sensitive to the C-terminals of tachykinins.

The characteristics of the tachykinin-evoked GABA release are very different from those of the ACh release. The GABA release needed a much higher concentration of SP and was Ca^{2+}-independent and TTX-resistant. Furthermore, the GABA release was evoked by an N-terminal analogue, SP_{1-10} amide, but not by a C-terminal analogue, SP_{5-11}. Spantide acted as an agonist, whereas $[D-Pro^4,D-Trp^{7,9,10}]SP_{4-11}$ acted as an antagonist. Some of these characteristics resemble those of the SP-evoked histamine release from mast cells.[13]

The physiological implication of this tachykinin-evoked GABA release is not clear at present. It is possible that our biochemical analyses could not detect the GABA release that is relevant to the physiological actions of tachykinins and that may be Ca^{2+}-sensitive. Recently, Schwartz described a GABA release from retinal horizontal cells that was induced by a depolarization in a Ca^{2+}-independent manner and suggested that it might be mediated by a carrier mechanism.[14] On the other hand, several investigators reported the presence of both Ca^{2+}-sensitive and Ca^{2+}-insensitive components in the GABA release from CNS tissues.[15] That the N-terminal analogue, SP_{1-10} amide, was effective in evoking a release of GABA may be related to the observation of Piercey and Einspahr that electrophoretic application of SP_{1-10} caused an excitation of dorsal horn neurons.[16]

REFERENCES

1. OTSUKA, M. & S. KONISHI. 1976. Substance P and excitatory transmitter of primary sensory neurons. Cold Spring Harbor Symp. Quant. Biol. **40:** 135–143.
2. MATSUTO, T., M. YANAGISAWA, M. OTSUKA, I. KANAZAWA & E. MUNEKATA. 1984. The excitatory action of the newly discovered mammalian tachykinins, neurokinin α and neurokinin β, on neurons of the isolated spinal cord of the newborn rat. Neurosci. Res. **2:** 105–110.
3. OTSUKA, M., S. KONISHI, M. YANAGISAWA, A. TSUNOO & H. AKAGI. 1982. Role of substance P as a sensory transmitter in spinal cord and sympathetic ganglia. *In* Substance P in the Nervous System. Ciba Foundation Symposium 91. R. Porter & M. O'Connor, Eds.: 13–34. Pitman. London.
4. YANAGISAWA, M., M. OTSUKA & J. E. GARCÍA-ARRARÁS. 1986. Effect of GABA and GABA-related drugs on the capsaicin-induced nociceptive reflex in the isolated spinal cord–tail preparation of the newborn rat. Neurosci. Res. Suppl. **3:** S127.
5. AKAGI, H., S. KONISHI, M. OTSUKA & M. YANAGISAWA. 1985. The role of substance P as a

neurotransmitter in the reflexes of slow time courses in the neonatal rat spinal cord. Br. J. Pharmacol. **84:** 663–673.

6. FUJIMORI, K. & K. YAMAMOTO. 1987. Determination of acetylcholine and choline in perchlorate extracts of brain tissue using liquid chromatography–electrochemistry with an immobilized-enzyme reactor. J. Chromatogr. **414:** 167–173.

7. SAKUMA, M., K. YOSHIOKA, M. YANAGISAWA, Y. ONISHI & M. OTSUKA. 1990. Tachykinins induce a release of acetylcholine from neonatal rat spinal cord. Jpn. J. Pharmacol. **52**(suppl. 1): 143P.

8. SAKUMA, M., N. KOBAYASHI, M. YANAGISAWA & M. OTSUKA. 1988. Substance P releases GABA from neurons in the isolated spinal cord of the newborn rat. Jpn. J. Pharmacol. **46**(suppl.): 60P.

9. YOSHIOKA, K., M. SAKUMA & M. OTSUKA. 1990. Cutaneous nerve–evoked cholinergic inhibition of monosynaptic reflex in the neonatal rat spinal cord: involvement of M_2 receptors and tachykininergic primary afferents. Neuroscience **38:** 195–203.

10. BARBER, R. P., P. E. PHELPS, C. R. HOUSER, G. D. CRAWFORD, P. M. SALVATERRA & J. E. VAUGHN. 1984. The morphology and distribution of neurons containing choline acetyl-transferase in the adult rat spinal cord: an immunocytochemical study. J. Comp. Neurol. **229:** 329–346.

11. CHARLTON, C. G. & C. J. HELKE. 1986. Ontogeny of substance P receptors in rat spinal cord: quantitative changes in receptor number and differential expression in specific loci. Dev. Brain Res. **29:** 81–91.

12. YANAGISAWA, M. & M. OTSUKA. 1990. Pharmacological profile of a tachykinin antagonist, spantide, as examined on rat spinal motoneurones. Br. J. Pharmacol. **100:** 711–716.

13. LOWMAN, M. A., R. C. BENYON & M. K. CHURCH. 1988. Characterization of neuropeptide-induced histamine release from dispersed skin mast cells. Br. J. Pharmacol. **95:** 121–130.

14. SCHWARTZ, E. A. 1987. Depolarization without calcium can release γ-aminobutyric acid from a retinal neuron. Science **238:** 350–355.

15. SZERB, J. C. 1979. Relationship between Ca^{2+}-dependent and independent release of [^{3}H]GABA evoked by high K^+, veratridine, or electrical stimulation from rat cortical slices. J. Neurochem. **32:** 1565–1573.

16. PIERCEY, M. F. & F. J. EINSPAHR. 1980. Use of substance P partial fragments to characterize substance P receptor of cat dorsal horn neurons. Brain Res. **187:** 481–486.

Substance P Actions on Sensory Neurons

IGOR SPIGELMAN[a] AND ERNEST PUIL[b]

[a] Playfair Neuroscience Unit
Toronto Western Hospital
Toronto, Ontario, Canada M5T 2S8

[b] Department of Pharmacology and Therapeutics
University of British Columbia
Vancouver, British Columbia, Canada V6T 1W5

INTRODUCTION

There is a great deal of evidence to support a neurotransmitter role for substance P (SP) in vertebrate sensory systems, especially those involved in transmission of nociceptive information and responses to tissue injury (for review, see references 1 and 2). The ionic mechanisms of SP actions on the postjunctional membranes that have been examined in various neuronal and nonneuronal preparations seem to depend on the target cell type (see below). Our findings of SP actions on the cell bodies of neurons in trigeminal root ganglia (TRG) provide a basis for suggesting a complex mechanism that may differ from the mechanisms proposed for the actions at postjunctional targets. In addition, this peptide may exert effects on sensory neurons at multiple sites within the trigeminal system.

SUBSTANCE P AS A NEUROTRANSMITTER

A strong case may be made to support the fact that the major criteria for identifying SP as a neurotransmitter in sensory systems have been fulfilled. SP is synthesized in small-diameter perikarya of sensory neurons[3] and is transported to their peripheral and central terminations.[4,5] SP-like immunoreactivity is localized to synaptic vesicles,[6] within axon terminals without elaborate synaptic structures, and in neuronal contacts with blood vessels.[7] Release of SP-like immunoreactivity has been observed in the periphery[8] and in the central nervous system[9] following stimulation of the peripheral nerve fibers. Excitatory actions of exogenous SP have been observed in spinal motoneurons,[9] in second-order sensory neurons of the spinal trigeminal nucleus,[10] and in postganglionic sympathetic neurons.[11–13] In addition, SP can evoke the release of various compounds from the endothelial cells lining blood vessels,[14] can increase fluid secretion from parotid acinar cells,[15] and can activate several cell types within the immune system.[16] In earlier studies, dialyzed TRG neurons and DRG neurons in culture were reported to be unaffected by SP applications.[17,18] In contrast, SP has been shown to greatly increase the excitability of TRG neurons[19] and ganglion cells in the retina.[20]

MECHANISMS OF SUBSTANCE P ACTIONS AT POSTJUNCTIONAL SITES

Application of SP to spinal cord and brain stem neurons in tissue culture increases their excitabilities by decreasing membrane conductance for K^+.[18,21] Similar membrane effects have been observed in T-lymphocytes.[22] In neurons of the inferior mesenteric ganglia, SP increases conductance for Na^+ in addition to reducing K^+ conductance.[23] In dorsal horn neurons, SP increases a transmembrane inward current that can be blocked selectively by calcium channel blockers such as Co^{2+}.[24,25] SP also can elevate intraneuronal $[Ca^{2+}]$ by releasing Ca^{2+} from internal stores, independent of its influx.[26] Similar increases in internal $[Ca^{2+}]$ have been demonstrated following SP application to mast cells.[27] On the other hand, Ca^{2+} currents as well as Ca^{2+}-dependent K^+ currents are reduced in postganglionic sympathetic neurons.[28] SP also has been reported to increase both a nonselective cationic conductance in parotid acinar cells[29] and a leak conductance that is strongly dependent on the internal $[Cl^-]$ in sympathetic neurons.[28]

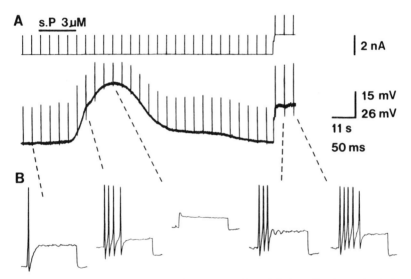

FIGURE 1. Dual effects of SP on spike discharge. A: Short (17 s) application evoked a large reversible depolarization. Resting potential was −58 mV in control conditions. Depolarizing current steps (100 ms, 3 Hz) were used to elicit a spike before SP application. B: Selected traces from A (dotted lines) are shown on a larger scale. Note the repetitive discharge during SP-induced depolarization and the absence of spikes during the peak response. Following recovery, repetitive discharge was evoked from about the same membrane potential at which repetitive discharge was observed during the SP depolarization.

SUBSTANCE P ACTIONS ON SENSORY NEURONS

A majority ($\approx 75\%$) of neurons in slices of TRG have exhibited depolarizing responses to bath applications of SP during intracellular recordings.[19,30] These depolarizations were dose-dependent, at first detected with 10^{-8} M applications, and were maximal at low micromolar concentrations. The abilities of TRG neurons to discharge spikes repetitively are increased during application of the peptide. However, during very large depolarizations, spike discharge is inhibited, presumably due to excessive Na^+ channel inactivation in spike genesis. The increases in repetitive discharge are due to the SP-induced depolarization rather than to any additional effect of the peptide (FIGURE 1). In specialized ganglion cells of the retina, SP may increase both the evoked and spontaneous spike discharges in the absence of detectable membrane depolarization.[20] Thus, the actions of SP on primary sensory neurons are excitatory as are its effects on postjunctional targets at the sites of release.

IONIC MECHANISM OF SUBSTANCE P ACTION ON SENSORY NEURONS

The tetrodotoxin-insensitive responses of TRG neurons to SP are associated with decreased input resistance, although increases in resistance were observed when changes in the membrane potential had been compensated with direct current (DC) injection. The current-voltage (I/V) relationships constructed during single-electrode voltage-clamp (SEVC) recording showed an inward shift in response to SP;

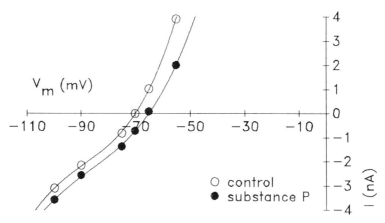

FIGURE 2. I/V relationships obtained from a holding potential of −70 mV in control conditions and during the peak response to substance P application (2 μM). Note the larger reduction in the outward currents compared to the relatively small increases in the inward currents.

greater effects were observed during depolarizing commands that evoked large K^+ currents in these neurons (FIGURE 2). The inability to extrapolate a reversal potential for the SP responses under these conditions suggested that the mechanism may involve activation as well as inactivation of membrane conductances. In ionic substitution experiments, substitution of Ca^{2+} by Co^{2+} did not significantly affect the SP-induced depolarizations in TRG neurons, suggesting that Ca^{2+} influx through Co^{2+}-sensitive channels is not involved in the responses to SP. Similarly, SP-induced increases in the excitability of retinal ganglion cells are maintained during applications of Co^{2+}.[20]

The responses to SP in TRG neurons were reduced by ≈46% in Na^+-deficient solutions, indicating a conductance increase for Na^+ in its mechanism of action (FIGURE 3). SP responses were almost completely abolished in Mg^{2+}-deficient solutions (FIGURE 4). Therefore, Mg^{2+} influx as well as Na^+ influx contribute to the

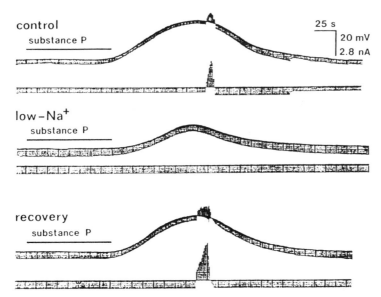

FIGURE 3. Reduction in the response to SP (3 μM) during perfusion with Na^+-deficient solution. Resting potentials were −53, −54, and −53 mV in control, low-Na^+, and recovery conditions, respectively. Ten minutes was allowed for recovery prior to each application of the peptide. (Reproduced with permission from the *Canadian Journal of Physiology and Pharmacology.*)

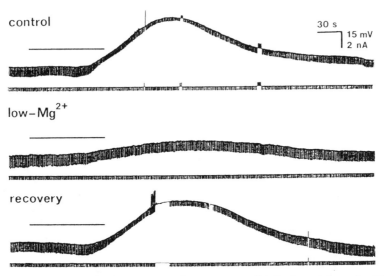

FIGURE 4. Reduction in the response of a neuron to SP (horizontal bars, 2 μM) in Mg^{2+}-deficient solutions. Resting potential was −75 mV during control conditions. Spontaneous depolarization followed recovery from substance P application (top right) and resting potential was maintained at −75 mV with DC injection for subsequent applications of SP at 18-min intervals. (Reproduced with permission from the *Journal of Neurophysiology.*)

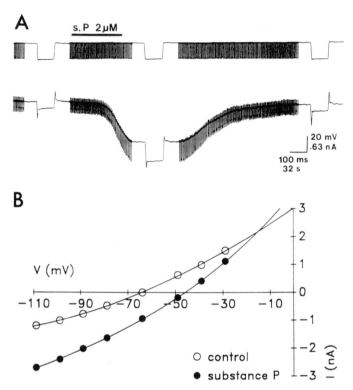

FIGURE 5. A: Effects of SP during K$^+$ channel blockade with 4-AP (1 mM), TEA (10 mM), and Cs$^+$ (3 mM). The upper trace shows the hyperpolarizing voltage commands at two chart recorder speeds. The holding potential was -60 mV. The bottom trace shows the currents evoked by the voltage commands. SP application increased the inward currents. Note the absence of the slow, time-dependent inward currents. B: I/V relationship obtained in another neuron during perfusion with K$^+$ channel blockers (4-AP, TEA, and Cs$^+$) and during concomitant application of substance P (2 μM). The holding potential was -64 mV; the resting membrane potential was -40 mV. The extrapolated intersection of the two curves is at -15.5 mV. (Adapted from the *Journal of Neurophysiology.*)

ionic mechanism, in addition to a probable decrease in K$^+$ conductance. By applying K$^+$ channel blockers, it was possible to isolate the inward current component of the SP response. With the presence of 4-aminopyridine (4-AP), tetraethylammonium (TEA), and Cs$^+$ in the perfusing solutions, SP evoked an inward shift in the holding current and a clear-cut increase in the evoked inward currents (FIGURE 5A). A reversal potential near -20 mV was extrapolated from the I/V curves under such conditions (FIGURE 5B). Responses to SP were also reduced in Mg^{2+}-deficient solutions that contained K$^+$ channel blockers. However, these reductions were much smaller ($\approx 30\%$) compared with those observed during current-clamp recordings without the concomitant application of K$^+$ channel blockers.[30] On the basis of these results, we proposed that the activation of membrane receptors for SP opens nonselective ionic channels, resulting in a net inward current; this leads to a K$^+$ current blockade that is dependent on the external [Mg^{2+}] (FIGURE 6). According to this scheme, Ca^{2+} influx is not essential for the depolarizing response to the peptide. A possible contribution of Cl^- to the inward current cannot be eliminated because the extrapolated reversal potential for the SP-induced responses was more negative (by ≈ 20 mV) than expected for a purely cationic conductance. A contribution of K^+ to the ionic mechanism of SP actions should also be considered because the K^+ channel blockers would not necessarily block K^+ efflux through nonselective channels activated by agonist interactions at membrane receptors.

PHYSIOLOGICAL IMPLICATIONS

The excitatory actions of SP on the perikarya of TRG neurons imply that the actions of this peptide are mimicked at the central and peripheral terminations of the neurons. The autoreceptor concept for SP is reinforced by the observed changes in presynaptic terminal excitability following SP application in the cat spinal cord.[31] In the peripheral nervous system, SP increases the excitability of presynaptic terminals in chick parasympathetic ganglia.[32] Also, prominent sensitizing effects of SP on responses to nociceptive stimulation and hyperalgesic agents have been observed at the peripheral terminations of rat sensory neurons.[33]

Another possible role would require a release of this peptide within the TRG following nociceptive stimulation or under pathological conditions (e.g., trigeminal neuralgia). The virtual absence of synaptic connections in sensory ganglia has led to a widespread view that the perikarya of sensory neurons are nothing more than metabolic factories that sustain cellular elements involved in the transfer of impulses from the periphery to the CNS.[34] However, the perikarya of neurons in sensory ganglia are capable of generating action potentials under normal[35,36] and pathological[37,38] conditions. In trigeminal neurons, SP-induced depolarizations can facilitate the generation of action potentials within the perikarya; the mechanism is suggested

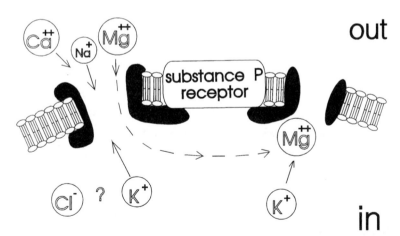

FIGURE 6. Proposed ionic mechanism of SP action in TRG neurons. Activation of receptors for SP leads to the activation of a nonselective ionic conductance. The increased internal $[Mg^{2+}]$, in turn, leads to the blockade of a K^+ conductance. These actions do not require Ca^{2+} influx through voltage-dependent Ca^{2+} channels. Efflux of Cl^- and K^+ may also contribute to the mechanism of SP-induced depolarization.

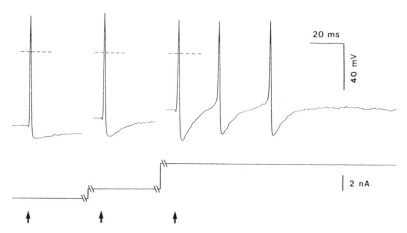

FIGURE 7. Effect of membrane potential changes on the action potential invasion of a TRG perikaryon (upper traces). Arrows indicate the brief stimuli (4.3 V, 0.5 ms) induced by an extracellular electrode positioned in the axonal field distal to the recording electrode. Middle traces correspond to the positive DC applied through the recording electrode. Note the additional spikes that followed the evoked spike when the resting potential was depolarized to −49 mV.

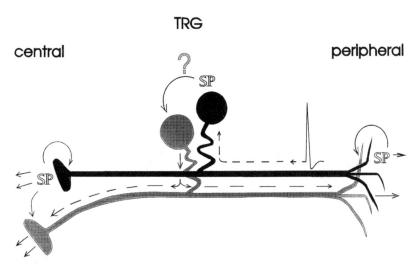

FIGURE 8. Proposed sites of SP actions on TRG neurons. Following the release of SP at the peripheral and central terminals, this peptide may act on autoreceptors at the sites of release and on the terminals of other sensory neurons. Assuming release of SP within the ganglion, the excitability of affected perikarya would be increased. During the SP-induced depolarizations, spikes invading from the periphery would lead to the generation of ectopic discharges, which in turn would travel to the central and peripheral terminations.

by the increase in repetitive discharge observed during SP-induced depolarizations and is depicted in FIGURE 7. The invasion of a single action potential into the perikaryon can result in the generation of ectopic spikes when the membrane potential is depolarized with DC, which mimics the depolarizing effects of SP on TRG neurons. In the event of SP release within the TRG, invasion of action potentials into neurons depolarized by SP would result in production of ectopic spikes that would travel to the central and peripheral terminations, thereby enhancing the overall excitability of the sensory neuron (FIGURE 8).

SUMMARY

SP is involved in sensory transmission as a mediator of excitation at target tissues following its release from the terminals of certain primary afferent fibers. In view of the pronounced SP effects on the perikarya of sensory neurons, it seems reasonable to suggest that its actions may extend to autoreceptors and to the enhancement of the excitabilities of sensory neurons that do not synthesize the peptide. This hypothesis would be strengthened by the demonstration of nonsynaptic release of SP within sensory ganglia, which would provide another site for interaction of SP with the various component cells of the sensory system.

REFERENCES

1. JESSELL, T. M. 1983. Substance P in the nervous system. Handbook Psychopharmacol. **16:** 1–105.
2. DUN, N. J. 1985. Substance P. *In* Neurotransmitter Actions in the Vertebrate Nervous System. M. A. Rogawski & J. L. Barker, Eds.: 385–410. Plenum. New York.
3. HARMAR, A., J. G. SCHOFIELD & P. KEEN. 1981. Substance P biosynthesis in dorsal root ganglia: an immunohistochemical study of ^{35}S-methionine and ^{3}H-proline incorporation *in vitro*. Neuroscience **6:** 1917–1922.
4. HOLTON, P. 1959. Further observations on substance P in degenerating nerve. J. Physiol. (London) **149:** 35.
5. BRIMIJOIN, S., J. M. LUNDBERG, E. BRODIN, T. HÖKFELT & G. NILSSON. 1980. Axonal transport of substance P in the vagus and sciatic nerves of the guinea pig. Brain Res. **191:** 443–457.
6. CUELLO, A. C., T. M. JESSELL, I. KANAZAWA & L. L. IVERSEN. 1977. Substance P localization in synaptic vesicles in rat central nervous system. J. Neurochem. **29:** 747–751.
7. BARBER, R. P., J. E. VAUGHN, J. R. SLEMMON, P. M. SALVATERRA, E. ROBERTS & S. E. LEEMAN. 1979. The origin, distribution, and synaptic relationships of substance P axons in rat spinal cord. J. Comp. Neurol. **184:** 331–351.
8. OLGART, L., B. GAZELIUS, E. BRODIN & G. NILSSON. 1977. Release of substance P–like immunoreactivity from the dental pulp. Acta Physiol. Scand. **101:** 510–512.
9. OTSUKA, M. & S. KONISHI. 1976. Substance P and excitatory transmitter of primary sensory neurons. Cold Spring Harbor Symp. Quant. Biol. **40:** 135–143.
10. ANDERSEN, R. K., J. P. LUND & E. PUIL. 1978. Enkephalin and substance P effects related to trigeminal pain. Can. J. Physiol. Pharmacol. **56:** 216–222.
11. DUN, N. J. & A. G. KARCZMAR. 1979. Effects of substance P on neurons in the inferior mesenteric ganglion of the guinea pig. J. Physiol. (London) **321:** 259–271.
12. KONISHI, S., A. TSUNOO & M. OTSUKA. 1979. Substance P and noncholinergic excitatory synaptic transmission in guinea pig sympathetic ganglia. Proc. Jpn. Acad. **55:** 525–530.
13. KRIER, J. & J. SZURSZEWSKI. 1979. Responses of neurons in the inferior mesenteric ganglion of the guinea pig to substance P. Fed. Proc. Fed. Am. Soc. Exp. Biol. **38:** 958.
14. BENY, J-L., P. C. BRUNET & H. HUGEL. 1986. Effect of mechanical stimulation, substance

P, and vasoactive intestinal polypeptide on the electrical and mechanical activities of circular smooth muscles from pig coronary arteries contracted with acetylcholine: role of endothelium. Pharmacology **33:** 61–68.

15. SOLTOFF, S. P., M. K. MCMILLIAN, L. C. CANTLEY, E. J. CRAGOE, JR. & B. R. TALAMO. 1989. Effects of muscarinic, alpha-adrenergic, and substance P agonists and ionomycin on ion transport mechanisms in the rat parotid acinar cell. J. Gen. Physiol. **93:** 285–319.

16. MCGILLIS, J. P., M. MITSUHASHI & D. G. PAYAN. 1990. Immunomodulation by tachykinin neuropeptides. Ann. N.Y. Acad. Sci. **594:** 85–94.

17. KRISHTAL, O. K. & V. I. PIDOPLICHKO. 1981. Receptor for protons in the membrane of sensory neurons. Brain Res. **214:** 150–154.

18. NOWAK, L. & R. L. MACDONALD. 1982. Substance P: the ionic basis for depolarizing responses of mouse spinal cord neurons in cell culture. J. Neurosci. **2**(8): 1119–1128.

19. SPIGELMAN, I. & E. PUIL. 1988. Excitatory effects of trigeminal neurons to substance P suggest involvement in sensory transmission. Can. J. Physiol. Pharmacol. **66:** 845–848.

20. ZALUTSKY, R. A. & R. F. MILLER. 1990. The physiology of substance P in the rabbit retina. J. Neurosci. **10**(2): 394–402.

21. STANSFIELD, P. R., Y. NAKAJIMA & K. YAMAGUCHI. 1985. Substance P raises neuronal excitability by reducing neuronal rectification. Nature **315:** 498–501.

22. SCHUMANN, M. A. & P. GARDNER. 1988. Substance P modulates potassium channels on T-lymphocytes through a GTP-binding protein. Soc. Neurosci. Abstr. **14**(1): 755.

23. MINOTA, S., N. J. DUN & A. G. KARCZMAR. 1981. Substance P induced depolarization in sympathetic neurons: not simple K-inactivation. Brain Res. **216:** 224–228.

24. MURASE, K., P. D. RYU & M. RANDIĆ. 1986. Substance P augments a persistent slow inward calcium-sensitive current in voltage-clamped spinal dorsal horn neurons of the rat. Brain Res. **365:** 369–376.

25. MURASE, K., P. D. RYU & M. RANDIĆ. 1989. Tachykinins modulate multiple ionic conductances in voltage-clamped rat spinal dorsal horn neurons. J. Neurophysiol. **61:** 854–865.

26. WOMACK, M. D., A. B. MACDERMOTT & T. M. JESSELL. 1988. Sensory transmitters regulate intracellular calcium in dorsal horn neurons. Nature **334:** 351–353.

27. MATTHEWS, G., E. NEHER & R. PENNER. 1989. Second messenger–mediated calcium influx in rat peritoneal cells. J. Physiol. (London) **418:** 105–130.

28. BLEY, K. R. & R. W. TSIEN. 1990. Inhibition of Ca^{2+} and K^+ channels in sympathetic neurons by neuropeptides and other ganglionic transmitters. Neuron **2:** 379–391.

29. SONG, S-Y., S. IWASHITA, K. NOGUCHI & S. KONISHI. 1988. Inositol triphosphate–linked calcium mobilization couples substance P receptors to conductance increase in a rat pancreatic acinar cell-line. Neurosci. Lett. **95:** 143–148.

30. SPIGELMAN, I. & E. PUIL. 1990. Ionic mechanism of substance P actions on neurons in trigeminal root ganglia. J. Neurophysiol. **64**(1): 273–281.

31. RANDIĆ, M., E. CARSTENS, M. ZIMMERMANN & D. KLUMPP. 1982. Dual effects of substance P on the excitability of single cutaneous primary afferent C- and A-fibers in the cat spinal cord. Brain Res. **233:** 389–393.

32. DRYER, S. E. & V. A. CHIAPINELLI. 1985. Substance P depolarizes nerve terminals in an autonomic ganglion. Brain Res. **336:** 190–194.

33. NAKAMURA-CRAIG, M. & T. W. SMITH. 1989. Substance P and peripheral inflammatory hyperalgesia. Pain **38:** 91–98.

34. LIEBERMAN, A. R. 1976. Sensory ganglia. *In* The Peripheral Nerve. D. N. Landon, Ed.: 188–278. Chapman & Hall. London.

35. MILETIĆ, V. & G. W. LU. 1988. EPSP-like activity recorded from cat dorsal root ganglion neurons. Soc. Neurosci. Abstr. **14**(1): 695.

36. HOFFERT, M. J., G. W. LU & V. MILETIĆ. 1988. Spontaneous activity of cat dorsal root ganglion neurons. Soc. Neurosci. Abstr. **14**(1): 695.

37. KIRK, E. J. 1974. Impulses in dorsal spinal nerve rootlets in cats and rabbits arising from dorsal root ganglia isolated from the periphery. J. Comp. Neurol. **155:** 165–176.

38. TAGINI, G. & E. CAMINO. 1973. T-Shaped cells of dorsal root ganglia can influence the pattern of afferent discharge. Pflügers Arch. **344:** 339–347.

In Situ Hybridization of Preprotachykinin mRNA in Cultured Vagal Sensory Neurons

The Effect of Nerve Growth Factor[a]

DAVID B. MacLEAN,[b] LORI HAYES,[b]
AND HARVEY SASKEN[c]

[b]Department of Medicine
[c]Department of Pathology
Brown University
Rhode Island Hospital
Providence, Rhode Island 02903

INTRODUCTION

Within the vagus nerve, substance P (SP) is localized in a subpopulation of unmyelinated sensory fibers derived from the jugular and nodose ganglia. Its release from the peripheral or central terminals of those sensory neurons may mediate a variety of local effector or afferent reflexes regulating cardiovascular, respiratory, or gastrointestinal function. To study the factors regulating SP biosynthesis in and release from vagal sensory neurons, we have developed dissociated cultures of neonatal rat vagal sensory neurons.[1–3] In these cultures, immunoreactive SP is present in approximately 20% of the neurons using immunocytochemical techniques. SP content measured by radioimmunoassay approximates 50–150 pg per plated ganglion; corrected for neuron survival, this is in the range predicted by *in vivo* studies of its axoplasmic transport in the rat cervical vagus nerve.[4,5]

Using this culture model, we have previously shown that SP content is regulated by nerve growth factor (NGF): SP content is doubled in NGF-treated versus NGF-deprived cultures despite no change in the number of surviving neurons. This effect is apparent whether NGF is present from the time of plating or whether it is withdrawn from cultures established in the presence of NGF,[1] demonstrating that the regulation by NGF is dynamic and not just an epiphenomenon of survival of an SP-expressing neuronal subpopulation. Basal and stimulated release of SP from NGF-treated cultures is increased proportionately to its increased content (unpublished observations).

Using immunocytochemical techniques, we have been unable to determine whether NGF increases the expression of SP immunoreactivity within a previously SP-containing subpopulation or whether it induces SP expression within a wider subset of cultured neurons. To study this further and to determine whether the increase in SP content is paralleled by an increase in the steady state level of its messenger RNA(s),[6–8] we have utilized quantitative *in situ* hybridization of preprotachykinin (PPT) mRNA. *In situ* hybridization, in addition to its greatly increased

[a]This study was partially supported by Grant No. NS18705 from the National Institutes of Health.

229

sensitivity compared to Northern blot analysis of extracted mRNA, allows analysis of mRNA expression at the individual cell level. Using this technique in these cultures, NGF increases the average level of expression of PPT mRNA, as well as inducing apparent expression in a larger subset of neurons. Based on image analysis, NGF also has a trophic effect on cultured neurons, significantly increasing their average size.

METHODS

Cell Culture

Sensory neuron cultures were established as previously described.[1-3] Briefly, (1–4)-day-old neonatal rats were anesthetized on ice and were decapitated. The vagal sensory ganglia (nodose and jugular) were dissected and dissociated enzymatically using sequential collagenase and neutral protease.[9] The ganglia were plated on laminin-coated 11-mm or 16-mm miniwells or, for *in situ* studies, on 8-chamber permanox Lab-tek tissue culture slides (Nunc Incorporated, Napierville, Indiana). Plating density was 1 ganglion equivalent per 30 mm^2. Cultures were established for 5 days in nutrient-supplemented L-15/10% fetal bovine serum (FBS), antibiotics, and 100 ng/mL of 7.5S NGF (Collaborative Research, Waltham, Massachusetts); then, they were maintained for a further 7–9 days in the presence or absence of NGF.

Measurement of Immunoreactive SP Content

Cultures in 11-mm miniwells, plated and treated as described earlier, were harvested in hot 1 M acetic acid and were sonicated and lyophilized for radioimmunoassay (RIA). Substance P was assayed as previously described using antiserum no. 190 at 1:64,000. Immunoreactive SP has been previously confirmed as authentic SP(1–11) using HPLC.[3]

Northern Blot Analysis and in Situ Hybridization

β-PPT Probe

Radiolabeled antisense β-PPT cRNA riboprobe was prepared from the plasmid pG1β-PPT, kindly provided by James Krause.[8] The plasmid contains the 0.56-kb β-PPT sequence inserted in the antisense orientation with respect to the T7 promoter site. The plasmid was linearized with Hind III and radiolabeled antisense β-PPT was transcribed using T7 polymerase and a riboprobe transcription kit according to the instructions of the manufacturer (Promega, Madison, Wisconsin). The isotopes used were, for Northern analysis, α-^{32}P-cytidine-5'-triphosphate (800 Ci/mmol) or, for *in situ* hybridization, ^{35}S-α-thiocytidine-5'-triphosphate (1000–1500 Ci/mmol) (NEN, Boston, Massachusetts). The final specific activities of the probes were $(2-5) \times 10^8$ cpm/μg. Sense probes were similarly constructed using Eco RI linearized probe and SP6 polymerase.

Northern Blot Analysis

All studies were performed using (12–14)-day-old cultures. Total RNA was extracted from cultures maintained in 16-mm wells using minor modifications of the method of Chirgwin.[10] The cells were harvested in 5 M guanidium thiocyanate, the suspension was centrifuged, and the supernatant was ultracentrifuged through a cesium chloride cushion. Control tissues were rapidly dissected from adult rats and were homogenized in guanidium and then the total RNA was isolated by ultracentrifugation. RNA from 4–6 culture wells (approximately 4 μg/well) was pooled before centrifugation. Total RNA (12–20 μg/sample) was separated on 0.6 M formaldehyde/ethidium bromide gels and was then transferred by electrophoresis to nylon filters (Zeta-Probe, Bio-Rad Laboratories, Richmond, California). RNA bands were sized using a (0.24–9.6)-kb RNA ladder (BRL, Gaithersburg, Maryland).

Northern blot hybridization was performed at 68 °C in hybridization buffer (5 Prime/3 Prime Incorporated, West Chester, Pennsylvania) containing 50% formamide, 10% dextran sulfate, and $(0.5–1.0) \times 10^6$ cpm/mL probe. The filters were washed under high stringency conditions ($0.1\times$ SSC, 0.1% SDS, at 65 °C) and then were processed for autoradiography. Autoradiograms were analyzed qualitatively using an LKB scanning laser densitometer.

In Situ *Hybridization*

For *in situ* hybridization, the cultures were washed twice in L-15 and then were fixed in 2% paraformaldehyde/5 mM MgCl as described by Lawrence and Singer for cultured cells.[11] Prior to hybridization, fixed slides were stored either at −70 °C for up to one month or, with somewhat better results, at 4 °C under 75% EtOH for 1–7 days.

Fixed slides were prepared for hybridization as described by Segerson *et al.*[12] Briefly, slides were exposed to sequential glycine/PBS and proteinase K (1 μg/mL), 3% paraformaldehyde/PBS to terminate proteolysis, and a 10-min incubation in 0.25% acetic anhydride/0.1 M triethanolamine. Following a 30-min prehybridization in $2\times$ SSC/50% formamide, the slides were incubated overnight at 55 °C in hybridization buffer/50% formamide/10% dextran sulfate containing $(2–3) \times 10^6$ cpm/mL probe. The slides were washed twice in $2\times$ SSC followed by two washes in $0.1\times$ SSC at 65 °C. Following dehydration in graded alcohol/0.3 M ammonium acetate, the slides were air-dried, dipped in NTB-2 emulsion (Eastman Kodak, Rochester, New York), and stored in a desiccated state for 8–14 days. The slides were developed in D-19, fixed, and counterstained with cresyl violet before undergoing image analysis.

Autoradiographic granules of *in situ* hybridized slides were quantitatively analyzed using the Bioquant Image Analysis System (R&M Biometrics, Nashville, Tennessee) linked to a Zeiss Axiophot light microscope. Individual cells within an oil immersion 400× field were outlined using a hand-guided mouse. Autoradiographic granules were highlighted by a pixel intensity thresholding technique. The areas (expressed in pixels) within each cell above, equal to, and below the granule density (transmission) were automatically calculated using a macroroutine. The thresholding technique was visually validated for each section, although it remained relatively uniform within each slide. No objects other than granules were of sufficient low intensity transmission (high density) to be highlighted by the thresholding determination (see FIGURE 3 later).

Control and NGF-treated cells were cultured in four wells each of the 8-chamber slides in varying patterns, so the image analysis was performed in a blind fashion. About 30 to 50 cells/well were analyzed using a predetermined sampling technique that included all cells, regardless of size or granule content, within a sampled field. Analysis of 150–200 cells in three separate experiments was performed. Cell area or granule density area (in pixels) was compared between groups using statistical software packages. Distribution histograms were compared using the nonparametric Kolmogorov-Smirnov test. Overall comparisons between treatment groups were performed using Student's t test.[13] Group values are expressed as the mean ± SD.

RESULTS

Substance P Content

Substance P immunoreactivity in NGF-treated cultures (maintained in 11-mm wells at the same time as those evaluated for PPT mRNA) was double of that in control cultures: NGF, 183 ± 24 pg, versus controls, 84 ± 15 pg per well, $P < 0.01$.

Northern Analysis of PPT mRNA

Using high stringency wash conditions, autoradiographs of blotted RNA extracted from sensory tissue revealed one major band at a position approximating 1100–1200 base pairs (bp). This corresponds to the size of the three described PPT mRNAs (α, β, and γ) that cannot be distinguished using standard formaldehyde gel electrophoresis.[7] Similar bands were present in lanes containing RNA from adult rat striatum, trigeminal, or vagal sensory ganglia, as well as from extracted cultures. No significant hybridization signal was detected in RNA extracted from cortex, cerebellum, or kidney, demonstrating the specificity of the probe hybridization under these conditions. In three experiments, assessing 4–8 culture wells per lane, NGF-treated cultures had similar quantities of total RNA as control cultures, but had 1.5–2 times the PPT hybridization signal. A representative autoradiogram is shown in FIGURE 1.

In Situ Hybridization

Because of the relative insensitivity of Northern analysis, sufficient cultures were not analyzed for statistical analysis. For this reason and in order to determine in which cell subpopulations PPT mRNA was expressed and/or regulated by NGF, analysis of PPT mRNA at the individual cell level was undertaken using the *in situ* hybridization methods described earlier. No autoradiographic granules were present above background levels in support (Schwann) cells or fibroblasts. Although many neurons had none or few granules, a significant subpopulation had numerous granules at levels that were four or more times above background levels. Using image analysis, this corresponded to greater than 120–200 pixels/cell (the range in several experiments) at or below the threshold of the light transmission through granules. A representative field is shown in FIGURE 2. An outlined neuron cell body, with superimposed granules highlighted by pseudocoloring, is shown in FIGURE 3.

A density distribution histogram of cells from NGF-treated or control cultures is shown in FIGURE 4. There is a significant shift to the right, that is, increased granules in NGF-treated cells: $P < 0.01$, Kolmogorov-Smirnov test. In this study, 70% of the control cells were below an arbitrary granule density of 200 pixels/cell compared with 45% of NGF-treated cells. In another study, PPT-negative cells were 78% and 54%, respectively. Furthermore, there were few cells in control cultures with very high granule density, which, in this study, was defined as above 400 pixels per cell. Averaged over all analyzed cells, the granule density was 127 ± 113 in control cells versus 359 ± 366 pixels per cell in NGF-treated cultures (mean ± SD, $P < 0.001$).

The image analysis routine also calculated the total cell size (area) of each analyzed cell body, based on the perimeter outlined by the system operator (as shown in FIGURE 3). A scattergram of studied cells defined by area versus granule density is shown in FIGURE 5. Although many of the points are near the abscissa (cells without granules), there is a general shift upwards and to the right (larger areas) in

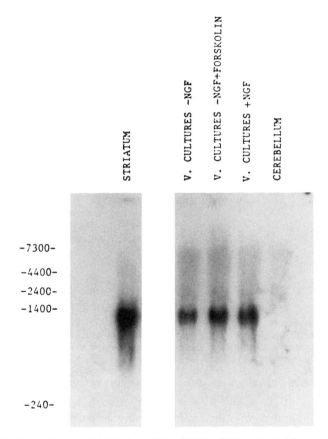

FIGURE 1. Autoradiogram of a Northern blot of PPT mRNA extracted from vagal sensory cultures and rat brain. Using high stringency wash conditions, only a single band was detected corresponding to the (1100–1200)-bp lengths of PPT mRNAs. The total RNA extracted from each group of cultures was similar and, in this study, 16 µg of RNA was run per lane. The band density in the lane of RNA extracted from NGF-deprived cultures is approximately one-half of that of the NGF-treated group. The blot also demonstrates that forskolin treatment of NGF-deprived cultures (10 µM for seven days) reversed the reduction in PPT mRNA (see DISCUSSION).

NGF-exposed cells. Averaged over all cells in this study, the area in control cells was 279 ± 126 µm^2 versus 372 ± 102 µm^2 in NGF-treated cultures ($P < 0.01$).

The distribution of cell size versus NGF-treated or control cells having granule densities above or below an arbitrary threshold of 120 pixels/cell is displayed as a

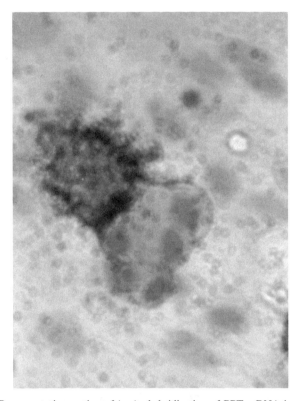

FIGURE 2. Representative section of *in situ* hybridization of PPT mRNA in cultured vagal sensory neurons showing dense autoradiographic granule accumulation in two neurons. Cultures were prepared in Lab-tek tissue culture chambers and were then fixed and studied as described in the text. Note the absence of granules overlying the background cells as well as several of the cresyl violet–stained neurons. Hybridization with radiolabeled sense cRNA probe did not result in similar granule accumulation within the neurons (not shown).

histogram in FIGURE 6. With the exception of very small diameter neurons (<260 μm^2), there is no appreciable shift in the cell size distribution between the NGF-treated and control groups in cells not containing significant granule numbers. Among all cells, there is a significant increase in average size in granule (PPT mRNA)–positive cells. However, within control (non-NGF-treated) cells of the predominant population of 180–500 μm^2, there is no significant increase in cell size in granule-positive cells. This suggests that the overall increase in cell size in granule-positive cells is due to an NGF effect on both PPT mRNA expression and cell size rather than due to a bias in cell sizing caused by the presence of the granules themselves. In contrast, the rightward shift in size distribution of larger diameter (>500 μm^2) PPT mRNA–positive neurons in control cultures may represent their relative independence from the trophic effect of NGF.

DISCUSSION

Among neuron lineages of the peripheral nervous system, nerve growth factor is both a survival and trophic agent.[14] Its survival effect is most evident regarding postganglionic sympathetic neurons and, to a lesser extent, fetal and neonatal DRG sensory neurons. These two cell types are both derived from the embryonic neural crest. On the other hand, a survival effect of NGF on the cranial sensory ganglia derived from the neural placode has not been demonstrated.[15,16] However, NGF is a well-characterized trophic factor for both neural crest–derived and placode-derived neurons. These trophic effects are most easily demonstrated in cultured neurons in which cell morphology can be directly observed. In cultured sympathetic or DRG ganglia, the neurite number and length increase.[17,18] *In vivo*, NGF has similar effects on neurite length and number and enhances neuronal recovery following axonal injury.[14,19,20] Although changes in neuron soma diameter have been less well characterized, Sato noted qualitative increases in cell size in cultured rabbit nodose ganglion neurons.[15]

Neurotransmitter levels in peripheral neurons are also regulated by NGF. In the developing rodent, in the adult rodent following nerve injury, or in cultured DRG neurons, SP levels are either enhanced or, in the case of nerve injury, maintained following exposure to NGF.[19–22] Immunoneutralization of endogenous NGF results in corresponding reductions in SP content.[23–25] These changes occur independent of cell survival, but (when noted) with similarly directed changes in nerve protein. In most

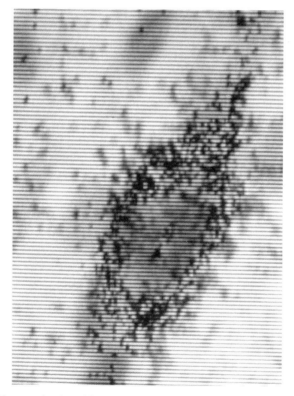

FIGURE 3. Photograph of a video monitor screen demonstrating the procedure of cell outlining and density thresholding of autoradiographic granules (pseudocolored) performed as part of the *in situ* hybridization image analysis routine. The outlined cell represents a medium-sized neuron (30 μm in diameter) that constituted a minority of the analyzed cells.

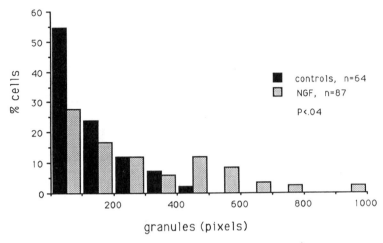

FIGURE 4. Distribution histogram of pixels per cell at or below granule density and representing PPT mRNA in cultured vagal sensory neurons. Cultures were established in normal NGF-supplemented media for five days and were then maintained with or without NGF for a further seven days prior to fixation and study. The rightward shift (increased pixels of granule density) in NGF-treated cultures was significant by Kolmogorov-Smirnov analysis ($P < 0.01$) and demonstrates the stimulation of a presumably previously latent expression of PPT mRNA in a larger subpopulation of cultured neurons.

of these studies, including our own regarding cultured vagal sensory neurons, the total changes in SP range over 40–200% of the baseline peptide content depending upon the withdrawal or supplementation of NGF.

In this study, we have confirmed our previous observations regarding the regula-

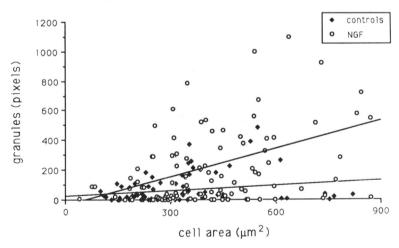

FIGURE 5. Scattergram of the values of pixels of granule density versus cell area of cells maintained with or without NGF and studied by *in situ* hybridization. The values of NGF-treated cells are shifted both upwards and to the right, demonstrating an effect of that trophic factor on both cell size and PPT mRNA expression.

tion of SP content by NGF in cultured neonatal vagal sensory neurons. We have extended these observations to demonstrate that this change in peptide content is associated with corresponding changes in preprotachykinin messenger RNA(s). Using Northern blot analysis, we were unable to differentiate among the three observed forms of PPT mRNA (α, β, and γ); in addition, we did not measure the expression of the other preprotachykinin products, for example, NKA. Based on the relatively uniform variation in the expression of these products in peripheral neural tissue,[6,8] it seems unlikely that their relative expression would be altered by NGF. Our study similarly quantitated steady state levels of mRNA, but did not address whether the changes in observed levels are secondary to either (or both) altered mRNA transcription or increased stability. Tubulin mRNA stability also changes in response to alterations in the axoplasmic transport system:[26] such changes in mRNA stability may be similarly important regarding transported neuropeptides.

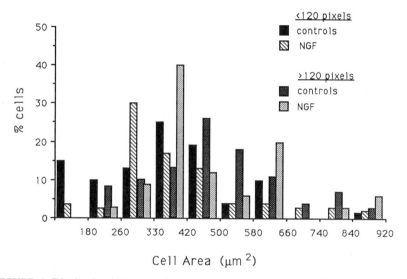

FIGURE 6. Distribution histogram of cell areas of NGF or control cultured neurons with overlying autoradiographic granules either below or above an arbitrary threshold of 120 pixels per cell. In the predominant population of 260–500 μm^2, PPT mRNA–positive cells (>120 pixels) are apparently increased in size in the NGF-treated group, whereas there is no shift in cell size of PPT-positive versus PPT-negative cells in NGF-deprived (control) cultures.

We did not examine sufficient numbers of cultures to statistically analyze NGF-induced changes in PPT mRNA determined by Northern analysis. Instead, exploiting the greatly increased sensitivity of quantitative *in situ* hybridization, we demonstrated an approximate 3-fold increase in PPT mRNA in NGF-treated cultures. In other models of neuropeptide regulation, for example, the hypothalamic-releasing hormone neurons of the paraventricular nucleus of the hypothalamus, there has been excellent correlation between Northern blot and *in situ* hybridization quantification of thyrotropin-releasing hormone or somatostatin mRNAs.[12,27,28] Our findings are somewhat different than those recently reported by Lindsay and Harmar regarding PPT mRNA expression in cultured adult rat DRG.[18] In that study, using exclusively Northern blot analysis, they reported that NGF induced 4-fold to 60-fold increases in PPT mRNA despite only 50–100% increases in peptide content. The reason for this observed difference in steady state changes in mRNA versus peptide content is unclear, but it has not been generally observed in other models of neuropeptide regulation.

In situ hybridization provides additional information regarding mRNA expression within individual cells that is not discernible using Northern analysis. As expected, granule density above background levels was not present in fibroblasts or Schwann cells. Our study confirmed that most PPT mRNA was expressed within a small to medium–sized neuronal population ranging between 200 and 500 μm^2 (18–25 μm in diameter).[29] However, PPT mRNA granules were also present in some larger diameter neurons. In addition, not only did NGF increase the apparent number of granules in the presumably normally expressing subpopulation, but the total number of cells with granule density above threshold was also approximately doubled. Thus, the overall 3-fold increase in the PPT mRNA signal was probably due to enhanced expression within individual neurons, but equally or more so to induction of a previously low level or latent expression of PPT mRNA within another subpopulation. This induction of expression occurred in small, medium, and large diameter neurons. Using immunocytochemical techniques, we have been unable to reliably detect a corresponding increased expression of immunoreactive peptide within this more extensive population. This increase in the number of neurons apparently expressing PPT mRNA is qualitatively similar to that found by Noguchi *et al.* in rat DRG following exposure to a noxious stimulus,[30] in which both the intensity and the percentage of cells with positive signal intensity significantly increased. Induction of vasopressin mRNA in the hypothalamus following adrenalectomy is another example of induction of a previously latent, but tissue-specific expression.[31]

Our quantitative image analysis also confirmed the general trophic effects of NGF, as discussed earlier, on cultured vagal neurons. Cell diameters were significantly increased, particularly in small- and medium-sized neurons. This effect was most notable in PPT mRNA–positive cells. A methodological artifact, for example, preferentially outlining a larger cell perimeter in granule-positive cells, cannot be retrospectively excluded. However, such a shift in size distribution in control treated cultures was less evident, particularly among small and midsized cells. Therefore, we believe it is more likely that the increased PPT mRNA expression and cell size are both comarkers of NGF sensitivity of those particular neurons.

The precise mechanism mediating the effect of NGF on PPT expression is unknown, but it is probably through the interaction with response element(s) on the PPT gene (see J. Krause, this volume). NGF's effect in other systems is mediated through both cyclic AMP– and phorbol ester–mediated transduction pathways[31,32] and a sequence analogous to the cAMP response element is present in the 5′ region of the PPT gene. A serum response element that may be more specific for NGF is also present. We have previously shown that the adenylate cyclase activator, forskolin, reverses the decline in SP levels following NGF withdrawal from the culture medium;[2] by Northern analysis, forskolin also enhances PPT mRNA expression in NGF-deprived cultures (see FIGURE 1). Similar *in situ* studies using forskolin and phorbol esters are in progress to determine their effect on individual vagal sensory neurons.

ACKNOWLEDGMENTS

We thank James Krause for provision of the PPT riboprobe and Paula Grabowski and Ron Lechan for technical advice. Betsy Tavares assisted in typing the manuscript.

REFERENCES

1. MacLEAN, D. B., S. F. LEWIS & F. B. WHEELER. 1988. Substance P content in cultured neonatal rat vagal sensory neurons: the effect of nerve growth factor. Brain Res. **457**: 53–62.
2. MacLEAN, D. B., B. BENNET, M. MORRIS & F. B. WHEELER. 1989. Differential regulation of calcitonin gene–related peptide and substance P in cultured neonatal rat vagal sensory neurons. Brain Res. **478**: 349–355.
3. MacLEAN, D. B., F. WHEELER & L. HAYES. 1990. Basal and stimulated release of substance P from dissociated cultures of vagal sensory neurons. Brain Res. **519**: 308–314.
4. MacLEAN, D. B. & S. F. LEWIS. 1984. Axoplasmic transport of somatostatin and substance P in the vagus nerve of the cat, guinea pig, and rat. Brain Res. **307**: 135–145.
5. MacLEAN, D. B. 1987. Adrenocorticotropin-adrenal regulation of transported substance P in the vagus nerve of the rat. Endocrinology **121**: 1540–1547.
6. NAWA, H., R. HIROSE, H. TAKASHIMA, S. INAYAMA & S. NAKANISHI. 1983. Nucleotide sequences of cloned cDNAs for two types of bovine brain substance P precursor. Nature **306**: 32–36.
7. KRAUSE, J. E., J. M. CHIRGWIN, M. S. CARTER, Z. S. XU & A. D. HERSHEY. 1987. Identification of three rat preprotachykinins encoding both substance P and neurokinin A. Proc. Natl. Acad. Sci. U.S.A. **84**: 881–885.
8. KRAUSE, J. E., J. D. CREMINS, M. S. CARTER, E. R. BROWN & M. R. McDONALD. 1989. Solution hybridization–nuclease protection assays for the sensitive detection of differentially spliced substance P– and neurokinin A–encoding messenger ribonucleic acids. Methods Enzymol. **168**: 634–652.
9. MATHIEU, C., A. MOISAND & M. J. WEBER. 1984. Acetylcholine metabolism by cultured neurons from rat nodose ganglia: regulation by a macromolecule from muscle-conditioned medium. Neuroscience **13**: 1373–1386.
10. CHIRGWIN, J. M., A. D. PRZYBYLA, R. J. MacDONALD & R. J. RUTTER. 1979. Isolation of biologically active ribonucleic acid from sources enriched in ribonuclease. Biochemistry **18**: 5294–5299.
11. LAWRENCE, J. B. & R. H. SINGER. 1986. Intracellular localization of messenger RNAs for cytoskeletal proteins. Cell **45**: 407–415.
12. SEGERSON, T. P., H. HOEFLER, H. CHILDERS, H. J. WOLFE, P. WU, I. M. D. JACKSON & R. M. LECHAN. 1987. Localization of thyrotropin-releasing hormone prohormone messenger ribonucleic acid in rat brain by *in situ* hybridization. Endocrinology **121**: 98–107.
13. SOKA, R. R. & F. J. ROHLF. 1981. Biometry, p. 440. Freeman. San Francisco.
14. PURVES, D., W. D. SNIDER & J. T. VOYVODIC. 1988. Trophic regulation of nerve cell morphology and innervation in the autonomic nervous system. Nature **336**: 123–128.
15. SATO, M. 1985. Different effects of nerve growth factor on cultured sympathetic and sensory neurons. Brain Res. **345**: 192–195.
16. LINDSAY, R. M., H. THOENEN & Y-A. BARDE. 1985. Placode and neural crest–derived sensory neurons are responsive at early developmental stages to brain-derived neurotrophic factor. Dev. Biol. **112**: 319–328.
17. CAMPENOT, R. B. 1977. Local control of neurite development by nerve growth factor. Proc. Natl. Acad. Sci. U.S.A. **74**: 4516–4519.
18. LINDSAY, R. M. & A. J. HARMAR. 1989. Nerve growth factor regulates expression of neuropeptide genes in adult sensory neurons. Nature **337**: 362–364.
19. LINDSAY, R. M. 1988. Nerve growth factors (NG < BDNF) enhance axonal regeneration, but are not required for survival of adult sensory neurons. J. Neurosci. **8**: 2394–2405.
20. GOEDERT, M., K. STOECKEL & U. OTTEN. 1981. Biological importance of the retrograde axonal transport of nerve growth factor in sensory neurons. Neurobiology **78**: 5895–5898.
21. MAYER, N., F. LEMBECK, M. GOEDERT & U. OTTEN. 1982. Effects of antibodies against nerve growth factor on the postnatal development of substance P–containing sensory neurons. Neurosci. Lett. **29**: 47–52.

22. KESSLER, J. A. & I. B. BLACK. 1980. Nerve growth factor stimulates the development of substance P in sensory ganglia. Proc. Natl. Acad. Sci. U.S.A. **77:** 649–652.

23. ROSS, M., S. LOFSTRANDH, P. D. GORIN, E. M. JOHNSON, JR. & J. P. SCHWARTZ. 1981. Use of an experimental autoimmune model to define nerve growth factor dependency of peripheral and central substance P–containing neurons in the rat. J. Neurosci. **1:** 1304–1311.

24. GORIN, P. D. & E. M. JOHNSON, JR. 1980. Effects of long-term nerve growth factor deprivation on the nervous system of the adult rat: an experimental autoimmune approach. Brain Res. **198:** 27–42.

25. SCHWARTZ, J. P., J. PEARSON & E. M. JOHNSON, JR. 1982. Effect of exposure to anti-NGF on sensory neurons of adult rats and guinea pigs. Brain Res. **244:** 378–381.

26. YEN, T. J., P. S. MACHLIN & D. W. CLEVELAND. 1988. Autoregulated instability of β-tubulin mRNAs by recognition of the nascent amino terminus of β-tubulin. Nature **334:** 580–586.

27. MACLEAN, D. B. & I. M. D. JACKSON. 1988. Molecular biology and regulation of the hypothalamic hormones. Bailliere's Clin. Endocrinol. Metab. **2:** 835–867.

28. DYESS, E. M., T. P. SEGERSON, Z. LIPOSITS et al. 1988. Triiodothyronine exerts direct cell-specific regulation of thyrotropin-releasing hormone gene expression in the hypothalamic paraventricular nucleus. Endocrinology **123:** 1191–1197.

29. HENKEN, D. B., A. TESSLER, M-F. CHESSELET, A. HUDSON, F. BALDINO, JR. & M. MURRAY. 1988. In situ hybridization of mRNA for β-preprotachykinin and preprosomatostatin in adult rat dorsal root ganglia: comparison with immunocytochemical localization. J. Neurol. **17:** 671–681.

30. NOGUCHI, K., Y. H. MORITA, H. KIYAMA, K. ONO & M. TOHYAMA. 1988. A noxious stimulus induces the preprotachykinin-A gene expression in the rat dorsal root ganglion: a quantitative study using in situ hybridization histochemistry. Mol. Brain Res. **4:** 31–35.

31. SAWCHENKO, P. E., L. W. SWANSON, J. RIVIER & W. W. VALE. 1984. Co-expression of corticotropin-releasing factor and vasopressin immunoreactivity in parvocellular neurosecretory neurons of the adrenalectomized rat. Proc. Natl. Acad. Sci. U.S.A. **81:** 1883–1887.

32. CREMINS, J., J. A. WAGNER & S. HALEGOUA. 1986. Nerve growth factor action is mediated by cyclic AMP– and Ca^{+2}/phospholipid-dependent protein kinases. J. Cell Biol. **103:** 887–893.

Effects of Substance P on Secretion of Catecholamines from Populations of Bovine Chromaffin Cells and on Calcium Transients in Individual Cells

J. A. KENT-BRAUN, L. K. LYFORD, D. J. GROSS,
AND E. W. WESTHEAD[a]

Program in Molecular and Cellular Biology
University of Massachusetts
Amherst, Massachusetts 01003

INTRODUCTION

As shown in this volume, substance P has a wide variety of effects on different cell types. Previous work has shown that substance P inhibits secretion of catecholamines from cells of the adrenal medulla. These include chromaffin cells from a variety of species, such as guinea pigs,[1] cattle,[2,3] and rats.[4] Substance P has also been shown to alter the desensitization of the nicotinic receptor in chromaffin cells. In experiments by Boksa and Livett[3] and by Khalil *et al.*,[5] it appeared that substance P decreased the rate of desensitization of the nicotinic receptor. On the other hand, electrophysiological studies using the patch-clamp technique demonstrated an enhanced rate of desensitization in the presence of substance P.[6] A direct interaction between substance P and the nicotinic receptor was deduced by Boksa and Livett[3] from the fact that substance P appeared to have no effect on secretion that was stimulated by direct depolarization of the cells. More recently, Yip, Boyd, and Leeman (this conference) have shown chemical evidence for the association of substance P with the nicotinic receptor of these cells.

METHODS

Chromaffin cells were isolated from adrenal medullae by collagenase digestion and centrifugation on a Percoll gradient, as described by Kilpatrick and Kirshner in 1980.[7] Cells were maintained in Eagle's minimal essential medium (Gibco, Grand Island, New York) containing 10% fetal bovine serum, 10 units per mL of penicillin, 2 mg/mL of gentomycin, and 2 μg/mL of nystatin at 37 °C under 5% CO_2 and 95% air. For the experiments described here, purified cells were plated onto fibronectin-coated quartz plates or coverslips. These plates were used either in a flowing system for studies of secretion from populations of cells or under the microscope for single cell calcium transient experiments. The flowing stream system for the study of secretion has been previously described.[8] In this system, stimulants are injected into a constantly flowing stream of buffer and catecholamines are measured immediately

---

[a] To whom all correspondence should be addressed.

downstream from the cells using electrochemical detection. For detection of calcium transients, cells were loaded at 37 °C for 30 min in a solution of 1 μM fura-2/AM and 10 μL/mL of pluronic F-127 (Molecular Probes, Eugene, Oregon). After washing three times with Locke's buffer, the coverslip was mounted in a cell-holder and was placed under the video imaging microscope. The imaging system is based on a Photometrics CCD instrumentation camera and has been described in a previous publication.[9]

Solutions: The Locke's buffer used in perfusing cells in both systems was composed of 154 mM NaCl, 5.6 mM KCl, 2.2 mM CaCl$_2$, 10 mM glucose, and 5 mM 4-(2-hydroxyethyl)-1-piperazinethanesulfonic acid (hepes buffer), pH 7.3.

RESULTS AND DISCUSSION

In the experiments of Boksa and Livett[3] and of Marley and Livett,[10] cells in the culture dishes were stimulated for 5 minutes in two successive incubations. During their first incubation, the cells were stimulated with a cholinergic agonist, with or without substance P (SP). After a very brief wash, they were incubated with stimulant alone. During the first incubation, the presence of substance P inhibited nicotinically stimulated catecholamine release. In the second incubation, those cells that had previously secreted in the presence of substance P released more catecholamine than cells that had been exposed only to the cholinergic agonist. Because cells that had previously been stimulated in the presence of substance P secreted more during the second incubation, it appeared that substance P inhibited the desensitization of the nicotinic response. Our preliminary experiments confirmed these results in detail and showed that DMPP (1,1-dimethyl-4-phenylpiperazinium iodide), a strictly nicotinic agonist, showed the same effects as other cholinergic agonists in the presence of substance P.

In order to examine in more detail the behavior of the cells during the incubation, we adapted the protocol of Livett and co-workers to our flow system. As seen in FIGURE 1, stimulation for 5 minutes, either in the presence of substance P or in its absence, produced almost complete desensitization; that is, the secretion decreased almost to baseline under both conditions. It is apparent from FIGURE 1 that the cells secrete considerably more in the absence of substance P than in the presence of substance P. The cells normally show a decrease in secretion upon repeated stimulation, but FIGURES 2A and 2B, in which only peak heights are shown, demonstrate that, in a series of five stimulations, the normal decrease response has the marked inhibitory effect of substance P superimposed on it. The surprising aspect of FIGURE 1 is that the secretory response in the presence of substance P declines much faster than the response in the absence of substance P. This is contrary to the interpretation that substance P decreases the desensitization to nicotinic stimulation, but is in accord with the more rapid desensitization of calcium entry seen by patch-clamp studies.[6]

The increased rate of desensitization in the presence of substance P apparent in FIGURE 1 is confirmed more quantitatively in FIGURE 3, in which, for the same five sequential stimulations shown in FIGURES 2A and 2B, the logarithm of the height of the declining phase of the secretory curve is plotted as a function of time. The approximately linear nature of the logarithmic function shows that desensitization follows first-order kinetics. The slope of such a curve is proportional to the rate constant and it is apparent that the slopes are much steeper in the presence of substance P.

The question then arises as to why the culture dish experiments, quoted earlier, do not seem to agree with these more detailed kinetic studies. The answer to this question appears in FIGURE 4. In this experiment, two separate incubations, as used in dish experiments, were replaced by the switching of the flowing stream from one that contained both substance P and nicotinic agonist to one that contained nicotinic agonist alone. Cells were stimulated until secretion stopped, that is, until desensitization was complete. When substance P was then removed from the bathing solution (but in the continued presence of DMPP), there was a second slow wave of secretion

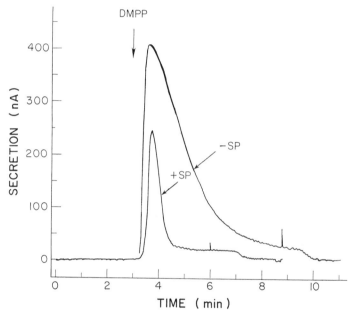

FIGURE 1. Catecholamine secretion and desensitization in response to 10 μM DMPP with (+) or without (−) 20 μM SP. The two curves were obtained by washing the cells for 10 min with Locke's buffer and then switching to buffer with the 10 μM DMPP solution until the cells were desensitized. The starting points of secretion have been made coincident to show the difference in curve shape. The rate constants for the desensitizations shown in these curves were −0.049 s^{-1} with SP and −0.007 s^{-1} without SP. From reference 11.

amounting to a substantial fraction of the secretion that was present in the first stimulation. It is this second burst of secretion that apparently accounts for the enhanced secretion during the second incubation in experiments in culture dishes. In control experiments in which no substance P is present at any point, there is, of course, no secondary secretion because the cells are in the constant presence of DMPP. In culture dish experiments with a prewash between the first and second incubations, the secretion that is seen in the second challenge with nicotinic agonist is a measure of the recovery from desensitization rather than the amount of

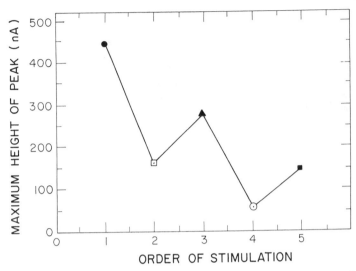

FIGURE 2A. Substance P lowered the maximum catecholamine release and increased the rate of desensitization during long pulses of 10 μM DMPP. The maximum heights of the long pulses in the absence (solid symbols) and presence (open symbols) of SP are plotted in the order that stimulation occurred. Note that the inhibition of secretion that occurred with SP was not due to the natural decline of peak height over time. The stimulations were separated by 20 minutes of washing with Locke's buffer. From reference 11.

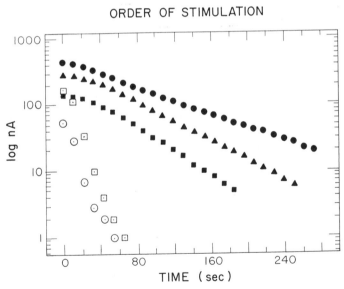

FIGURE 2B. Logarithmic plots of the decreasing phase of secretion from the experiment in FIGURE 2A. Symbols correspond to the peak height symbols of FIGURE 2A. Rapid desensitization occurred in the presence of SP (open symbols). From reference 11.

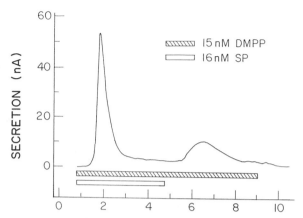

FIGURE 3. Stimulation with 15 μM DMPP, immediately after desensitizing stimulation with 16 μM SP plus 15 μM DMPP, resulted in a second peak with a lower rate of desensitization. Hatched and open bars below the traces show changes in the buffer composition. From reference 11.

remaining undesensitized receptor activity when the first incubation is as long as five minutes. A scheme that might explain these results is the following:

$$\text{Closed Receptor} \rightleftharpoons \text{Open Receptor} \rightleftharpoons \text{Desensitized Receptor}$$
$$\updownarrow$$
$$\text{Closed Receptor–SP}$$

In this scheme, receptors are opened by the binding of nicotinic agonist. Substance P effectively sequesters nicotinic receptors so that they cannot respond to agonist, thus causing inhibition; however, those receptors also cannot become desensitized. Upon removal of substance P and in the continued presence of nicotinic agonist, receptors that had been previously sequestered by substance P would become available. If the removal of substance P from the receptor is not rapid, there will be a gradual increase in the number of responding receptors that will then begin to desensitize. This would give the kind of broad response upon removal of substance P that we see in FIGURE 4.

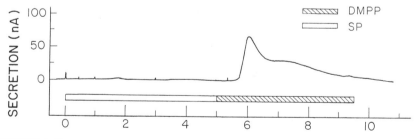

FIGURE 4. Secretory response to 15 μM DMPP stimulation after preincubation with 20 μM SP alone. Preincubation with SP led to a slow, biphasic rate of desensitization during stimulation by DMPP. From reference 11.

The question of whether substance P enhances or inhibits desensitization becomes a semantic one. In FIGURE 4, it is clear that the cells have become desensitized to their particular set of circumstances, but they have not become desensitized fully to the nicotinic agonist. The important distinction is that the rate constant for the desensitization reaction has not changed. What has happened is that some of the receptors appear to have been removed from the desensitization process simultaneously with their inhibition. This sequestration of initially competent receptors appears to explain, at least in part, the apparent change in the rate of desensitization.

Boyd and Leeman[12] have proposed a different scheme in which substance P binds to the desensitized form of the receptor. Their model was based on careful study of the kinetics of receptor desensitization in PC12 cells, using sodium permeability as the indicator of receptor activity. Their model would not explain the secondary response to DMPP after removal of substance P in our system, but the models may be reconciled with further study.

The simple scheme shown earlier serves only as a starting point for the consideration of the effect of substance P. Although Yip *et al.* (this conference) provide evidence for direct association of substance P with the nicotinic receptor, the scheme functions equally well if sequestration is accomplished by an indirect action of substance P, for example, phosphorylation of the receptor.

CHANGES IN CALCIUM TRANSIENTS

It has been shown previously[13,14] that the entry of calcium across the plasma membrane appears to be a necessary and sufficient condition for secretion. In order to see the effects of substance P on the cytosolic calcium transients caused by nicotinic agonist, we turned to single cell imaging experiments, in which the calcium concentration of the cytosol is measured by the fluorescence of the calcium-binding dye, fura-2. With this technique, we can examine a number of individual cells simultaneously under exactly the same stimulating conditions and can observe their individual responses. We would expect the results of these experiments to correlate well with the electrophysiological experiments of Clapham and Neher, who measured the effects of substance P on calcium currents.[6] The first unexpected result of these experiments was that substance P alone could increase the calcium concentration in the cytosol. The data in FIGURE 5 show examples of this. The second unexpected result was that the response of individual cells was highly variable, which is in contrast to the behavior of the cells when stimulated with DMPP. FIGURE 5 shows the fura-2 fluorescence ratio (which increases as cytoplasmic calcium concentration increases) for five individual cells in a single field as the cells are exposed to different solutions. The time is continuous; the noise-free lines indicate the time during which the cells were being washed with Locke's solution in the dark.

Reading from left to right in FIGURE 5, the cells were first stimulated for 1 minute with 50 µM DMPP and then were washed with Locke's solution. All cells responded quickly and with similar increases in cytosolic Ca^{2+}. At 1000 s, cells were treated for 5 minutes with 20 µM substance P (SP). The responses of the five cells varied considerably. Cells 1 and 4 responded quickly; cell 1 showed elevated Ca^{2+} for the entire 5 minutes of exposure to SP, whereas cell 4 showed a transient rise followed by a partial return to baseline. Cell 2 showed no response for 1.5 minutes and then a sharp transient rise followed by a return near baseline and small oscillations. Cell 5 showed a very weak response and cell 3 showed a delayed response with a 2-min plateau. After a wash and rest, a solution of 20 µM SP plus 50 µM DMPP was added.

Again, the responses varied. Cell 1, which showed a strong and prolonged response to SP alone, showed a rapid transient response, whereas cell 3, for example, showed a weaker, but prolonged response. After 5 minutes, during which the Ca^{2+} in three of the cells remained well above baseline, SP was removed by washing with Locke's solution containing only 50 μM DMPP. In every cell, there was a renewed increase in Ca^{2+}, but both the degree of increase and the desensitization (return of Ca^{2+} to baseline) were different. Finally, after a wash and rest, a pulse of DMPP showed that all five cells responded immediately and similarly as they did upon the first stimulation with DMPP.

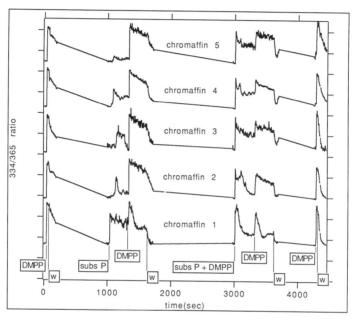

FIGURE 5. Changes of cytosolic calcium concentration in individual cells in response to stimulation. The ratio of fluorescence of fura-2 at two excitation wavelengths is plotted versus time as a measure of cytosolic Ca^{2+} concentration. Cells on a single coverslip were bathed in different solutions as indicated by the boxes at the bottom of the figure. Solutions were changed very rapidly on this time scale at the times indicated by vertical lines. A marked difference in the uniformity of response is seen when comparing stimulations by DMPP and SP.

In many experiments of this type, we have seen oscillations of Ca^{2+} concentration in the presence of SP. In FIGURE 5, oscillations can be seen in cells 1 and 2 when treated with SP alone and in cell 4 when treated with SP and DMPP. The oscillatory effects seen in FIGURES 1 and 3 probably result from calcium release from internal stores. If substance P releases calcium from internal stores, it presumably does so via inositol 1,4,5-triphosphate (IP_3) release. Livett's laboratory (personal communication) looked for effects of substance P on phosphatidylinositol phosphate turnover, but did not find any. However, the stimulated rise in IP_3 is transient in most cells, often peaking within 10–15 seconds. If the cells respond individually, with delays of 1 or 2 minutes, then the concentration of IP_3 in a cell population may rise very slowly and stay very low, even though it reaches a sharp peak of concentration at some particular time in individual cells. These effects of substance P on the cytosolic calcium concentration of chromaffin cells suggest that substance P interactions with these cells are more complex than the binding to and inhibition of the nicotinic receptor. On one hand, the elevation of cytosolic Ca^{2+} could suggest that SP is a partial nicotinic agonist. On the other hand, the varied response of individual cells suggests a process of elevation of some intermediate to a threshold concentration. The intermediate could be IP_3. It seems likely that SP can bind to some receptor in addition to the nicotinic receptor—perhaps to a tachykinin receptor or to the muscarinic receptor that is known to mediate IP_3 release. Further studies with SP in the absence of extracellular Ca^{2+} are needed to test the hypothesis that SP triggers Ca^{2+} release from internal stores.

REFERENCES

1. ROLE, L. W., S. E. LEEMAN & R. L. PERLMAN. 1981. Somatostatin and substance P inhibit catecholamine secretion from isolated cells of guinea-pig adrenal medulla. Neuroscience **6**(9): 1813–1821.
2. MIZOBE, F., V. KOZOUSEK, D. M. DEAN & B. G. LIVETT. 1979. Pharmacological characterization of adrenal paraneurons: substance P and somatostatin as inhibitory modulators of the nicotinic response. Brain Res. **178**: 555–566.
3. BOKSA, P. & B. G. LIVETT. 1984. Substance P protects against desensitization of the nicotinic response in isolated adrenal chromaffin cells. J. Neurochem. **42**: 618–627.
4. OEHME, P., K. HECHT, H. D. FAULHABER, K. NIEBER, I. ROSKE & R. RATHSACK. 1987. Relationship of substance P to catecholamines, stress, and hypertension. J. Cardiovasc. Pharmacol. **S12**: S109–S111.
5. KHALIL, Z., P. D. MARLEY & B. G. LIVETT. 1988. Effect of substance P on nicotine-induced desensitization of cultured bovine adrenal chromaffin cells: possible receptor subtypes. Brain Res. **459**: 282–288.
6. CLAPHAM, D. E. & E. NEHER. 1984. Substance P reduces acetylcholine-induced currents in isolated bovine chromaffin cells. J. Physiol. **347**: 255–277.
7. KILPATRICK, D. L., F. H. LEDBETTER, K. A. CARSON, A. KIRSHNER, R. SLEPETIS & N. KIRSHNER. 1980. Stability of bovine adrenal medulla cells in culture. J. Neurochem. **35**(3): 692–697.
8. HERRERA, M., L-S. KAO, D. J. CURRAN & E. W. WESTHEAD. 1985. Flow-injection analysis of catecholamine secretion from bovine adrenal medulla cells on microbeads. Anal. Biochem. **144**: 218–227.
9. LINDERMAN, J. J., L. J. HARRIS, L. L. SLAKEY & D. J. GROSS. 1990. Charge-coupled device imaging of rapid calcium transients in cultured arterial smooth muscle cells. Cell Calcium **11**: 131–144.
10. MARLEY, P. D. & B. G. LIVETT. 1987. Effects of opioid compounds on desensitization of the nicotinic response of isolated bovine adrenal chromaffin cells. Biochem. Pharmacol. **36**(18): 2937–2944.
11. LYFORD, L. K., J. A. KENT-BRAUN & E. W. WESTHEAD. 1990. Substance P enhances desensitization of the nicotine response in bovine chromaffin cells, but enhances secretion upon removal. J. Neurochem. **55**: in press.
12. BOYD, N. D. & S. E. LEEMAN. 1987. Multiple actions of substance P that regulate the functional properties of acetylcholine receptors of clonal rat PC12 cells. J. Physiol. **389**: 69–97.
13. DOUGLAS, W. W. 1968. Stimulus-secretion coupling: the concept and clues from chromaffin and other cells. Br. J. Pharmacol. **34**: 451–474.
14. KIM, K. T. & E. W. WESTHEAD. 1989. Cellular responses to Ca^{2+} from extracellular and intracellular sources are different as shown by simultaneous measurements of cytosolic Ca^{2+} and secretion from bovine chromaffin cells. Proc. Natl. Acad. Sci. U.S.A. **86**: 9881–9885.

Substance P Interactions with the Nicotinic Response

BRUCE G. LIVETT AND XIN-FU ZHOU

Department of Biochemistry
University of Melbourne
Parkville, Victoria 3052, Australia

INTRODUCTION

Substance P (SP), a member of a family of neuropeptides, the tachykinins, that share certain common functions and the C-terminal amino acid sequence Phe-X-Gly-Leu-Met-NH$_2$, is present in primary sensory neurons in the peripheral and central nervous system of vertebrates where it functions as a neurotransmitter.[1] In addition to its role as a neurotransmitter, SP can act as a neuromodulator: At a number of sites in the nervous system where SP has no action on its own, it modifies the actions of acetylcholine (ACh) on the nicotinic acetylcholine receptor (nAChR).[2] Both inhibitory and facilitatory actions of SP on nicotinic responses have been reported.

First, inhibitory actions of SP on the nicotinic response: Belcher and Ryall[3] and Krnjevic and Lekić[4] showed in the cat spinal cord that electrophoretically adminis-tered SP inhibits the ACh-evoked nicotinic activation of Renshaw cells, but has no effect on the excitation caused by either muscarinic agonists or excitatory amino acids (FIGURE 1). At the frog neuromuscular junction, Steinacker[5] showed that SP (10^{-6}–10^{-4} M) exhibits an initial phase of synaptic inhibition and then a later phase (60–180 min) of synaptic facilitation. At the Mauthner fiber–giant fiber synapse in the hatchetfish, SP shows predominantly presynaptic and postsynaptic inhibitory action[6] and, in rat and chick sympathetic ganglia, SP inhibits the nicotinic depolariza-tion of ganglionic neurons.[7,8] In isolated bovine adrenal chromaffin cells, SP inhibits the ACh- and nicotine-evoked release of catecholamines (CA), but not that evoked by K$^+$, veratridine, or muscarinic agonists[9–12] (FIGURE 2).

In addition, SP enhances ACh-induced desensitization and reduces the number of bursts evoked by ACh.[13] In PC12 cells, SP inhibits the increase in nicotinic agonist–induced ^{23}Na influx and enhances the desensitization of this nicotinic response.[14–17] Furthermore, in perfused rat adrenal gland slices, SP inhibits both presynaptic ACh release and postsynaptic CA release evoked by electrical field stimulation.[18]

Second, facilitatory actions of SP on the nicotinic response: In addition to the aforementioned inhibitory actions, SP shows facilitatory actions in a number of neuronal and endocrine systems. In isolated bovine chromaffin cells, SP (10^{-5} M), present together with high concentrations of ACh or nicotine, completely protects against nicotinic desensitization.[19,20] SP also protects against desensitization of ^{45}Ca^{2+} uptake in these cells.[21] The ability of SP (10^{-6} M) to exhibit inhibitory or facilitatory effects on CA secretion depends on the concentration of nicotinic agonist used[22] (FIGURE 3). Neurokinin A (NKA) and neurokinin B (NKB) also protect against nicotinic desensitization.[23] In the cat spinal cord, SP shows a facilitatory effect on the excitation evoked by nicotine in a minority of the Renshaw cells tested[3] and, at the frog neuromuscular junction, SP facilitates synaptic transmission in the later phase.[5] Likewise, in guinea pig sympathetic ganglionic neurons, physiological studies show

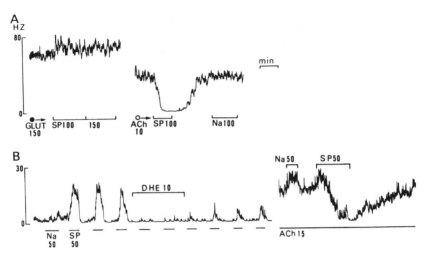

FIGURE 1. Microelectrophoretic administration of SP to two Renshaw cells (A and B). A: Substance P (SP) had no effect on the excitation maintained by continuous administration of glutamic acid (GLUT), but abolished the firing evoked by ACh. A current control ejecting Na^+ had no effect. B: SP caused an excitation that was not maintained during administration. The simultaneous administration of dihydro-β-erythroidine (DHE) abolished the excitatory effect of SP. The ordinate scale shows the frequency of firing (Hz). Microphoretic currents are expressed in nA. (From reference 71.)

that SP (10^{-6} M) facilitates both nerve-stimulated EPSP and ACh-evoked depolarization[24] (FIGURE 4). In PC12 cells, SP increases the response to nicotinic agonists in two ways: (1) by preventing the slow component of agonist-evoked desensitization (which is Ca^{2+}-dependent) and (2) by protecting against carbachol-induced deactivation of the nicotinic response (TABLE 1).[17]

EXPERIMENTAL METHODS

We have studied substance P as a modulator of the nicotinic response in the adrenal medulla [catecholamine (CA) secretion] using four different preparations: (1) isolated bovine adrenal chromaffin cells maintained in monolayer culture; (2) the isolated perfused rat adrenal gland preparation; (3) an anesthetized rat cannulated *in situ*; and (4) conscious freely moving rats with indwelling cannulae for drug administration and blood sampling.

First, in studies on bovine adrenal chromaffin cells in culture, substance P exhibited two actions on CA secretion evoked by ACh and nicotinic agonists.[19,20,22,23] At SP concentrations > 10^{-7} M, SP inhibited nicotinic CA secretion in a dose-dependent manner. Between 10^{-7} M and 10^{-6} M, this inhibition was reversible by $DArg^1, DPro^2, DTrp^{7,9}, Leu^{11}$-SP (RPTTL-SP), an SP antagonist.[22] At high concentrations of ACh or nicotine, SP (10^{-9}–10^{-5} M) facilitated CA secretion by protecting against nicotinic desensitization. This protection against nicotinic desensitization was also reversed by RPTTL.[22] These actions of SP were contingent and long-lasting. In this respect, SP acts as a true neuromodulator, having no direct effect by itself, but acting to modulate the actions of the classical transmitter ACh. Of a number of related tachykinins tested, only neurokinin A and neurokinin B were effective and these were 30-fold less effective than SP in their ability to inhibit the nicotinic response and to protect against nicotinic desensitization. All three mammalian tachykinins were approximately 10-fold more potent at protecting against desensitization than at inhibiting the nicotinic response.[23] This compares with (i) somatostatin, which was 10-fold less active than SP at inhibiting the nicotinic response[10,25] (FIGURE 2) and had no effect on protection,[26] and (ii) the enkephalins, which were 100-fold less potent as inhibitors and failed to protect against nicotinic desensitization.[27]

Second, in studies on isolated perfused rat adrenal glands *in vitro*, SP again acted biphasically. The effects of both short-term and long-term stimulation were examined. Following short-term stimulation[28] (6 min, 10 Hz)—(i) At low concentrations, SP (10^{-7}–3×10^{-6} M) potentiated the release of CA by up to 56%, whereas it inhibited the release of ^{3}H-ACh by up to 60%; (ii) at higher concentrations, SP (3×10^{-5} M) inhibited the release of CA by 39% and inhibited the release of ^{3}H-ACh by 33%. We conclude that the potentiation of CA release by SP is primarily the result of a postsynaptic event rather than a presynaptic facilitation of ACh release from splanchnic nerve terminals. Following long-term stimulation[29] (60 min, 10 Hz) (FIGURE 5)—First, SP (10^{-6} M) potentiated the release of CA evoked by a subse-

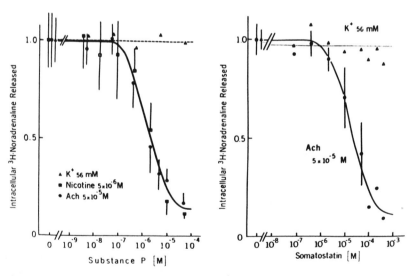

FIGURE 2. Left panel: Effect of substance P on [^{3}H]NA secretion from primary monolayer cultures of bovine adrenal chromaffin cells evoked by ACh (●), nicotine (■), and K^{+} (▲). Note that SP inhibited the nicotinic response in a dose-dependent manner, but had no effect on the secretion evoked by 56 mM K^{+}. The response to the various agonists has been normalized to 1.0, which is the response to an EC$_{50}$ concentration of agonist alone (i.e., in the absence of SP). The percentage of the total intracellular [^{3}H]NA released (mean ± SD) in the presence of the secretogogue alone was as follows: 5×10^{-5} M ACh, 21.6 ± 3.1% ($n = 14$); 5×10^{-6} M nicotine, 16.8 ± 2.4% ($n = 5$); 56 mM K^{+}, 15.1 ± 1.8% ($n = 4$). Right panel: Effect of somatostatin on the [^{3}H]NA release from the cells evoked by ACh and K^{+}. The percentage of the total intracellular [^{3}H]NA released (mean ± SD) in the presence of the secretogogue alone was as follows: 5×10^{-5} M ACh, 21.1 ± 1.7% ($n = 6$); 56 mM K^{+}, 12.5 ± 0.7% ($n = 4$). (From reference 10.)

quent period of field stimulation at 1 Hz. SP also potentiated CA secretion if perfused through the adrenal gland at the end of the 10-Hz stimulation period. Second, SP (10^{-7}–10^{-6} M) potentiated the release of ^{3}H-ACh evoked by a 1-Hz field stimulation. However, SP did not potentiate the release of CA evoked by 1-Hz stimulation if not preceded by a period of 10-Hz stimulation or in the absence of electrical stimulation. This indicates that SP was acting as a neuromodulator rather than as a neurotransmitter. Following neonatal capsaicin treatment or capsaicin perfusion[30]—In response to prolonged field stimulation, CA secretion declined more

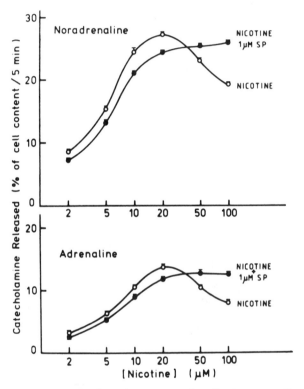

FIGURE 3. Dose-response curves for endogenous noradrenaline (upper panel) and adrenaline (lower panel) release induced by different concentrations of nicotine from cultured bovine chromaffin cells in the absence (O) and presence (●) of 10^{-6} M SP. Results for each concentration are given as the mean ± SD ($n = 8$). (From reference 22.)

rapidly in glands from rats pretreated as neonates with capsaicin than from glands of vehicle-pretreated rats. When SP (10^{-6} M) was present in the perfusion stream, CA secretion increased more in the glands from capsaicin-pretreated rats than from the glands of vehicle-pretreated rats. These findings raise the possibility that endogenous SP in the splanchnic nerve and adrenal gland may prevent desensitization of CA secretion and that exogenous SP can reverse the desensitization induced by prolonged high frequency field stimulation. Because these results suggested that SP *in vivo* in the splanchnic nerve may maintain adrenal CA secretion during stress,

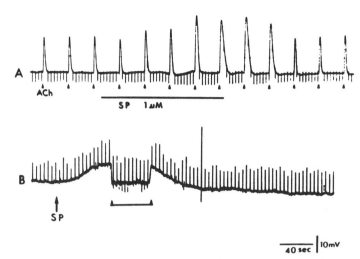

FIGURE 4. Potentiation of nicotinic depolarizations by SP in two guinea pig inferior mesenteric ganglion (IMG) neurons. A: ACh depolarizations were induced by pressure ejection of ACh (arrowheads, 20-ms pulse duration). Hyperpolarizing electronic potentials (small downward deflections) elicited by constant hyperpolarizing current pulses (not shown) were used to monitor the membrane input resistance change. SP (1 μM) was applied to the ganglion by superfusion as indicated by the bar. B: Subthreshold f-EPSPs (small upward deflections) were induced by stimulation of the right hypogastric nerve. The amplitude of the f-EPSPs was slightly increased on the rising phase of the SP depolarization that was induced by pressure ejection of SP (arrow, 100-ms pulse duration). A greater (38%) increase of the f-EPSPs could be detected when the membrane potential was restored to the resting level by hyperpolarizing currents (between the two arrowheads). Recordings from A and B were obtained from two separate IMG neurons. (From reference 24.)

additional experiments were carried out in anesthetized animals and in freely moving conscious rats where this hypothesis could be tested directly (see discussion later). Following nicotinic and muscarinic stimulation[31]—SP (10^{-10}–10^{-7} M) changed the time course of CA secretion evoked by nicotine, resulting in an increase in CA

TABLE 1. Inhibition of Carbamylcholine-induced Receptor Deactivation by SP

Preincubation Condition	Initial Rate of $^{22}Na^+$ Influx Measured after a 20-min Recovery Period[a]	Percentage of Extent of Deactivation[b]
Buffer only	100	0
100 μM carbamylcholine	75 ± 5	23
100 μM carbamylcholine + 1 μM SP	96 ± 6	<5
1 mM carbamylcholine	58 ± 6	42
1 mM carbamylcholine + 1 μM SP	83 ± 5	<17
1 μM SP	95 ± 7	<5

[a]Initial rate measurements are expressed as the percentage of control values ± SD ($n = 4$).
[b]Deactivation is defined as the nonrecoverable component of the permeability response expressed as a percentage of control values. (From reference 17.)

secretion in the first four minutes and a decrease in the following six minutes. SP (10^{-9}–10^{-5} M) had no effect on the CA secretion evoked by muscarine.

Third, studies on the anesthetized rat cannulated *in situ* showed that the adrenal could not maintain its neurogenic output of catecholamines in response to stress if SP was depleted from the splanchnic nerve of the rat by neonatal pretreatment with capsaicin.[32-34] Three stressors were studied: insulin hypoglycemia, cold stress, and

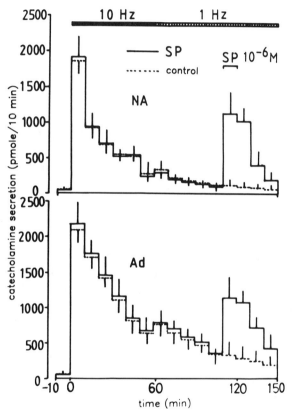

FIGURE 5. Effect of SP on CA secretion evoked by prolonged field stimulation from perfused rat adrenal glands. The glands were stimulated at 10 Hz, 60 volts, and 3-ms pulse duration continuously for 60 min and then with 1 Hz for 90 min. SP at 1 μM was present in the perfusion stream for 10 min after 2 hours (during stimulation with 1 Hz) as shown in the figure. The 10-min fractions were collected continuously for CA assay. Data are plotted as the means ± SEM of five experiments. (From reference 29.)

histamine stress. With all three, the neurogenic component of adrenal CA release was abolished in the capsaicin-pretreated animals. These results suggest that SP-containing (capsaicin-sensitive) components in the splanchnic nerve are essential for maintaining adrenal CA output in response to metabolic and physical stress.

Last, in studies on conscious freely moving rats with indwelling cannulae for drug administration and blood sampling, a number of different stressors have been studied. First, insulin-induced hypoglycemia[35]—Adrenaline (Ad) and noradrenaline (NA) were released in response to the hypoglycemia, but there was no difference in the response of vehicle- and capsaicin-pretreated animals. It is possible that the nature of the stimulus necessary to evoke CA release masked any effects of the capsaicin-sensitive components in the splanchnic nerve or, more likely, that the pharmacology was complicated by the presence of somatostatin, which we previously showed could inhibit the nicotinic response of the adrenal medullary chromaffin cells. Second, 2-deoxyglucose (2-DG)[36]—Infusion of 2-DG produced a marked release of adrenaline into the circulation, but once again this adrenal CA release was not inhibited by prior treatment of the rats with capsaicin as neonates. Third, cold stress, swimming stress, hypovolemic stress, and immobilization stress[37]—Capsaicin-sensitive sensory neurons in the conscious rat were required for the plasma CA response to cold stress and for the early phase of swimming stress (both of which activate pathways primarily concerned with release of NA from sympathetic nerve terminals). They were not required for the plasma CA response to hypovolemic stress and immobilization stress. These results indicate that, in the freely moving conscious rat under conditions of stress, SP-containing capsaicin-sensitive sensory fibers are involved in the maintenance of plasma NA levels (derived from NA released from sympathetic nerve endings), but not in the maintenance of plasma Ad levels (derived from the adrenal medulla). This contrasts with the situation in the anesthetized rat[37] and in isolated perfused rat adrenal glands,[28-31] where capsaicin-sensitive sensory fibers are involved in the modulation of adrenal CA secretion.

DISCUSSION

How does SP inhibit the nicotinic response? Several lines of evidence have shown that SP does not act as a classical competitive antagonist, but rather as a compound that modulates receptor activity by binding to a distinct regulatory site.[14,15,17,38] Studies on PC12 cells have shown that the site of action of SP is localized to the nicotinic receptor–ionophore complex, possibly within the ion channel itself, because the effects of SP are competed for by histrionicotoxin.[14] In the absence of nicotinic agonists, SP alone can interact with the nicotinic receptors to lessen the responsiveness of PC12 cells to subsequent nicotinic activation.[15,17] In the presence of nicotinic agonists, SP enhances the rate of nicotinic desensitization by changing the state of the receptor-linked ionophore complex.[16,17] In bovine chromaffin cells, we found that SP has no effect on voltage-sensitive channels activated by K^+ depolarization or veratridine and does not affect secretion evoked by Ca^{2+} ionophores such as A23187. Although SP inhibits the carbachol-evoked calcium uptake in isolated bovine chromaffin cells, it does not interact directly with calcium channels[21] and there is no evidence that SP influences intracellular Ca^{2+} levels in chromaffin cells.

How does SP facilitate the nicotinic response? Several ideas have been proposed: SP may increase the nicotinic response by changing the conductance of the ion channels. It has been reported that SP at 10^{-7} M depolarizes sympathetic neurons in the guinea pig by increasing sodium permeability and decreasing potassium permeability.[39] In autonomic ganglia, SP (10^{-7}–4×10^{-6} M) mimics the noncholinergic slow excitatory postsynaptic potential (EPSP).[40] Moreover, it has been shown that SP at 10^{-7} M depolarizes rat chromaffin cells from the adrenal medulla by approximately 20 mV.[41] SP at $(3–20) \times 10^{-6}$ M, by pressure ejection, enhances one type of Ca^{2+} current[42] and suppresses voltage-sensitive K^+ conductance[43] in isolated smooth muscle cells. Furthermore, in a neuronal cell line, SP at micromolar concentrations enhances sodium uptake.[44]

It is possible that SP plays a facilitatory role via second messenger systems. It is well known that SP can stimulate hydrolysis of phospholipids and produce accumulation of inositol trisphosphate and diacylglycerol in many tissues including guinea pig ileum, rat hypothalamus,[45] hamster urinary bladder,[46] rat parotid gland,[47] and rat skin.[48] Although SP has no effect on metabolism of phosphatidylinositol phosphates (PIP) in bovine chromaffin cells,[49] it does have a stimulating effect on PIP metabolism in the rat adrenal medulla.[50,51] An increase in cytosolic mobilization of calcium by inositol 1,4,5-trisphosphate and the activation of protein kinase C by diacylglycerol may prime the calcium-sensitive secretory process so as to facilitate secretion by nicotine.[52]

The following questions also arise: Why does SP show both inhibitory and facilitatory actions in the same preparation[3,13,14,20] and what physiological role does SP play *in vivo*? In attempting to answer these questions, several factors should be considered. First, it is known that at least three tachykinin receptors are present in mammalian tissues. Different receptor subtypes may regulate different responses.[53] Second, the effect of SP on the nicotinic response may depend on the physiological status of the preparation. For example, SP can show analgesic or hyperanalgesic effects on mice depending on its previous stress experience.[54] Third, SP can exhibit different effects with different concentrations.[28] With higher concentrations, SP may show inhibitory effects; at lower concentrations, SP may show facilitatory effects. Finally, the effect of SP may be dependent upon the time scale.[31] At different time scales, SP may have different effects. For example, electrophysiological studies on adrenal chromaffin cells demonstrated that SP enhanced ACh-induced desensitization within seconds,[13] but biochemical studies in the same preparation showed that SP protected against nicotinic desensitization of CA secretion over five minutes.[20] In PC12 cells, SP enhanced the fast phase of Na^+ uptake, but inhibited the slow phase of the nicotinic desensitization and protected against deactivation of the nicotinic response (TABLE 1).[17,55]

What is the physiological significance of these modulatory actions of SP? The various observations that SP protected the nicotinic response *in vitro* against desensitization led to the idea that SP may function *in vivo* to maintain CA output during stress. In support of this hypothesis, Khalil *et al.* have used capsaicin-pretreated rats in which SP was specifically depleted in the splanchnic nerve and have investigated the effect of SP-containing capsaicin-sensitive nerve fibers on adrenal CA output in response to stress in the anesthetized rat. Their results showed that, in the capsaicin-pretreated rat, adrenal CA output was abolished in response to either insulin-hypoglycemic stress[32,33] or the neural component of histamine-induced stress.[34] The finding was confirmed by Amann and Lembeck,[56] who found that urinary adrenaline levels were reduced in the capsaicin-pretreated rat after insulin hypoglycemia. These results suggested that SP may be involved in the regulation of stress-induced adrenal CA secretion. Oehme and Krivoy[54] reported an inhibitory effect of SP on stress-induced disorders and suggested that the "anti-stress effect" of SP may be mediated by an influence of SP on adrenal CA. *In vivo* dialysis has been used to show that SP is released locally in the rat adrenal in response to mild stress, where it is thought to exert a paracrine influence on CA release.[57] This view is supported by the inability of capsaicin-pretreated rats to secrete adrenal CA in response to hypoglycemic, cold, and histamine stress[32–34] and in response to electrical stimulation of the adrenal gland.[30,37]

Given the difficulty that others have had in demonstrating a role for presynaptic adrenoceptors in transmitter release *in vivo*, it may not be too surprising that our attempts to demonstrate control of peripheral adrenal CA release by neuropeptides *in vivo* were inconclusive.

The remarkable capacity of the conscious animal to regulate homeostasis indicates that other mechanisms exist that can overcome the desensitization behavior of the adrenal nicotinic response. The exact nature of these mechanisms remains to be determined, but it is likely that postsynaptic components of the "secretory cocktail"[58] and release of other peptides presynaptically, such as vasoactive intestinal polypeptide (VIP)[59] and angiotensin II,[60] influence the nicotinic receptor response to a variety of stressors. Moreover, both C-terminal and N-terminal residues are important for SP action: Structure-activity studies have demonstrated the importance of the SP C-terminus in SP action as a neurotransmitter.[61] The N-terminal residues are also important for certain actions of SP. Studies with N-terminal and C-terminal SP fragments on pain control in mice[54,62] have shown that the N-terminal sequence possesses the hyperalgesic component and the C-terminus possesses the analgesic component of action. Furthermore, N-terminal fragments excite cat dorsal horn neurons,[63] produce enhanced rearing in rats (a motor effect unique to SP),[64] prevent the stress-induced involution of the rat thymus,[65] and inhibit angiotensin-converting enzyme (ACE) activity.[66,67] As discussed earlier, these functional studies led to the concept of SP as a bifunctional regulatory molecule or "regulide".[54]

In adrenal chromaffin cells, SP, NKA, and NKB are more effective at protecting against nicotinic desensitization than in inhibiting nicotinic CA secretion,[23] and NKA and NKB are 30 times less potent than SP in these actions. There is a high degree of sequence homology in the C-terminal regions of these three peptides, which contain the sequence common to all tachykinins; however, the N-terminal regions differ markedly. This indicates that the N-terminal residues are important for the activity of tachykinins on chromaffin cells. In addition, all N-terminal fragments of SP show potency in competing for ³H-SP binding to bovine adrenal medulla membranes (see following discussion).

Structure-function studies with SP and analogues in isolated chromaffin cells and PC12 cells have shown that SP is the most potent peptide in modulating nicotinic receptor functions.[16,17,19,23] The other mammalian tachykinins and C-terminal or N-terminal SP fragments are much less potent than SP. The functional studies show that both C- and N-terminal sequences of SP are required for the inhibitory action on nicotinic function.

Removal of the highly charged amino-terminal residue, Arg-Pro-Lys, results in a greater than 30-fold loss in activity (TABLE 2).[17] Recent receptor binding studies by Geraghty *et al.*[68] have shown that bovine adrenal medullary membranes possess a novel class of SP binding sites distinct from the classical NK$_1$, NK$_2$, and NK$_3$ receptors. SP binding sites in the adrenal medulla require both the N- and C-terminal structures of SP (TABLE 3). It is of interest that the N-terminal fragment SP(1–9) was equipotent with the C-terminal fragment SP(3–11) in both the functional studies on PC12 cells[17] and the receptor binding studies on adrenal medullary membranes[68] (compare TABLES 2 and 3). The SP receptor on adrenal chromaffin cells has certain similarities to the mast cell SP receptor[69] and to the N-terminal-directed receptor in the central nervous system,[63] suggesting that this novel SP receptor may be more widely distributed.

The nicotinic receptor on adrenal chromaffin cells: Much of what is known about the nicotinic acetylcholine receptor (nAChR) comes from studies of *Torpedo* and *Electrophorus electricus* electric organs and from skeletal muscle. These nAChRs have been shown to be multiply phosphorylated by at least three protein kinase systems, namely, cAMP-dependent protein kinase, protein kinase C, and tyrosine kinase. The phosphorylation of these receptors has a regulatory effect on the rate of

TABLE 2. Relative Potencies of SP Fragments and Analogues in Inhibiting Carbamylcholine-stimulated $^{22}Na^+$ Influx in PC12 Cells[a]

	Fragments	Relative Potency
	Carboxy-terminal fragments	
SP	Arg-Pro-Lys-Pro-Gln-Gln-Phe-Phe-Gly-Leu-Met-NH$_2$	100
SP$_{3-11}$	Lys-Pro-Gln-Gln-Phe-Phe-Gly-Leu-Met-NH$_2$	25
SP$_{4-11}$	Pro-Gln-Gln-Phe-Phe-Gly-Leu-Met-NH$_2$	3
SP$_{6-11}$	Gln-Phe-Phe-Gly-Leu-Met-NH$_2$	3
SP$_{7-11}$	Phe-Phe-Gly-Leu-Met-NH$_2$	5
SP$_{8-11}$	Phe-Gly-Leu-Met-NH$_2$	0.8
	Amino-terminal fragments	
SP COOH	Arg-Pro-Lys-Pro-Gln-Gln-Phe-Phe-Gly-Leu-Met-COOH	3
SP ester	Arg-Pro-Lys-Pro-Gln-Gln-Phe-Phe-Gly-Leu-Met-OMe	50
SP$_{1-10}$	Arg-Pro-Lys-Pro-Gln-Gln-Phe-Phe-Gly-Leu-NH$_2$	38
SP$_{1-9}$	Arg-Pro-Lys-Pro-Gln-Gln-Phe-Phe-Gly-NH$_2$	25
SP$_{1-9}$ COOH	Arg-Pro-Lys-Pro-Gln-Gln-Phe-Phe-Gly-COOH	0.4
SP$_{1-8}$	Arg-Pro-Lys-Pro-Gln-Gln-Phe-Phe-NH$_2$	6
	Peptide analogues	
[Nle^{11}]-SP	Arg-Pro-Lys-Pro-Gln-Gln-Phe-Phe-Gly-Leu-Nle-NH$_2$	63
[Tyr^8]-SP	Arg-Pro-Lys-Pro-Gln-Gln-Phe-Tyr-Gly-Leu-Met-NH$_2$	83
eledoisin	pGlu-Pro-Ser-Lys-Asp-Ala-Phe-Ile-Gly-Leu-Met-NH$_2$	<0.3
physalaemin	pGlu-Ala-Asp-Pro-Asp-Lys-Phe-Tyr-Gly-Leu-Met-NH$_2$	1.0
neurokinin A	His-Lys-Thr-Asp-Ser-Phe-Val-Gly-Leu-Met-NH$_2$	6

[a]Increasing concentrations of the various peptides examined were added with 500 μM carbamylcholine, and tracer $^{22}Na^+$ taken up by PC12 cells in 60 s was determined. The data were analyzed by constructing inhibition curves for each peptide. From these plots, the concentration of peptide that reduces the permeability response by 50% (IC$_{50}$) was estimated. Values are expressed relative to the parent compound; SP = 100%; IC$_{50}$ = 250 nM. (From reference 17.)

TABLE 3. Competition by Substance P (SP) and SP Fragments for Specific [^{3}H]SP Binding[a]

Peptide	Amino Acid Sequence											K_d (nM)	PR (%)
	1	2	3	4	5	6	7	8	9	10	11		
SP	Arg-Pro-Lys-Pro-Gln-Gln-Phe-Phe-Gly-Leu-Met-NH$_2$											2.14 ± 1.28	100
NKA	His-Lys-Thr-Asp-Ser-Phe-Val-Gly-Leu-Met-NH$_2$											32 ± 12	6.7
NKB	Asp-Met-His-Asp-Phe-Phe-Val-Gly-Leu-Met-NH$_2$											~4000	<0.50
SP(3–11)	Lys-Pro-Gln-Gln-Phe-Phe-Gly-Leu-Met-NH$_2$											54 ± 15	4.0
SP(5–11)	Gln-Gln-Phe-Phe-Gly-Leu-Met-NH$_2$											>10,000	>0.05
SP(7–11)	Phe-Phe-Gly-Leu-Met-NH$_2$											>10,000	>0.05
SP(9–11)	Gly-Leu-Met-NH$_2$											>10,000	>0.05
SP(1–3)	Arg-Pro-Lys											3570 ± 703	0.06
SP(1–4)	Arg-Pro-Lys-Pro											411 ± 98	0.52
SP(1–6)	Arg-Pro-Lys-Pro-Gln-Gln											438 ± 89	0.49
SP(1–7)	Arg-Pro-Lys-Pro-Gln-Gln-Phe											383 ± 78	0.56
SP(1–9)	Arg-Pro-Lys-Pro-Gln-Gln-Phe-Phe-Gly											58 ± 19	3.7
Tuftsin	Thr-Lys-Pro-Arg											12,800 ± 2120	0.02

[a]Values for the equilibrium dissociation constants (K_d) were derived using the nonlinear curve fitting program LIGAND and are the geometric mean ± SE (approximate) of 3–5 determinations. PR = potency relative to SP. (From reference 69.)

desensitization.[70] In cells of neuronal origin, including the adrenal medulla, SP has been implicated in modulating nicotinic receptor desensitization;[12–14,17,22] however, the role of SP in phosphorylation of these neuronal AChRs has not been studied.

In conclusion, the studies discussed in this report indicate that the neuropeptide SP has powerful modulatory effects on the nicotinic receptor, both on chromaffin cells and elsewhere in the nervous system, by an action on a novel class of tachykinin receptor. Future work will be directed at experiments designed to look at the molecular form(s) of the endogenous SP molecule(s) in the adrenal medulla, the relationship of the novel SP binding site to the functional nicotinic receptor, and the role of SP and congeners in desensitization of the nicotinic receptor.

REFERENCES

1. MARLEY, P. D. & B. G. LIVETT. 1985. Neuropeptides in the autonomic nervous system. CRC Crit. Rev. Clin. Neurobiol. **1:** 201–283.
2. LIVETT, B. G. 1987. Peptide modulation of adrenal chromaffin cell secretion. *In* Stimulus-Secretion Coupling in Chromaffin Cells. Volume II. K. Rosenheck & P. I. Lelkes, Eds.: 177–204. CRC Press. Boca Raton, Florida.
3. BELCHER, G. & R. W. RYALL. 1977. Substance P and Renshaw cells: a new concept of inhibitory synaptic interactions. J. Physiol. (London) **272:** 105–119.
4. KRNJEVIC, K. & D. LEKIC. 1977. Substance P selectively blocks excitation of Renshaw cells by acetylcholine. Can. J. Physiol. Pharmacol. **55:** 958–961.
5. STEINACKER, A. 1977. Calcium-dependent presynaptic action of substance P at the frog neuromuscular junction. Nature **267:** 268–270.
6. STEINACKER, A. & S. M. HIGHSTEIN. 1976. Pre- and post-synaptic action of substance P at the Mauthner fiber–giant fiber synapse in the hatchetfish. Brain Res. **114:** 128–133.
7. AKASU, T., M. KOJIMA & K. KOKETSU. 1983. Substance P modulates the sensitivity of the nicotinic receptor in amphibian cholinergic transmission. Br. J. Pharmacol. **80:** 123–131.
8. ROLE, L. W. 1984. Substance P modulation of acetylcholine-induced currents in embryonic chicken sympathetic and ciliary ganglion neurons. Proc. Natl. Acad. Sci. U.S.A. **81:** 2924–2928.
9. LIVETT, B. G., V. KOZOUSEK, F. MIZOBE & D. M. DEAN. 1979. Substance P inhibits nicotinic activation of chromaffin cells. Nature **278:** 256–257.
10. MIZOBE, F., V. KOZOUSEK, D. M. DEAN & B. G. LIVETT. 1979. Pharmacological characterization of adrenal paraneurons: substance P and somatostatin as inhibitory modulators of the nicotinic response. Brain Res. **178:** 555–566.
11. ROLE, L. W., S. E. LEEMAN & R. L. PERLMAN. 1981. Somatostatin and substance P inhibit catecholamine secretion from isolated cells of guinea-pig adrenal medulla. Neuroscience **6:** 1813–1821.
12. HIGGINS, L. S. & D. K. BERG. 1988. A desensitized form of neuronal acetylcholine receptor detected by ³H-nicotine binding on bovine adrenal chromaffin cells. J. Neurosci. **8:** 1436–1446.
13. CLAPHAM, D. E. & E. NEHER. 1984. Substance P reduces acetylcholine-induced currents in isolated bovine chromaffin cells. J. Physiol. (London) **347:** 255–277.
14. STALLCUP, W. B. & J. PATRICK. 1980. Substance P enhances cholinergic receptor desensitization in a clonal nerve cell line. Proc. Natl. Acad. Sci. U.S.A. **77:** 634–638.
15. SIMASKO, S. M., J. A. DURKIN & G. A. WEILAND. 1987. Effects of substance P on nicotinic acetylcholine receptor function in PC12 cells. J. Neurochem. **49:** 253–260.
16. SIMASKO, S. M., J. R. SOARES & G. A. WEILAND. 1985. Structure-activity relationship for substance P inhibition of carbamylcholine-stimulated ²²Na⁺ flux in neuronal (PC12) and non-neuronal (BC3H1) cell lines. J. Pharmacol. Exp. Ther. **235:** 601–605.
17. BOYD, N. D. & S. E. LEEMAN. 1987. Multiple actions of substance P that regulate the functional properties of acetylcholine receptors of clonal rat PC12 cells. J. Physiol. (London) **389:** 69–97.

18. NIEBER, K. & P. OEHME. 1987. Effect of substance P (SP) and the N-terminal SP-analogue SP(1–4) on the pre- and post-synaptic transmitter release in rat adrenal gland slices. Biomed. Biochim. Acta **46:** 103–109.
19. LIVETT, B. G. & P. BOKSA. 1984. Receptors and receptor modulation in cultured chromaffin cells. Can. J. Physiol. Pharmacol. **62:** 467–476.
20. BOKSA, P. & B. G. LIVETT. 1984. Substance P protects against desensitization of nicotinic response in isolated adrenal chromaffin cells. J. Neurochem. **42:** 618–627.
21. BOKSA, P. 1985. Effect of substance P on carbachol-stimulated $^{45}Ca^{2+}$ uptake into cultured adrenal chromaffin cells. J. Neurochem. **45:** 1895–1902.
22. KHALIL, Z., P. D. MARLEY & B. G. LIVETT. 1988. Effect of substance P on nicotine-induced desensitization of cultured bovine adrenal chromaffin cells: possible receptor subtypes. Brain Res. **459:** 282–288.
23. KHALIL, Z., P. D. MARLEY & B. G. LIVETT. 1988. Mammalian tachykinins modulate the nicotinic secretory response of cultured bovine adrenal chromaffin cells. Brain Res. **459:** 289–297.
24. JIANG, Z. G. & N. J. DUN. 1986. Facilitation of nicotinic response in the guinea pig prevertebral neurons by substance P. Brain Res. **363:** 196–198.
25. BOKSA, P., S. ST. PIERRE & B. G. LIVETT. 1982. Characterization of substance P and somatostatin receptors on adrenal chromaffin cells using structural analogues. Brain Res. **245:** 275–282.
26. MOELLER, I., S. J. BUNN & P. D. MARLEY. 1989. Actions of somatostatin on perfused bovine adrenal glands and cultured bovine adrenal medullary cells. Brain Res. **484:** 192–202.
27. LIVETT, B. G., P. D. MARLEY, D. C-C. WAN & X-F. ZHOU. 1990. Peptide regulation of adrenal medullary function. J. Neural Transm. (Suppl.) **29:** 77–89.
28. ZHOU, X-F. & B. G. LIVETT. 1990. Substance P has biphasic effects on catecholamine secretion evoked by electrical stimulation of perfused rat adrenal glands *in vitro*. J. Autonom. Nerv. Syst. In press.
29. ZHOU, X-F. & B. G. LIVETT. 1990. Substance P increases catecholamine secretion from perfused rat adrenal glands evoked by prolonged field stimulation. J. Physiol. (London) **425:** 321–334.
30. ZHOU, X-F. & B. G. LIVETT. 1990. Role of capsaicin-sensitive neurons in the regulation of catecholamine secretion from perfused rat adrenal glands. Eur. J. Pharmacol. In press.
31. ZHOU, X-F., P. D. MARLEY & B. G. LIVETT. 1990. Substance P modulates the time-course of nicotinic, but not muscarinic catecholamine secretion from perfused rat adrenal glands. Br. J. Pharmacol. Submitted.
32. KHALIL, Z., P. D. MARLEY & B. G. LIVETT. 1984. Neonatal capsaicin treatment prevents insulin-stress-induced adrenal catecholamine secretion *in vivo*: possible involvement of sensory nerves containing substance P. Neurosci. Lett. **45:** 65–70.
33. KHALIL, Z., B. G. LIVETT & P. D. MARLEY. 1986. The role of sensory fibres in the rat splanchnic nerve on adrenal medullary secretion from the rat adrenal medulla and sympathetic nerves. J. Physiol. (London) **370:** 201–215.
34. KHALIL, Z., B. G. LIVETT & P. D. MARLEY. 1987. Sensory fibres modulate histamine-induced catecholamine secretion from the rat adrenal medulla and sympathetic nerves. J. Physiol. (London) **391:** 511–526.
35. ZHOU, X-F., K. H. JHAMANDAS & B. G. LIVETT. 1990. Capsaicin-sensitive nerves are required for glucostasis, but not for catecholamine output during hypoglycemia in rats. Am. J. Physiol. (Endocrinol. Metab.) **258:** E212–E219.
36. ZHOU, X-F. & B. G. LIVETT. 1990. Effect of capsaicin-sensitive sensory nerves on plasma glucose and catecholamine levels during 2-deoxyglucose-induced stress in conscious rats. Br. J. Pharmacol. In press.
37. ZHOU, X-F. & B. G. LIVETT. 1990. Capsaicin-sensitive neurons are involved in the plasma catecholamine response to selective stressors. J. Physiol. (London). Submitted.
38. WEILAND, G. A., J. A. DURKIN, J. M. HENLEY & S. M. SIMASKO. 1987. Effects of substance P on the binding of ligands to nicotinic acetylcholine receptors. Mol. Pharmacol. **32:** 625–632.

39. DUN, N. J. & S. MINOTA. 1981. Effect of substance P on neurones of the inferior mesenteric ganglia of the guinea-pig. J. Physiol. (London) **321:** 259–271.

40. KONISHI, S., S-Y. SONG, T. OGAWA & I. KANAZAWA. 1989. Tachykinins produce fast and slow depolarizations in sympathetic neurons of rat coeliac–superior mesenteric ganglia. Brain Res. **490:** 162–165.

41. RICHTER, R. & C. H. GRUNWALD. 1987. Effect of substance P on the membrane potential of rat adrenal chromaffin cells. Biomed. Biochim. Acta **46:** 837–840.

42. CLAPP, L. H., M. B. VIVAUDOU, J. J. SINGER & J. V. WALSH, JR. 1989. Substance P, like acetylcholine, augments one type of Ca^{2+} current in isolated smooth muscle cells. Pflügers Arch. **413:** 565–567.

43. SIMS, S. M., J. V. WALSH, JR. & J. J. SINGER. 1986. Substance P and acetylcholine both suppress the same K^+ current in dissociated smooth muscle cells. Am. J. Physiol. **251:** C580–C587.

44. REISER, G. & B. HAMPRECHT. 1988. Characterization of a substance P receptor activating a cation permeability in neuronal cell lines. Eur. J. Pharmacol. **145:** 273–280.

45. WATSON, S. P. & C. P. DOWNES. 1983. Substance P induced hydrolysis of inositol phospholipids in guinea-pig ileum and rat hypothalamus. Eur. J. Pharmacol. **93:** 245–253.

46. BRISTOW, D. R., N. R. CURTIS, N. SUMAN-CHAUHAN, K. J. WATLING & B. J. WILLIAM. 1987. Effects of tachykinins on inositol phospholipid hydrolysis in slices of hamster urinary bladder. Br. J. Pharmacol.

47. ROLLANDY, I., C. DREUX, V. IMHOFF & B. ROSSIGNOL. 1989. Importance of the presence of the N-terminal tripeptide of substance P for the stimulation of phosphatidylinositol metabolism in rat parotid gland: a possible activation of phospholipases C and D. Neuropeptides **13:** 175–185.

48. THOMAS, K. L., P. V. ANDREWS, Z. KHALIL & R. D. HELME. 1989. Substance P induced hydrolysis of inositol phospholipids in rat skin in an *in vivo* model of inflammation. Neuropeptides **13:** 191–196.

49. BUNN, S. J., P. D. MARLEY & B. G. LIVETT. 1990. Receptor stimulated formation of inositol phosphates in cultures of bovine adrenal medullary cells: the effects of bradykinin, bombesin, and neurotensin. Neuropeptides **15:** 187–194.

50. MINENKO, A. & P. OEHME. 1987. Substance P action on inositol phospholipids in rat adrenal medulla slices. Biomed. Biochim. Acta **46:** 461–467.

51. MINENKO, A., B. GABRYSIAK & P. OEHME. 1988. Decreased SP-stimulated diesteratic hydrolysis of inositol phospholipids in adrenal medulla slices from spontaneously hypertensive rats. Biomed. Biochim. Acta **47:** 31–37.

52. CHEEK, T. R., A. J. O'SULLIVAN, R. B. MORETON, M. J. BERRIDGE & R. D. BURGOYNE. 1989. Spatial localization of the stimulus-induced rise in cytosolic Ca^{2+} in bovine adrenal chromaffin cells: distinct nicotinic and muscarinic patterns. FEBS Lett. **247:** 429–434.

53. MASU, Y., H. TAMASKI, Y. YOKOTA & S. NAKANISHI. 1988. Tachykinin precursors and receptors: molecular genetic studies. Regulat. Peptides **22:** 9–12.

54. OEHME, P. & W. A. KRIVOY. 1983. Substance P: a peptide with unusual features. TIPS **4:** 521–523.

55. BOYD, N. D. 1987. Two distinct kinetic phases of desensitization of acetylcholine receptors of clonal rat PC12 cells. J. Physiol. (London) **389:** 45–67.

56. AMANN, R. & F. LEMBECK. 1986. Capsaicin sensitive afferent neurons from the peripheral glucose receptors mediate the insulin-induced increase in adrenaline secretion. Naunyn-Schmiedeberg's Arch. Pharmacol. **334:** 71–76.

57. VAUPEL, R., H. JARRY, H-T. SCHLOMER & W. WUTTKE. 1988. Differential response of substance P–containing subtypes of adrenomedullary cells to different stressors. Endocrinology **123:** 2140–2145.

58. SIETZEN, M., M. SCHOBER, R. FISCHER-COLBRIE, D. SCHERMAN, G. SPERK & H. WINKLER. 1987. Rat adrenal medulla: levels of chromogranins, enkephalins, dopamine B–hydroxylase, and the amine transporter are changed by nervous activity and hypophysectomy. Neuroscience **22:** 131–139.

59. WAKADE, A. R. 1988. Noncholinergic transmitter(s) maintains secretion of catechol-

amines from rat adrenal medulla for several hours of continuous stimulation of splanchnic neurons. J. Neurochem. **50:** 1302–1308.

60. BUNN, S. J. & P. D. MARLEY. 1989. Effects of angiotensin II on cultured, bovine adrenal medullary cells. Neuropeptides **13:** 121–132.

61. HANLEY, M. R. & L. L. IVERSEN. 1980. Substance P receptors. *In* Neurotransmitter Receptors Part I. Series B. Volume 9. S. J. Enna & H. T. Yamamura, Eds.: 71–105. Chapman & Hall. London.

62. OEHME, P., H. HILSE, E. MORGENSTERN & E. GORES. 1980. Substance P: does it produce analgesia or hyperalgesia? Science **208:** 305–307.

63. PIERCY, M. F., P. J. K. DOBREY, F. J. EINSPAHR, L. A. SCHROEDER & N. MASIQUES. 1982. Use of substance P fragments to differentiate substance P receptors of different tissues. Regulat. Peptides **3:** 337–349.

64. HALL, M. E., P. GRANTHAM, J. LIMOLI & J. M. STEWART. 1987. Effects of substance P and neurokinin A (substance K) on motor behavior: unique effect of substance P attributable to its amino-terminal sequence. Brain Res. **420:** 82–94.

65. OEHME, P., K. HECHT, J. JUMATOV, H. REPKE, H. HILSE & A. CORDOVA. 1987. Prevention of stress-induced involution of the thymus in rats by substance P (SP1–11) and its N-terminal fragment SP1–4. Pharmazie **42:** 34–36.

66. ROGERSON, F. M., B. G. LIVETT, D. SCANLON & F. A. O. MENDELSOHN. 1989. Inhibition of angiotensin converting enzyme by N-terminal fragments of substance P. Neuropeptides **14:** 213–217.

67. SIEMS, W. E., N. W. KOMISSAROWA, P. OEHME, K. D. JENTZSCH & A. M. CHENRNUKH. 1983. Studies on the action of substance P and partial sequences of this compound on the angiotensin I converting enzyme activity. Pharmazie **38:** 256–257.

68. GERAGHTY, D. P., B. G. LIVETT, F. M. ROGERSON & E. BURCHER. 1990. A novel substance P binding site in bovine adrenal medulla. Neurosci. Lett. **112:** 267–281.

69. DEVILLIER, P., M. RENOUX, J-P. GIROUD & D. REGOLI. 1985. Peptides and histamine release from rat peritoneal mast cells. Eur. J. Pharmacol. **117:** 89–96.

70. HUGANIR, R. L., A. H. DELCOUR, P. GREENGARD & G. P. HESS. 1986. Phosphorylation of the nicotinic acetylcholine receptor regulates its rate of desensitization. Nature **321:** 774–776.

71. RYALL, R. W. & G. BELCHER. 1977. Substance P selectively blocks nicotinic receptors on Renshaw cells: a possible synaptic inhibitory mechanism. Brain Res. **137:** 376–380.

PART V

Substance P and the Inflammatory and Immune Response

PATRICK W. MANTYH

Molecular Neurobiology Lab
Veterans Administration Medical Center
Minneapolis, Minnesota 55417

Several lines of evidence indicate that tachykinin neuropeptides [substance P (SP), neurokinin A (NKA), and neurokinin B (NKB)] play a role in regulating the inflammatory and immune response both in peripheral tissues (such as the lung, joint, and colon) and in the central nervous system. To explore the possible involvement of tachykinins in these processes, we have used quantitative receptor autoradiography to examine alterations in the location and level of tachykinin binding sites in surgical specimens from patients with inflammatory bowel disease and in the rabbit optic nerve after neuronal injury. Results from these experiments demonstrate that binding sites for SP, but not for NKA or NKB, are ectopically expressed in high concentrations (1000–2000 times normal) by small arterioles and lymph nodules in human surgical samples of colon from patients with inflammatory bowel disease, but not from colon tissue obtained from normals. In the central nervous system, section of the rabbit optic nerve, which results in a proliferation of type-1 astrocytes that form the glial scar and that have been hypothesized to block neuronal regeneration, is also accompanied by a dramatic up-regulation of SP (but not NKA or NKB) binding sites. These data suggest that SP may be involved in the response to tissue injury both in peripheral tissues such as the colon and in the CNS after neuronal injury.

INFLAMMATORY BOWEL DISEASE

Neurons with cell bodies located in dorsal root ganglia (DRG) are known to convey specific features of somatic sensory information from peripheral tissues to the central nervous system. Recently, several neuropeptides have been identified within a subpopulation of these sensory neurons.[1] The most extensively characterized of these sensory neuropeptides is SP, a member of the mammalian tachykinin family that also includes NKA and NKB. Although it is clear that SP and NKA are expressed by sensory neurons,[2] it appears that NKB is not expressed in detectable levels in DRG or in most peripheral tissues.

Several of these sensory neuropeptides, most notably SP, have been associated with neurons specifically implicated in the conduction of nociceptive information. Therefore, intrathecal injection of SP produces biting and scratching behavior, consistent with a role for SP as a peptide neurotransmitter associated with primary afferent nociceptors;[3] SP release in the spinal cord is inhibited by opiate analgesics;[4] depletion of SP by capsaicin (a neurotoxin that is relatively selective for unmyelinated sensory neurons,[5] including those containing SP) is associated with a loss of specific nociceptive response; and release of SP in the spinal dorsal horn in response to normally innocuous stimuli is enhanced in polyarthritic rats.[6]

It has become increasingly evident in the last decade that a specific class of DRG neurons conveying *afferent* somatosensory information from peripheral tissues to the spinal cord are involved in the *efferent* regulation of the peripheral tissues they innervate. Thus, SP-containing DRG neurons have been implicated both in the *afferent* central transmission of nociceptive information and in the *efferent* regulation of inflammation and sensitization of joint sensory endings in a chronic pain state, for example, arthritis.[7,8] Support for this concept includes the following observations: the bulk of the SP synthesized by DRG neurons is transported to the peripheral terminals rather than to the spinal cord;[9] SP is a potent vasodilator in several peripheral tissues;[10] terminals of SP-containing sensory neurons are observed in association with blood vessels;[11] electrical stimulation of these peripheral nerves at intensities that release SP in peripheral tissues reproduces many of the physiological changes seen in acute inflammation,[12] including plasma extravasation;[7] and SP binding sites in experimental animals are expressed by several tissues involved in the inflammatory and immune response.[13]

What emerges from these observations is the hypothesis that sensory neurons containing SP and/or other neuropeptides are involved both in conveying nociceptive information to the spinal cord and in regulating the inflammatory and immune responses in the peripheral tissues they innervate. Hence, the same sensory neuropeptide released by a sensory neuron may signal tissue damage in the spinal cord and may participate in regulating the inflammation, immune response, and (ultimately) wound healing in the affected peripheral tissue.

To test whether this hypothesis is applicable to human inflammatory diseases, we examined the changes in tachykinin neuropeptide receptor binding sites in chronic inflammatory bowel disease (IBD) patients, where surgical removal of the affected tissue is used to ameliorate the disease in severe cases. IBD is a generic term that refers to chronic inflammatory diseases of the intestine that are of unknown etiology, principally ulcerative colitis and Crohn's disease. Ulcerative colitis is an inflammatory, ulcerating process of the colon; Crohn's disease is an inflammation of the intestine characterized by nodular granulomatous inflammatory lesions throughout the entire wall that may involve any part of the intestine, but that primarily attack the distal small intestine and colon.[14] Because surgical removal of the inflamed colon is used in severe cases of IBD, we used these surgical specimens to ask whether significant alterations in either the location or the levels of SP binding sites occur in these human inflammatory diseases. What we found was that SP binding sites were unique among the binding sites examined in that they were dramatically up-regulated in the inflamed colon tissue (FIGURE 1) and that this dramatic up-regulation appeared to be restricted to cells involved in mediating the inflammatory and immune response (FIGURE 2), that is, small arterioles and lymph nodules.

A key question that remains to be answered, though, was the following: what was the normal function of the neuropeptide-containing sensory neurons, which were the presumed source of the SP that would occupy these SP binding sites? One observation that suggests a normal function for these neuropeptide-containing sensory neurons is that one of the most pronounced deficits in neonatal capsaicin-treated rats (the neurotoxin destroys primarily the neuropeptide-containing C-fibers) is that the skin and fur lose their luster and that these animals lack a normal wound-healing response; that is, these animals have numerous small wounds that do not appear to be healing.[15,16] Such a lack of the normal trophic or wound-healing response after sensory denervation can also be inferred from the ulceration of the cornea, which follows trigeminal deafferentation.[17] Together, these observations suggest that, in a pathological state, SP appears to be involved in regulating a hyperinflammatory and immune response and that, in the normal condition, these sensory neuropeptide-

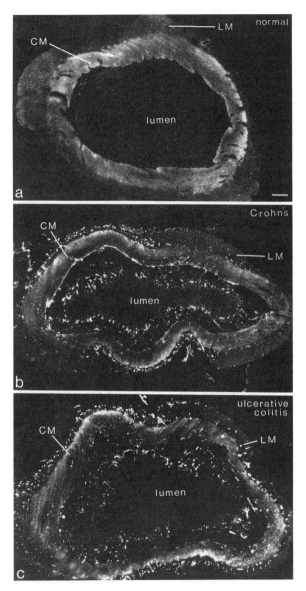

FIGURE 1. Dark-field autoradiograms showing the distribution of substance P (SP) binding sites in transverse sections of colon obtained from the margins of extensive resection for carcinoma (a) and with patients with Crohn's disease (b) and ulcerative colitis (c). In these dark-field autoradiograms, the tritium-sensitive film was used as the negative; white silver grains represent areas of high concentration of SP binding sites. Whereas a moderate concentration of SP receptor binding sites is expressed by the external circular muscle (CM) and the tunica media of a large artery in the serosa in normal colon (a), arterioles, venules, and lymph nodules express very high levels of SP receptor binding sites in both Crohn's disease (b) and ulcerative colitis (c). Abbreviations: CM, external circular muscle; LM, external longitudinal muscle. Line bar = 1.4 mm.

containing neurons may have a trophic action on tissues they innervate and may also regulate wound healing after injury.

As noted here, SP and other sensory neurotransmitters appear to be released centrally in the spinal cord to signal pain and peripherally to produce vasodilatation, plasma extravasation, and homing of leukocytes to the area of injury. Because there cannot be tissue repair until there has been an appropriate inflammatory and immune response,[18] the initial action of SP may be to promote and direct the inflammatory and immune responses in the damaged tissue. After the infection and

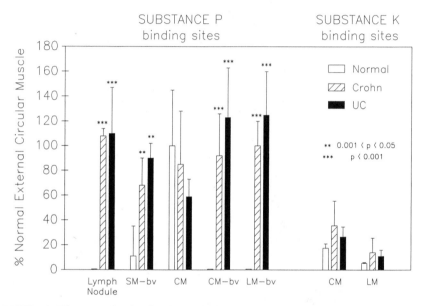

FIGURE 2. Histogram showing the changes in the location and concentration of SP and NKA (also known as substance K, SK) binding sites in the surgical specimens of normal colon obtained from carcinoma resection (open bars), Crohn's disease (hatched bars), and ulcerative colitis (dark bars). In this histogram, 100% specific binding is that concentration of specific SP binding sites expressed by the smooth muscle of the normal external circular muscle (CM). Whereas SP receptor binding sites are undetectable in blood vessels (bv) vascularizing the circular (CM) and longitudinal muscle (LM) and in the lymph nodules of normal patients, they reach levels in the Crohn's and ulcerative colitis patients that are the highest observed in the human GI tract. Distinct binding sites for NKB were not detected in any area of the human GI tract. Abbreviations: bv, blood vessel (arteriole or venule); CM, external circular muscle; LM, external longitudinal muscle; SM, submucosa.

damaged tissue have been cleared, SP and other neuropeptide growth factors continue to be released; however, their effects would now be directed towards mitogenesis and tissue remodeling. Two sensory neuropeptides, SP and NKA, have been shown to be potent mitogens for myocytes and fibroblasts in culture.[19] The key to this hypothesis is that SP should be both stimulatory and inhibitory towards the same cells, depending on the context of other chemical signals present. This multifunctional role for SP is not unprecedented for other peptide growth factors as it has been shown that another peptide, transforming growth factor-β, stimulates the growth of certain fibroblasts *in vitro* in the presence of platelet-derived growth factor, but inhibits the growth of the same cells if epidermal growth factor is present.[20,21] In human inflammatory diseases, it may be that ectopic expression of SP or its binding site is not the primary pathology, but rather that the pathology may involve whatever other factors are needed to switch SP action from the "catabolic" mode, where inflammatory and immune responses are promoted, to the "anabolic" process of tissue growth. What remains to be determined is what factors regulate SP binding site expression and what the physiological consequences of SP release and SP binding site activation are in both normal and inflamed tissues.

GLIAL EXPRESSION OF SUBSTANCE P RECEPTORS AFTER NEURONAL INJURY

A major question in neurobiology is why damaged mammalian central nervous system (CNS) neurons do not regenerate *in vivo*. In recent years, the focus of attention has shifted from CNS neurons themselves, which appear to have the capacity to regenerate, to CNS glia, which apparently inhibit the regrowth of axons in the CNS. Thus, it has been demonstrated that, after injury, regenerating axons grow a short distance until they reach the glial scar, at which time they appear to stop growing and degenerate.[22-27]

The major cellular constituent of a CNS glial scar is the reactive astrocyte.[25] Unlike fibroblasts, which form scars in nonneural tissue by secreting large amounts of collagenous extracellular matrix, astrocytes form scars by extending numerous processes that become packed with intracellular glial filaments.[28] Astrocytes proliferate in response to injury[29] and it appears that these "reactive astrocytes" are biochemically different from the major class of astrocytes that are present in the normal, nonlesioned brain.[25] Recently, several neuropeptides, including bombesin, NKA, and substance P, have been shown to be mitogenic[30,31] for several cell types that may be involved in the inflammatory and wound-healing responses in peripheral tissues.[32] *In vitro* studies suggest that glia are potential targets for a variety of neurotransmitters,[33] including SP,[34-37] somatostatin,[38,39] and vasoactive intestinal peptide.[36,38,39] By analogy with the inflammatory and immune responses that occur in response to injury in peripheral tissues, neuropeptides may also regulate glial mitogenesis and glial response to injury of the CNS. However, because glial cells exhibit different functional properties depending on their biochemical environment,[33] it is imperative to demonstrate that these receptor binding sites, which have been shown to be expressed by glia *in vitro*, are also expressed by glia *in vivo*.

To determine if similar neurotransmitter receptors are also expressed by glia *in vivo*, we examined the glial scar in the transected optic nerve of the albino rabbit using quantitative receptor autoradiography. Receptor binding sites for radiolabeled calcitonin gene–related peptide, cholecystokinin, galanin, somatostatin, SP, and vasoactive intestinal peptide were examined. Specific receptor binding sites for each of these neurotransmitters were identified in the rabbit forebrain, but were not detected in the normal optic nerve or tract. In the transected optic nerve and tract, only receptor binding sites for SP were expressed at detectable levels.[40] The density of SP receptor binding sites observed in this glial scar is among the highest observed in the rabbit forebrain (FIGURE 3). Ligand displacement and saturation experiments indicate that the SP receptor binding site expressed by the glial scar has pharmacological characteristics similar to those of NK-1 receptors in the rabbit striatum (FIGURE 4), the rat brain, and the rat and canine gut. These results demonstrate that glial cells *in vivo* express high concentrations of SP receptor binding sites after transection of retinal ganglion cell axons.

Because SP has been shown to regulate inflammatory and immune responses in peripheral tissues, SP may also, by analogy, be involved in regulating the glial response to injury in the central nervous system. This is consistent with previous *in vitro* studies that demonstrated that SP receptors are present in (2–3)-week-old primary cultures of cortical astrocytes from newborn mice and that addition of substance P to these astrocyte cultures stimulates phosphatidylinositol turnover.[37] SP has also been shown to stimulate the cyclooxygenase pathway of arachidonic acid metabolism in (2–3)-week-old cultures of rat astrocytes and to evoke the formation of prostaglandin E and thromboxane B_2 in a dose-dependent manner.[34] These studies together with the present results are consistent with the suggestion that "reactive astrocytes" that proliferate after neuronal injury—and that are hypothesized to play

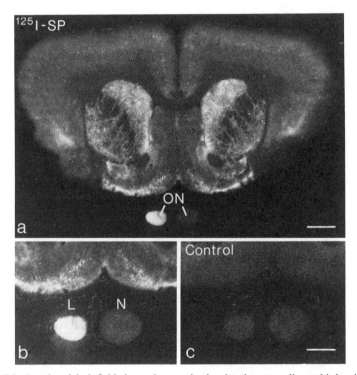

FIGURE 3. A series of dark-field photomicrographs showing the autoradiographic localization of SP receptor binding sites in a coronal section of the rabbit brain (animal #05) 99 days after unilateral transection of the optic nerve (ON). Autoradiograms a and b show the total binding, whereas c is the nonspecific binding. The control section (c) illustrating the nonspecific binding was treated identically to the adjacent section, which shows the total binding (b) except that nonradioactive SP (1 μM) was added to the incubation medium. In all the dark-field autoradiograms, the highest density of white silver grains represents the highest concentration of binding sites. The specific binding is obtained by subtracting the binding in c from b. Whereas the lesioned (L) optic nerve is reduced in size, it expresses a high density of specific receptor binding sites relative to the larger normal (N) optic nerve, in which specific binding sites are not detectable. Line bar (a) = 1.9 mm; (b & c) = 1.2 mm.

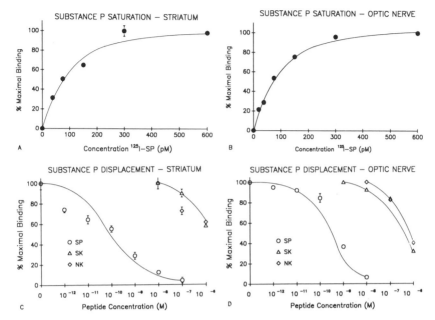

FIGURE 4. Saturation (A,B) and displacement (C,D) curves for SP receptor binding sites expressed by the striatum (A,C) and the lesioned optic nerve (B,D) 99 days after transection (rabbit #04). Note that both the saturation and displacement curves for SP receptor binding sites in the normal striatum (A,C) and the transected optic tract (B,D) are similar, suggesting that the SP receptor binding site expressed by the lesioned optic nerve is similar to the SP receptor binding site expressed by the normal striatum. The data shown are from a representative experiment. Each point represents the mean of triplicate determinations.

a role in inhibiting neuronal regeneration[25]—express functional SP receptors. These data suggest that, when glia are separated from neurons either *in vitro* or *in vivo* after the transection and degeneration of retinal ganglion cell axons, the glia that survive and proliferate express SP receptors.

SUMMARY

These findings suggest that SP may have proinflammatory actions in both the peripheral tissue and the central nervous system after tissue injury. Although the possibility that the same neuropeptide could have actions in both the brain and the peripheral tissues is certainly not without precedent, there is a key difference in the source of the ligand in these tissues. Unlike peripheral tissues such as the gastrointestinal tract or skin, where there is a dense innervation by SP-containing dorsal root ganglion neurons, the brain lacks such a sensory innervation. This important difference raises the question as to the possible origin of the SP that could occupy the SP receptors expressed by the CNS glia after neuronal injury. Whereas the answer to this question is currently unknown, an important clue may be the findings that circulating leukocytes have been reported to synthesize neuropeptides such as ACTH, opiates,[41] and SP.[42]

To begin to fully understand the role that SP may play in coordinating the inflammatory and immune response to tissue injury, we must first understand where SP fits into the cascade of events that occur after tissue injury, what events lead to nociceptor sensitization (which may lead to an increase in SP release), and what regulates SP receptor expression (which may be involved in the direction of leukocytes to the site of injury, plasma extravasation, or the proliferation/hypertrophy of reactive astrocytes). Although this may seem like a daunting task, several recent advances including the cloning of the three mammalian tachykinin receptors and the introduction of highly potent and specific SP receptor antagonists[43] should make this a highly fruitful field of investigation.

REFERENCES

1. HUNT, S. P. 1983. *In* Chemical Neuroanatomy. P. C. Emson, Ed.: 53–84. Raven Press. New York.
2. MAGGIO, J. E. & J. C. HUNTER. 1984. Brain Res. **307:** 370–373.
3. HYLDEN, J. L. K. & G. WILCOX. 1981. Brain Res. **217:** 212–215.
4. JESSEL, T. J. & L. L. IVERSEN. 1977. Nature **268:** 549–551.
5. NAGY, J. I., S. P. HUNT, L. L. IVERSEN & P. C. EMSON. 1981. Neuroscience **6:** 1923–1934.
6. OKU, R., M. SATOH & H. TAKAGI. 1987. Neurosci. Lett. **74:** 315–319.
7. LEMBECK, F. & P. HOLZER. 1979. Naunyn-Schmiedeberg's Arch. Pharmacol. **310:** 175–183.
8. LEVINE, J. D., S. J. DARDICK, M. F. ROEZEN, C. HELMS & A. I. BASBAUM. 1986. J. Neurosci. **6:** 3423–3429.
9. BRIMIJOIN, S., J. M. LUNDBERG, E. BRODIN, T. HÖKFELT & G. NILSSON. 1980. Brain Res. **191:** 443–457.
10. LUNDBERG, J. M., E. BRODIN, X. HUA & A. SARIA. 1984. Acta Physiol. Scand. **120:** 217–227.
11. FURNESS, J., R. E. PAPKA, N. G. DELLA, M. COSTA & R. L. ESKAY. 1982. Neuroscience **7:** 447–459.
12. CHAHL, L. A. & R. J. LADD. 1976. Pain **2:** 25–34.
13. MANTYH, P. W., C. R. MANTYH, T. GATES, S. R. VIGNA & J. E. MAGGIO. 1988. Neuroscience **25:** 817–838.
14. ROSENBERG, I. H. 1985. *In* Cecil Textbook of Medicine. Wyngaarden & Smith, Eds.: 740–756. Saunders. Philadelphia.
15. BUCK, S. H. & T. F. BURKS. 1983. Trends Pharmacol. Sci. **4:** 84–87.
16. NAGY, J. I., S. P. HUNT, L. L. IVERSEN & P. C. EMSON. 1981. Neuroscience **6:** 1923–1934.
17. BEUERMAN, R. W. & B. SCHIMMELPFENNIG. 1980. Exp. Neurol. **69:** 196–201.
18. GALLIN, J. I. & A. S. FAUCI. 1982. Advances in Host Defense Mechanisms. Vol. 1—Phagocytic Cells. Raven Press. New York.
19. NILSSON, J., A. M. VON EULER & C. J. DALSGAARD. 1985. Nature **315:** 61–63.
20. ROBERTS, A. B., M. A. ANZANO, L. M. WAKEFIELD, N. ROCHE, D. F. STERN & M. B. SPORN. 1985. Proc. Natl. Acad. Sci. U.S.A. **82:** 119–123.
21. SPORN, M. B. & A. B. ROBERTS. 1988. Nature **332:** 217–219.
22. AGUAYO, A. J., S. DAVID & G. M. BRAY. 1981. J. Exp. Biol. **95:** 231–240.
23. EYSEL, U. T. & L. PEICHL. 1985. Exp. Neurol. **88:** 757–766.
24. LIUZZI, F. J. & R. J. LASEK. 1987. Science **237:** 642–645.
25. MILLER, R. H., E. R. ABNEY, S. DAVID, C. FRENCH-CONSTANT, R. LINDSAY, R. PATEL, J. STONE & M. RAFF. 1986. J. Neurosci. **6:** 22–29.
26. RAMON Y CAJAL, S. 1928. Degeneration and Regeneration of the Nervous System. Vol. II, p. 583–596. Oxford University Press. London/New York.
27. VILLEGAS-PEREZ, M. P., M. VIDAL-SANZ, G. M. BRAY & A. J. AGUAYO. 1988. J. Neurosci. **8:** 265–280.
28. MAXWELL, D. S. & L. KRUGER. 1965. J. Cell Biol. **25:** 141–157.
29. LATOV, N., N. GAJANAN, E. A. ZIMMERMAN, W. G. JOHNSON, A. SILVERMAN, R. DEFENDINI & L. COTE. 1979. Dev. Biol. **72:** 381–384.

30. LOPEZ-RIVAS, A., S. A. MENDOZA, E. NANBERG, J. SINNETT-SMITH & E. ROZENGURT. 1987. Proc. Natl. Acad. Sci. U.S.A. **84:** 5768–5772.
31. ZICHE, M., L. MORBIDELLI, M. PACINI, P. DOLARA & C. A. MAGGI. 1990. Br. J. Pharmacol. **100:** 11–14.
32. MANTYH, C. R., T. S. GATES, R. P. ZIMMERMAN, M. L. WELTON, E. P. PASSARO, JR., S. R. VIGNA, J. E. MAGGIO, L. KRUGER & P. W. MANTYH. 1988. Proc. Natl. Acad. Sci. U.S.A. **85:** 3235–3239.
33. MURPHY, S. & B. PEARCE. 1987. Neuroscience **22:** 381–394.
34. HARTUNG, H. P., K. HEININGER, B. SCHAFER & K. V. TOYKA. 1988. FASEB J. **3:** 48–51.
35. PERRONE, M. H., R. D. LEPORE & W. SHAIN. 1986. J. Pharmacol. Exp. Ther. **238:** 389–395.
36. ROUGON, G., M. NOBLE & A. W. MUDGE. 1983. Nature **305:** 715–717.
37. TORRENS, Y., J. C. BEAUJOUAN, M. SAFFROY, M. C. DAGUET DE MONTETY, L. BERGSTROM & J. GLOWINSKI. 1986. Proc. Natl. Acad. Sci. U.S.A. **83:** 9216–9220.
38. CHNEIWEISS, H., J. GLOWINSKI & J. PREMONT. 1985. J. Neurochem. **44:** 779–786.
39. EVANS, T., K. D. MCCARTHY & T. K. HARDEN. 1984. J. Neurochem. **43:** 131–138.
40. MANTYH, P. W., D. JOHNSON, C. BOEHMER, M. CATTON, H. VINTERS, J. MAGGIO, H. TOO & S. VIGNA. 1988. Proc. Natl. Acad. Sci. U.S.A. **86:** 5193–5197.
41. BLALOCK, J. E., K. L. BROST & E. M. SMITH. 1985. J. Neuroimmunol. **10:** 31.
42. WEINSTOCK, J. V., A. BLUM, J. WALDER & R. WALDER. 1988. J. Immunol. **141:** 961–966.
43. SNIDER, R. M., J. W. CONSTANTINE, J. A. LOWE, K. P. LONGO, W. S. LEBEL, H. A. WOODY, S. E. DROZDA, M. C. DESAI, F. J. VINICK, R. W. SPENCER & H. J. HESS. 1991. Science **251:** 435–437.

Role of Peptidergic Sensory Neurons in Gastric Mucosal Blood Flow and Protection[a]

P. HOLZER,[b,c] I. TH. LIPPE,[b] H. E. RAYBOULD,[c]
M. A. PABST,[d] E. H. LIVINGSTON,[c] R. AMANN,[b]
B. M. PESKAR,[e] B. A. PESKAR,[f] Y. TACHÉ,[c]
AND P. H. GUTH[c]

[b]Department of Experimental and Clinical Pharmacology
University of Graz
A-8010 Graz, Austria

[c]Center for Ulcer Research and Education
University of California at Los Angeles
and
Veterans Administration Wadsworth Medical Center
Los Angeles, California

[d]Department of Histology and Embryology
University of Graz
A-8010 Graz, Austria

[e]Department of Experimental Clinical Medicine
[f]Department of Pharmacology and Toxicology
University of Bochum
Bochum, Federal Republic of Germany

INTRODUCTION

Apart from autonomic and enteric neurons, the gastric mucosa and submucosa are richly innervated by primary afferent neurons that arise from two different sources. One group consists of "spinal" sensory neurons that originate from cell bodies in the dorsal root ganglia and that reach the stomach via the splanchnic and mesenteric nerves, a route whereby they pass through the celiac ganglion.[1,2] The other group consists of vagal sensory nerve fibers that have their cell bodies in the nodose ganglion.[2] The nerve endings of these afferent nerve fibers in the stomach form a particularly dense plexus around submucosal blood vessels.[1-4] Other sensory nerve endings supply the mucosa and the enteric nerve plexuses. This localization suggests that afferent nerve endings could be involved in the regulation of many gastrointestinal functions, especially blood flow. The functional implications of some of these afferent neurons can be examined by virtue of their sensitivity to capsaicin. This drug enables the selective manipulation of the state of activity of certain primary afferent neurons with unmyelinated (C-) or thinly myelinated (Aδ-) nerve fibers.[5-7]

[a]This work was supported by the Austrian Scientific Research Council (Grant Nos. 5552 and 7845), the Max Kade Foundation, the National Institute of Health, Veterans Administration Research Funds, and the Franz Lanyar Foundation of the Medical Faculty of the University of Graz.

There are two actions of capsaicin that can be taken use of: acute administration of low nontoxic doses of the drug can be employed to stimulate capsaicin-sensitive afferent neurons, whereas systemic administration of high neurotoxic doses of capsaicin can be used to produce a long-lasting functional and neurochemical ablation of the neurons sensitive to the drug.

There is ample evidence that capsaicin-sensitive sensory neurons not only serve a sensory and afferent role, but also display a local effector function initiated by the release of neuropeptide transmitters from their peripheral nerve endings.[7] Sensory neuropeptides such as substance P and calcitonin gene–related peptide (CGRP) are involved in inflammatory reactions of the skin, eye, and respiratory tract, which are interpreted as protecting or as promoting repair of damaged tissue.[7] It is hence tempting to speculate that capsaicin-sensitive sensory neurons in the gastric mucosa and submucosa are of significance in gastric mucosal protection against injury. These neurons are particularly sensitive to chemical noxious stimuli and there is accumulating evidence that capsaicin-sensitive primary afferent neurons in general are sensitive to hydrogen ions.[8-11] Considering that the gastric mucosa is constantly exposed to the chemical hazard of hydrogen ions, we hypothesized that capsaicin-sensitive sensory neurons subserve a protective role in the gastric mucosa by sensing pending injury due to acid influx and by signaling for appropriate measures of defense and repair. We therefore set out to examine (1) whether ablation of capsaicin-sensitive neurons would weaken—and stimulation of these neurons would strengthen—the ability of the gastric mucosa to resist experimentally imposed injury, (2) whether capsaicin-sensitive sensory neurons are involved in the physiological control of gastric mucosal circulation, and (3) whether peptides such as substance P (SP) and calcitonin gene–related peptide (CGRP) are mediators of the protective and vasodilator role of sensory neurons.

ABLATION OF SENSORY NEURONS AGGRAVATES GASTRIC INJURY

Defunctionalization of sensory neurons, by treating rats with a high dose of capsaicin (≥ 50 mg/kg) subcutaneously at least a week before the experiments, does not cause gastric mucosal damage by itself. However, mucosal lesion formation in response to a variety of endogenous and exogenous factors including acid,[12,13] indomethacin,[14,15] ethanol,[14,16,17] and platelet-activating factor[18] is significantly exacerbated. This aggravation of injury is seen on both the macroscopic and microscopic levels and suggests that sensory neurons control mechanisms of gastric mucosal defense against injurious factors.

STIMULATION OF SENSORY NEURONS INCREASES GASTRIC MUCOSAL BLOOD FLOW AND RESISTANCE AGAINST INJURY

Szolcsányi and Barthó[12] were the first to show that intragastric administration of capsaicin, to stimulate sensory nerve endings, protected the rat gastric mucosa from acid injury. In taking up this lead, we were able to demonstrate that intragastric administration of capsaicin also prevented injury produced by ethanol[19-21] or acidified aspirin.[22] All experiments were performed on urethane-anesthetized rats, with the stomach being continuously perfused via catheters in the esophagus and pylorus. The protective effect of capsaicin administered together with the injurious stimuli was dose-related (10–640 μM) and manifested itself in a reduction of macroscopically visible damage and in prevention of histologically deep injury (FIGURE 1). Capsaicin, though, failed to prevent superficial injury to the mucosa, especially in the ethanol injury model,[20,21] as shown by both light and scanning electron microscopy (FIGURE 1).

Experiments designed to delineate the mechanisms of sensory nerve–induced gastric mucosal protection demonstrated that the protective effect of capsaicin against experimental gastric injury is unlikely to be accounted for by a reduction of gastric acid output[23] or by increases in the secretion of bicarbonate or mucus (unpublished observations). There is good evidence, however, that the protective effect of capsaicin is related to an increase in gastric mucosal blood flow. Using the aniline[23] or hydrogen gas[20,21] clearance technique, we showed that gastric mucosal blood flow was significantly enhanced after intragastric administration of capsaicin. This increase in gastric mucosal blood flow was also seen when capsaicin was administered together with an injurious concentration of 25% ethanol.[20,21] The gastric mucosal vasodilatation caused by 10–640 µM capsaicin was closely correlated

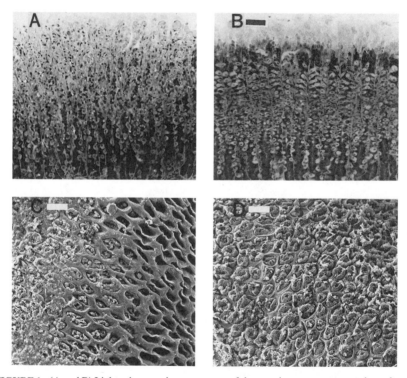

FIGURE 1. (A and B) Light microscopic appearance of the gastric corpus mucosa taken after a 30-min perfusion of the stomach of urethane-anesthetized rats with 25% ethanol containing either no (A) or 160 µM capsaicin (B). Calibration bar: 100 µm. The graphs show that capsaicin attenuated the depth of gastric mucosal erosions induced by ethanol. (C and D) Scanning electron microscopic appearance of the gastric corpus mucosa taken after a 30-min perfusion of the stomach of urethane-anesthetized rats with 25% ethanol containing either no (C) or 160 µM capsaicin (D). Calibration bar: 50 µm. The graphs show that capsaicin did not prevent ethanol-induced damage to the gastric surface epithelium.

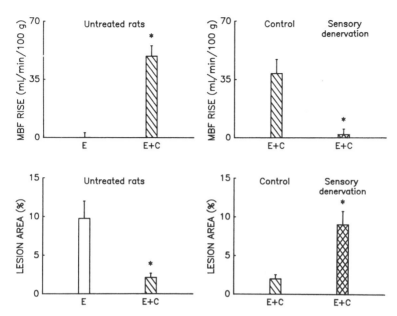

FIGURE 2. Effect of intragastric capsaicin (C, 160 μM) on gastric mucosal blood flow (MBF) and on gross injury produced by ethanol (E, 25%) in the gastric mucosa. The stomach of urethane-anesthetized rats was perfused with ethanol containing either no or 160 μM capsaicin for a period of 30 min, after which gross injury was quantitated and expressed as a percentage of the total area of the glandular mucosa.[20] MBF was measured by the hydrogen gas clearance technique.[20] The graphs show the increases in MBF over the basal MBF measured before exposure to ethanol or ethanol plus capsaicin. The left panels illustrate that capsaicin increased MBF and reduced ethanol injury in the stomachs of untreated rats. These effects of intragastric capsaicin were abolished after sensory denervation (treatment of the experimental animals with a total dose of 125 mg/kg capsaicin subcutaneously 10 days before the experiment, control rats receiving the vehicle) as depicted in the right panels. Means ± SEM, $n = 8$; ∗ = $P < 0.05$ (U test) versus E (left panels) or control (right panels). Data are taken from reference 21.

($P < 0.01$) with a reduction of gross lesion formation (FIGURE 2, left panels).[21] Because intragastric administration of capsaicin had no effect on blood pressure, it can be inferred that the increase in mucosal blood flow resulted from mucosal vasodilatation.

Further experiments established that both the capsaicin-induced mucosal vasodilatation and the protection from ethanol injury were mediated by sensory neurons.[19,21,23] As shown in FIGURE 2 (right panels), ablation of capsaicin-sensitive neurons ("sensory denervation") completely abolished the capsaicin-induced increase in gastric mucosal blood flow and significantly aggravated the gross injury caused by ethanol. According to the neuropharmacology of capsaicin,[5-7] this observation indicates that intragastric capsaicin protects the rat gastric mucosa by stimulation of sensory neurons. Other experiments revealed that the protective effect of capsaicin does not involve the autonomic nervous system and thus is most likely due to a local neural mechanism within the stomach.[19] However, both the vasodilatory and protective effects of intragastric capsaicin were inhibited by tetrodotoxin, a blocker of nerve conduction.[21] Tetrodotoxin (60 ng/min) was infused close arterially to the stomach by way of a catheter inserted retrogradely in the splenic artery. This observation indicates that the gastric effects of capsaicin involve nerve conduction and hence are brought about by a neural reflex within the gastric wall.

CALCITONIN GENE–RELATED PEPTIDE AS A MEDIATOR OF GASTRIC MUCOSAL VASODILATATION AND PROTECTION INDUCED BY SENSORY NERVE STIMULATION

Inherent in the assumption that capsaicin-induced protection of the gastric mucosa results from a local neural mechanism within the stomach is the question as to what mediator substances are released from capsaicin-sensitive nerve endings that strengthen gastric mucosal resistance. Prostaglandins and other eicosanoids that play a role in maintaining mucosal integrity have been ruled out as mediators of sensory nerve–mediated gastric mucosal protection. This conclusion is derived from the finding that indomethacin administered at doses shown to inhibit gastric prostaglandin synthesis failed to alter the protective action of intragastric capsaicin against ethanol injury.[20] Furthermore, capsaicin given intragastrically at a dose known to prevent ethanol-induced injury did not affect the *ex vivo* formation of prostaglandin E_2, 6-oxo-prostaglandin $F_{1\alpha}$, and leukotriene C_4.[20]

Sensory nerve endings in the stomach arising from dorsal root ganglion neurons contain a number of putative peptide transmitters that, at least in part, coexist in the same nerve fibers.[1-4] Particularly well established is the presence of CGRP and substance P in these neurons.[1-4] We found that capsaicin (10 μM) administered intra-arterially to the vascularly perfused rat stomach induced a large increase in the release of CGRP into the venous effluent (FIGURE 3).[24] Identical data were obtained by an independent laboratory.[25] High performance liquid chromatography of the released material indicated that the majority of the immunoreactivity corresponded to authentic CGRP.[24] Other work has shown that substance P is also released by capsaicin in the rat and guinea pig stomach.[26]

Because both substance P and CGRP possess vasodilator properties in a number of vascular beds,[7] it appears likely that these two peptides could mediate the vasodilator and protective effects of capsaicin in the gastric mucosa. This hypothesis was tested by investigating whether close arterial administration of peptides to the rat stomach is able to increase gastric mucosal blood flow and protect the mucosa from experimental injury. Using the hydrogen gas clearance technique, we observed that infusion of rat alpha-CGRP, the prevalent form of CGRP in primary afferent neurons of the rat,[27] increased gastric mucosal blood flow at doses (15 pmol/min) that were too low to cause systemic hypotension (FIGURE 4).[28] Higher doses of the peptide (75 pmol/min) facilitated blood flow to a larger extent, but also lowered blood pressure. In contrast, neither substance P (125 or 625 pmol/min) nor neurokinin A (50 or 250 pmol/min) changed the gastric mucosal blood flow, although the higher dose of each peptide caused significant hypotension.[28] These findings suggest that substance P and neurokinin A are unlikely to mediate the gastric mucosal vasodilator effect of intragastric capsaicin, which is consistent with a previous finding that substance P fails to alter the gastric clearance of aminopyrine, an indirect measure of mucosal blood flow.[29] CGRP, on the contrary, is a very potent vasodilator in the gastric mucosa of the rabbit[30] and (as the present study has shown) the rat and, thus, it mimicks the vasodilator effect of capsaicin.

Further experiments have confirmed the hypothesis that CGRP is the primary mediator of sensory nerve–mediated gastric mucosal protection. Close arterial

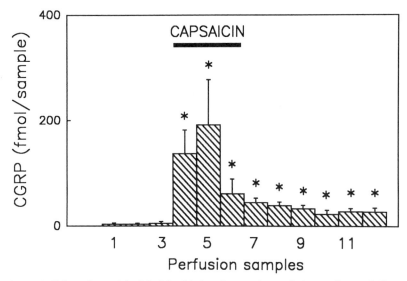

FIGURE 3. Effect of capsaicin (10 μM, added to the vascular perfusion medium as indicated) on the release of immunoreactive calcitonin gene–related peptide (CGRP) into the venous effluent of the vascularly perfused stomach of the rat. Each perfusion sample consisted of 60 drops. Means ± SEM, $n = 4$; * = $P < 0.05$ (Quade test) versus precapsaicin values. Data are taken from reference 24.

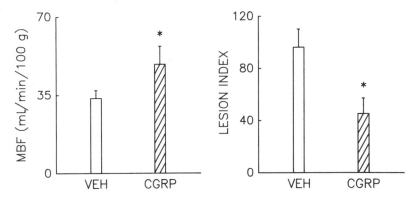

FIGURE 4. Effect of close arterial infusion of calcitonin gene–related peptide (rat alpha-CGRP, 15 pmol/min) into the rat stomach on gastric mucosal blood flow (MBF) (left panel) and on gross lesion formation in response to ethanol (right panel). In the latter case, the stomach of urethane-anesthetized rats was perfused with 25% ethanol for a period of 30 min, after which gross injury was estimated semiquantitatively by calculating a lesion index.[31] MBF was measured by the hydrogen gas clearance technique.[28] The infusion of CGRP was started 5 min before the measurement of MBF or the start of the ethanol perfusion. Means ± SEM, $n = 6$; * = $P < 0.05$ (U test) versus infusion of vehicle (VEH). Data are taken from references 28 and 31.

infusion of CGRP to the rat stomach, at the same dose (15 pmol/min) that stimulated gastric mucosal blood flow,[28] prevented the gross injury produced by 25% ethanol (FIGURE 4) or acidified aspirin,[31] which are the two injury models in which capsaicin previously had been found to be protective.[19,22] Thus, CGRP is able to strengthen the resistance of the rat gastric mucosa against injurious factors, an effect that is very likely related to its potent vasodilator action. Subcutaneous[32] or intravenous[33] administration of CGRP also has been found to reduce damage imposed experimentally on the rat gastric mucosa. In view of the inactivity of substance P and neurokinin A in increasing gastric mucosal blood flow, we did not examine their effect on gastric mucosal lesion formation. There is some information, though, that subcutaneous administration of substance P fails to reduce experimental injury, whereas some neurokinin A–related peptides, injected subcutaneously, may afford protection against lesion formation in the rat mucosa.[34]

A PHYSIOLOGICAL ROLE FOR SENSORY NEURONS IN THE GASTRIC MUCOSA

The data described in the previous sections of this article clearly indicate that stimulation of sensory neurons in the stomach strengthens the resistance of the gastric mucosa against injury by way of an increase in gastric mucosal blood flow. CGRP is an important candidate mediator of sensory neurons in producing these effects. This hypothesis is in keeping with the concept that maintenance or facilitation of mucosal blood flow is an important mechanism of gastric mucosal protection.[35,36] The question, therefore, arises as to the physiological or pathophysiological conditions under which capsaicin-sensitive sensory neurons are called into effect to facilitate gastric mucosal blood flow. Because these neurons are sensitive to acid,[8–11] we examined whether augmented back-diffusion of acid into the gastric mucosa is a condition under which sensory neurons are stimulated and whether this could lead to a well-documented increase in gastric mucosal blood flow.[37,38] In our experimental model, acid back-diffusion into the gastric mucosa was induced by disrupting the gastric mucosal barrier with 15% ethanol in the presence of exogenous acid (0.15 N HCl). This procedure caused a marked and sustained increase in gastric mucosal blood flow (FIGURE 5) and enhanced acid loss from the gastric perfusion medium by a factor of more than five, indicating acid back-diffusion.[13] As shown in FIGURE 5 (left panel), sensory denervation by subcutaneous pretreatment of rats with a high dose of capsaicin significantly inhibited the blood flow increase caused by barrier disruption in the presence of exogenous acid.[13] A significant exacerbation of gross lesion formation and a significant increase in the mucosal depth of the lesions[13] were associated with this inhibition of the blood flow response. Mean arterial blood pressure, basal mucosal blood flow, and acid loss from the gastric perfusion medium were not altered by ablation of capsaicin-sensitive sensory neurons.[13]

Additional proof that the blood flow response to acid back-diffusion is mediated by neurons came from experiments in which tetrodotoxin, a blocker of nerve conduction, was infused close arterially to the stomach (0.2 nmol/min).[13] This drug suppressed the blood flow increase evoked by acid back-diffusion (FIGURE 5, right panel) and aggravated gross damage in the gastric mucosa.[13] The mean arterial blood pressure was not significantly affected by this dose of tetrodotoxin. As reported previously,[38] atropine failed to change the gastric blood flow response to acid back-diffusion, indicating that postganglionic parasympathetic neurons or cholinergic vasodilator neurons of the enteric nervous system are not implicated.[13] Also unlikely is an involvement of the sympathetic nervous system because stimulation of sympathetic efferent neurons causes mucosal vasoconstriction.[36] However, the inhibitory effect of tetrodotoxin indicates that the rise in blood flow due to acid back-diffusion involves nerve conduction. It would seem, therefore, that acid back-diffusion is monitored by sensory nerve endings that, in turn, signal for an increase in blood flow to the mucosa by way of a local neural reflex in the stomach. In analogy with the local effector function of sensory nerve endings in the skin, eye, and respiratory tract,[7] it may be hypothesized that vasodilatation involves only sensory neurons and is the result of an axon reflex between different branches of sensory nerve fibers in the stomach. This explanation, though, does not take account of a possible implication of the enteric nervous system, which also needs to be considered in view of the morphological evidence that sensory nerve endings are in contact with enteric neurons.[39]

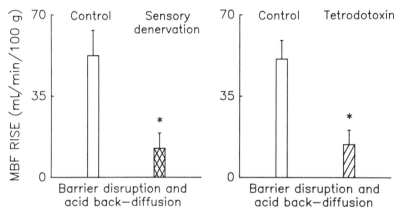

FIGURE 5. Effect of sensory denervation (see FIGURE 2) and tetrodotoxin on the increase in gastric mucosal blood flow (MBF RISE) caused by barrier disruption and acid back-diffusion. The stomach of urethane-anesthetized rats was perfused with 0.15 N HCl and acid back-diffusion was induced by breaking the gastric mucosal barrier with 15% ethanol. Tetrodotoxin (60 ng/min) or its vehicle (control) was infused close arterially to the stomach,[13] with the infusion starting 30 min before barrier disruption. MBF was measured by the hydrogen gas clearance technique. Means ± SEM, $n = 8$; * = $P < 0.05$ (U test) versus control.

A separate study investigated the origin of the sensory neurons that mediate gastric mucosal vasodilatation in response to acid back-diffusion. To selectively ablate vagal or spinal sensory neurons, the cervical vagus nerve trunks or the celiac ganglia were treated with capsaicin (1%) for 30 min, with the control rats receiving the vehicle.[40] The gastric mucosal vasodilator response to acid back-diffusion was measured 10–14 days after the local nerve treatments. Perivagal capsaicin treatment failed to change the rise in blood flow evoked by barrier disruption in the presence of exogenous acid and gross damage of the mucosa was likewise unaltered. In contrast, periceliac treatment with capsaicin significantly inhibited the mucosal vasodilator response to acid back-diffusion and significantly exacerbated mucosal lesion formation.[40] Neither perivagal nor periceliac capsaicin treatment had any effect on the substance P content of the gastric wall as measured by radioimmunoassay. The CGRP content was unchanged after perivagal treatment, but was reduced by 73% after periceliac capsaicin treatment.[40] These data confirm previous reports that most of the gastric CGRP originates from spinal ganglion neurons,[2,4,27] whereas substance P derives primarily from enteric neurons. Furthermore, the present data indicate that gastric mucosal vasodilatation in response to acid back-diffusion is, at least in part, mediated by primary afferent neurons of dorsal root ganglion origin. The results also are consistent with the hypothesis that CGRP is the principal candidate mediator of gastric mucosal vasodilatation evoked by sensory nerve stimulation.

SUMMARY

The present findings have revealed a new aspect of how mechanisms of gastric mucosal resistance to injury are called into effect and are coordinated by the nervous system. Capsaicin-sensitive sensory neurons in the stomach play a physiological role in monitoring acid influx into the superficial mucosa. Once activated, they strengthen gastric mucosal defense against deep injury, with a key process in this respect being an increase in blood flow through the gastric mucosa. This concept opens up completely new perspectives in the physiology and pathophysiology of the gastric mucosa if we consider that the long-term integrity of the gastric mucosa may be under the subtle control of acid-sensitive sensory neurons and that, vice versa, improper functioning of these neural control mechanisms may predispose to gastric ulcer disease.

The present observations also indicate that some of the peptides contained in gastric sensory nerve endings might fulfill a transmitter or mediator role in controlling gastric mucosal blood flow and integrity. Whereas substance P and neurokinin A are unlikely to play a role in the regulation of gastric mucosal blood flow, there is severalfold evidence that CGRP is very important in this respect. This peptide, which in the rat gastric mucosa originates exclusively from spinal sensory neurons,[2,4,27] is released upon stimulation of sensory nerve endings and is extremely potent in facilitating gastric mucosal blood flow and in protecting the mucosa from injurious factors. Selective ablation of spinal sensory neurons containing CGRP weakens the resistance of the gastric mucosa against acid injury, which is most likely due to inhibition of protective vasodilator reflexes. We now aim at providing direct pharmacological evidence that antagonism of endogenously released CGRP results in similar pathophysiological consequences as ablation of capsaicin-sensitive sensory neurons.

REFERENCES

1. SHARKEY, K. A., R. G. WILLIAMS & G. J. DOCKRAY. 1984. Sensory substance P innervation of the stomach and pancreas—demonstration of capsaicin-sensitive sensory neurons in the rat by combined immunohistochemistry and retrograde tracing. Gastroenterology 87: 914–921.
2. GREEN, T. & G. J. DOCKRAY. 1988. Characterization of the peptidergic afferent innervation of the stomach in the rat, mouse, and guinea pig. Neuroscience 25: 181–193.
3. FURNESS, J. B., R. E. PAPKA, N. G. DELLA, M. COSTA & R. L. ESKAY. 1982. Substance P–like immunoreactivity in nerves associated with the vascular system of guinea pigs. Neuroscience 7: 447–459.
4. STERNINI, C., J. R. REEVE & N. BRECHA. 1987. Distribution and characterization of

calcitonin gene–related peptide immunoreactivity in the digestive system of normal and capsaicin-treated rats. Gastroenterology **93**: 852–862.

5. SZOLCSÁNYI, J. 1984. Capsaicin-sensitive chemoceptive neural system with dual sensory-efferent function. *In* Antidromic Vasodilatation and Neurogenic Inflammation. L. A. Chahl, J. Szolcsányi & F. Lembeck, Eds.: 27–52. Akad. Kiadó. Budapest.

6. BUCK, S. H. & T. F. BURKS. 1986. The neuropharmacology of capsaicin: review of some recent observations. Pharmacol. Rev. **38**: 179–226.

7. HOLZER, P. 1988. Local effector functions of capsaicin-sensitive sensory nerve endings: involvement of tachykinins, calcitonin gene–related peptide, and other neuropeptides. Neuroscience **24**: 739–768.

8. CLARKE, G. D. & J. S. DAVISON. 1978. Mucosal receptors in the gastric antrum and small intestine of the rat with afferent fibres in the cervical vagus. J. Physiol. (London) **284**: 55–67.

9. CERVERO, F. & H. A. McRITCHIE. 1982. Neonatal capsaicin does not affect unmyelinated efferent fibers of the autonomic nervous system: functional evidence. Brain Res. **239**: 283–288.

10. MARTLING, C-R. & J. M. LUNDBERG. 1988. Capsaicin-sensitive afferents contribute to the acute airway edema following tracheal instillation of hydrochloric acid or gastric juice in the rat. Anesthesiology **68**: 350–356.

11. BEVAN, S. & J. C. YEATS. 1989. Protons activate a sustained inward current in a subpopulation of rat isolated dorsal root ganglion (DRG) neurons. J. Physiol. (London) **417**: 81P.

12. SZOLCSÁNYI, J. & L. BARTHÓ. 1981. Impaired defense mechanism to peptic ulcer in the capsaicin-desensitized rat. *In* Gastrointestinal Defense Mechanisms. G. Mózsik, O. Hänninen & T. Jávor, Eds.: 39–51. Pergamon/Akad. Kiadó. Elmsford, New York/Budapest.

13. HOLZER, P., E. H. LIVINGSTON & P. H. GUTH. 1990. Sensory neurons signal for an increase in rat gastric mucosal blood flow in response to acid back-diffusion. Gastroenterology **98**: A175.

14. HOLZER, P. & W. SAMETZ. 1986. Gastric mucosal protection against ulcerogenic factors in the rat mediated by capsaicin-sensitive afferent neurons. Gastroenterology **91**: 975–981.

15. EVANGELISTA, S., C. A. MAGGI & A. MELI. 1986. Evidence for a role of adrenals in the capsaicin-sensitive "gastric defense mechanism" in rats. Proc. Soc. Exp. Biol. Med. **182**: 568–569.

16. EVANGELISTA, S., C. A. MAGGI & A. MELI. 1987. Influence of peripherally administered peptides on ethanol-induced gastric ulcers in the rat. Gen. Pharmacol. **18**: 647–649.

17. ESPLUGUES, J. V. & B. J. R. WHITTLE. 1990. Morphine potentiation of ethanol-induced gastric mucosal damage in the rat: role of local sensory afferent neurons. Gastroenterology **98**: 82–89.

18. ESPLUGUES, J. V., B. J. R. WHITTLE & S. MONCADA. 1989. Local opioid-sensitive afferent sensory neurones in the modulation of gastric damage induced by PAF. Br. J. Pharmacol. **97**: 579–585.

19. HOLZER, P. & I. T. LIPPE. 1988. Stimulation of afferent nerve endings by intragastric capsaicin protects against ethanol-induced damage of gastric mucosa. Neuroscience **27**: 981–987.

20. HOLZER, P., M. A. PABST, I. T. LIPPE, B. M. PESKAR, B. A. PESKAR, E. H. LIVINGSTON & P. H. GUTH. 1990. Afferent nerve–mediated protection against deep mucosal damage in the rat stomach. Gastroenterology **98**: 838–848.

21. HOLZER, P., E. H. LIVINGSTON & P. H. GUTH. 1990. Close correlation between sensory nerve–induced increase in rat gastric mucosal blood flow and prevention of ethanol injury. Gastroenterology **98**: A60.

22. HOLZER, P., M. A. PABST & I. T. LIPPE. 1989. Intragastric capsaicin protects against aspirin-induced lesion formation and bleeding in the rat gastric mucosa. Gastroenterology **96**: 1425–1433.

23. LIPPE, I. T., M. A. PABST & P. HOLZER. 1989. Intragastric capsaicin enhances rat gastric acid elimination and mucosal blood flow by afferent nerve stimulation. Br. J. Pharmacol. **96**: 91–100.

24. HOLZER, P., B. M. PESKAR, B. A. PESKAR & R. AMANN. 1990. Release of calcitonin gene–related peptide induced by capsaicin in the vascularly perfused rat stomach. Neurosci. Lett. **108:** 195–200.
25. GRAY, J. L., N. W. BUNNETT, S. J. MULVIHILL & H. T. DEBAS. 1989. Capsaicin stimulates release of calcitonin gene–related peptide (CGRP) from the isolated perfused rat stomach. Gastroenterology **96:** A181.
26. RENZI, D., P. SANTICIOLI, C. A. MAGGI, C. SURRENTI, P. PRADELLES & A. MELI. 1988. Capsaicin-induced release of substance P–like immunoreactivity from the guinea pig stomach *in vitro* and *in vivo*. Neurosci. Lett. **92:** 254–258.
27. VARRO, A., T. GREEN, S. HOLMES & G. J. DOCKRAY. 1988. Calcitonin gene–related peptide in visceral afferent nerve fibers: quantification by radioimmunoassay and determination of axonal transport rates. Neuroscience **26:** 927–932.
28. HOLZER, P., Y. TACHÉ & P. H. GUTH. 1990. The vasodilator peptides alpha-CGRP and VIP, but not substance P and neurokinin A, increase rat gastric mucosal blood flow. Gastroenterology **98:** A175.
29. YOKOTANI, K. & M. FUJIWARA. 1985. Effects of substance P on cholinergically stimulated gastric acid secretion and mucosal blood flow in rats. J. Pharmacol. Exp. Ther. **232:** 826–830.
30. BAUERFEIND, P., R. HOF, A. HOF, M. CUCALA, S. SIEGRIST, CH. VON RITTER, J. A. FISCHER & A. L. BLUM. 1989. Effects of hCGRP I and II on gastric blood flow and acid secretion in anesthetized rabbits. Am. J. Physiol. **256:** G145–G149.
31. LIPPE, I. T., M. LORBACH & P. HOLZER. 1989. Close arterial infusion of calcitonin gene–related peptide into the rat stomach inhibits aspirin- and ethanol-induced hemorrhagic damage. Regulat. Peptides **26:** 35–46.
32. MAGGI, C. A., S. EVANGELISTA, S. GIULIANI & A. MELI. 1987. Anti-ulcer activity of calcitonin gene–related peptide in rats. Gen. Pharmacol. **18:** 33–34.
33. KOLVE, E. & Y. TACHÉ. 1989. Intracisternal alpha-CGRP prevents gastric ulcer formation in the rat. Gastroenterology **96:** A266.
34. EVANGELISTA, S., I. T. LIPPE, P. ROVERO, C. A. MAGGI & A. MELI. 1989. Tachykinins protect against ethanol-induced gastric lesions in rats. Peptides **10:** 79–81.
35. GANNON, B., J. BROWNING & P. O'BRIEN. 1982. The microvascular architecture of the glandular mucosa of rat stomach. J. Anat. **135:** 667–683.
36. GUTH, P. H. & F. W. LEUNG. 1987. Physiology of the gastric circulation. *In* Physiology of the Gastrointestinal Tract. L. R. Johnson, Ed.: 1031–1053. Raven Press. New York.
37. WHITTLE, B. J. R. 1977. Mechanisms underlying gastric mucosal damage induced by indomethacin and bile salts, and the actions of prostaglandins. Br. J. Pharmacol. **60:** 455–460.
38. BRUGGEMAN, T. M., J. G. WOOD & H. W. DAVENPORT. 1979. Local control of blood flow in the dog's stomach: vasodilatation caused by acid back-diffusion following topical application of salicylic acid. Gastroenterology **77:** 736–744.
39. NEUHUBER, W. L. 1987. Sensory vagal innervation of the rat esophagus and cardia: a light and electron microscopic anterograde tracing study. J. Auton. Nerv. Syst. **20:** 243–255.
40. RAYBOULD, H. E., P. HOLZER, C. STERNINI & V. E. EYSSELEIN. 1990. Selective ablation of spinal sensory neurons containing CGRP inhibits the increase in rat gastric mucosal blood flow due to acid back-diffusion. Gastroenterology **98:** A198.

The Tachykinin Neuroimmune
Connection in Inflammatory Pain

EBERHARD WEIHE,[a] DONATUS NOHR,[a]
SABINE MÜLLER,[a] MARKUS BÜCHLER,[b]
HELMUT FRIESS,[b] AND HANS-JOACHIM ZENTEL[a]

[a]Anatomical Institute
Johannes Gutenberg University
D-6500 Mainz, Federal Republic of Germany

[b]Department of General Surgery
University Clinics Ulm
D-7900 Ulm, Federal Republic of Germany

INTRODUCTION

The present study is based on light microscopic (LM) enzyme and double fluorescence immunohistochemistry and evaluates the responsiveness of neuroimmune systems to more or less acute or chronic inflammatory pain conditions. First, in the well-established rat models of Freund's adjuvant–induced chronic polyarthritis and unilateral inflammation, also referred to as monoarthritis,[1,2] the responses of peripheral nerves and of central (spinal) neurons are evaluated. Second, our study of human chronic inflammatory pain concentrates on peripheral tissues in examining neuroimmune responses in chronic alcohol-induced pancreatitis and in Crohn's disease as compared to organ donors.[3]

It was our main aim to outline a novel concept of the possible importance of a neuroimmune axis in sustaining mechanisms of acute inflammatory pain in the rat and of chronic inflammatory pain in humans. For this purpose, antibodies/antisera against peptides and immune cell antigens were used as summarized in TABLES 1 and 2 or as explained in the text. The essential chemoanatomical findings of the neuroimmune response are summarized in FIGURES 1–3 and are exemplarily documented in FIGURES 4 and 5.

THE NEUROIMMUNE CONNECTION OF PEPTIDERGIC NERVES IN INFLAMED PAWS OF FREUND'S ADJUVANT–INDUCED POLYARTHRITIS AND MONOARTHRITIS IN THE RAT

In both polyarthritic and monoarthritic rats, inflamed paws contained an increased number of nerve fibers staining for substance P (SP) and for calcitonin gene–related peptide (CGRP) as compared to nonimmunized animals and contralateral noninflamed paws, respectively. CGRP-immunoreactive (ir) fibers outnumbered SP-ir fibers. Moreover, all fibers containing SP also appeared to contain CGRP. The SP-negative, but CGRP-positive fibers had a larger diameter than the SP/CGRP costained fibers. The increase in the number of SP-ir and CGRP-ir fibers

TABLE 1. List of Antisera/Antibodies against Peptides and Rat Macrophages

Antigen	Donor Species	Working Dilution	Source	Code
Met-enkephalyl-Arg-Gly-Leu (ME-RGL)	rabbit	1:20,000	Yanaihara	R 0171
Dynorphin A(1–17) (DYN)	rabbit	1:5000	Arendt	SUSI
Neuropeptide Y (NPY)	rabbit	1:8000	Yanaihara	R 0258
Substance P (SP)	rat monoclone	1:300	Seralab	MAS 035b
Calcitonin gene–related peptide (CGRP)	rabbit	1:6000	Peninsula	RAS 6012 N
Vasoactive intestinal poly-peptide (VIP)	rabbit	1:25,000	CRB	CA 340
Peptide histidine isoleucine (PHI)	rabbit	1:25,000	Yanaihara	R 8403
Macrophages, dendritic cells, monocytes (ED1)	mouse	1:1000	Serotec	MCA 341

was particularly obvious in the epidermis of inflamed skin. The question arises as to whether the increased density of these peptidergic fibers reflects inflammation-induced sprouting or an increase in the content of peptide message in fibers that, under noninflammatory conditions, contain peptide levels too low to be visualized. We favor the view that there is real sprouting in the inflamed tissues because the sensitivity of our immunocytochemical method was very high. We used the streptavidin-biotin system (Amersham) and the nickel-enhanced diaminobenzidine/horseradish peroxidase reaction. This supersensitive method revealed no differences in the number of peptide-stained ganglionic cells and ganglionic fibers of ipsisegmental dorsal root ganglia when comparing control animals and contralateral noninflamed

TABLE 2. List of Monoclonal Antibodies against Surface Antigens of Human Immune Cells

Antigen	Specificity	Working Dilution	Source	Code
Leukocyte common antigen (LC)	leukocytes including: granulocytes lymphoid cells macrophages	1:10	Dianova	M503
UCHL1 (T cell)	most thymocytes activated T cells proportion of resting T cells	1:50	Dakopatts	M742
4 KB 5 (B cell)	most B cells	1:50	Dakopatts	M754
MAC 387 (MAC)	monocytes macrophages granulocytes	1:500	Camon	E026

sides with polyarthritic animals and ipsilateral inflamed sides, respectively.[4] Therefore, we assume that the increased density of SP/CGRP and CGRP fibers in inflamed
paws implies and reflects peripheral sprouting. We are currently undertaking
quantitative studies with pan-neural marker antibodies to evaluate this concept
further.

Specific mast cell staining techniques revealed a striking increase in the number
of mast cells in inflamed paw. SP/CGRP fibers and fibers staining for CGRP alone
contacted mast cells in noninflamed paws, but the number of contacts was much
higher in inflamed paws. In addition, SP/CGRP fibers and those staining for CGRP
alone were seen in close vicinity to macrophages. Neuromacrophage contacts
appeared to be more frequent in inflamed paws. This is not surprising because

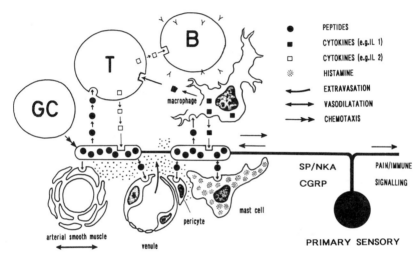

FIGURE 1. Diagram based on immunohistochemical observations in inflamed paws of arthritic
rats schematically summarizing our hypothetical conceptions of a neuroimmune dialogue in
acute inflammation. The term "acute" is in contrast to the term "chronic" devoted to long-term
inflammatory pain in humans, although the arthritic model is often referred to as chronic. We
assume that substance P and neurokinin A as well as CGRP are released and influence various
target structures. Inversely, mediators of immune cells are conceived to act on the sensory nerve
endings.

macrophages identified as ED1-positive cells and SP/CGRP-ir as well as CGRP-ir
fibers were increased in numbers as compared to noninflamed paw tissue. The
coincidence of increased mast cell numbers and putative peripheral sprouting of
peptidergic nerves may be regulated by an increased peripheral level of nerve growth
factor (NGF) and possibly other growth factors.[5] NGF regulates the gene expression
of tachykinins and CGRP in primary sensory neurons and appears to be correlated
with an increased number of mast cells. In fact, the mRNA levels for tachykinins and
CGRP are increased in dorsal root ganglia ipsilateral to peripheral inflammation as
revealed by quantitative *in situ* hybridization.[6] Furthermore, NGF has striking
immunomodulatory actions.[5] The peripheral "soup" of inflammatory mediators
possibly interfering in the neuroimmune dialogue and modifying nociceptor mechanisms is much more complex.[7,8]

The fact that the antisera against the other peptides listed in TABLE 1 revealed no inflammation-induced increase in nerve fiber staining may underline the anatomical specificity of the response. The presumed SP/CGRP sensory system is apparently selectively activated. On the other hand, we recently gained the impression that the density of immunoreactive fibers containing neuropeptide Y (NPY) was equally decreased as the staining for tyrosine hydroxylase (TH), which is the rate-limiting and marker enzyme of catecholaminergic postganglionic sympathetic fibers. Because NPY is well known to coexist in TH-positive postganglionic sympathetic fibers, the seemingly concomitant decrease of two coexisting messenger systems is not too surprising. The fact that the sympathetic nervous system and particularly β_2-receptors possibly play a role in nociceptive mechanisms has been recently argued by

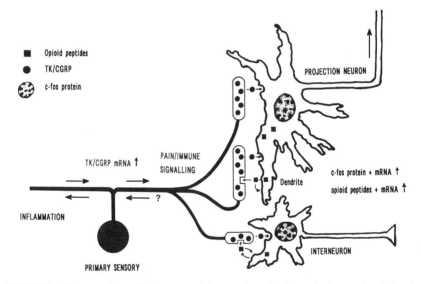

FIGURE 2. Diagram schematically summarizing our hypothesis on the integrational circuits and the molecular anatomy of pain/immune signaling in the dorsal horn of the spinal cord. The diagram is based on our own immunohistochemical investigations and on current concepts in the literature.[12] For the reason of simplicity, the postsynaptic target relations of the interneuron are not depicted. Note particularly our schematic representation of a possible dendritic release of opioids putatively acting on SP/CGRP nociceptor endings. We assume that the SP/CGRP release is presynaptically suppressed. Furthermore, SP and CGRP release from nociceptor endings is likely to excite projection neurons and interneurons. For further details, see the text.

Basbaum and colleagues.[2] Interestingly, NPY has prejunctional modulatory actions on peripheral terminals of capsaicin-sensitive sensory fibers[9] that can be assumed to contain SP/CGRP. In guinea pig airways, capsaicin-sensitive neurons are suppressed by NPY.[10] Therefore, pain is possibly due to a deficiency of postganglionic sympathetic messenger systems like NPY that suppress the activity of nociceptors peripherally. Because platelets contain and probably release NPY, presumed tachykinin and CGRP sensory fibers could be modulated by neuronal and nonneuronal sources of NPY. This may play a so far unelucidated role in inflammatory processes.

The prominent features of the peripheral inflamed tissue in the Freund's adjuvant–induced arthritis were the increase in mast cells and the massive infiltration of mixed populations of lymphocytes, granulocytes, and macrophages that were

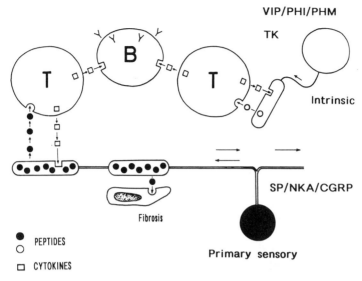

FIGURE 3. Diagram schematically summarizing our hypothesis on the chemical anatomy of chronic inflammatory pain in human disease based on our immunohistochemical findings in chronic alcohol-induced pancreatitis and Crohn's disease. We assume mutual communication between nerve fibers and sensory or intrinsic neurons. Peptides released from nerves may influence immune cells, and cytokines released from immune cells may act on nerve fibers. Cytokine action on primary sensory (nociceptor) endings may be critical in peripheral sustaining mechanisms of chronic inflammatory pain. The neuroimmune communication may be amplified by cascadal interactions between immune cells.

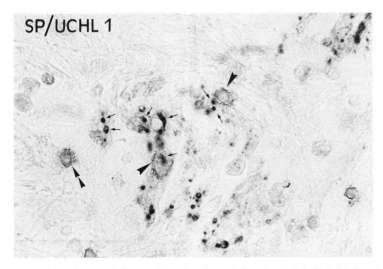

FIGURE 4. Light microscopic immunohistochemistry of chronic painful alcohol-induced pancreatitis. A high-power micrograph showing the close interrelation of substance P–immunoreactive nerve fibers (arrows) with T cells identified by UCHL1 staining (arrowheads). Note also the absence of tachykininergic input to a T cell (double arrowhead).

arranged around inflammatory vacuoles and blood vessels. Blood vessels were maximally dilated and particularly densely innervated by CGRP-ir fibers. CGRP and SP/CGRP costained fibers branched off from the vasculature to intermingle with mast cells and various infiltrated immune cells. Some of these immune cells displayed staining for opioids as originally reported previously.[4] This suggested a possible function of endogenous neuropeptides as "neurocytokines", possibly playing a role in peripheral opioid antinociceptive mechanisms. Taken together, the complex chemoanatomy of the likely neuroimmune interactions coming into play in the inflamed paws is presented in FIGURE 1.

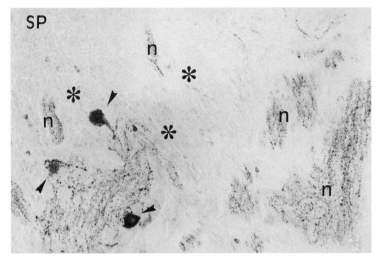

FIGURE 5. Light microscopic immunohistochemistry of a terminal ileum of Crohn's disease. A low-power micrograph showing large numbers of nerves (n) containing many SP-containing nerve fibers surrounded by immune infiltrates (∗). Note the immunopositive intrinsic neurons (arrowheads).

SUSTAINED OPIOID/c-fos COEXPRESSION IN SPINAL NEURONS CONTROLLED BY INCREASED SP/CGRP RELEASE FROM PRIMARY SENSORY ENDINGS IN ARTHRITIC RATS

Opioid immunoreactivity was generally absent from spinal cord neurons of control animals and from the spinal half contralateral to the inflamed paw in monoarthritis. Multiple opioid stainings in spinal neurons and fibers were strikingly enhanced bilaterally in polyarthritis and ipsilaterally in monoarthritis as compared to control rats.[11] Immunoreactivities for dynorphin A(1–17) and several other prodynorphin (PRO-DYN) derivatives like DYN A(1–8), DYN B, and α-neoendorphin were increased in large superficial dorsal horn neurons of the Waldeyer type and in small neurons of the substantia gelatinosa, as well as in large neurons and neurons of intermediate size located in the deep dorsal horn, particularly in lamina V. Immunoreactivity for the proenkephalin derivative, met-enkephalyl-Arg-Gly-Leu (ME-RGL), was increased in deep dorsal horn neurons. Marginal neurons of the

Waldeyer type appeared to be less frequently stained for the PRO-ENK octapeptide than for DYN.

Because of the very high density of octapeptide-ir fibers in the substantia gelatinosa, cellular staining of small neurons for octapeptide could not be assessed with certainty. Due to the much higher overall density of the PRO-ENK fiber system, differences in fiber density between controls and arthritic rats were not obvious. Analysis of consecutive sections revealed a substantial coincidence of PRO-ENK-related and PRO-DYN-related staining of deep dorsal horn neurons.

Double immunofluorescence revealed a close interrelation of both PRO-DYN and PRO-ENK responsive neurons with SP or CGRP fibers or with fibers staining for both SP and CGRP. The CGRP fibers and endings in the dorsal horn can be reasonably assumed to originate from primary afferents, whereas spinal SP fibers have mixed origins from primary afferents, intrinsic spinal neurons, and descending systems of supraspinal origin.[12] Therefore, we conclude that the close association of CGRP varicose fibers with dendrites and somata of opioid neurons reflects primary afferent input to a specifically responsive population of dorsal horn neurons.[13] Both large and small dorsal horn opioid neurons staining for PRO-ENK or PRO-DYN (or both) were the target of presumed primary afferent CGRP fibers. This view is in accordance with observations by Takahashi *et al.* that DYN A(1–8) neurons "lit up" in inflammation-received CGRP input.[14] However, this study needed colchicine treatment as a cofactor to visualize the perikaryal opioid staining. Moreover, some of the deep dorsal horn opioid neurons were seen to have characteristics of projection neurons. In fact, retrograde labeling combined with immunocytochemistry revealed rostral projections of such opioid neurons, whereas the small opioid neurons were characterized as interneurons.[15] Interestingly, it was shown by electron microscopic (EM) immunocytochemistry that DYN A(1–8) monkey dorsal horn neurons received synaptic axosomatic and axodendritic CGRP inputs that were in line with the interpretation of our light microscopic results.[16]

However, it should be pointed out again that we cannot be confident that the SP input to opioid neurons "lit up" in arthritis is of primary afferent origin.[12,13] Our current efforts, though, with triple-staining methods providing evidence that SP/ CGRP costained fibers target opioid neurons do give us reason to conclude that there is a primary afferent SP input to the spinal neurons. The fact that SP varicose fibers not containing CGRP target opioid neurons also implies that these receive a nonprimary sensory tachykinin input as well.[12] We could not answer the question of whether this non-SP/CGRP population is derived from intrinsic SP neurons that apparently produce increased levels of mRNA in the response to peripheral inflammation.[17] It remained equally unclear whether opioid responsive neurons receive a descending tachykininergic input.

Our data, based on LM immunocytochemistry, do not provide direct evidence for synaptic input. This has to be resolved by EM immunocytochemistry applied to the arthritic model directly. However, it can be argued that synaptic release of SP or CGRP may not be necessary for a functional interrelation between the presumed nociceptor endings and the responsive opioid neurons. In fact, nonsynaptic mechanisms and diffusion of bioactive peptides over a certain target distance are accepted possibilities. Nevertheless, we think that our chemoanatomical data in conjunction with those cited here[14,16] provide evidence for the view that there is a close functional link between putative nociceptive primary afferents containing SP and CGRP or CGRP alone and spinal opioid neurons.

SP and CGRP release in the dorsal horn is increased under inflammatory conditions,[18] as is the mRNA for both peptides in the segmentally related dorsal root ganglia.[6,19] The increase of SP, of course, can also be derived from intrinsic SP neurons. An increase of SP originating from intrinsic spinal neurons is most likely the case because spinal levels of tachykinin mRNA are elevated.[17] The question arises as to whether the increased spinal release of SP and CGRP from presumed nociceptor endings and of SP from endings of intrinsic and supraspinal origin is functionally coupled to the increase in peptide mRNA and message of opioid target neurons.[12,13] At present, this question cannot be answered, but some speculations about the possibly mutual functional interrelation between the primary afferent and the opioid responsive neurons can be made.

We assume that the CGRP/SP fibers targeting the opioid neurons are primarily fulfilling nociceptive transmission. However, we have to take into account that they do not only signal pain, but also inflammation. Alternatively, separate entities of SP/CGRP fibers may signal pain and inflammation differentially. Perhaps some of the activated SP/CGRP primary afferents belong to the group of "silent nociceptors" (according to Schaible) that bombard the CNS during inflammation while being quiescent in noninflammatory conditions.[20] It may well be that this group is specifically up-regulated in peptide gene expression, resulting in enhanced release of the pronociceptive peptides SP/CGRP from spinal sensory endings. It would be interesting to know whether spinal glutamate release is also enhanced in arthritis because coexistence of glutamate and SP in small-diameter afferents has been recently demonstrated.[12,13]

The c-fos Connection

Immediate-early genes of the c-fos and c-jun family are involved in signal-transcription coupling of the opioid genes.[21] The fos oncoprotein encoded by the c-fos oncogene binds to the AP 1 binding region, which is located in a regulatory element of the PRO-ENK gene and is essential for basal and induced levels of transcription.[21]

Evidence for an up-regulation of c-fos gene expression and an increase in the spinal levels of fos protein upon noxious stimulation has first been immunohistochemically mapped by Hunt,[22] who showed "lighting up" of nuclear fos immunoreactivity in a substantial number of dorsal horn neurons. A transient increase in fos gene expression[23] and message preceding the ongoing increase in PRO-ENK- and PRO-DYN-mRNA and opioid peptides was measured by Draisci and Iadarola.[24]

Therefore, it seemed logical to anticipate and search for the possible coexistence of nuclear fos protein and opioids in the arthritis model. Whereas fos protein immunoreactivity was virtually absent in control animals and in the spinal halves of noninflamed sides, substantial numbers of dorsal horn neurons exhibiting fos-positive nuclear staining were "lit up" bilaterally in polyarthritis and ipsilaterally in monoarthritis. More than 50% of these fos-positive neurons clearly exhibited positive opioid staining in their perikarya. The intensity of fos staining varied from very strong to weak. The coincidence of opioid and fos expression in identical neurons could be even greater because of the underestimation of marginal fos or opioid staining due to methodological reasons. However, some fos-positive and opioid-negative neurons and some opioid-positive and fos-negative neurons were certainly present. In the region lateral to the central canal and in the ventral horn, nuclear fos staining was regularly "lit up" in arthritis, whereas concomitant staining of neuronal cell bodies for opioids was absent from these regions. This reflects that the fos response is not specific for opioid neurons. In fact, fos gene up-regulation is a stereotypic response in signal-secretion coupling and also applies to other peptide families and even growth factors.

Based on our double immunofluorescence studies showing a close interrelation between SP/CGRP fibers and opioid neurons, we expected that SP/CGRP fibers would target PRO-ENK and PRO-DYN neurons cocontaining c-fos. By using a newly developed and highly sensitive immunoenzymatic procedure of sequential application of primary and secondary antibodies and detection systems, we succeeded in demonstrating a close interrelation of SP/CGRP fibers with dendrites and somata of both PRO-DYN/c-fos and PRO-ENK/c-fos costained neurons. Details of our strategy to triple-label opioids, c-fos, and SP/CGRP have been presented at the INRC conference in 1990[25] and will be published elsewhere. Our results obtained in an ongoing process of inflammation-induced pain in the polyarthritic and monoarthritic rat are, in principle, in accordance with the cocontainment of opioids and c-fos in dorsal horn neurons in the more acute carrageenan-induced inflammation.[26]

We are tempted to propose that the sustained up-regulation of c-fos immunoreactivity and, implicitly, of c-fos oncogene expression may reflect the pertained mechanism of up-regulation of signal-transcription coupling in dorsal horn opioid neurons under chronic pain. The involvement of other immediate-early genes in response to noxious stimulatory events also has to be taken into regard.[27] Interestingly, systemic opiates suppress the noxious stimulus–induced fos protein expression in dorsal horn neurons.[28]

The specific stimulus continuously triggering enhanced c-fos gene expression as the mediating signal of enhanced opioid expression may consist of the permanently increased release of SP/CGRP and, possibly, of cocontained glutamate from nearby nociceptor endings. Speculatively, though, we might argue that dendritic release of opioids from intrinsic spinal neurons (both projection neurons and segmental interneurons) could be a so far unrecognized mechanism for presynaptic control of the release of messengers from spinal nociceptor endings. In line with this concept is the suppressing effect of opioids on the *in vitro* release of CGRP from afferent fibers in rat spinal cord.[29] Our concept of the chemoanatomical basis of integrative spinal mechanisms in pain/immune signaling is summarized in FIGURE 2.

THE NEUROIMMUNE DIALOGUE AS A SUSTAINING MECHANISM OF CHRONIC INFLAMMATORY PAIN IN HUMAN DISEASES

Although the arthritic rat has been introduced as an animal model of chronic inflammatory pain,[1,2] it is pertinent to analyze the chemoanatomy of the chronic pain conditions in humans.[3] In this study, we concentrated on possible changes of peptidergic innervation in peripheral tissues in the course of long-term inflammatory pain. By focusing on tachykinins, we investigated peptidergic patterns in patients suffering from chronic alcohol-induced pancreatitis or from Crohn's disease. Pancreatic nerves of patients suffering from chronic pancreatitis were increased in their number and diameter and exhibited strikingly intensified costaining of fibers for SP/CGRP.[3] In addition to the SP/CGRP costained population, there was an increase of SP fibers not containing CGRP. These changes mainly occurred in the interlobular tissues. The iuxtaneural areas were often infiltrated by inflammatory cells that partly formed follicular accumulations. SP and CGRP fibers were found to be sprouted into follicular and nonfollicular accumulations of lymphocytes. Costaining for immune cell surface antigens and neural peptides or neuronal marker proteins revealed mainly a close interrelation of nerve fibers with T cells and also with some B cells, whereas neuromacrophage contacts were only rarely encountered. Neuro–T cell contacts of tachykininergic fibers were particularly pronounced. In control tissues of organ donors, some neuro–T cell and neuro–B cell interrelations and some rare neuromacrophage contacts of tachykininergic fibers were present, but infiltrations and follicular accumulations of inflammatory cells were absent.

Tachykinin immunoreactivity was mainly absent from intrinsic pancreatic neurons of organ donor tissue. In contrast, we recently gained the impression that an increased number of intrinsic neurons exhibited staining for tachykinins in chronic pancreatitis. CGRP immunoreactivity was absent from intrinsic neurons both in donor pancreas and in pancreatitis. VIP/PHI immunoreactivity and, to a lesser extent, NPY immunoreactivity were regularly present in substantial numbers of intrinsic neurons in pancreatitis and in donor pancreas. Surprisingly, we observed an increased number of fibers costained for tachykinins and VIP/PHI in pancreatitis, whereas coexistence of SP/CGRP was not unexpected.[12,13] We argue that the SP/CGRP population is of primary sensory origin, whereas the population staining for SP, but not for CGRP, and the SP population costaining for VIP/PHI and/or NPY belong to the intrinsic (postganglionic parasympathetic?) innervation of the pancreas.

Having provided evidence for an intrinsic innervation of the pancreas that appears to be more pronounced in pancreatitis, we can conclude that there is not only a tachykininergic response of the sensory nervous system, but also of the intrinsic nervous system. Thus, tachykininergic fibers closely interrelated with the inflammatory cells in pancreatitis may originate from sensory and intrinsic systems. Therefore, we have to assume that neuroimmune mechanisms may be controlled by tachykinins released from both neural origins. This is in contrast to the situation in peripheral somatic tissue where intrinsic/postganglionic parasympathetic innervation is absent. Whether tachykinin gene expression in pancreatic intrinsic neurons is up-regulated by cytokines, anticipatably increased in the chronically inflamed pancreas, is an attractive question to answer in the light of the recently described interleukin-1 (IL-1)–induced up-regulation of tachykinin gene expression in cultured sympathetic neurons.[30] Our current immunocytochemical evidence indicates that, indeed, there may be some coregulation of the intrinsic tachykinin and VIP/PHI response to pancreatitis. However, the main change in the neuronal tachykinin system under pancreatitis appears to be attributable to the primary sensory compartment, which is identified as being costained for CGRP.

Because nerves in chronic pancreatitis exhibit ultrastructural features of barrier-loss at the level of the perineural sheath, there may be free access of various cytokines and inflammatory mediators to nociceptor fibers in passage as well as to those closely intermingled with T cells and other leukocytes (FIGURE 4). Hence, the anatomical constellation is provided for an intensified neuroimmune cross talk under chronic inflammation. The predominant neuroimmune interrelation appears to be at the neuro–T cell level, but neurogranulocyte intercommunications are also conceivable because the number of neuroimmune cell contacts was somewhat higher when immune cells were stained with antileukocyte common antigen than with anti-T cell monoclonals. Chronic pancreatitis is accompanied by fibrosis of the pancreatic tissue.[3] We may speculate that neuropeptides like SP, present in increased numbers of fibers, may contribute to the development of fibrosis. This is deduced from the mitogenic and trophic action profiles of tachykinins.[31] In contrast to the inflammation of relatively short duration in the arthritic rat, mast cells appear to be absent in the long-term chronic inflammatory process over years in humans, at least in pancreatitis. This chronic pain and inflammatory condition is clearly characterized by predominance of the neuro–T cell connection as compared to the prominence of the neuro–mast cell connection in the arthritic rats.

A possible involvement of endogenous neuropeptides in Crohn's disease has been recognized by using VIP immunocytochemistry.[32] VIP fibers appeared to be increased in numbers throughout the wall of the diseased bowel. Submucous and myenteric neurons appeared to be affected. In contrast, no characteristic change in SP innervation of the gut in Crohn's disease was reported. Our current observations, though, indicate that there is a striking increase in the number of fibers staining for tachykinins in Crohn's disease as compared to healthy tissue obtained during routine surgical therapy undertaken for other reasons. In particular, the tachykinin-ir fibers were found to form frequent and close contacts with the strikingly increased inflammatory cells throughout the gut wall of patients suffering from Crohn's disease. The neuro–T cell connection was the predominant form of neuroimmune interconnection and was similar to the constellation in chronic pancreatitis.

In contrast to pancreatitis, large populations of intrinsic neurons of the normal human gut and of the bowel in Crohn's disease were strongly immunoreactive for tachykinins. The number of intrinsic neurons staining for SP appeared to be higher in Crohn's disease than in normal gut. The tachykininergic neuroimmune connection is regularly present in the entire normal gastrointestinal system. Thus, tachykininergic fibers regularly target lymphocytes in the lamina propria and in the accumulated lymph follicles, although only at the marginal zones. This pattern is very similar to that shown by VIP/PHI fibers. It appears that, under Crohn's disease, the basically present neuroimmune constellation, although qualitatively unchanged, is quantitatively altered (up-regulated), resulting in a striking augmentation of the neuroimmune target interrelations.

The density of CGRP fibers was unchanged in Crohn's disease and was much lower than that of SP fibers. Assuming that CGRP fibers are mainly of primary sensory origin, supported by the absence of CGRP from intrinsic gut neurons, we may conclude that the sensory innervation with small-diameter peptidergic fibers in the human gut is minimal. Alternatively, non-CGRP peptides like VIP may be of sensory origin as evidenced by the recently demonstrated capsaicin-sensitivity of VIP release in the human intestine.[33] In any case, the observed change of tachykinin innervation in Crohn's disease may be mainly of intrinsic origin. Perhaps cytokines regulate the increase in VIP as well as in tachykinin innervation due to chronic inflammatory bowel disease. The particular increase in tachykinin innervation seems to be correlated with a selective increase in substance P receptor density in Crohn's disease (see the discussion by Mantyh in this volume).

CONCLUSIONS AND FUTURE DIRECTIONS

We assume that the neuroimmune connection generally plays a role in normal somatic (e.g., cutaneous) as well as normal visceral (e.g., gastroenteropancreatic) functions and is of particular importance under chronic inflammatory conditions. It is tempting to postulate that neuroimmune mechanisms are relevant for the perception, sustaining, and perpetuation mechanisms of chronic inflammatory pain. A disturbed neuroimmune dialogue may initiate and sustain pain and there may even be a psycho-neuroimmune-endocrine link. It may be worthwhile to develop drugs for the therapy of pain that normalize disturbed neuroimmune cross talk. Perhaps the combination of immune therapy with pain therapy is an attractive strategy.

REFERENCES

1. MILLAN, M. J. 1990. K-Opioid receptors and analgesia. TIPS **11**(2): 70–76.
2. BASBAUM, A. I., D. MENETREY, R. PRESLEY & J. D. LEVINE. 1988. The contribution of the nervous system to experimental arthritis in the rat. *In* The Arthritic Rat as a Model of Clinical Pain? J. M. Besson & G. Guilbaud, Eds.: 41–53. Elsevier. Amsterdam/New York.
3. WEIHE, E., M. BÜCHLER, S. MÜLLER, H. FRIESS, H. J. ZENTEL & N. YANAIHARA. 1990. Peptidergic innervation in chronic pancreatitis. *In* Chronic Pancreatitis. H. G. Beger, M. Büchler, H. Ditschuneit & P. Malfertheiner, Eds.: 83–105. Springer-Verlag. Berlin/New York.
4. WEIHE, E., D. NOHR, M. J. MILLAN, C. STEIN, S. MÜLLER, C. GRAMSCH & A. HERZ. 1988. Peptide neuroanatomy of adjuvant-induced arthritic inflammation in rat. Agents Actions **25**(3/4): 255–259.
5. OTTEN, U. H. 1991. What extra-neural trophic factors influence peripheral and central nerve function? *In* Towards a New Pharmacotherapy of Pain (Dahlem Konferenzen). A. Basbaum & J. M. Besson, Eds.: 353–363. Wiley. New York.
6. NOGUCHI, K., Y. MORITA, H. KYAMA, K. ONO & M. TOHYAMA. 1988. A noxious stimulus induces the preprotachykinin-A gene expression in the dorsal root ganglion: a quantitative study using *in situ* hybridization histochemistry. Mol. Brain Res. **4**: 31–35.
7. HANDWERKER, H. O. 1991. What peripheral mechanisms contribute to nociceptive transmission and hyperalgesia? *In* Towards a New Pharmacotherapy of Pain (Dahlem Konferenzen). A. Basbaum & J. M. Besson, Eds.: 5–19. Wiley. New York.
8. DRAY, A. & J. N. WOOD. 1991. Non-opioid molecular signalling systems involved in nociceptive transmission and antinociception? *In* Towards a New Pharmacotherapy of Pain (Dahlem Konferenzen). A. Basbaum & J. M. Besson, Eds.: 21–34. Wiley. New York.
9. GIULIANI, S., C. A. MAGGI & A. MELI. 1989. Prejunctional modulatory action of neuropeptide Y on peripheral terminals of capsaicin-sensitive sensory nerves. Br. J. Pharmacol. **98**: 407–412.
10. GRUNDEMAR, L., N. GRUNDSTRÖM, I. G. M. JOHANSSON, R. G. G. ANDERSSON & R. HÅKANSON. 1990. Suppression by neuropeptide Y of capsaicin-sensitive sensory nerve–mediated contraction in guinea-pig airways. Br. J. Pharmacol. **99**: 473–476.
11. WEIHE, E., M. J. MILLAN, V. HÖLLT, D. NOHR & A. HERZ. 1989. Induction of the gene encoding pro-dynorphin by experimentally induced arthritis enhances staining for dynorphin in the spinal cord of the rats. Neuroscience **31**: 77–95.
12. DUGGAN, A. W. & E. WEIHE. 1991. Central transmission of impulses in nociceptors: events in the superficial dorsal horn. *In* Towards a New Pharmacotherapy of Pain (Dahlem Konferenzen). A. Basbaum & J. M. Besson, Eds. Wiley. New York.
13. WEIHE, E. 1990. Neuropeptides in primary sensory neurons. *In* The Primary Sensory Neuron—A Survey of Recent Morphofunctional Aspects. W. Zenker & W. Neuhuber, Eds.: 127–159. Plenum. New York.
14. TAKAHASHI, O., R. J. TRAUB & M. A. RUDA. 1988. Demonstration of calcitonin gene–related peptide immunoreactive axons contacting dynorphin A(1–8) immunoreactive spinal neurons in a rat model of peripheral inflammation and hyperalgesia. Brain Res. **475**: 168–172.
15. NAHIN, R. L., J. L. K. HYLDEN, M. J. IADAROLA & R. DUBNER. 1989. Peripheral inflammation is associated with increased dynorphin immunoreactivity in both projection and local circuit neurons in the superficial dorsal horn of the rat lumbar spinal cord. Neurosci. Lett. **96**: 247–252.
16. CARLTON, S. M. & E. S. HAYES. 1989. Dynorphin A(1–8) immunoreactive cell bodies, dendrites, and terminals are postsynaptic to calcitonin gene–related peptide primary afferent terminals in the monkey dorsal horn. Brain Res. **504**: 124–128.
17. MINAMI, M., Y. KURAISHI, K. KAWAMURA, T. YAMAGUCHI, Y. MASU, S. NAKANISHI & M. SATOH. 1989. Enhancement of preprotachykinin A gene expression by adjuvant-induced inflammation in the rat spinal cord: possible involvement of substance P–containing spinal neurons in nociception. Neurosci. Lett. **98**: 105–110.

18. OKU, R., M. SATOH & H. TAKAGI. 1987. Release of substance P from the spinal dorsal horn is enhanced in polyarthritic rats. Neurosci. Lett. **74:** 315–319.
19. IADAROLA, M. J. & G. DRAISCI. 1988. Elevation of spinal cord dynorphin mRNA compared to dorsal root ganglion peptide mRNAs during peripheral inflammation. *In* The Arthritic Rat as a Model of Clinical Pain? J. M. Besson & G. Guilbaud, Eds.: 173–183. Elsevier. Amsterdam/New York.
20. MCMAHON, S. B. & M. KOLTZENBURG. 1990. Novel classes of nociceptors: beyond Sherrington. TINS **13**(6): 199–201.
21. SONNENBERG, J. L., F. J. RAUSCHER III, J. I. MORGAN & T. CURRAN. 1989. Regulation of proenkephalin by fos and jun. Science **246:** 1622–1625.
22. HUNT, S. P., A. PINI & G. EVAN. 1987. Induction of c-fos-like protein in spinal cord neurons following sensory stimulation. Nature **328:** 632–634.
23. HÖLLT, V., I. HAARMANN, M. J. MILLAN & A. HERZ. 1987. Prodynorphin gene expression is enhanced in the spinal cord of chronic arthritic rats. Neurosci. Lett. **73:** 90–94.
24. DRAISCI, G. & M. J. IADAROLA. 1989. Temporal analysis of increases in c-fos, preprodynorphin, and preproenkephalin mRNAs in rat spinal cord. Mol. Brain Res. **6:** 31–37.
25. WEIHE, E., M. J. IADAROLA, D. NOHR, S. MÜLLER, M. J. MILLAN, N. YANAIHARA, C. STEIN & A. HERZ. 1990. Sustained expression and colocalization of proenkephalin and prodynorphin opioids and c-fos protein in dorsal horn neurons revealed in arthritic rats. Excerpta Med. Int. Congr. Ser. **914:** 92–94.
26. RUDA, M. A., K. KOWALSKI, R. J. TRAUB, A. SOLODKIN & M. J. IADAROLA. 1990. Colocalization of opioid peptide and fos protein in a rat model of peripheral inflammation and hyperalgesia. Pain (Suppl.) **5:** S102.
27. HERDEGEN, T., J. D. LEAH, T. WALKER, B. BASLER & M. ZIMMERMAN. 1990. Activated neurons in CNS pain pathways detected via early and protooncogene-protein products. Pain (Suppl.) **5:** 97.
28. PRESLEY, R. W., D. MENETREY, J. D. LEVINE & A. I. BASBAUM. 1990. Systemic morphine suppresses noxious stimulus–evoked fos protein–like immunoreactivity in the rat spinal cord. J. Neurosci. **10**(1): 323–335.
29. POHL, M., M. C. LOMBARD, S. BOURGOIN, A. CARAYON, J. J. BENOLIEL, A. MAUBORGNE, J. M. BESSON, M. HAMON & F. CESSELIN. 1989. Opioid control of the *in vitro* release of calcitonin gene–related peptide from primary afferent fibers projecting in the rat cervical cord. Neuropeptides **14:** 151–159.
30. JONAKAIT, G. M. & R. P. HART. 1990. Interleukin-1 increases substance P and preprotachykinin mRNA in injured sympathetic ganglion neurons. First International Congress ISNIM, Florence, Italy.
31. DALSGAARD, C. J., A. HULTGARDH-NILSSON, A. HAEGERSTRAND & J. NILSSON. 1989. Neuropeptides as growth factors: possible roles in human diseases. Regulat. Peptides **25:** 1–9.
32. BISHOP, A. E., J. M. POLAK, M. G. BRYANT, S. R. BLOOM & S. HAMILTON. 1980. Abnormalities of vasoactive intestinal peptide–containing nerves in Crohn's disease. Gastroenterology **79:** 853–860.
33. MAGGI, C. A. 1990. Capsaicin and primary afferent neurons: from basic science to human therapy? J. Auton. Nerv. Syst. In press.

Substance P Afferents Regulate ACTH-Corticosterone Release[a]

JOSEF DONNERER,[b] RAINER AMANN,[b]
GERHARD SKOFITSCH,[c] AND FRED LEMBECK[b]

[b]Department of Experimental and Clinical Pharmacology
[c]Department of Zoology
University of Graz
A-8010 Graz, Austria

INTRODUCTION

The investigation into the physiological role of primary afferent C-fibers containing substance P, neurokinin A, calcitonin gene–related peptide, and other related peptides as their neurotransmitters was facilitated by their sensitivity towards capsaicin. Because this class of afferent neurons can be selectively eliminated by a treatment with capsaicin,[1] their role in various physiological and pathophysiological states could be investigated in the whole organism without relying on exogenous stimuli to excite them. It was thus found that afferent peptidergic fibers register through their peripheral terminals a whole range of nociceptive and nonnociceptive information processed centrally into protective autonomic reflexes and hormone secretion.[2,3]

The systemic capsaicin pretreatment of rats can be performed at either neonatal or adult age with a dose of 50 mg/kg sc; this impairs afferent C-fibers and a few A-delta fibers without affecting central or efferent autonomic nerves of the same fiber diameter. After a neonatal treatment, the impairment is permanent, making it possible to then correlate, at adult age, the deficits in neuronal function to the capsaicin-sensitive afferent neurons.

THE STRESS RESPONSE IN THE CAPSAICIN-TREATED RAT

The activation of the hypothalamic-pituitary-adrenal axis by stressful neural stimuli is mediated by different pathways to the hypothalamus, with hypothalamic norepinephrine and 5-hydroxytryptamine having a stimulatory effect in the mediation of these responses.[4] During infection or in response to acute inflammatory stimuli, the hypothalamic-pituitary axis is activated by humoral factors as well (e.g., interleukin-1).[5] The main stimulatory hypothalamic factor for the release of adrenocorticotropin (ACTH) from the anterior pituitary is the corticotropin-releasing factor (CRF), with the involvement of vasopressin, oxytocin, and angiotensin.[6] ACTH then induces the synthesis and secretion of corticosteroids from the adrenal cortex. The physiological function of these steroids secreted during stress or injury is

[a]This research was supported by the Austrian Scientific Research Funds (Grant Nos. P6646M and P7676M), the Pain Research Commission of the Austrian Academy of Sciences, the Franz Lanyar Foundation at the Medical Faculty of the University of Graz, and the Austrian National Bank (Grant No. 3378).

not so much to protect against the source of stress, but to adjust the organism to the immunological and inflammatory defense mechanisms that are activated by stress.[7,8]

Although it has been long known that sensory neurons transmit impulses to the central nervous system that induce the release of ACTH and corticosterone,[4] the identification of this class of neurons has not been put forward. With capsaicin as a tool to impair selectively primary afferent C-fibers, this task has become possible.

To establish functionally that the efferent pathway in the stress response is not influenced by the neonatal capsaicin treatment, both the ability of the anterior pituitary gland to respond to an infusion of CRF with a secretion of ACTH and the response of the adrenal cortex to secrete corticosterone upon an ACTH injection were tested in rats pretreated with capsaicin and were found to be identical to control animals.[9,10] Similarly, those stressful stimuli that excite specific sensor systems (olfaction, optic, vestibular, taste) or that cause emotional disturbances like the open field situation or restraint conditions have induced the same ACTH release in capsaicin-treated animals and controls, indicating that they activate central neural pathways independent of capsaicin-sensitive afferents.[9,11,12]

However, those stimuli that excited somatosensory or viscerosensory systems were not able to induce the same ACTH and corticosterone release in the capsaicin-treated rats as they did in controls. These latter types of stimuli include exposure to a cold environment (6 °C) in the awake animal,[11] standard neck surgery with cannulation of blood vessels, and ip injection of formalin in the pentobarbital-anesthetized rat[9] (see FIGURE 1). The ACTH response can be measured quite well in pentobarbital anesthesia because this anesthetic does not itself influence ACTH levels as gaseous (ether, halothane) or injectable substances like urethane do.[12]

In extending the studies of Feldman *et al.*[13] on sciatic nerve stimulation, we could demonstrate that the electrical afferent stimulation of all types of A-fibers does not raise ACTH levels in plasma, but that such a rise necessitates the additional activation of C-fibers, indicating the exclusive involvement of these fibers in the activation of the ACTH-corticosterone response.[12] This specific C-fiber-mediated response could not be observed in the capsaicin-treated rats.

Capsaicin-treated rats can also be used to search for an involvement of peptidergic afferents in a stress response where the involvement of peripheral afferents is not expected a priori. During morphine withdrawal, a pronounced secretion of ACTH can be seen and we found that this surge was reduced by 50% in the capsaicin-treated rats, indicating the involvement of afferent peptidergic nerves.[12] The morphine withdrawal symptoms were reduced in the capsaicin-treated rats by Sharpe and Jaffe,[14] and Bell *et al.*[15] proposed under these same conditions an increased input from small-diameter primary afferent fibers as visualized by the [14C]2-deoxyglucose technique.[16] We could demonstrate that a normal release of neuropeptides from primary afferents during opiate withdrawal causes overshooting reflex responses in general through the supersensitivity of receptors situated postsynaptically to C-fiber afferents or through the hyperexcitability of neurons located further centrally.[17]

Nicotine is known to stimulate not only chemoreceptors and baroreceptors, but also free terminals of afferent paravascular C-fibers.[18] This is in addition to its effects within the central nervous system. We also could demonstrate that a portion of the ACTH release elicited by an iv injection of nicotine in the rat is mediated by capsaicin-sensitive afferents.[10]

Furthermore, the impaired activation of central neural pathways in the brain stem by a cold stress in the capsaicin-treated rat can be demonstrated by using the [14C]2-deoxyglucose technique to measure neuronal metabolic activity.[16] With this method, it has already been shown that noxious stimulation of afferent trigeminal C-fibers increases the metabolic rate of the trigeminal sensory complex.[19] We also

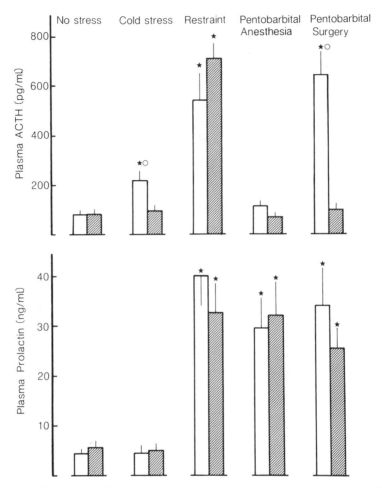

FIGURE 1. Plasma ACTH and prolactin concentrations in vehicle-pretreated rats (open columns) or capsaicin-pretreated rats (hatched columns) in various stressful situations: cold exposure (6 °C) for 30 min; restraining movements in a Plexiglas cylinder for 10 min; pentobarbital anesthesia (50 mg/kg ip) 10 min earlier; and anesthesia and surgery. The values represent the mean ± SEM of 5–7 observations. Significance of differences: * = $P < 0.05$ compared to the stress-free situation; ○ = $P < 0.05$ compared to capsaicin-pretreated rats. (Reproduced by permission from reference 10.)

demonstrated for a 45-min cold exposure that metabolic activity, corresponding to [^{14}C]2-deoxyglucose accumulation, in the whole cerebellum, in the reticular formation, and in the termination area of the trigeminal nerves was higher in controls than in capsaicin-treated rats (FIGURE 2).

During cold stress, the impaired ACTH secretion is followed by a disturbed corticosterone secretion and an altered body core temperature control in the capsaicin-treated animals, leading to a significant lowering of the colon temperature

60 and 90 min after the start of the cold exposure (FIGURE 3). Whether a disturbed corticosterone secretion is the sole factor involved in the impaired control of the body core temperature cannot be concluded; a release of adrenaline from the adrenal medulla and of noradrenaline from the sympathetic nerves might also be involved. However, because it has been shown that the adrenaline release is also dependent upon proper functioning of afferent C-fibers during certain dysregulations such as hypoglycemia or hypotonia and hemorrhagia,[20] it can be expected that adrenaline release could probably be impaired as well when afferent fibers registering cold are missing.

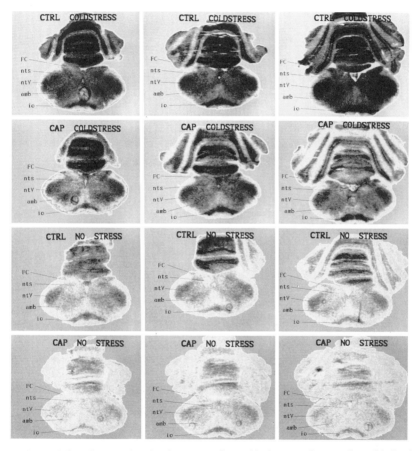

FIGURE 2. Microphotographs showing autoradiographic images of coronal rat hindbrain sections corresponding to the atlas of Palkovits and Jacobowitz.[38] From left to right: approximately 7400, 7000, and 6050 μm posterior to the intra-aural plane of control (CTRL) rats and rats pretreated with capsaicin on the second day of life (CAP) either without stress or after cold stress (45 min at 6 °C). All animals received a single dose of [^{14}C]2-deoxyglucose (10 μCi/100 g body weight) into the tail vein either at the onset of cold exposure or 45 min prior to decapitation. Terms: (amb) nucleus accumbens; (FC) fasciculus cuneatus; (nts) nucleus tractus solitarii; (ntV) nucleus spinalis nervi trigemini; (io) nucleus olivarius inferior.

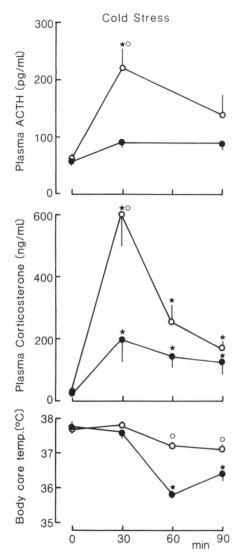

FIGURE 3. Time course of plasma ACTH and corticosterone levels as well as body core temperature during cold exposure (6 °C) of rats pretreated with vehicle (open circles) or capsaicin (filled circles) as neonates. The values represent the mean ± SEM of 6–8 observations: ∗ = $P < 0.05$ compared to the control condition; ○ = $P < 0.05$ compared to the capsaicin-pretreated rats. (Modified from reference 10 and used with permission.)

Interestingly, the secretion of another proposed stress hormone—prolactin—is regulated in a quite different manner. We found that those somatosensory stimuli that induce ACTH secretion via activation of peptidergic afferents do not cause any release of prolactin (e.g., during cold stress), whereas emotional stimuli like restraint conditions cause the release of both pituitary hormones (FIGURE 1). Although pentobarbital anesthesia does not raise the levels of ACTH, prolactin levels are markedly elevated during this type of anesthesia. This different control in the release of the stress hormones, ACTH and prolactin, may be explained by their different hypothalamic releasing and inhibiting factors.[21]

OTHER REFLEXES AND NEUROENDOCRINE REGULATIONS MEDIATED BY CAPSAICIN-SENSITIVE AFFERENT NEURONS

Aside from the endocrine responses described earlier, the secretion of other hormones like vasopressin (stimulated by neuronal messages from the portal vein[22]) and the decidua formation in the rat uterus (evoked by stimulation of afferent neurons in the cervix and mediated by prolactin and progesterone release[23]) are also initiated by impulses transmitted to the CNS by capsaicin-sensitive peptidergic afferents.

Many autonomic adrenergic reflexes are induced by activation of capsaicin-sensitive afferents: (1) the activation of the adrenal medulla (adrenaline release) generated by hypoglycemia, by hypovolemia, or by hypotension; this afferent information travels most probably within the vagus nerve;[20] (2) the reflex increase in the adrenergic tone responsible for the control of the blood pressure during pentobarbital anesthesia;[24] (3) the short depressor reflexes induced by intra-arterial injection of capsaicin or by afferent splanchnic or mesenteric nerve stimulation; and (4) the long-lasting reflex vasodilatation in the tail and paws of rats through inhibition of the cutaneous adrenergic vasoconstrictor tone when heat-sensitive afferent neurons are stimulated (heat-loss thermoregulation).[2]

These findings establish the peptidergic afferent neuron system as an important pathway for the endocrine and neuronal regulatory mechanisms responsible for endogenous homeostasis of the organism.[25] They also change our view of the function and sensory characteristics of afferent peptidergic nerves and their receptors and sensors. They are not only responding to noxious thermal, chemical, and mechanical stimuli, but also to changes in the composition of the intravascular or interstitial fluid and to changes in the perfusion pressure of arteries; note that both events are not specifically recognized as C-fiber stimuli thus far. Because many of those regulations are initiated without reaching the level of consciousness, the peptidergic afferents can also be seen as the afferent pathway of the autonomic nervous system.[26]

To determine which part of the information carried by the capsaicin-sensitive nerves is transmitted by a specific peptide, substance P, for example, presents some uncertainty because there are several peptides colocated in the capsaicin-sensitive afferent nerve fibers and in their corresponding B-type dorsal root ganglion cells.[27] Yet, there is a whole body of evidence pointing towards the specific involvement of substance P in certain sensory functions. Although the simultaneous release of all the neuropeptides present in dorsal root afferents from spinal cord slices can be demonstrated *in vitro* upon excitation of all capsaicin-sensitive endings or upon K[+]-depolarization,[28] these experiments do not simulate the selective stimulation of a certain group of sensors on peptidergic peripheral terminals.

During *in situ* experiments using perfusion techniques of the spinal subarachnoid space[29] or antibody microprobes placed into the dorsal horn,[30,31] it was found that, in the cat, electrical C-fiber excitation and noxious thermal and mechanical stimuli could cause the release of substance P. In contrast, in the rabbit, only noxious mechanical and inflammatory stimulation caused the release of substance P[32] and, in the rat, noxious cold stimuli and movements of inflamed joints caused the release of substance P.[33,34]

This all points to species differences in the connection between substance P–containing afferents and different nociceptors. All these experiments give a good background to the assumption that, during noxious C-fiber stimulation, the release of the stress hormones is mediated by substance P in the dorsal spinal cord; however, for the nonnoxious stimuli described herein, such a connection has yet to be proved.

Nonetheless, the information transmitted by capsaicin-sensitive afferents may not only be solely carried by substance P, but also by coexisting and coreleased peptides in primary afferents.

The consequences of a disturbed ACTH-corticosterone response in stressful, threatening situations may be manyfold. For example, in cold stress, the maintenance of the temperature regulation could be, at least in part, a consequence of a proper steroid secretion from the adrenal cortex, although adrenaline may be a more important factor. A defect in CRF secretion during inflammatory diseases can facilitate the continuation of the inflammation and the development of an autoimmune disease.[35,36] Consequences are also to be expected for diseases accompanied by neuropathy, as in diabetics when these individuals are exposed to hypoglycemia.[37]

REFERENCES

1. GAMSE, R., P. HOLZER & F. LEMBECK. 1980. Br. J. Pharmacol. **68:** 207–213.
2. LEMBECK, F. 1987. *In* Substance P and Neurokinins. J. L. Henry, R. Couture, A. C. Cuello, G. Pelletier, R. Quirion & D. Regoli, Eds.: 380–387. Springer-Verlag. Berlin/New York.
3. LEMBECK, F. 1988. Acta Physiol. Scand. **133:** 435–454.
4. FELDMAN, S. 1985. Fed. Proc. Fed. Am. Soc. Exp. Biol. **44:** 169–175.
5. RIVIER, C., R. CHIZZONITE & W. VALE. 1989. Endocrinology **125:** 2800–2805.
6. RIVIER, C. & P. PLOTZKY. 1986. Annu. Rev. Physiol. **48:** 475–494.
7. MUNCK, A., P. M. GUYRE & N. J. HOLBROOK. 1984. Endocr. Rev. **5:** 25–44.
8. FLOWER, R. J. 1988. Br. J. Pharmacol. **94:** 987–1015.
9. AMANN, R. & F. LEMBECK. 1987. Br. J. Pharmacol. **90:** 727–731.
10. DONNERER, J. & F. LEMBECK. 1990. Endocrinology **126:** 921–926.
11. LEMBECK, F. & R. AMANN. 1986. Brain Res. Bull. **16:** 541–543.
12. DONNERER, J. & F. LEMBECK. 1988. Br. J. Pharmacol. **94:** 647–652.
13. FELDMAN, S., N. CONFORTI, I. CHOWERS & R. A. SIEGEL. 1981. Exp. Brain Res. **42:** 486–488.
14. SHARPE, L. G. & J. H. JAFFE. 1986. Neurosci. Lett. **71:** 213–218.
15. BELL, J. A., A. S. KIMES & E. D. LONDON. 1988. Eur. J. Pharmacol. **150:** 171–174.
16. SOKOLOFF, L., M. REIVICH, C. KENNEDY, M. H. DES ROSIERS, C. S. PATLAK, K. D. PETTIGREW, O. SAKURADA & M. SHINOHARA. 1977. J. Neurochem. **28:** 897–916.
17. DONNERER, J. 1989. Br. J. Pharmacol. **96:** 767–772.
18. JUAN, H. 1982. Pain **12:** 259–264.
19. SHETTER, A. G. & W. H. SWEET. 1979. *In* Advances in Pain Research and Therapy. Vol. 3. J. J. Bonica, Ed.: 337–342. Raven Press. New York.
20. DONNERER, J. 1988. Naunyn-Schmiedeberg's Arch. Pharmacol. **338:** 282–290.
21. LENOX, R. H., G. J. KANT, G. R. SESSIONS, L. L. PENNINGTON, E. H. MOUGEY & J. L. MEYERHOFF. 1980. Neuroendocrinology **30:** 300–308.
22. STOPPINI, L., F. BARJA, R. MATHISON & J. BAERTSCHI. 1984. Neuroscience **11:** 903–912.
23. TRAURIG, H., R. E. PAPKA & M. E. RUSH. 1988. Cell Tissue Res. **253:** 573–581.
24. DONNERER, J., R. SCHULIGOI & F. LEMBECK. 1989. Naunyn-Schmiedeberg's Arch. Pharmacol. **340:** 740–743.
25. DONNERER, J., A. EGLEZOS & R. D. HELME. 1990. *In* The Neuroendocrine-Immune Network. S. Freier, Ed.: 69–83. CRC Press. Boca Raton, Florida.
26. PRECHTL, J. C. & T. L. POWLEY. 1990. Behav. Brain Sci. In press.
27. LUNDBERG, J. M. & T. HÖKFELT. *In* Progress in Brain Research. Vol. 68. T. Hökfelt, K. Fuxe & P. Pernow, Eds.: 241–262. Elsevier. Amsterdam/New York.
28. SARIA, A., R. GAMSE, J. PETERMANN, J. A. FISCHER, E. THEODORSSON-NORHEIM & J. M. LUNDBERG. 1986. Neurosci. Lett. **63:** 310–314.
29. GO, V. L. W. & T. L. YAKSH. 1987. J. Physiol. **391:** 141–167.
30. HUTCHINSON, W. D. & C. R. MORTON. 1989. Pain **37:** 357–363.

31. DUGGAN, A. W., C. R. MORTON, Z. Q. ZHAO & I. A. HENDRY. 1987. Brain Res. **403:** 345–349.
32. KURAISHI, Y., N. HIROTA, Y. SATO, N. HANASHIMA, H. TAKAGI & M. SATOH. 1989. Neuroscience **30:** 241–250.
33. TISEO, P. J., M. W. ADLER & L. Y. LIU-CHEN. 1990. J. Pharmacol. Exp. Ther. **252:** 539–545.
34. OKU, R., M. SATOH & H. TAKAGI. 1987. Neurosci. Lett. **74:** 315–319.
35. STERNBERG, E. M., W. S. YOUNG, R. BERNARDINI, A. E. CALOGERO, G. P. CHROUSOS, P. W. GOLD & R. L. WILDER. 1989. Proc. Natl. Acad. Sci. U.S.A. **86:** 4771–4775.
36. STERNBERG, E. M., J. M. HILL, G. P. CHROUSOS, T. KAMILARIS, S. J. LSIWAK, P. W. GOLD & R. L. WILDER. 1989. Proc. Natl. Acad. Sci. U.S.A. **86:** 2374–2378.
37. HORIE, H., T. HANAFUSA, M. MATSUYAMA, M. NAMBA, K. KONAKA, S. TARUI, A. YAMATODANI & H. WADA. 1984. Horm. Metab. Res. **16:** 398–401.
38. PALKOVITS, M. & D. M. JACOBOWITZ. 1974. J. Comp. Neurol. **157:** 29–42.

Substance P and Related Peptides Associated with the Afferent and Autonomic Innervation of the Uterus[a]

H. H. TRAURIG,[b] R. E. PAPKA,[c] AND R. L. SHEW[c]

[b]Department of Anatomy and Neurobiology
University of Kentucky Medical Center
Lexington, Kentucky 40536

[c]Department of Anatomical Sciences
University of Oklahoma Health Sciences Center
Oklahoma City, Oklahoma 26901

INTRODUCTION

Recent investigations have revealed subgroups of afferent and autonomic neurons innervating the female rat reproductive organs based on their content of one or more chemical markers for noradrenaline, acetylcholine, and various peptides. These nerves innervate selected targets in the reproductive organs, forming coded circuits that regulate (in concert with the hormonal milieu) myometrial contractions, blood flow, and other visceral responses important in reproductive function and behavior (see references 1 and 2). Also, the expression of some transmitter markers and certain nerve actions are responsive to the hormonal environment.[1-5]

Primary afferent nerves, arising principally from T_{13} and L_1 dorsal root ganglia (DRG), accompany autonomic fibers in ovarian-oviductal or hypogastric nerves to innervate the cranial or caudal portions of the rat uterine horns, respectively.[4-6] Afferent nerves innervating uterine cervix and other pelvic viscera arise principally from L_6-S_1 DRGs, follow the pelvic nerves, and intermingle with hypogastric fibers in the hypogastric plexus.[3,7-11] Many of these fibers traverse the paracervical ganglia (PG), which are autonomic ganglia innervating the uterus and located bilaterally in the vaginal-cervical parametrium. Sensory and postganglionic autonomic fibers are distributed to the uterus via independent nerve trunks or as perivascular and paravascular plexuses. Innervation densities are greatest in the oviductal isthmus, the utero-oviductal junction, and the uterine cervix—regions serving sphincter-like functions[3,7,12]—suggesting that sensory nerves could play significant roles in gamete transport, pacing the passage of blastocysts into the uterine lumen and regulating parturition.[3,13]

The objectives of this report are to:

(1) review some characteristics and functional roles of primary afferent and autonomic nerves innervating the rat uterus;
(2) illustrate some actions of substance P (SP) and calcitonin gene–related peptide (CGRP) on myometrial contractions.

[a]Original studies by H. H. Traurig and R. E. Papka were supported by NIH Grant No. 1-R01-NS22526, the Alumni Research Fund, and the Presbyterian Health Foundation (University of Oklahoma).

PRIMARY AFFERENT INNERVATION OF THE UTERUS

Subpopulations of nerves, distinguished by their content of immunoreactivities (-I) for SP,[6,8,11,12,14–16] neurokinin A (NKA),[8,14,15] CGRP,[7–9,11,12,14–17] cholecystokinin-octapeptide (CCK),[8,14–16] galanin (GAL),[16,18] or other peptides,[1,2] innervate the rat uterus. The uterine nerves containing these peptides can be considered primary afferent nerves because (1) they are insensitive to 6-hydroxydopamine, a noradrenergic neurotoxin;[7,10,11,19,20] (2) autonomic neurons, which innervate the uterus, do not contain immunoreactivity for these peptides;[7,9,11,14,16,18,19] (3) axonal tracing studies demonstrate that many uterine nerves containing SP-, NKA-, CCK-, CGRP-, or GAL-I emanate from lumbosacral DRGs;[6–11,16,18] (4) some subgroups of peptide-containing uterine nerves are destroyed by capsaicin (CAP),[7,11,14–16] a sensory neurotoxin; and (5) *in situ* hybridization techniques using cDNA probes in rat have revealed $L_{4,5}$ DRG sensory neurons expressing mRNAs encoding precursor molecules for SP,[21] CGRP,[22] or GAL.[23]

Nerves immunoreactive for SP form a moderate plexus of fibers and varicose terminals throughout the rat uterus. Many fibers and terminals are arranged as subepithelial plexuses in the endometrium and some appear to penetrate the epithelium, especially the mucosa of the portio vaginalis of the cervix. The anatomical position of these fibers and terminals is ideal for them to serve sensory functions. SP-I fibers and terminals also course among the myometrial and mesometrial smooth muscle fascicles, suggesting that they might influence myometrial contractions. Other SP fibers are associated with uterine blood vessels, particularly those in the mesometrium, and thus may participate in the regulation of uterine blood flow.[11,12,14–16] Furthermore, anatomical studies revealed SP-I varicose terminals surrounding many PG autonomic neurons, providing a basis for sensory-autonomic circuitry that could participate in the regulation of autonomic transmission to the uterus.[11,16,19] Axonal tracing studies have shown that uterine SP-I sensory nerves arise from a subgroup of small neurons[6,8,10,11] that comprise 20–30% of the neurons in lumbosacral DRGs.[21,24] Finally, studies employing selective rhizotomies[25] and neurotoxins[11,16,25] have revealed that the central processes of SP-I sensory neurons terminate in the dorsal horn of the spinal cord.

Nerves and terminals immunoreactive for NKA or SP have similar distribution patterns and innervation densities in female reproductive organs, in PG, and in the spinal cord, suggesting the coexistence of these tachykinins in a subpopulation of sensory neurons.[8,14–16,25] In fact, small sensory neurons in rat lumbosacral DRGs contain immunoreactivities for SP and NKA that are coincident with mRNAs encoding β-preprotachykinin, the precursor for these peptides.[21] Virtually all PG and uterine SP- or NKA-I coded fibers and terminals, including most terminals in the dorsal horn of the lumbosacral spinal cord, are destroyed by CAP[11,15,16] and thus are C-type primary afferent nerves (see reference 26).

Sensory nerves and terminals immunoreactive for CGRP innervate uterine and PG targets in a pattern similar to that for tachykinin-I nerves, but the CGRP-I innervation density is greater.[7,9,11,14–16,19] Therefore, CGRP-I fibers and varicose terminals form extensive plexuses in the endometrium and some terminals are intraepithelial, especially in the cervix, again suggesting that such nerves could have a sensory function. Other CGRP-I varicose fibers are intimately associated with myometrial smooth muscle fascicles and blood vessels and form pericellular, basket-like arrangements around many PG neurons.[9,11,14–17,19] CGRP-I uterine nerves have been traced to lumbosacral DRGs[7–9] where CGRP-I neurons comprise about 50% of the DRG neuronal population.[9–11,22] However, distinct subgroups of small and large CGRP-I lumbosacral DRG neurons have been revealed in the rat.[11,16] Hence, about half of the CGRP-I neurons are small-sized sensory ganglion cells and most of these also contain immunoreactivities, in various combinations, for CCK, SP, and/or GAL.[2,10,11,16,24] The small CGRP-I neurons and their peripheral and central terminals are sensitive to CAP and therefore are C-type primary afferent nerves.[7,10,11,15,16] However, a few CGRP-I uterine nerve fibers are CAP-insensitive, especially those terminals surrounding many of PG autonomic neurons;[14,19] they probably arise from the subgroup of large, CAP-resistant, CGRP-I DRG neurons and may also contain other peptides.[1,2,16,24] For example, mRNAs for β-CGRP and preprotachykinin are preferentially expressed in small L_5 DRG neurons in the rat, whereas larger DRG neurons express α-CGRP mRNA, but not preprotachykinin mRNA.[22] Possibly α-CGRP and β-CGRP—and thus the large and small neurons that preferentially express these peptides—have different sensory and/or effector functions in the uterus.

CCK-I nerves and terminals innervate endometrium, myometrium, uterine vasculature, and PG; however, the CCK-I innervation density is less than that observed for CGRP-I nerves.[8,14,19] Virtually all CCK-I nerves and small sensory neurons in the rat are also immunoreactive for SP[16,24] and/or CGRP.[16] In the rat uterus, most CCK-I nerve fibers are CAP-sensitive, except those forming pericellular arrangements of terminals around PG neurons.[15,19] Because some CGRP-I terminals in PG are also CAP-resistant, it is possible that CGRP-I and CCK-I coexist in sensory terminals in PG.

A sparse innervation of the rat uterus by GAL-I sensory nerves has been reported.[16,18] GAL-I fibers travel parallel to and in close association with myometrial smooth muscle fascicles and uterine blood vessels. Some GAL-I nerve fibers innervate the endometrium, but do not form subepithelial plexuses or penetrate the epithelium. In contrast, GAL-I varicose nerve terminals form prominent basket-like plexuses closely enveloping many PG neurons.[16,18] Most uterine and PG GAL-I terminals are CAP-insensitive and thus do not belong to the C-type subgroup of uterine sensory nerves. There may be several subgroups of GAL-I neurons in lumbosacral DRGs that give origin to uterine sensory nerves in the rat because many, but not all, also contain CGRP-I, whereas others contain CGRP- and SP-I as well as GAL-I.[16,23] In addition, more rat lumbosacral DRG neurons may contain GAL-I than is detectable with present immunohistochemical techniques because the number of neurons expressing mRNA for GAL markedly increases following nerve injury.[23]

FUNCTIONAL INTERACTIONS

The distributions and characteristics of subgroups of sensory neurons containing SP-, NKA-, CCK-, CGRP-, and GAL-I and innervating selected targets in the rat uterus provide morphological support for their role in the conduction of sensory modalities to the spinal cord (see references cited earlier). In addition, SP-, NKA-, CCK-, CGRP-, and GAL-I sensory nerve terminals are associated with the vasculature and myometrium, suggesting functional interactions. Available evidence supports the view that sensory nerves also participate in "local effector" functions by releasing peptides from their peripheral terminals in rat tissues.[27,28] For example, following electrical stimulation[29] or exposure to depolarizing agents such as CAP or high potassium concentrations,[11,30,31] SP, NKA, and CGRP are released from primary afferent central[11,30] and peripheral processes,[29] including those in rat genitourinary organs.[31] Furthermore, data suggest that these peptides could influence blood flow,[32] inflammatory responses,[33,34] and nonvascular smooth muscle contractions.[17,27,28,33,35]

Many studies illustrate intimate morphological associations between peptide-containing, varicose nerve terminals and myometrial smooth muscle fascicles, suggesting functional relationships.[7,9,11,12,15–18] Accumulating data suggest that uterine sensory nerves may also serve efferent roles in rat myometrium.[17] For example, in an *in vitro* model of uterine horn, derived from estrogen-primed, intact rats, SP (10^{-7} to 10^{-4} M) directly induced concentration-dependent myometrial contractions (FIGURE 1a). In contrast, myometrial contractions induced by acetylcholine (10^{-5} M or 10^{-6} M) were inhibited by CGRP (10^{-9} to 10^{-6} M) in a concentration-dependent manner. CGRP had no effect on baseline tension in these preparations (FIGURE 1b).[17] These results

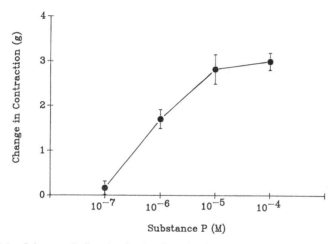

FIGURE 1a. Substance P directly stimulated uterine horn contractions in a concentration-dependent manner (12 rats, 3–13 observations per point). Uteri were obtained from Sprague-Dawley rats, treated the previous day with diethylstilbestrol (50 μg/rat). Whole uterine horns were immediately suspended in a tissue bath, containing Van Dyke–Hastings solution, and a resting tension of 0.5–1.0 g was applied. All test solutions were added directly to the bath medium. (See text for details.) Uterine contractions were measured isometrically and were recorded. Data are expressed as the mean change in gram tension (±SEM). (For methods, see reference 17.)

in rat uterus corroborate the findings of contractile actions of SP and inhibition by CGRP in rat[35] and human[36] myometrium. Furthermore, these data suggest that, following sensory stimulation, SP and/or CGRP could be released from "sensory" terminals in the uterus and could directly augment (SP) or inhibit (CGRP) myometrial contractions. However, it has not as yet been demonstrated that these peptides are actually released from rat uterine sensory nerves.

GAL-I sensory nerves are few in the rat myometrium.[16,18] However, galanin evokes a concentration-dependent contraction of rat uterine horn, a response insensitive to tetrodotoxin.[18] Hence, if GAL were released from sensory terminals, it could exert a direct contractile effect on the myometrium similar to the effect of SP.

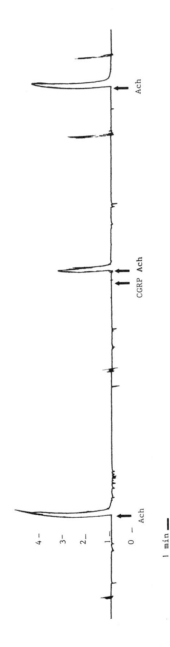

FIGURE 1b. Similar conditions as described in the caption to FIGURE 1a. Ordinate units represent the gram tension, with the resting tension set at 0.5–1.0 grams. Acetylcholine chloride (ACh, 10^{-5} M)–stimulated uterine contraction is illustrated (left arrow). Following a wash, CGRP (10^{-8} M) inhibited the contractile effect of ACh added one minute later (center arrows). Subsequently, ACh (10^{-5} M) again induced uterine contraction in the same preparation (right arrow). CGRP had no effect on the basal uterine tension. (Reproduced with permission from reference 17.)

The portio vaginalis of the uterine cervix plays an important role in reproductive function in the rat. This region of the cervix is richly supplied by SP-, NKA-, CCK-, and CGRP-I sensory nerves, which are ideally arranged to transmit nociceptive and nonnociceptive stimuli to the spinal cord and could participate in visceral reflexes and neuroendocrine responses.[7,9,11,15] For example, it is well established that uterine cervix innervation is essential in the rat to convey copulatory or copulomimetic stimuli to the spinal cord and, in turn, to hypothalamic centers, resulting in alterations of gonadotropin secretion patterns favoring prolactin release. Prolactin, a luteotropin in the rat, facilitates corpus luteal progesterone secretion necessary for nidation and maintenance of early pregnancy or pseudopregnancy (see references 15 and 37). Neonatal CAP treatment[15] or local application of CAP to the lumbosacral cord in adults[37] results in an effective sensory denervation of the cervix and interrupts transmission of stimuli to the spinal cord. Rats so treated are infertile in subsequent adult life; moreover, application of electrical or mechanical copulomimetic stimuli to the cervix fails to induce pseudopregnancy. This suggests that the neural limb of the neuroendocrine copulation (luteal) response consists of C-type primary afferent nerves innervating the cervix and containing such peptides as SP, NKA, CCK, CGRP, and possibly others.[15,37]

Other functional roles for sensory nerves innervating the rat uterine cervix have been revealed. The uterus is most sensitive to distension in the cervical region—where innervation density is greatest[6,12,15]—compared to uterine sensitivity at the uterine-oviductal junction.[3] Electrophysiological studies demonstrate that C-type sensory fibers innervating the uterus travel in the pelvic and hypogastric nerves and are sensitive to mechanical or noxious stimuli.[3-5] Because the efficacy of stimuli to elicit uterine sensory nerve transmission fluctuates with the estrous cycle,[4,5] it is possible that the hormonal milieu could influence sensory nerve function. The selective sensory innervation of the uterus is further revealed in that vaginocervical stimulation during mating alters uterine contractility patterns, favoring sperm transport through the endocervical canal.[13] A similar uterine response was elicited by experimental stimulation of the cervix, but not of the perineal region.[3,13] Furthermore, uterine sensory nerves are responsive to the temporal and spatial aspects of experimentally induced uterine distensions,[5] suggesting roles for C-type sensory nerves in pacing parturition. In support of this suggestion is the observation that, as fetuses pass through the cervical canal, activation of hypogastric and pelvic sensory nerve transmission is augmented, which, in turn, could facilitate the regulation of myometrial contractions necessary for parturition.[3] Finally, vaginocervical stimulation induces analgesia[3,38] and this analgesic effect is markedly reduced in rats following the destruction of peptide-containing, C-type sensory nerves with CAP. This response may be important in attenuating pain during parturition.[38]

AFFERENT-AUTONOMIC INTERACTIONS

Morphological evidence reveals that several subgroups of sensory nerves, containing SP-, NKA-, CGRP-, CCK-, and GAL-I, form pericellular arrangements of varicose terminals around subgroups of PG autonomic neurons.[7,9-11,16,18,19] Therefore, it is conceivable that stimulation of sensory nerves could release these peptides in the PG, thus influencing autonomic transmission to the uterine vasculature and myometrium. Accordingly, SP, NKA, and CGRP generate excitatory postsynaptic potentials (EPSP) in guinea pig[39-41] and rat[42] autonomic ganglia. Moreover, CCK facilitates nicotinic autonomic transmission,[43] whereas GAL is inhibitory.[44] Stimulation of afferent roots associated with autonomic ganglia evokes EPSPs and this response is blocked by CAP.[39] This is consistent with the observations that most SP-, most NKA-, and some CGRP- and CCK-I PG pericellular varicose terminals are CAP-sensitive;[16,19] thus, they probably arise from C-type sensory nerves. However, most CGRP-, most CCK-, and all GAL-I terminals probably arise from another subgroup of sensory neurons because they are CAP-insensitive and we have not observed immunoreactivities for these peptides in peripheral autonomic neurons innervating the rat uterus.[16,19] Hence, a complex afferent-autonomic circuitry is evident that probably plays important roles in regulating visceral reflexes and responses in the rat uterus (FIGURE 2).

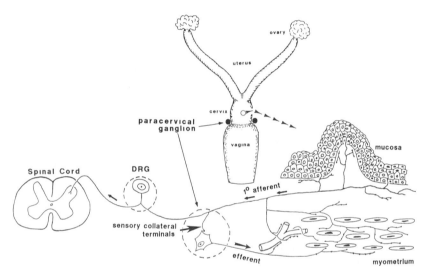

FIGURE 2. A schematic representation of the anatomical arrangements of peptide-containing primary afferent nerves innervating the rat uterus. In addition to conveying stimuli to the spinal cord, peptide-containing sensory nerves may release peptides from their terminals in the uterus and autonomic ganglia innervating the uterus. These peptides could influence blood flow, myometrial contractions, and autonomic transmission. (See text for discussion.)

CONCLUSIONS

The rat uterus is innervated by subgroups of nerves containing SP-, NKA-, CCK-, CGRP-, and GAL-I, originating from lumbosacral DRG and characterized by anatomical arrangements suggesting sensory functions. Many of these subgroups are C-type sensory neurons and play important roles in reproduction. SP-, NKA-, CCK-, CGRP-, and GAL-I sensory nerve varicose terminals are also associated with the myometrium, the vasculature, and the autonomic ganglia that innervate the uterus (FIGURE 2). Evidence suggests that sensory nerves may also serve effector roles by releasing these peptides in autonomic ganglia and peripheral tissues, thereby influencing autonomic transmission and a number of physiological processes. Accumulating data demonstrate that, if released from sensory terminals in the rat uterus, SP and CGRP could exert direct actions on myometrial contraction (FIGURES 1a and 1b).

REFERENCES

1. OWMAN, C. & M. STJERNQUIST. 1988. Origin, distribution, and functional aspects of aminergic and peptidergic nerves in the male and female reproductive tracts. *In* Handbook of Chemical Neuroanatomy. Vol. 6: The Peripheral Nervous System. A. Bjorklund, T. Hökfelt & C. Owman, Eds.: 445–544. Elsevier. Amsterdam/New York.
2. TRAURIG, H. H. & R. E. PAPKA. 1990. Sensory and autonomic innervation of the female reproductive tract: some characteristics and functional roles. *In* Myometrial Contractility. R. Garfield, Ed.: 253–265. Serono Symposia. Norwalk, Massachusetts.
3. PETERS, L. C., M. B. KRISTAL & B. R. KOMISARUK. 1987. Sensory innervation of the external and internal genitalia of the female rat. Brain Res. **408:** 199–204.
4. BERKLEY, K. J., A. ROBBINS & Y. SATO. 1988. Afferent fibers supplying the uterus in the rat. J. Neurophysiol. **59:** 142–163.
5. ROBBINS, A., Y. SATO, H. HOTTA & K. J. BERKLEY. 1990. Responses of hypogastric nerve afferent fibers to uterine distension in estrous or metestrous rats. Neurosci. Lett. **110:** 82–85.
6. NANCE, D. M., J. BURNS, C. M. KLEIN & H. W. BURDEN. 1988. Afferent fibers in the reproductive system and pelvic viscera of female rats: anterograde tracing and immunocytochemical studies. Brain Res. Bull. **21:** 701–709.
7. GHATEI, M. A., J. GU, P. K. MULDERRY, M. A. BLANK, J. M. ALLEN, J. F. B. MORRISON, J. M. POLAK & S. R. BLOOM. 1985. Calcitonin gene–related peptide (CGRP) in the female rat urogenital tract. Peptides **6:** 809–815.
8. TRAURIG, H. H., R. E. PAPKA & L. URBAN. 1985. Origin of peptide-containing nerves in the female reproductive system. Anat. Rec. **211:** 199A–200A.
9. INYAMA, C. O., J. WHARTON, H. C. SU & J. M. POLAK. 1986. CGRP-immunoreactive nerves in the genitalia of the female rat originate from dorsal root ganglia T_{11}-L_3 and L_6-S_1: a combined immunocytochemical and retrograde tracing study. Neurosci. Lett. **69:** 13–18.
10. SU, H. C., J. WHARTON, J. M. POLAK, P. K. MULDERRY, M. A. GHATEI, S. J. GIBSON, G. TERENGRI, J. F. B. MORRISON, J. BALLESTA & S. R. BLOOM. 1986. Calcitonin gene–related peptide immunoreactivity in afferent neurons supplying the urinary tract: combined retrograde tracing and immunohistochemistry. Neuroscience **18:** 727–747.
11. FRANCO-CERECEDA, A., H. HENKE, J. M. LUNDBERG, J. B. PETERMANN, T. HÖKFELT & J. A. FISCHER. 1987. Calcitonin gene–related peptide (CGRP) in capsaicin-sensitive substance P–immunoreactive sensory neurons in animals and man: distribution and release by capsaicin. Peptides **8:** 399–410.
12. PAPKA, R. E., J. P. COTTON & H. H. TRAURIG. 1985. The comparative distribution of neuropeptide tyrosine, vasoactive intestinal polypeptide–, substance P–immunoreactive, acetylcholinesterase-positive, and noradrenergic nerves in the reproductive tract of the female rat. Cell Tissue Res. **242:** 475–490.
13. TONER, J. P. & N. T. ADLER. 1986. Influence of mating and vaginocervical stimulation on rat uterine activity. J. Reprod. Fertil. **78:** 239–249.
14. PAPKA, R. E. & H. H. TRAURIG. 1987. Substance K–, substance P–, and calcitonin gene–related peptide–immunoreactive nerves in female reproductive organs. *In* Substance P and Neurokinins. J. L. Henry *et al.*, Eds.: 229–231. Springer-Verlag. Berlin/New York.
15. TRAURIG, H. H., R. E. PAPKA & M. E. RUSH. 1988. Effects of capsaicin on reproduction function in the female rat: role of peptide-containing primary afferent nerves innervating the uterine cervix in the neuroendocrine copulatory reflex. Cell Tissue Res. **253:** 573–581.
16. PAPKA, R. E. & H. H. TRAURIG. 1989. Galanin-immunoreactive nerves in the female rat

paracervical ganglion and uterine cervix: distribution and reaction to capsaicin. Cell Tissue Res. **257:** 41–51.

17. SHEW, R., R. E. PAPKA & D. L. MCNEILL. 1990. Calcitonin gene–related peptide in the rat uterus: presence in nerves and effects on uterine contraction. Peptides **11:** 583–589.

18. STJERNQUIST, M., E. EKBLAD, C. OWMAN & F. SUNDLER. 1988. Immunocytochemical localization of galanin in the rat male and female genital tracts and motor effects *in vitro.* Regulat. Peptides **20:** 335–343.

19. PAPKA, R. E., H. H. TRAURIG & P. KLENN. 1987. The paracervical ganglia of the female rat: histochemistry and immunohistochemistry of neurons, SIF cells, and nerve terminals. Am. J. Anat. **179:** 243–257.

20. PAPKA, R. E. & H. H. TRAURIG. 1988. Distribution of subgroups of neuropeptide Y–immunoreactive and noradrenergic nerves in the female rat uterine cervix. Cell Tissue Res. **252:** 533–541.

21. HENKEN, D. B., A. TESSLER, M-F. CHESSELET, A. HUDSON, F. BALDINO & M. MURRAY. 1988. *In situ* hybridization of mRNA for β-preprotachykinin and preprosomatostatin in adult rat dorsal root ganglia: comparison with immunocytochemistry localization. J. Neurocytol. **17:** 671–681.

22. NOGUCHI, K., E. SENBA, Y. MORITA, M. SATO & M. TOHYAMA. 1990. Co-expression of α-CGRP and β-CGRP mRNAs in the rat dorsal root ganglion cells. Neurosci. Lett. **108:** 1–5.

23. VILLAR, M. J., R. CORTES, E. THEODORSSON, Z. WIESENFELD-HALLIN, M. SCHALLING, J. FAHRENKRUG, P. C. EMSON & T. HÖKFELT. 1989. Neuropeptide expression in rat dorsal root ganglion cells and spinal cord after peripheral nerve injury with special reference to galanin. Neuroscience **33:** 587–604.

24. TUCHSCHERER, M. M. & V. S. SEYBOLD. 1985. Immunohistochemical studies of substance P, cholecystokinin-octapeptide, and somatostatin in dorsal root ganglia of the rat. Neuroscience **14:** 593–605.

25. DALSGAARD, C. J., A. HAEGERSTRAND, E. BRODIN, E. THEODORSSON-NORHEIM & T. HÖKFELT. 1985. Neurokinin A–like immunoreactivity in rat primary sensory neurons: coexistence with substance P. Histochemistry **83:** 407–414.

26. BUCK, S. H. & T. F. BURKS. 1986. The neuropharmacology of capsaicin: review of some recent observations. Pharmacol. Rev. **38:** 179–226.

27. HOLZER, P. 1988. Local effector functions of capsaicin-sensitive sensory nerve endings: involvement of tachykinins, calcitonin gene–related peptide, and other neuropeptides. Neuroscience **24:** 739–768.

28. MAGGI, C. A. & A. MELI. 1988. The sensory-efferent function of capsaicin-sensitive sensory nerves. Gen. Pharmacol. **19:** 1–43.

29. WHITE, D. M. & R. D. HELME. 1985. Release of substance P from peripheral nerve terminals following electrical stimulation of the sciatic nerve. Brain Res. **336:** 27–31.

30. SARIA, A., R. GAMSE, J. PETERMANN, J. A. FISCHER, E. THEODORSSON-NORHEIM & J. M. LUNDBERG. 1986. Simultaneous release of several tachykinins and calcitonin gene–related peptide from rat spinal cord slices. Neurosci. Lett. **63:** 310–314.

31. SANTICIOLI, P., C. A. MAGGI, P. GEPPETTI, E. DEL BIANCO, E. THEODORSSON & A. MELI. 1988. Release of calcitonin gene–related peptide immunoreactivity (CGRP-LI) from organs of the genitourinary tract in rats. Neurosci. Lett. **92:** 197–201.

32. FUJIMORI, A., A. SAITO, S. KIMURA & K. GOTO. 1990. Release of calcitonin gene–related peptide (CGRP) from capsaicin-sensitive vasodilator nerves in the rat mesenteric artery. Neurosci. Lett. **112:** 173–178.

33. MAGGI, C. A., P. SANTICIOLI, L. ABELLI, M. PARLANI, M. CAPASSO, B. CONTE, S. GIULIANI & A. MELI. 1987. Regional differences in the effects of capsaicin and tachykinins on motor activity and vascular permeability of the rat lower urinary tract. Naunyn-Schmiedeberg's Arch. Pharmacol. **335:** 636–645.

34. FINK, T. & E. WEIHE. 1988. Multiple neuropeptides in nerves supplying mammalian lymph nodes: messenger candidates for sensory and autonomic neuroimmunodulation? Neurosci. Lett. **90:** 39–44.

35. BEK, T., B. OTTESEN & J. FAHRENKRUG. 1988. The effect of galanin, CGRP, and ANP on spontaneous smooth muscle activity in the rat uterus. Peptides **9:** 497–500.

36. SAMUELSON, U. E., C. J. DALSGAARD, J. M. LUNDBERG & T. HÖKFELT. 1985. Calcitonin gene–related peptide inhibits spontaneous contractions in human uterus and fallopian tube. Neurosci. Lett. **62:** 225–230.

37. NANCE, D. M., T. R. KING & P. W. NANCE. 1987. Neuroendocrine and behavioral effects of intrathecal capsaicin in adult female rats. Brain Res. Bull. **18:** 109–114.

38. RODRIGUEZ-SIERRA, J. F., G. SKOFITSCH, B. R. KOMISARUK & D. M. JACOBOWITZ. 1988. Abolition of vagino-cervical stimulation–induced analgesia by capsaicin administered to neonatal, but not adult rats. Physiol. Behav. **44:** 267–272.

39. TSUNOO, A., S. KONISHI & M. OTSUKA. 1982. Substance P as an excitatory transmitter of primary afferent neurons in guinea pig sympathetic ganglia. Neuroscience **7:** 2025–2037.

40. SARIA, A., R. C. MA, N. J. DUN, E. THEODORSSON-NORHEIM & J. M. LUNDBERG. 1987. Neurokinin A in capsaicin-sensitive neurons of the guinea pig inferior mesenteric ganglia: an additional putative mediator for the non-cholinergic excitatory postsynaptic potential. Neuroscience **21:** 951–958.

41. DUN, N. & N. MO. 1988. Calcitonin gene–related peptide evokes fast and slow depolarizing responses in guinea pig coeliac neurons. Neurosci. Lett. **87:** 157–162.

42. KONISHI, S., S-I. SONG, T. OGAWA & I. KANAZAWA. 1989. Tachykinins produce fast and slow depolarizations in sympathetic neurons of rat coeliac–superior mesenteric ganglia. Brain Res. **490:** 162–165.

43. MO, N. & N. J. DUN. 1986. Cholecystokinin octapeptide depolarizes guinea pig inferior mesenteric ganglion cells and facilitates nicotinic transmission. Neurosci. Lett. **64:** 263–268.

44. TAMURA, K., J. M. PALMER & J. D. WOOD. 1987. Galanin suppresses nicotinic synaptic transmission in the myenteric plexus of guinea-pig small intestine. Eur. J. Pharmacol. **136:** 445–446.

Neuroanatomical Relationships of Substance P and Sex Steroid Hormone–sensitive Neurons Involved in Sexual Behavior[a]

JEFFREY D. BLAUSTEIN, KIRSTEN H. NIELSEN,
YVON DELVILLE, JOANNE C. TURCOTTE, AND
DEBORAH H. OLSTER

Department of Psychology
and
Neuroscience and Behavior Program
University of Massachusetts
Amherst, Massachusetts 01003

INTRODUCTION

The ovarian steroid hormones, estradiol and progesterone, regulate sexual behavior in many species.[1] In estrous-cycling guinea pigs, as in ovariectomized animals, estradiol primes and progesterone then facilitates the expression of sexual behavior. Many of the effects of ovarian hormones on behaviors and on reproductive physiology are due to actions of steroid hormones on neurotransmitter/neuropeptide systems in the brain.[2,3] Our strategy for investigating the interactions between steroid hormones and neuropeptides in the regulation of female sexual behavior in guinea pigs has been first to identify neural sites of action of sex steroid hormones on sexual behavior and then to determine the possible neurotransmitters and neuropeptides involved in the cellular mechanisms of action of steroid hormones on sexual behavior.

Previous studies on the neuroanatomical site where estradiol and progesterone regulate female sexual behavior in guinea pigs, as with studies on rats, implicated the mediobasal hypothalamus as a site for induction of sexual receptivity in guinea pigs. Estradiol implants located in the mediobasal hypothalamus and the preoptic area induced female sexual behavior in response to subsequent progesterone treatment.[4] Similarly, progesterone implants located in the mediobasal hypothalamus were sufficient to facilitate sexual receptivity in estradiol-primed animals.[5] The presence of high concentrations of estrogen receptors and estradiol-induced progestin receptors is consistent with a role for this area in hormonal regulation of sexual behavior.[6] However, in our present studies, it was necessary to define further a specific site of action for the hormones in the regulation of sexual behavior in guinea pigs.

[a]This research was supported by the following grants: National Institutes of Health Grant Nos. NS 19327 and RCDA NS 00970 (to J. D. Blaustein) and HD 23483 (to D. H. Olster); BRSG Grant No. RR 07048 (University of Massachusetts); and a Healey Endowment Grant from the University of Massachusetts (to J. D. Blaustein).

In order to identify more precisely the neural sites of action of sex steroid hormones on sexual behavior in guinea pigs, we have focused on neurons containing intracellular estrogen and progestin receptors. The results of a variety of earlier experiments have supported the idea that the effects of estradiol and progesterone on female sexual behavior in rodents require interaction with these intracellular, hormone-specific receptors.[6] Radioligand binding assays have demonstrated that certain brain nuclei contain estrogen receptors.[7] As with behavioral response to progesterone, the concentration of cytosol progestin receptors in the hypothalamus and preoptic area increases after estradiol priming.[8–10] Subsequent treatment of these estradiol-primed animals with progesterone results in the facilitation of female sexual behavior and in a transient accumulation of cell nuclear progestin receptors in the hypothalamus and preoptic area.[11,12] Treatment with either an estrogen[13] or progestin[14] antagonist inhibits sexual behavior. Taken together, these experiments provide strong evidence that intracellular, neural estrogen and progestin receptors are critically involved in mediating the effects of estradiol and progesterone, respectively, on guinea pig sexual behavior.[6]

Typically, *in vitro* binding assays have been used to study the regulation of neural steroid hormone receptor concentration. Although this technique is valuable in quantifying the concentration of receptors, it provides very limited neuroanatomical resolution, even on microdissected tissue.[7,15,16] In addition, this technique does not enable us to determine the neurotransmitters and neuropeptides present in steroid receptor–containing neurons nor the projections of these neurons. With the recent development of antibodies to estrogen and progestin receptors, we and others have developed immunocytochemical techniques to study the cell-by-cell localization of estrogen[17,18] and progestin receptors[19–21] in the guinea pig brain. We have used these techniques to study the site of action of estradiol and progesterone for the induction of sexual behavior and the relationships of steroid hormone–sensitive neurons to neurotransmitter/neuropeptide systems.

Many neurotransmitters and neuropeptides have been implicated in the regulation of progesterone-facilitated female sexual behavior in rodents.[2,3] One peptide that facilitates lordosis, when infused into the brain of estradiol-primed rats, is the tachykinin, substance P.[22] Substance P–immunoreactive (SP-IR) neurons are present throughout the ventral hypothalamus of female rats, and neurons containing both substance P and estrogen receptors are present in the ventrolateral area of the ventromedial nucleus of the hypothalamus in rats,[23] a postulated critical site of action of sex steroid hormones on sexual behavior.[24–26]

In the experiments to be discussed, we first identified a neural site of action for sex steroid hormones on guinea pig female sexual behavior. We then investigated the colocalization of substance P with progestin receptors in this area under different hormonal conditions. We have now begun studies of the relationships of the projections from this area and of SP-IR neurons to steroid receptor–containing neurons in another part of the brain believed to be involved in female sexual behavior, namely, the midbrain central gray.

IMMUNOCYTOCHEMICAL METHODS

In all experiments, recently ovariectomized Hartley strain guinea pigs (Charles River Breeding Laboratories, Wilmington, Massachusetts) were used. The perfusion and immunocytochemical techniques have already been described.[17,19] In general, animals are perfused with a fixative such as acrolein or, in some cases, Zamboni's fixative. Brains are cut on either a vibratome or a freezing microtome. Free-floating sections are incubated with monoclonal antibodies to progestin receptors. These include the mouse monoclonal antibodies mPRII (Transbio Sarl, Paris, France) directed against rabbit uterine progestin receptors and the PR 6 antibody directed against the chick oviduct progestin receptor. In the indirect immunoperoxidase procedure, sections are incubated in a secondary goat anti-mouse antiserum followed by mouse monoclonal peroxidase-antiperoxidase complex (PAP, Sternberger-Meyer Immunocytochemicals, Jarrettsville, Maryland). To enhance the immunostaining, a multiple-bridge procedure is used in which incubations in the secondary and tertiary antibodies are repeated. The peroxidase is then visualized with diaminobenzidine, resulting in a brown reaction product. In double-label experiments, an antibody against substance P (Incstar Corporation, Stillwater, Minnesota) is then used for immunocytochemical colocalization in the same brain sections. In this case, the procedure is nearly identical, except that α-naphthol or diaminobenzidine with nickel intensification is used to visualize the immunoreactivity of the second substance. For estrogen receptor localization, a rat monoclonal antibody directed against human estrogen receptors (H 222; Abbott Research Laboratories) is used followed by goat anti-rat antiserum and rat monoclonal PAP. In some experiments, a fluorescent technique is used in which immunoreactivities are visualized using a fluorescein-conjugated or rhodamine-conjugated secondary immunoglobulin.

In anterograde tract–tracing experiments, *Phaseolus vulgaris* Leucoagglutinin was iontophoretically applied to the brain. After two weeks, animals were perfused and sections were stained by an avidin-biotin technique with nickel-intensified diaminobenzidine as the chromogen.

RESULTS

Progestin Receptor Immunostaining

We have observed progestin receptor immunostaining throughout the medial preoptic area and mediobasal hypothalamus of estradiol-treated guinea pigs.[19] Although we have detected PR-IR cells using our sensitive multiple-bridge procedure in locations that have not been observed in other investigations, the areas with the highest numbers of progestin receptor–immunoreactive (PR-IR) cells agree with other investigations of progestin receptor immunostaining in guinea pig brain.[20,21] Very few PR-IR cells are evident in ovariectomized guinea pigs that are not given estradiol replacement. In estradiol-injected animals, at the most rostral level examined, PR-IR cells were present in highest numbers in the medial preoptic nucleus, the anterior hypothalamic nucleus, the periventricular preoptic area, and the medial preoptic area. At the mid-rostrocaudal level, the largest accumulation of PR-IR cells was seen in and around the arcuate nucleus, the dorsomedial nucleus of the hypothalamus, and the ventrolateral hypothalamic area (VLH) (FIGURE 1). We use the term VLH in guinea pigs to refer to the area ventral and lateral to the ventromedial nucleus of the hypothalamus, including the ventrolateral nucleus of the hypothalamus (VLN), the area just rostral to the VLN, and a crescent-shaped band of PR-IR cells extending laterally and dorsally to the level of the fornix. At caudal hypothalamic levels, a large number of PR-IR cells was observed in the caudal aspect of the arcuate nucleus and in the dorsal and ventral premammillary nuclei. A few scattered, labeled cells were observed in the posterior hypothalamic area surrounding the cerebral aqueduct.

Presence of Estrogen Receptor–Immunoreactivity in Progestin
Receptor–Immunoreactive Cells

Because the occurrence of sexual behavior in estradiol-primed guinea pigs requires facilitation by progesterone,[27] we have focused on cells containing progestin receptors in our studies. Although there is a basal level of progestin receptors throughout the brain of ovariectomized rats[9,28] and guinea pigs,[8] estradiol treatment increases the concentration only in those areas containing high concentrations of estrogen receptors. We have suggested that progestin receptors are induced by estradiol in cells that contain estrogen receptors. In preliminary immunocytochemical experiments, we and others observed estradiol-induced PR-IR[19,21] only in areas

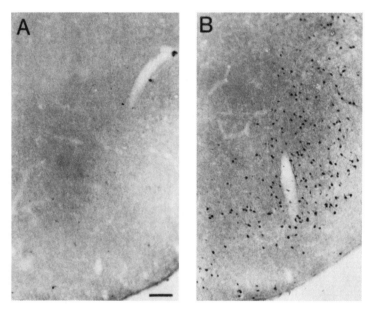

FIGURE 1. PR-IR in the arcuate nucleus and ventrolateral hypothalamus of estradiol-primed ovariectomized guinea pigs injected with (A) vehicle control or (B) 20 µg of estradiol benzoate per day for four days prior to perfusion. Magnification bar = 100 µm.

that contained estrogen receptor–immunoreactive (ER-IR) cells. Because these studies did not eliminate the possibility that estradiol could modulate the concentration of progestin receptors by an indirect, intercellular mechanism, we performed a colocalization experiment to determine if the cells that contain PR-IR also contain ER-IR.

Using a fluorescent immunocytochemical technique, we determined that estradiol-induced progestin receptors are present exclusively in cells that contain estrogen receptors. Consistent with the recent findings of Warembourg *et al.*,[18] estradiol-induced PR-IR in all areas was found only in cells that also contained ER-IR.[29] The neuroanatomical sites at which this relationship was observed included the VLH, the arcuate nucleus, the periventricular-preoptic area, the medial preoptic nucleus, the anterior hypothalamic nucleus, and the medial preoptic area. However, although virtually all PR-IR cells also contain ER-IR, the converse is not true. The amygdala presents the opposite extreme; in this area, many ER-IR cells are evident, but PR-immunoreactivity is not. Nevertheless, throughout the regions studied in the hypothalamus and preoptic area, most medium-intensity to highly fluorescent ER-IR cells contain PR-IR, but a small number of ER-IR cells do not contain PR-IR. This result suggests that, in studies in which neuropeptides are colocalized with PR-IR, most of the PR-IR cells undoubtedly also contain ER-IR.

The VLH: A Site of Action for Estradiol Induction of Progesterone-facilitated Sexual Behavior

In an attempt to define discrete areas within the mediobasal hypothalamus in which estradiol primes guinea pigs for progesterone facilitation of female sexual behavior, the behavioral response to progesterone was evaluated after bilateral implantation of estradiol-containing cannulae into the hypothalamus of ovariecto-mized guinea pigs. After behavioral testing, animals were perfused and hypothalamic PR-IR was determined as a means of assessing the extent of diffusion of estradiol (i.e., levels sufficient to induce PR-IR) from the implant site. In our first experiments, 28-gauge cannulae containing either 1% or 10% estradiol diluted in cholesterol were implanted in various sites within the mediobasal hypothalamus. Two days later, progesterone was injected and guinea pigs were tested for sexual behavior. The results of this experiment narrowed the sensitive area to the rostral part of the mediobasal hypothalamus; the posterior portion was insensitive even to the larger doses of estradiol. In a second study, smaller, 33-gauge cannulae containing the same dilutions of estradiol were used to locate more precisely the sensitive sites. Only cannulae located at the rostral and ventral aspect of the VLH induced behavioral responsiveness to progesterone (FIGURE 2). Although many animals with implants in this region failed to express sexual receptivity after progesterone treatment, few or no PR-IR cells were seen in many of these animals. Further analysis revealed that the presence of PR-IR in the rostral VLH was correlated with response to progesterone treatment. Further supporting a role for the rostral, ventral VLH, estradiol-induced PR-IR in the arcuate nucleus did not correlate with sexual receptivity. These data suggest that activation of the VLH by very low levels of estradiol may be sufficient to allow progesterone to facilitate female sexual behavior in guinea pigs.

The results of other experiments have implicated the VLH as a likely site of action for the behavioral effects of estradiol and progesterone. For example, administration of low, discrete doses of 17β-estradiol is as effective as higher, single doses of estradiol benzoate in priming ovariectomized guinea pigs[30,31] and rats[32] to display progesterone-facilitated lordosis. Furthermore, although both of these estradiol treatments induce cytosol progestin receptors in the mediobasal hypothalamus and preoptic area,[30,31] the concentrations of progestin receptors are significantly lower in estradiol-pulse-treated females as compared to estradiol benzoate–treated females as measured by in vitro binding assays.[31] Immunocytochemistry for progestin receptors was used to define more precisely the areas of progestin receptor–containing cells within the hypothalamus and preoptic area that might be differentially responsive to the inductive effects of these two estradiol treatments.[31] The lower concentration of progestin receptors in the mediobasal hypothalamus–preoptic area following the estradiol-pulse treatment appears to reflect the induction of PR-IR in fewer cells in the arcuate nucleus and medial preoptic–anterior hypothalamic nuclei. PR-IR staining intensity was also significantly weaker in the arcuate nucleus of estradiol-pulse-injected animals. Most interestingly, in some areas, including the VLH (as well as the medial preoptic area and the periventricular preoptic area), neither the numbers nor the staining intensity of PR-IR cells differed between groups of animals receiving the different estradiol treatments.

Conversely, it is well known that progesterone treatment results in decreased

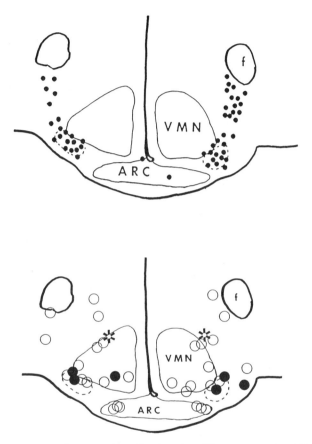

FIGURE 2. (Bottom panel) Localization of implant sites (33-gauge cannulae; 1% estradiol) in the rostral aspect of the mediobasal hypothalamus. Filled symbols = cannulae location of animals that were sexually receptive in response to progesterone; unfilled symbols = nonresponders. (Top panel) Reconstruction of the PR-IR observed in the rostral aspect of the mediobasal hypothalamus in sexually receptive animals implanted with 33-gauge cannulae containing 1% or 10% estradiol. The reconstruction is based on the median cell counts of sexually receptive animals for different zones within this area. Terms: VMN = ventromedial nucleus of the hypothalamus, ARC = arcuate nucleus, and f = fornix. The ventrolateral nucleus of the hypothalamus (dashed line) is included for reference, even though it is only present in slightly caudal levels. Each dot corresponds to one PR-IR cell.

sensitivity to its own facilitative action (desensitization) (see reference 6 for review). We have observed that an injection of progesterone, which is known to down-regulate progestin binding in the brain, does indeed down-regulate PR-IR throughout the brain.[33] Although decreases were seen in all areas studied in the preoptic area and hypothalamus, the VLH was the most responsive site studied. In the VLH, injection of progesterone caused a large decrease in PR-IR by 12 h after injection, which increased further by 24 h after injection.

Because progestin receptor immunostaining changes in a manner consistent with the involvement of progestin receptors in this area in female sexual behavior, the results of these experiments provide additional support for the concept that the VLH is important in the hormonal induction of sexual receptivity in guinea pigs. With this rationale, we have begun to study the neurotransmitter/neuropeptide content of the PR-IR neurons in the VLH and the relationships of these neurons to neurons in other parts of the brain.

Colocalization of SP-IR and PR-IR in the VLH

Because substance P may play a role in steroid hormone–induced lordosis in rats[22] and because SP-IR neurons are present in approximately the same hypothalamic areas in which estradiol primes guinea pigs for progesterone-facilitated lordosis,[34] we used a double-antibody immunocytochemical technique to determine if substance P–immunoreactivity is present in the progestin receptor–containing neurons of estradiol-primed, ovariectomized guinea pigs.[35]

In colchicine-treated guinea pigs that had received a high dose of estradiol-17β (20-mm Silastic capsules implanted seven days prior to perfusion), both SP-IR neurons and PR-IR neurons were observed in the previously reported locations throughout the hypothalamus and preoptic area. As described previously in rats,[34,36,37] high concentrations of SP-IR cell bodies were observed in the medial preoptic area, the anterior hypothalamus, the suprachiasmatic nucleus, the caudal arcuate nucleus, and the ventromedial and ventrolateral nucleus of the hypothalamus, becoming more sparse when extending toward the lateral hypothalamic and dorsal hypothalamic areas.

The double-label immunocytochemical technique in which sections were stained for PR-IR and SP-IR revealed their colocalization in the same neurons almost exclusively in the VLH. In the caudal arcuate nucleus and the preoptic periventricular area, populations of PR-IR neurons and SP-IR neurons were both present, but PR-IR neurons rarely contained SP-IR (<0.1%). Within the VLH, however, approximately 35% of the PR-IR neurons also contained SP-IR (FIGURES 3 and 4). Although the numbers of cells containing SP-IR and PR-IR varied in different regions of the VLH, the proportion of PR-IR cells containing SP-IR was consistent across the rostral, mid, and caudal divisions of the VLH (TABLE 1). It should be emphasized that, because virtually all cells containing PR-IR also contain ER-IR, intraneuronal colocalization of SP-IR with PR-IR implies its colocalization with ER-IR as well. This colocalization of SP-IR and ovarian steroid hormone–immunoreactivity in the VLH is consistent with the hypothesis that substance P is involved in hormonally induced lordosis in rodents.

In another experiment that suggests indirectly a role for substance P in hormone-induced sexual behavior in guinea pigs, we have found that the highly effective, pulsatile mode of estradiol administration described earlier induces PR-IR in the VLH selectively in neurons that contain substance P.[38] Specifically, we have looked at the degree of cellular colocalization of SP-IR and PR-IR after treatment with either Silastic capsules filled with estradiol (20 mM for 1 week) or pulses of estradiol (2 μg of estradiol at 11 and 39 h prior to perfusion). The total number of PR-IR cells in the VLH and the number of SP-IR cells in the VLH/ventromedial nucleus did not differ significantly between treatment groups, although the number of PR-IR cells appeared somewhat lower in the pulse-treated animals. However, the percentage of PR-IR cells that contained SP-IR in the VLH was twice as high in the estradiol-pulse-treated animals as compared to the estradiol-capsule-treated animals (52% versus 36%, respectively; TABLE 2). These data demonstrate that neurons within the VLH

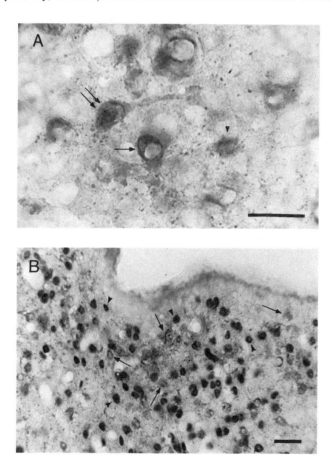

FIGURE 3. Substance P–immunoreactivity (cytoplasmic staining) and progestin receptor–immunoreactivity (darker cell nuclear staining) in the hypothalamus. (A) High power photomicrograph of the VLH: Double arrows point to a neuron immunoreactive for both substance P and progestin receptors. The single arrow points to a neuron containing only substance P–immunoreactivity and the arrowhead points to a neuron containing only progestin receptor–immunoreactivity. (B) Lower power photomicrograph of the caudal arcuate showing the presence of both SP- and PR-IR neurons, but no colocalization: Single arrows = examples of neurons containing SP-IR only; arrowheads = cells containing PR-IR only. Scale bars = 25 μm. In original photomicrographs,[35] cytoplasmic SP-IR is a readily distinguishable pink, α-naphthol reaction product, whereas cell nuclear PR-IR is a brown diaminobenzidine reaction product.

that show induction of PR-IR after a minimal, behaviorally effective estradiol treatment are likely to contain SP-IR. This suggests that substance P is present in those PR-IR neurons in the VLH that are likely to be involved in steroid hormone induction of sexual behavior in female guinea pigs.

VLH and Substance P Projections to Estrogen-sensitive Neurons in the Midbrain Central Gray

In order to begin to characterize the cells with which ovarian steroid hormone–sensitive neurons in the VLH interact, we did an anterograde tract–tracing study. Efferent projections from the rostral VLH were traced using *Phaseolus vulgaris* Leucoagglutinin (Pha-L), which was applied iontophoretically into the brains of

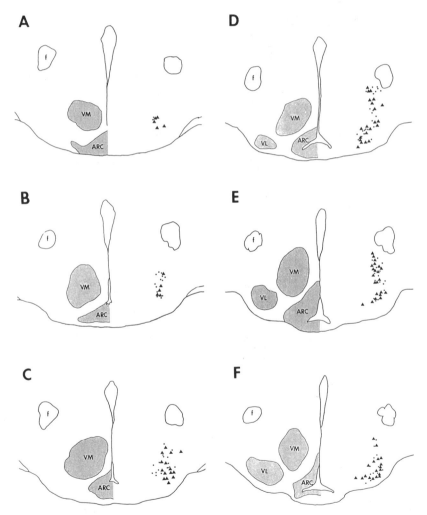

FIGURE 4(A–F). Camera lucida drawings of the VLH showing the distribution of individual neurons containing PR-IR (circles) and PR-IR neurons that are also SP-IR (triangles). A–C represent the rostral VLH and D–F represent the mid-VLH. Abbreviations: ARC = arcuate nucleus, DM = dorsomedial hypothalamic nucleus, PO = posterior hypothalamic nucleus, VL = ventrolateral hypothalamic nucleus, VM = ventromedial hypothalamic nucleus, f = fornix, and mt = mammillothalamic tract.

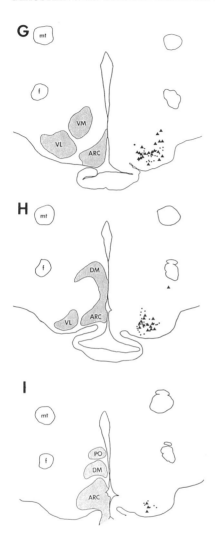

FIGURE 4(G–I). Same as the caption to FIG-URE 4(A–F), except G–I are equivalent to the caudal VLH.

ovariectomized guinea pigs. After a survival period of two weeks, the guinea pigs were perfused and the Pha-L was visualized immunocytochemically. Pha-L injection sites were small and were localized in sites containing high concentrations of steroid receptor–containing cells. The majority of Pha-L-labeled projections were observed ipsilateral to the injection site, but occasional axons were labeled in the same contralateral structures. The following areas received the heaviest projections: the bed nucleus of the stria terminalis, the medial preoptic area, the anterior hypothalamus, the tuber cinereum, the ventromedial nucleus, the dorsomedial and dorsolateral hypothalamus, the posterior hypothalamus, the dorsal longitudinal fasciculus, the midbrain central gray, and the recess inferior colliculus. The latter three areas also received the heaviest contralateral projections. Areas with fewer labeled terminals and fibers included the diagonal band of Broca, the lateral septum, the medial

TABLE 1. Colocalization of PR-IR and SP-IR in the Ventrolateral Hypothalamus of Estradiol-primed Ovariectomized Guinea Pigs[a]

Subdivision of the VLH	Number of Cells with PR-IR[b]	Number of PR-IR Cells with SP-IR[b]	Percentage of Colocalization
rostral	145.3 ± 15.9	45.5 ± 2.3	32.0 ± 1.9
mid	303.8 ± 24.0	113.0 ± 5.3	38.0 ± 4.0
caudal	350.8 ± 81.0	112.2 ± 25.9	34.6 ± 3.6
all sections	792.3 ± 107.5	270.8 ± 28.1	35.1 ± 3.4

[a]Values are expressed as the mean ± SEM; $n = 4$.
[b]Counted in every fourth section.

and cortical amygdala, the lateral preoptic area, the paraventricular nucleus, the arcuate nucleus, the premammillary nucleus, the dorsal tegmental area, and the pontine central gray. Fibers with few or no terminals were observed in the median forebrain bundle, the stria terminalis, and the medial lemniscus. Many of these projections, including the one to the midbrain central gray, are similar to the efferents from the ventrolateral-ventromedial nucleus in rats,[39,40] the area apparently analogous to the VLH in guinea pigs.

The midbrain central gray is one of the major projection sites of the steroid receptor–rich region of the VLH in guinea pigs. Furthermore, estrogen receptor–containing neurons of the rat VMH project to this area and the midbrain central gray also contains ER-IR neurons in guinea pigs.[17] Therefore, we visualized VLH projections with a double-label immunocytochemical procedure, which included immunostaining for both the anterograde tracer (Pha-L) and the estrogen receptors in the same sections. Within this area, as well as in the medial preoptic area and periventricular preoptic area, many apparent terminals of projections from the VLH were found closely associated with ER-IR neurons, suggestive of synaptic contacts.

Although the projections of the specific VLH neurons in which we have colocalized SP-IR and PR-IR in guinea pigs are unknown, the anterograde tract–tracing study indicates that many of these rostral VLH neurons project to the midbrain central gray. Furthermore, in rats, substance P–containing neurons of the ventromedial hypothalamus do, in fact, project to the midbrain central gray.[41] In guinea pigs, we have found an interesting relationship between substance P and steroid hormone receptors within the midbrain central gray.[42] First, SP-IR fibers and terminals and ER-IR neurons are present in the same areas of the central gray (FIGURE 5). In guinea pigs, ER-IR cell nuclei were observed at all levels of the central gray, increasing in numbers more caudally. Most ER-IR nuclei were found slightly ventrolateral to the cerebral aqueduct, where SP-IR fibers and terminals appear most dense. By using a multiple-bridging technique to enhance ER-IR immunostaining, we have been able to visualize ER-IR in the cytoplasmic processes as well as in

TABLE 2. Colocalization of PR-IR and SP-IR in the Ventrolateral Hypothalamus in Guinea Pigs Receiving Different Estradiol Treatments[a]

Estradiol Treatment	Number of Cells with PR-IR[b]	Number of PR-IR Cells with SP-IR[b]	Percentage of Colocalization
Pulses	1184.2 ± 232.2	626.0 ± 135.3	52.0 ± 1.4
Silastic capsules	1660.4 ± 287.9	594.6 ± 122.7	36.5 ± 4.0

[a]Values are expressed as the mean ± SEM; $n = 5$.
[b]Counted in every fourth section.

cell nuclei. This enabled us to observe SP-IR punctate structures, suggestive of terminal boutons, in close association with a small number of ER-IR cell processes and, more frequently, with ER-IR cell bodies (FIGURES 5 and 6). This overlap of SP-IR innervation with ER-IR neurons, together with the presence of an abundance of substance P receptors in the midbrain central gray of rats[36,43–46] and guinea pigs,[47] suggests a neuroanatomical substrate for the facilitative effects of substance P on sexual behavior that has been described in rats.[22]

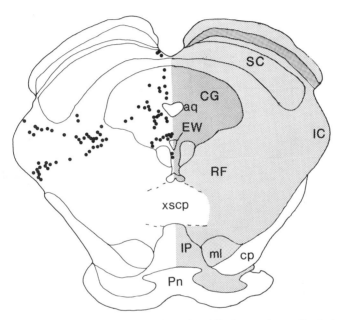

FIGURE 5. Camera lucida drawing of the guinea pig midbrain at an intercollicular level of the midbrain showing the distribution of estrogen receptor–immunoreactive cells (dots) and substance P–immunoreactivity (shaded areas). Abbreviations: CG = central gray, EW = Edinger-Westphal nucleus, IC = inferior colliculus, IP = interpeduncular nucleus, RF = reticular formation, SC = superior colliculus, Pn = pontine nuclei, aq = cerebral aqueduct, cp = cerebral peduncle, ml = medial lemniscus, and xscp = decussation of the superior cerebral peduncle. Dots on the left side of the figure represent ER-IR cells and the shading on the right side represents the intensity of SP-IR fibers and terminals.

Substance P and Sexual Behavior in Guinea Pigs

We have observed two distinct anatomical relationships of substance P to PR-IR and ER-IR neurons in guinea pigs in sites where sex steroid hormones are believed to regulate sexual behavior. In the VLH, we have observed intracellular colocalization of SP-IR with PR-IR (and therefore of ER-IR as well); in the midbrain central gray, we have observed SP-IR punctate structures closely associated with ER-IR neurons. These relationships suggest the possible involvement of substance P in mediating the behavioral effects of estradiol and progesterone on sexual behavior. In a preliminary test of this hypothesis, ovariectomized guinea pigs were injected with estradiol and progesterone and they were tested for lordosis. Once sexual receptivity was confirmed (by 6–8 h after progesterone injection), antiserum to substance P was infused into the midbrain central gray, lateral to the cerebral aqueduct, and behavioral testing was continued. By the time of the first test for lordosis at 30 minutes after infusion, sexual receptivity was nearly totally inhibited. Although this is a very preliminary experiment, the results are consistent with an earlier experiment in rats[22] and with the hypothesized role and site of action of substance P on sexual behavior.

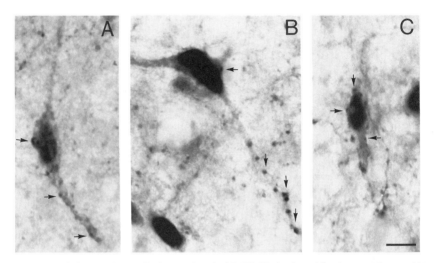

FIGURE 6. Substance P terminals associated with ER-IR in the midbrain central gray: (A) high power photomicrograph of SP-IR punctate structures closely associated with an ER-IR neuron in the midbrain central gray; note the lightly stained cytoplasm with darkly stained punctate structures associated with the process and soma (arrows); (B) high power photomicrograph of a large ER-IR neuron in the midbrain central gray with darkly stained SP-IR punctate structures along one process; (C) high power photomicrograph of an ER-IR neuron in the midbrain central gray with small darkly stained punctate structures surrounding the cell nucleus and process. Scale bar = 10 μm.

DISCUSSION

We have applied immunocytochemical and tract-tracing techniques to the study of substance P involvement in the behavioral effects of steroid hormones in the brain. We first mapped the distribution of ER-IR and PR-IR cells in the guinea pig brain and observed, as predicted, densities of PR-IR and ER-IR neurons within the hypothalamus in addition to other areas. These techniques have enabled us to begin to unravel the neuroanatomy of estradiol- and progesterone-responsive areas for female sexual behavior. We have focused our studies on the VLH because implants of estradiol prime guinea pigs to respond to progesterone and because PR-IR cells in the VLH consistently respond in concordance with the behavioral effects of the hormonal treatments used. For example, in this area, PR-IR is induced similarly by either high doses of estradiol-17β or minimal pulsatile treatment of estradiol. In addition, PR-IR in this area is more responsive than in other neuroanatomical areas to an injection of progesterone that results in behavioral refractoriness to progesterone.

We have begun studies of the neurotransmitters found in ovarian hormone receptor–containing neurons in the VLH and anatomically related areas.[35,48-50] Although we have observed some colocalization of enkephalin with PR-IR in neurons in this area,[50] the relationship of PR-IR neurons to substance P is the strongest that we have seen. We have demonstrated with double-label immunocytochemistry that, although substance P–immunoreactivity and progestin receptor–immunoreactivity occur throughout the guinea pig hypothalamus and caudal preoptic area, they are found in the same neurons almost exclusively in the VLH. In the caudal arcuate nucleus and in the periventricular preoptic area, the populations of PR-IR neurons and SP-IR neurons coexist, but PR-IR neurons are rarely immunoreactive for substance P. However, within the VLH, many of the PR-IR neurons also contain substance P–immunoreactivity. Although we have observed that approximately 35% of the PR-IR neurons in this area also contain SP-IR, this percentage could be influenced by a variety of factors including the physiological state of the animal. In support of this idea, we have observed that the proportion of PR-IR cells containing SP-IR increases by 50% when a minimal, estradiol-priming regimen that results in progesterone-facilitated sexual behavior is used.

The amount of colocalization of substance P–immunoreactivity and progestin receptors in guinea pigs is generally consistent with that reported for [³H]estradiol-concentrating neurons and SP-IR in rats.[23] However, Akesson and Micevych[23] also reported finding some colocalization in the arcuate and ventral premammillary nuclei. One explanation for finding colocalization in slightly different areas is that Akesson and Micevych examined [³H]estradiol-concentrating neurons, whereas we examined PR-IR neurons. Because virtually all PR-IR neurons in guinea pigs are also immunoreactive for estrogen receptors, but not all ER-IR neurons contain PR-IR,[18,29] it is possible that some SP-IR neurons contain estrogen receptors, but not progestin receptors. Another obvious cause could be the species difference. For example, the amount of tyrosine hydroxylase colocalization with progestin receptors differs substantially between rats[51,52] and guinea pigs,[48] as does the amount of luteinizing hormone–releasing hormone colocalization with progestin receptors.[49,51]

Earlier work in rats suggests that substance P levels in the hypothalamus may vary over the estrous cycle[53,54] and that messenger RNA levels for substance P may be influenced directly by estradiol (see reference 55, but compare with reference 56). Although this suggests that substance P production may be affected by ovarian hormones, the effects on substance P levels have been inconsistent. The reported fluctuations in substance P levels vary in the direction of the change, in the neuroanatomical location, and in the stage of the estrous cycle at which they occur. We have not observed any obvious effect of estradiol priming on substance P–immunoreactivity. However, because the purpose of our control experiments was merely to determine that the estradiol treatment did not substantially affect the amount of colocalization between PR-IR and SP-IR, immunostaining was not quantified. Furthermore, the immunostaining procedure was not optimized to be sensitive to changes in the concentrations of substance P.

In rats, facilitation of sexual behavior has been observed after infusion of substance P into the midbrain central gray and inhibition has been observed after infusion of an antiserum to substance P.[22] Although we do not have definitive data implicating substance P or other tachykinins in the hormonal regulation of sexual behavior in guinea pigs, there is now a substantial neuroanatomical foundation for expecting this to be the case. In guinea pigs,[35] as in rats,[23] there is substantial colocalization of SP-IR with steroid receptors in cells in a well-defined neuroanatomical area that has been implicated in sexual behavior. A major projection site of this area in both rats[39,40] and guinea pigs[57] is the midbrain central gray. In guinea pigs, we have shown with very discrete iontophoretic application of Pha-L that the steroid receptor–rich rostral VLH projects to the midbrain central gray. These projections appear to enter the midbrain central gray dorsally and ramify lateral and ventrolateral to the cerebral aqueduct in the same area where many ER-IR cells are also located. Some of these projections are closely associated with ER-IR cells and appear to form synaptic contacts. Similarly, many of the ER-IR neurons in this area have SP-IR terminals closely associated and perhaps synapsing upon them. Because of the fact that, in rats, at least some of the SP-IR fibers and terminals in the midbrain central gray arise from the steroid receptor–rich area of the ventrolateral-ventromedial hypothalamus[41] that has been implicated in the regulation of sexual behavior, it is likely that many of these SP-IR terminals associated with ER-IR neurons in the midbrain central gray of guinea pigs are projections from the VLH.

Based upon work in rats, it has been suggested that the midbrain central gray serves as a relay point for descending hypothalamic projections involved in hormonal regulation of lordosis.[58] Electrical stimulation of this area facilitates,[59] whereas lesions disrupt sexual behavior.[60] Furthermore, applications of a variety of neuropeptides and hormones, including corticotropin-releasing hormone,[61] β-endorphin,[61,62] luteinizing hormone–releasing hormone,[63,64] and prolactin,[65] all influence sexual behavior in rats when applied to the midbrain central gray.

In addition to delineating further the neuropeptide systems that are involved in the regulation of behavior and physiology, these studies on the neuroanatomical relationships between steroid receptor–containing neurons and substance P neurons are beginning to shed new light on the cellular processes involved in response to sex steroid hormones. Defining groups of gonadal hormone receptor–containing neurons on the basis of their inputs, projections, or presence of particular neuropeptides or neurotransmitters should provide new insights into the hormonal regulation of cells involved in one fundamental reproductive process, namely, female sexual behavior.

ACKNOWLEDGMENTS

We thank Robin Lempicki and Carol Sacks for expert technical assistance, David Toft for generously supplying the PR 6 monoclonal antibody, and Geoffrey Greene and Abbott Laboratories for supplying the H 222 antibody.

REFERENCES

1. CLEMENS, L. G. & D. R. WEAVER. 1985. The role of gonadal hormones in the activation of feminine sexual behavior. *In* Handbook of Behavioral Neurobiology. Volume 7: Reproduction. N. Adler, D. W. Pfaff & R. Goy, Eds.: 183–227. Plenum. New York.
2. MEYERSON, B. J., C. O. MALMNAS & B. J. EVERITT. 1985. Neuropharmacology, neurotransmitters, and sexual behavior in mammals. *In* Handbook of Behavioral Neurobiology. Volume 7: Reproduction. N. Adler, D. W. Pfaff & R. Goy, Eds.: 495–536. Plenum. New York.
3. PFAFF, D. W. & S. SCHWARTZ-GIBLIN. 1988. Cellular mechanisms of female reproductive behaviors. *In* The Physiology of Reproduction. E. Knobil & J. Neill, Eds.: 1487–1568. Raven Press. New York.
4. MORIN, L. P. & H. H. FEDER. 1974. Intracranial estradiol benzoate implants and lordosis behavior of ovariectomized guinea pigs. Brain Res. **70:** 95–102.
5. MORIN, L. P. & H. H. FEDER. 1974. Hypothalamic progesterone implants and facilitation

of lordosis behavior in estrogen-primed ovariectomized guinea pigs. Brain Res. **70:** 81–93.

6. BLAUSTEIN, J. D. & D. H. OLSTER. 1989. Gonadal steroid hormone receptors and social behaviors. *In* Advances in Comparative and Environmental Physiology, Vol. 3. J. Balthazart, Ed.: 31–104. Springer-Verlag. Berlin/New York.

7. RAINBOW, T., B. PARSONS, N. MACLUSKY & B. MCEWEN. 1982. Estradiol receptor levels in rat hypothalamic and limbic nuclei. J. Neurosci. **2:** 1439–1445.

8. BLAUSTEIN, J. D. & H. H. FEDER. 1979. Cytoplasmic progestin receptors in guinea pig brain: characteristics and relationship to the induction of sexual behavior. Brain Res. **169:** 481–497.

9. MOGUILEWSKY, M. & J. P. RAYNAUD. 1977. Progestin binding sites in the rat hypothalamus, pituitary, and uterus. Steroids **30:** 99–109.

10. PARSONS, B., N. J. MACLUSKY, L. KREY, D. W. PFAFF & B. S. MCEWEN. 1980. The temporal relationship between estrogen-inducible progestin receptors in the female rat brain and the time course of estrogen activation of mating behavior. Endocrinology **107:** 774–779.

11. BLAUSTEIN, J. D. & H. H. FEDER. 1980. Nuclear progestin receptors in guinea pig brain measured by an *in vitro* exchange assay after hormonal treatments that affect lordosis. Endocrinology **106:** 1061–1069.

12. BROWN, T. J. & J. D. BLAUSTEIN. 1985. Loss of hypothalamic nuclear-bound progestin receptors: factors involved and the relationship to heat termination in female guinea pigs. Brain Res. **358:** 180–190.

13. WALKER, W. A. & H. H. FEDER. 1977. Anti-estrogen effects on estrogen accumulation in brain cell nuclei: neurochemical correlates of estrogen action of female sexual behavior in guinea pigs. Brain Res. **134:** 467–478.

14. BROWN, T. J. & J. D. BLAUSTEIN. 1986. Abbreviation of the period of sexual behavior in female guinea pigs by the progesterone antagonist, RU 486. Brain Res. **373:** 103–113.

15. PARSONS, B., T. RAINBOW, N. MACLUSKY & B. MCEWEN. 1982. Progestin receptor levels in rat hypothalamic and limbic nuclei. J. Neurosci. **2:** 1446–1452.

16. THORNTON, J. E., B. NOCK, B. S. MCEWEN & H. H. FEDER. 1986. Estrogen induction of progesterone receptors in microdissected hypothalamic and limbic nuclei of female guinea pigs. Neuroendocrinology **43:** 182–188.

17. BLAUSTEIN, J. D. & J. C. TURCOTTE. 1989. Estrogen receptor–immunostaining of neuronal cytoplasmic processes as well as cell nuclei in guinea pig brain. Brain Res. **495:** 75–82.

18. WAREMBOURG, M., A. JOLIVET & E. MILGROM. 1989. Immunohistochemical evidence of the presence of estrogen and progesterone receptors in the same neurons of the guinea pig hypothalamus and preoptic area. Brain Res. **480:** 1–15.

19. BLAUSTEIN, J. D., J. C. KING, D. O. TOFT & J. TURCOTTE. 1988. Immunocytochemical localization of estrogen-induced progestin receptors in guinea pig brain. Brain Res. **474:** 1–15.

20. DON CARLOS, L. L., G. L. GREENE & J. I. MORRELL. 1989. Estrogen plus progesterone increases progestin receptor immunoreactivity in the brain of ovariectomized guinea pigs. Neuroendocrinology **50:** 613–623.

21. WAREMBOURG, M., F. LOGEAT & E. MILGROM. 1986. Immunocytochemical localization of progesterone receptor in the guinea pig central nervous system. Brain Res. **384:** 121–131.

22. DORNAN, W. A., C. W. MALSBURY & R. B. PENNEY. 1987. Facilitation of lordosis by injection of substance P into the midbrain central gray. Neuroendocrinology **45:** 498–506.

23. AKESSON, T. R. & P. E. MICEVYCH. 1988. Estrogen concentration by substance P–immunoreactive neurons in the medial basal hypothalamus of the female rat. J. Neurosci. Res. **19:** 412–419.

24. RUBIN, B. S. & R. J. BARFIELD. 1980. Priming of estrous responsiveness by implants of 17β-estradiol in the ventromedial hypothalamic nucleus of female rats. Endocrinology **106:** 504–509.

25. RUBIN, B. S. & R. J. BARFIELD. 1983. Progesterone in the ventromedial hypothalamus facilitates estrous behavior in ovariectomized, estrogen-primed rats. Endocrinology **113:** 797–804.

26. DAVIS, P. G., M. S. KRIEGER, R. J. BARFIELD, B. S. MCEWEN & D. W. PFAFF. 1982. The

site of action in intrahypothalamic estrogen implants in feminine sexual behavior: an autoradiographic analysis. Endocrinology **111**: 1581–1586.

27. COLLINS, V. J., J. I. BOLING, E. W. DEMPSEY & W. C. YOUNG. 1938. Quantitative studies of experimentally induced sexual receptivity in the spayed guinea pig. Endocrinology **23**: 188–196.

28. MACLUSKY, N. J. & B. S. MCEWEN. 1978. Oestrogen modulates progestin receptor concentrations in some rat brain regions, but not in others. Nature **274**: 276–278.

29. BLAUSTEIN, J. D. & J. C. TURCOTTE. 1989. Estradiol-induced progestin receptor immuno-reactivity is found only in estrogen receptor–immunoreactive cells in guinea pig brain. Neuroendocrinology **49**: 454–461.

30. WILCOX, J. N., S. R. BARCLAY & H. H. FEDER. 1984. Administration of estradiol-17β in pulses to guinea pigs: self-priming effects of estrogen on brain tissues mediating lordosis. Physiol. Behav. **32**: 483–488.

31. OLSTER, D. H. & J. D. BLAUSTEIN. 1990. Biochemical and immunocytochemical assess-ment of neural progestin receptors following estradiol treatments that eliminate the sex difference in progesterone-facilitated lordosis in guinea pigs. J. Neuroendocrinol. **2**: 79–86.

32. SODERSTEN, P., P. ENEROTH & S. HANSEN. 1981. Induction of sexual receptivity in ovariectomized rats by pulse administration of oestradiol-17β. J. Endocrinol. **89**: 55–62.

33. BLAUSTEIN, J. D. & J. C. TURCOTTE. 1990. Down-regulation of progestin receptors in guinea pig brain: new findings using an immunocytochemical technique. J. Neurobiol. **21**: 675–685.

34. LJUNGDAHL, A., T. HÖKFELT & G. NILSSON. 1978. Distribution of substance P–like immunoreactivity in the central nervous system of the rat. I. Cell bodies and nerve terminals. Neuroscience **3**: 861–943.

35. NIELSEN, K. H. & J. D. BLAUSTEIN. 1990. Many progestin receptor–containing neurons in the guinea pig ventrolateral hypothalamus contain substance P: immunocytochemical evidence. Brain Res. **517**: 175–187.

36. SHULTS, C. W., R. QUIRION, B. CHRONWALL, T. N. CHASE & T. L. O'DONOHUE. 1984. A comparison of the anatomical distribution of substance P and substance P receptors in the rat central nervous system. Peptides **5**: 1097–1128.

37. TSURUO, Y., S. HISANO, Y. OKAMURA, N. TSUKAMOTO & S. DAIKOKU. 1984. Hypothalamic substance P–containing neurons: sex-dependent topographical differences and ultra-structural transformations associated with stages of the estrous cycle. Brain Res. **305**: 331–341.

38. OLSTER, D. H. & J. D. BLAUSTEIN. 1990. Behaviorally effective estradiol pulses induce progestin receptors selectively in substance P–containing cells in the ventrolateral hypothalamus of female guinea pigs. Program of the 20th Annual Meeting of the Society for Neuroscience. Abstract no. 315.2.

39. KRIEGER, M. S., C. A. CONRAD & D. W. PFAFF. 1979. An autoradiographic study of the efferent connections of the ventromedial nucleus of the hypothalamus. J. Comp. Neurol. **183**: 785–815.

40. MORRELL, J. I. & D. W. PFAFF. 1982. Characterization of estrogen-concentrating hypotha-lamic neurons by their axonal projections. Science **217**: 1273–1276.

41. DORNAN, W. A., T. R. AKESSON & P. E. MICEVYCH. 1988. Substance P immunoreactive neurons in the ventromedial nucleus project to the dorsal midbrain central gray. Program of the 18th Annual Meeting of the Society for Neuroscience. Abstract no. 115.6.

42. TURCOTTE, J. C. & J. D. BLAUSTEIN. 1989. The distribution of neurons having estrogen receptor–immunoreactivity and substance P innervation overlaps in the midbrain central gray of guinea pigs. Program of the 19th Annual Meeting of the Society for Neuroscience. Abstract no. 250.12.

43. LIU, R. P. C. & M. L. SWENBERG. 1988. Autoradiographic localization of substance P ligand binding sites and distribution of immunoreactive neurons in the periaqueductal gray of the rat. Brain Res. **474**: 73–79.

44. MANTYH, P. W., T. GATES, C. R. MANTYH & J. E. MAGGIO. 1989. Autoradiographic localization and characterization of tachykinin receptor binding sites in the rat brain and peripheral tissues. J. Neurosci. **9**: 258–279.

45. QUIRION, R., C. W. SHULTS, T. W. MOODY, C. B. PERT, T. N. CHASE & T. L. O'DONOHUE.

1983. Autoradiographic distribution of substance P receptors in rat central nervous system. Nature **303**: 714–716.

46. SAFFROY, M., J. BEAUJOUAN, Y. TORRENS, J. BESSEYRE, L. BERGSTROM & J. GLOWINSKI. 1988. Localization of tachykinin binding sites (NK1, NK2, NK3 ligands) in the rat brain. Peptides **9**: 227–241.

47. QUIRION, R. & T-V. DAM. 1985. Multiple tachykinin receptors in guinea pig brain: high densities of substance K (neurokinin A) binding sites in the substantia nigra. Neuropeptides **6**: 191–204.

48. BLAUSTEIN, J. D. & J. C. TURCOTTE. 1989. A small population of tyrosine hydroxylase–immunoreactive neurons in the guinea pig arcuate nucleus contains progestin receptor–immunoreactivity. J. Neuroendocrinol. **1**: 333–338.

49. KING, J. C., J. D. BLAUSTEIN & G. R. SEILER. 1989. Colocalization of luteinizing hormone–releasing hormone in neurons containing progestin receptors in guinea pig brain. Program of the 19th Annual Meeting of the Society for Neuroscience. Abstract no. 82.11.

50. OLSTER, D. H. & J. D. BLAUSTEIN. 1990. Immunocytochemical colocalization of progestin receptors and β-endorphin or enkephalin in the hypothalamus of female guinea pigs. J. Neurobiol. **21**: 768–780.

51. FOX, S. R., R. E. HARLAN, B. D. SHIVERS & D. W. PFAFF. 1990. Chemical characterization of neuroendocrine targets for progesterone in the female rat brain and pituitary. Neuroendocrinology **51**: 276–283.

52. SAR, M. 1988. Distribution of progestin-concentrating cells in rat brain: colocalization of [^{3}H]ORG.2058, a synthetic progestin, and antibodies to tyrosine hydroxylase in hypothalamus by combined autoradiography and immunocytochemistry. Endocrinology **123**: 1110–1118.

53. FRANKFURT, M., R. A. SIEGEL, I. SIM & W. WUTTKE. 1986. Estrous cycle variations in cholecystokinin and substance P concentrations in discrete areas of the rat brain. Neuroendocrinology **42**: 226–231.

54. MICEVYCH, P. E., D. W. MATT & V. L. W. GO. 1988. Concentrations of cholecystokinin, substance P, and bombesin in discrete regions of male and female rat brain: sex differences and estrogen effects. Exp. Neurol. **100**: 416–425.

55. BROWN, E. R., R. E. HARLAN & J. E. KRAUSE. 1990. Gonadal steroid regulation of substance P (SP) and SP-encoding messenger ribonucleic acids in the rat anterior pituitary and hypothalamus. Endocrinology **126**: 330–340.

56. ROMANO, G. J., T. I. BONNER & D. W. PFAFF. 1989. Preprotachykinin gene expression in the mediobasal hypothalamus of estrogen-treated and ovariectomized control rats. Exp. Brain Res. **76**: 21–26.

57. SHEN, C. L. 1983. Efferent projections from the lateral hypothalamus in the guinea pig: an autoradiographic study. Brain Res. Bull. **11**: 335–347.

58. PFAFF, D. W. 1980. Estrogens and Brain Function: Neural Analysis of a Hormone-controlled Mammalian Reproductive Behavior. Springer-Verlag. New York/Berlin.

59. SAKUMA, Y. & D. W. PFAFF. 1979. Facilitation of female reproductive behavior from mesencephalic central gray in the rat. Am. J. Physiol. **R237**: 278–284.

60. SAKUMA, Y. & D. W. PFAFF. 1979. Mesencephalic mechanisms for integration of female reproductive behavior in the rat. Am. J. Physiol. **R237**: 285–290.

61. SIRINATHSINGHJI, D. J. S. 1985. Modulation of lordosis behavior in the female rats by corticotropin releasing factor, β-endorphin, and gonadotropin releasing hormone in the mesencephalic central gray. Brain Res. **336**: 45–55.

62. SIRINATHSINGHJI, D. J. S. 1984. Modulation of lordosis behavior of female rats by naloxone, β-endorphin, and its antiserum in the mesencephalic central gray: possible mediation via GnRH. Neuroendocrinology **39**: 222–230.

63. RISKIND, P. & R. L. MOSS. 1979. Midbrain central gray: LHRH infusion enhances lordotic behavior in estrogen-primed ovariectomized rats. Brain Res. Bull. **4**: 203–205.

64. SAKUMA, Y. & D. W. PFAFF. 1980. LH-RH in the mesencephalic central gray can potentiate lordosis reflex of female rats. Nature **283**: 566–567.

65. HARLAN, R. E., B. D. SHIVERS & D. W. PFAFF. 1983. Midbrain microinfusions of prolactin increase the estrogen-dependent behavior, lordosis. Science **219**: 1451–1453.

Effects of Various Tachykinins on Pituitary LH Secretion, Feeding, and Sexual Behavior in the Rat[a]

SATYA P. KALRA, ABHIRAM SAHU, MICHAEL G. DUBE,
AND PUSHPA S. KALRA

Department of Obstetrics and Gynecology
University of Florida College of Medicine
Gainesville, Florida 32610

INTRODUCTION

In recent years, there has been an explosion in our knowledge of how the hypothalamus regulates reproduction and related behaviors, such as sexual and appetitive behaviors. Isolation, chemical characterization, and the study of the mode of action of a large number of neuropeptides have directly contributed to this rapid unraveling of hypothalamic function. These peptidergic signal molecules are of diverse chemical nature and are produced and released locally in the hypothalamus to exert either an inhibitory or excitatory influence on postsynaptic target sites. In addition, it is apparent that a majority of these newly discovered messenger molecules possess the potent ability to simultaneously influence reproduction and related behaviors. A careful evaluation of their action has further revealed that it is possible to assign these neuropeptides to two broad categories—(i) the core circuitry that normally regulates pituitary gonadotropin release and sexual and appetitive behaviors and (ii) the modulatory circuitry that transmits information from the internal and external environments to the core circuitry.[1,2] It seems that endogenous opioid peptides, neuropeptide Y (NPY), and adrenergic transmitter systems are key components of the core network that regulates the episodic discharge of luteinizing hormone-releasing hormone (LHRH) for the basal and cyclic release of LH from the anterior pituitary.[1-3] All of these neurotransmitters and neuromodulators also participate in the hypothalamic control of sexual and appetitive behaviors.[4-6]

The members of the tachykinin family of peptides are found in hypothalamic sites previously implicated in the control of reproduction, sexual, and appetitive behaviors.[6-16] Therefore, we have undertaken a systematic investigation of the effects of the members of these classes of tachykinins,[17] substance P (SP), neurokinin A (NKA), neuropeptide K (NPK), and neurokinin B (NKB), on pituitary LH secretion and sexual and appetitive behaviors in an attempt to analyze their physiological role in either the core or modulatory network integrating these hypothalamic functions.

[a]This investigation was supported by the following grants from the National Institutes of Health: Nos. HD 08634 (to S. P. Kalra), HD 11362 (to P. S. Kalra), and DK 37273 (to P. S. Kalra and S. P. Kalra).

EFFECTS OF TACHYKININS ON LH RELEASE IN FEMALE RATS

Substance P

The effects of SP on LH release have been examined in many laboratories. McCann and co-workers[18,19] reported that intracerebroventricular injection of SP rapidly stimulated LH release in ovariectomized (ovx) and estrogen-primed ovx rats. Because central administration of anti-SP serum in these rats inhibited LH release, it suggested a physiological excitatory role of SP in the control of LH release in female rats. Furthermore, Ohtsuka *et al.*[20] showed that, in the presence of estrogen, SP stimulated hypothalamic release of LHRH *in vitro*. On the other hand, Kerdelhué *et al.*[21] are of the opinion that SP acts as an inhibitory hypothalamic signal because administration of antiserum to SP at noon on proestrus prematurely evoked LH release and because injection of SP in the lateral cerebroventricle of the proestrous rat blocked the preovulatory discharge of LH. In addition, SP attenuated LHRH-induced LH release from the pituitary. More recently, Parnet *et al.*[22] found no temporal changes in SP concentrations in relevant hypothalamic sites in conjunction with the preovulatory discharge of LH. Because of these conflicting observations, we have reinvestigated the effect of SP on LH release. Our results showed that there was no appreciable change in plasma LH levels after intracerebroventricular administration of either 0.5 or 1.25 n*m* SP in ovx rats (unpublished). Also, SP was ineffective in stimulating LH release in ovarian steroid–primed ovx rats. The reasons for these conflicting findings on the effects of SP on LH release are currently unknown, but these inconsistencies underscore the possibility that the role, if any, of SP in the hypothalamic control of LH release may be minimal.

Neuropeptide K, Neurokinin A, and Neurokinin B

On the other hand, NPK and NKA, the peptides derived from β-preprotachykinin mRNA, exert inhibitory effects on LH release in ovx and ovarian steroid–primed ovx rats.[15-17] Intraventricular injection of NPK (0.5–1.25 n*m*) in ovx rats resulted in a rapid decrease in pituitary LH release. The suppression of plasma LH levels was dose-related and lasted for 4 h. In the ovarian steroid–primed rats, similar low doses of NPK produced little change in plasma LH, but higher doses transiently increased LH release.[23] The potent inhibitory effects of NPK on LH release were also apparent in another experimental design. We studied the effects of NPK on the stimulatory feedback effects of progesterone on LH release in estrogen-primed ovx rats. The results showed that NPK (0.5 or 1.25 n*m*) injected either twice (1300 and 1500 h) or once (1300 h) completely blocked the LH surge induced by progesterone.[24] In contrast, NKA, the carboxy-terminal sequence of NPK, and NKB (the derivative of γ-preprotachykinin mRNA) were completely ineffective in suppressing LH release under these conditions (unpublished).

That the suppressive effects of NPK on LH release are exerted centrally was indicated by our findings that intravenous injections in even higher doses failed to alter LH release in ovx rats. Moreover, the decrease in LH release after intraventricular NPK injection appeared to be due to suppression of LHRH secretion from the hypothalamus. We tested the effects of the NK-1 receptor agonist, [Sar^9,Met(O_2)^{11}]SP, and the NK-2 receptor agonist, [Nle^{10}]NKA(4–10), on basal and evoked LHRH release *in vitro* from the hypothalami of estrogen-primed ovx rats.[25-27] The NK-1 (SP) receptor agonist was ineffective in altering either basal or KCl-induced hypothalamic LHRH release. On the other hand, the NK-2 agonist (10^{-7}–10^{-5} M) significantly decreased the basal output as well as the KCl-evoked efflux of LHRH from the hypothalamus.

Thus, our studies show that, among the members of the tachykinin family so far tested, NPK is most active in suppressing LH release in ovx and ovarian steroid–primed ovx rats. Furthermore, we propose that NPK efferents in the hypothalamus exert an inhibitory influence on LHRH secretion, an action presumably mediated, in part, by activation of NK-2 receptor subtypes in the vicinity of the LHRH network in the hypothalamus.

EFFECTS OF TACHYKININS ON LH RELEASE IN MALE RATS

Encouraged by the findings that NPK suppressed LH release in a reliable fashion in female rats, we investigated the effects of NPK and NKA on LH release in male rats. As in female rats, we observed that intraventricular injection of NPK in castrated male rats readily inhibited LH release; both the duration and magnitude of LH suppression were similar in both sexes (unpublished). However, intraventricular injection of NKA also suppressed LH release in orchidectomized rats. Both the magnitude and duration of LH suppression were relatively smaller after NKA than after NPK administration. On the other hand, the effects of NPK and NKA on LH release in intact male rats were different. Doses of NPK and NKA that readily inhibited LH release in castrated rats stimulated LH release in intact male rats. Plasma LH in these rats rose within 10 min after NPK and NKA administration and remained elevated for up to 30 min (unpublished).

The unexpected revelation that NPK and NKA exert different effects on LH release in intact and castrated male rats prompted us to explore the possibility that tachykinins may act at two sites—one in the hypothalamus to inhibit LHRH release and the other at the level of pituitary gonadotrophs to stimulate LH release. It is well known that, after intraventricular injection, these peptides can reach the anterior pituitary via the hypophyseal portal veins. To test this possibility, we assessed the effects of NPK and NKA on LH release in vitro from hemipituitaries of intact male rats. Interestingly, NPK (1 μM) significantly stimulated LH release from the hemipituitaries of intact male rats. Seemingly then, tachykinins have the ability to affect LH release directly from the pituitary and we can argue that this action may partly be responsible for stimulation of LH release after intraventricular administration of NPK and NKA in intact rats. Brown et al.[12] failed to detect NPK in the anterior pituitary. Therefore, the physiological significance of the stimulatory effects of NPK on LH release from the pituitaries of male rats remains to be ascertained. However, because the pituitary contains NKA,[12] it is possible to suggest that stimulation of LH release by NPK from the pituitaries may be a result of NKA (NK-2) receptor activation.

In summary, our studies show that the products of β-preprotachykinin mRNA, NPK and NKA, exert profound effects on the LH release in both sexes and that NPK appears to be relatively more effective than NKA in suppressing LH release. Our preliminary studies show that NPK and NKA preferentially interact with NK-2 tachykinin receptor subtypes in the hypothalamus to inhibit LHRH release, and the relative differences in effectiveness of NPK and NKA may be attributed to differences either in the rate of metabolism of the two peptides or in the binding to tachykinin receptors.

EFFECTS OF TACHYKININS ON SEX BEHAVIOR

There is evidence to suggest that SP facilitates copulatory behavior in male rats and lordosis in female rats.[28,29] In view of our findings that NPK is an inhibitory peptidergic system in the hypothalamus, we studied the effects of NPK administration on copulatory behavior of sexually active male rats (unpublished). These studies showed that injection of 0.125 n*m* NPK into the third ventricle slightly increased the intromission latency, but the other parameters of copulatory behavior were unaffected. However, 0.5 n*m* NPK markedly disrupted all parameters of copulatory behavior. In fact, a majority of sexually active males displayed no interest when sexually receptive female rats were introduced into the arena. However, there was no evidence of locomotor impairment in these rats. That suppression of copulatory behavior by NPK in sexually active males is mediated centrally was shown by findings that similar (0.5 n*m*) or higher (3.14 n*m*) doses of NPK intraperitoneally produced no deficit in copulatory behavior. In fact, at high doses (3.14 n*m*), a slight enhancement in sexual performance, as indicated by a significant decrease in ejaculatory latency and postejaculatory interval, was evident in these rats.

EFFECTS OF TACHYKININS ON FEEDING BEHAVIOR

There are many clinical reports that suggest that eating disorders are often associated with impaired or subnormal reproductive functions. The concurrency of these two centrally mediated symptoms can often be seen in obesity, in anorexia nervosa, and in patients with diabetes. We have proposed that either a deficit or an inappropriate release and action of key neurochemical signals in the hypothalamus may underlie the close association of eating disorders and reproductive failure.[1,2,4] With this in mind and with the fact that NPK exerted profound effects on pituitary gonadotrophs, we studied the effect of NPK on feeding behavior in rats.[30] We observed that neither peripheral nor central injections of NPK stimulated feeding in male and female rats. On the other hand, NPK not only suppressed feeding in rats in three experimental paradigms, but intraperitoneal injections were more effective than central ones in decreasing food intake. In the first series of experiments in food-deprived rats, intraperitoneal injection of NPK (1.25 and 3.14 n*m*) significantly delayed the onset of feeding and decreased the cumulative 1 and 2 h food intake in a dose-related fashion. Moreover, the suppressive effects were specific to feeding because other ingestive behaviors, such as drinking, were not affected by NPK. Interestingly, NKA was completely ineffective in these food-deprived rats.

The effect of NPK on the normal dark-phase feeding behavior was assessed in the second series of experiments. As seen in food-deprived rats, intraperitoneal injection of NPK 15 min before lights off delayed the onset of ingestive behavior and the cumulative 1 and 2 h food intake was significantly decreased. In the third series of experiments, the effects of NPK on NPY-induced feeding were evaluated. Once again, we observed that intraperitoneal, and not central, injection of NPK (0.5–3.4 n*m*) significantly decreased feeding evoked by intraventricular NPY in satiated rats.

The evidence that intraperitoneal injections of NPK suppressed normal feeding during the dark phase of the daily light-dark cycle and feeding evoked by NPY, as well as following food-deprivation, strongly suggests that NPK may primarily be a peripheral signal capable of modulating feeding behavior in the rat. The reasons why central NPK is less effective than peripherally administered NPK are not yet known. However, it is noteworthy that two known satiety peptides, cholecystokinin and bombesin, are more effective in suppressing feeding when administered intraperitoneally than when administered into the cerebral ventricles. Presumably, NPK acts like other satiety-producing peripheral peptidergic signals and, therefore, these observations raise the possibility that some of the clinical symptoms in the gastrointestinal tract of carcinoid patients may be mediated by the reportedly high circulating NPK concentrations in these patients.

SUMMARY

Our investigations of the four tachykinins tested have shown that NPK characteristically evoked a spectrum of biological effects in male and female rats. NPK suppressed pituitary LH release by inhibiting the release of hypothalamic LHRH, presumably by activation of NK-2 tachykinin receptor subtypes. However, NPK may also act at the level of gonadotrophs to stimulate LH release in male rats. Central injection of NPK rapidly disrupted copulatory behavior in sexually active male rats. NPK also suppressed feeding, but, in this case, peripheral injections were more effective than central injections. Taken together, these observations strongly imply that NPK may be an inhibitory messenger molecule in the hypothalamic control of reproduction, sexual, and feeding behaviors.

ACKNOWLEDGMENT

We thank Sally McDonell for secretarial assistance.

REFERENCES

1. KALRA, S. P. 1986. Neural circuitry involved in control of LHRH secretion: a model for the preovulatory LH release. *In* Frontiers in Neuroendocrinology. Volume 9. W. F. Ganong & L. Martini, Eds.: 31–75. Raven Press. New York.
2. KALRA, S. P., L. G. ALLEN, J. T. CLARK, W. R. CROWLEY & P. S. KALRA. 1986. Neuropeptide Y—an integrator of reproductive and appetitive functions. *In* Neural and Endocrine Peptides and Receptors. T. W. Moody, Ed.: 353–366. Plenum. New York.
3. KALRA, S. P., P. S. KALRA, A. SAHU, L. G. ALLEN & W. R. CROWLEY. 1987. The steroid-neuropeptide connection in the control of LHRH secretion. *In* Regulation of Ovarian and Testicular Function. V. B. Mahesh, D. S. Dhindsa, E. Anderson & S. P. Kalra, Eds.: 65–84. Plenum. New York.
4. KALRA, S. P., J. T. CLARK & P. S. KALRA. 1988. The role of adrenergic and neuropeptidergic systems in the regulation of male sexual behavior. *In* Andrology and Human Reproduction. Vol. 47 (Serono Symposia). A. Negro-Vilar, A. Isidori, J. Paulson, R. Abdelmassih & M. P. P. de Castro, Eds.: 203–212. Raven Press. New York.
5. MORLEY, J. E. 1987. Neuropeptide regulation of appetite and weight. Endocr. Rev. **8:** 256–287.
6. LEIBOWITZ, S. F. 1980. Neurochemical systems of the hypothalamus: control of feeding and drinking behavior and water-electrolyte excretion. *In* Handbook of the Hypothalamus. Vol. 3 (Part A). P. Morgane & J. Panksepp, Eds.: 299–437. Dekker. New York.
7. SIMMERLY, R. B. & L. W. SWANSON. 1987. The distribution of neurotransmitter-specific cells and fibers in the anteroventral periventricular nucleus: implications of control of gonadotropin secretion in the rat. Brain Res. **400:** 11–34.
8. YAMANO, M., S. INAGAKI, S. KITO & M. TOHYAMA. 1986. A substance P–containing

pathway from the hypothalamic ventromedial nucleus to the medial preoptic area of the rat: an immunohistochemical analysis. Neuroscience **18:** 395–402.

9. LUNGDAHL, A., T. HÖKFELT & G. NILSSON. 1978. Distribution of substance P–like immunoreactivity in the central nervous system of the rat. I. Cell bodies and nerve terminals. Neuroscience **3:** 861–943.

10. MIKKELSEN, J. D., P. J. LARSEN, M. MOLLER, H. VILHARDT & T. SOERMARK. 1989. Substance P in the median eminence and pituitary of the rat: demonstration of immunoreactive fibers and specific binding sites. Neuroendocrinology **50:** 100–108.

11. TATEMOTO, K., J. M. LUNDBERG, H. JORNVALL & V. MUTT. 1985. Neuropeptide K: isolation, structure, and biological activities of a novel brain tachykinin. Biochem. Biophys. Res. Commun. **128:** 947–953.

12. BROWN, E. A., R. E. HARLAN & J. E. KRAUSE. 1990. Gonadal steroid regulation of substance P (SP) and SP-encoding messenger ribonucleic acid in the rat anterior pituitary and hypothalamus. Endocrinology **126:** 330–340.

13. VALENTINO, K. L., K. TATEMOTO, J. HUNTER & J. D. BARCHAS. 1986. Distribution of neuropeptide K–immunoreactivity in the rat central nervous system. Peptides **7:** 1043–1059.

14. MEISTER, B., S. CECCATELLI, T. HÖKFELT, N. E. ANDEN, M. ANDEN & E. THEODORSSON. 1989. Neurotransmitters, neuropeptides, and binding sites in the rat mediobasal hypothalamus: effects of monosodium glutamate (MSG) lesions. Exp. Brain Res. **76:** 343–368.

15. HARLAN, R. E., M. M. GARCIA & J. E. KRAUSE. 1989. Cellular localization of substance P– and neurokinin A–encoding preprotachykinin mRNA in the female rat brain. J. Comp. Neurol. **287:** 179–212.

16. WARDEN, M. K. & W. S. YOUNG, JR. 1988. Distribution of cells containing mRNA's encoding substance P and neurokinin B in the rat central nervous system. J. Comp. Neurol. **272:** 90–113.

17. HELKE, C. J., J. E. KRAUSE, P. W. MANTYH, R. COUTURE & M. J. BANNON. 1990. Diversity in mammalian tachykinin peptidergic neurons: multiple peptides, receptors, and regulatory mechanisms. FASEB J. **4:** 1607–1615.

18. VIJAYAN, E. & S. M. McCANN. 1979. *In vivo* and *in vitro* effects of substance P and neurotensin on gonadotropin and prolactin release. Endocrinology **105:** 64–68.

19. ARISAWA, M., L. DEPALATIS, R. HO, G. SNYDER, W. H. YU, G. PAN & S. M. McCANN. 1990. Stimulatory role of substance P on gonadotropin release in ovariectomized rats. Neuroendocrinology **51:** 523–529.

20. OHTSUKA, S., A. MIYAKE, T. NISHIZAKI, K. TASAKA, T. AONO & B. TANIZAWA. 1987. Substance P stimulates gonadotropin releasing hormone release from rat hypothalamus *in vitro* with involvement of oestrogen. Acta Endocrinol. **115:** 247–252.

21. KERDELHUÉ, B., M. VALENA & Y. LANGLOIS. 1987. Stimulation de la secretion de la LH et de la FSH hypophysaires apres re immunoneutralisation de la P endogene, chex la ratle cyclique. C. R. Acad. Sci. Ser. D (Paris) **286:** 977–979.

22. PARNET, P., V. LENOIR, M. PALKOVITS & B. KERDELHUÉ. 1990. Estrous cycle variations in gonadotropin-releasing hormone, substance P, and β-endorphin contents in the median eminence, the arcuate nucleus, and the preoptic nucleus in the rat: a detailed analysis of proestrous changes. J. Neuroendocrinol. **2:** 291–296.

23. SAHU, A., W. R. CROWLEY, K. TATEMOTO, A. BALASUBRAMANIAM & S. P. KALRA. 1987. Effects of neuropeptide Y, NPY analog (norleucine[4]-NPY), galanin, and neuropeptide K on LH release in ovariectomized (ovx) and ovx estrogen progesterone–treated rats. Peptides **8:** 921–926.

24. KALRA, S. P., M. G. DUBE & A. SAHU. 1989. Neuropeptide K inhibits progesterone-induced LH surge in estrogen-primed ovariectomized rats. Annu. Meet. Soc. Neurosci. (October 29 to November 3, 1989; Phoenix, Arizona) **15:** 1339.

25. SAFFROY, M., J. C. BEAUJOUAN, Y. TORRENS, J. BESSEYRE, L. BERGSTROM & J. GLOWINSKI. 1988. Localization of tachykinin binding sites (NK$_1$, NK$_2$, and NK$_3$ ligands) in the rat brain. Peptides **9:** 227–241.

26. QUIRION, R. & T-V. DAM. 1988. Multiple neurokinin receptors: recent developments. Regulat. Peptides **22:** 18–24.

27. DRAPEAU, G., P. D'ORLEANS-JUSTE, S. DION, N-E. RHALEB, N. ROUISSI & D. REGOLI. 1987. Selective agonists for substance P and neurokinin receptors. Neuropeptides **10:** 43–54.
28. DORNAN, W., C. W. MALSBURY & R. B. PENNY. 1987. Facilitation of lordosis by injection of substance P into the midbrain central gray. Neuroendocrinology **45:** 498–506.
29. DORNAN, W. A. & C. W. MALSBURY. 1989. Neuropeptides and male sexual behavior. Neurosci. Biobehav. Rev. **13:** 1–15.
30. SAHU, A., P. S. KALRA, M. G. DUBE & S. P. KALRA. 1988. Neuropeptide K suppresses feeding in the rat. Regulat. Peptides **23:** 135–143.

Significance of Substance P– and Enkephalin–Peptide Systems in the Male Genital Tract[a]

B. V. RAMA SASTRY, V. E. JANSON, AND L. K. OWENS

Departments of Pharmacology and Anesthesiology
Vanderbilt University School of Medicine
Nashville, Tennessee 37232-6600

INTRODUCTION

There is considerable evidence that substance P and enkephalins interact with presynaptic receptors and influence the neuronal release of chemical transmitters. Mechanisms of these effects of substance P and enkephalins are not well delineated. However, there is some evidence that both substance P and enkephalins influence the neuronal release of the primary chemical transmitters, namely, acetylcholine,[1-6] norepinephrine,[7,8] and dopamine.[8,9] There are also similarities in the distribution of substance P and methionine enkephalin in the central and peripheral nervous systems. Substance P and methionine enkephalin exhibit opposing effects on nociception, on uptake of Ca^{++} ions by the nervous tissue, on release of acetylcholine and modulation of cholinergic function, and on release of norepinephrine and modulation of adrenergic function. Peripheral branches of certain primary afferent neurons liberate substance P as a neurotransmitter in autonomic postganglionic cells and cause long-lasting increases in the excitability of ganglion cells to the primary transmitter, acetylcholine.[10]

Furthermore, the male genital system, its glands (seminal vesicles, prostate, epididymis), and plexi (vesicle, prostatic, cavernous) have rich autonomic and sensory or afferent innervation.[11] The nerves of the vas deferens and seminal vesicles are derived chiefly from the hypogastric and vesicle plexi. Those derived from the hypogastric plexus have both sympathetic and afferent components. The nerves derived from the vesicle plexus are mainly parasympathetic with few sympathetic fibers. The preganglionic parasympathetic fibers innervating the vas deferens as well as the seminal vesicles are components of the pelvic nerve. The chemical transmission at various synapses in the plexi of the male genital system may be modulated by substance P and enkephalins. Stimuli for reflex neural pathways for erection, emission, ejaculation, orgasm, and detumescence are coordinated through these plexi. Erection and glandular secretions are regulated by cholinergic impulses, whereas emission and ejaculation seem to be regulated by adrenergic impulses.[12] The excitation and the detumescence of the orgasmic experience are also modified by the neuromodulators of the autonomic and sensory nervous systems. In order to understand the modulation of chemical transmission in the male reproductive tract, the rat epididymis, prostate gland, seminal vesicles, and spermatozoa as well as human seminal plasma and spermatozoa were analyzed for substance P, methionine enkephalin, and leucine enkephalin by selective radioimmunoassays. The effects of substance

[a]This work was supported by grants from the USPHS-NIH (No. HD 10607) and the Council for Tobacco Research (U.S.A.), Incorporated.

P and enkephalins and their antagonists on human sperm motility and on chemical transmission in the rat vas deferens were determined.

METHODS

Extraction of Peptides from Spermatozoa, Seminal Plasma, and Tissues of Accessory Sex Glands

The collection of human ejaculates, the separation and washing of spermatozoa, the source of bull spermatozoa, and the collection of rat epididymal spermatozoa have been described in our previous publications.[13,14] Seminal vesicles and prostate glands were dissected from rats. All of these tissues were extracted for peptides by procedures described previously.[15–17] The final preparations were waxy residues, which were stored at -20 °C for radioimmunoassays.

Radioimmunoassays for Substance P and Enkephalins

Standard substance P, methionine enkephalin, leucine enkephalin, and β-endorphin were purchased from commercial sources. Rabbit anti–substance P, anti-met-enkephalin, anti-leu-enkephalin, anti-β-endorphin, [^{125}I]methionine enkephalin, [^{125}I]-leucine enkephalin, [^{125}I]β-endorphin, and [^{125}I]substance P were supplied by the Immuno Nuclear Corporation or the Incstar Corporation (Stillwater, Minnesota). Each antibody has 100% cross-reactivity with its corresponding antigen-peptide and negligible cross-reactivity with other peptides. For example, anti–substance P has 100% cross-reactivity with standard substance P and $<0.002\%$ cross-reactivity with other mammalian (neurokinin A, neurokinin B) and nonmammalian (eledoisin, physalaemin) tachykinins that are structurally related to substance P. Similarly, the antibody of methionine enkephalin has cross-reactivity of 100% with standard methionine enkephalin, 1.6% with leucine enkephalin, and 0.002% with substance P and β-endorphin.

Details of the radioimmunoassays for substance P and enkephalins were described by several authors.[18–20] The essential features of these assays and their application to tissue extracts were described in references 16 and 17.

Pharmacological Activities of Substance P and Enkephalins on the Rat Vas Deferens

The biological activities of the tissue extracts of the male reproductive tract were characterized using rat vas deferens that was subjected to electrical field stimulation by electrodes. The conditions of the assay using rat vas deferens were similar to those used by Henderson et al.[21] with mouse vas deferens. This preparation was sensitive to substance P as well as to opioid peptides. In this preparation, substance P enhanced the contraction height of responses to norepinephrine, which was released during intramural stimulation. Enkephalins depressed the contraction heights, an effect opposite to that of substance P. Therefore, the nature of the antagonism of substance P and leucine enkephalin on adrenergic transmission in the rat vas deferens was investigated.

Effects of Substance P and Other Peptides on the Motile Behavior of Human Spermatozoa

The motile behavior and the motility index of human spermatozoa in the presence and absence of (a) substance P and its antagonists and (b) enkephalins and their antagonists were determined according to the methods described in references 14 and 22. Each human ejaculate was divided into samples of 0.4 mL and placed in plastic tubes. Each tube contained about 56–82 million sperm cells. Test substances were dissolved in phosphate buffered saline (276 mOsM, pH 7.4). Solutions (0.1 mL) containing the test substances were added to the tubes containing the sperm samples. Equal volumes of phosphate buffered saline were added to the control tubes. The tubes were kept at laboratory temperature. At various times, the motility index of each sperm sample was determined. One drop of each sperm sample (100–200 cells) was placed on a microscope slide and the motile behavior of the spermatozoa was observed using an inverted research microscope equipped with a turret condenser

TABLE 1. Immunoreactivities for Substance P and Enkephalins[a]

Species and Tissue	Substance P	Methionine Enkephalin	Leucine Enkephalin	β-Endorphin
Human[b]				
spermatozoa	2145 ± 661	538 ± 174	1080 ± 650	570 ± 290
seminal plasma	572 ± 60	2228 ± 63	$>9000^d$	—[d]
Bull[c]				
spermatozoa	114 ± 80	899 ± 124	$>3728^d$	390 ± 190
Rat[b]				
spermatozoa	932 ± 33	244 ± 80	166 ± 96	68 ± 68
cauda epididymis	$>15,000$	1300 ± 191	2467 ± 814	1585 ± 486
seminal vesicles	777 ± 113	1360 ± 121	9663 ± 1508	56 ± 35
prostate	5379 ± 1793	976 ± 307	3246 ± 1188	1176 ± 337

[a]All values are expressed as pg/mg protein and are means ± SE from 3–4 observations.
[b]Quoted from reference 17.
[c]Unpublished observations from our laboratory.
[d]Exact values could not be reported due to interfering substances.

(for long working distance) and a closed circuit TV system. Observations of the behavior of the spermatozoa were made by two or three individuals watching the TV monitor simultaneously and were graded by a double-blind technique. Two variables were measured for each sperm sample: (1) the percentage of spermatozoa showing movement and (2) the average degree of motility estimated on a scale of 0 to 4. Grades were designated to sperm samples showing the following motility patterns: 0 for spermatozoa standing still; 1 for movement in place; 2 for circular movement or very sluggish movement across the field; 3 for progressive movement with wide, slow, whiplash action of the tails; and 4 for rapid progressive movement with rapid whiplash action of the tails. To determine the motility index, the percentage of spermatozoa showing motility in each sample was multiplied by the square of the value for the degree of motility. Further details have been described in references 14 and 22.

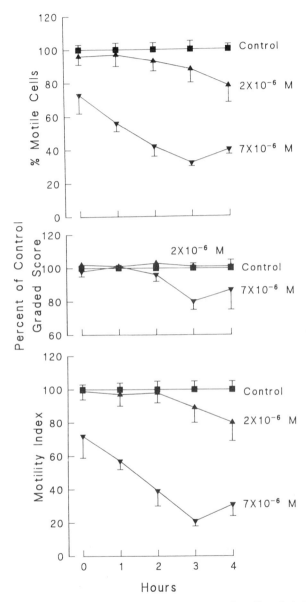

FIGURE 1. Influence of substance P (SP) on the percentage of motile cells in human sperm samples, graded score, and motility index as a function of time. Each point is expressed as a percentage of its corresponding control. Each point and vertical bar represents a mean ± SE from eight values.

RESULTS

Occurrence of Substance P and Opioid Peptides in the Male Genital Tract

The occurrence of substance P, methionine enkephalin, leucine enkephalin, and β-endorphin in tissues of the mammalian genital tract was demonstrated by sensitive

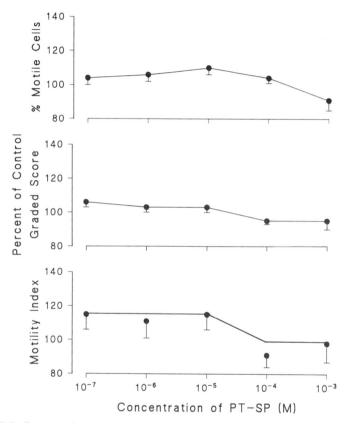

FIGURE 2. Concentration-response curves for the effects of [D-Pro^2,D-Trp^{7,9}]–substance P (PT-SP) on motile cells, graded score, and motility index of human sperm. PT-SP was added to the sperm sample and the parameters were measured at the end of four hours of contact time. All values are expressed as percentages of the corresponding controls. Each point and vertical bar represents a mean ± SE from 12–15 observations.

radioimmunoassays (TABLE 1). The level of substance P was about three times higher in human spermatozoa than in seminal plasma. In contrast, enkephalin levels were higher in human seminal plasma than in spermatozoa. This raises a question about the glandular source that contributes to high levels of enkephalins in seminal plasma. To understand this source, the cauda epididymis, seminal vesicles, and prostate glands from rats were extracted for bioactive peptides and were analyzed for substance P and enkephalins. Cauda epididymis and prostate gland contained higher levels of substance P than seminal vesicles, whereas seminal vesicles contained higher levels of enkephalins than cauda epididymis and prostate gland. The predominant enkephalin in human seminal plasma is leucine enkephalin.

Effects of Substance P and Substance P Antagonists on Human Sperm Motility

Exogenous substance P exhibited a biphasic effect on sperm motility. It caused a small increase (15–18%) in the motility index at very low concentrations (4×10^{-7} M). The predominant effect of exogenous substance P was depression of the motility index (FIGURE 1) at concentrations higher than 10^{-6} M ($EC_{50} = 2.5 \times 10^{-6}$ M) after a

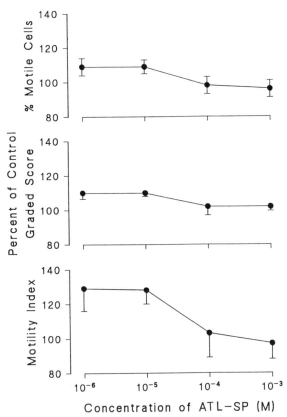

FIGURE 3. Concentration-response curves for the effects of [D-Arg,D-Trp[7,9],Leu[11]]–substance P (ATL-SP, spantide) on motile cells, graded score, and motility index of human sperm. ATL-SP was added to the sperm sample and the readings were taken after four hours of contact time of the sperm sample with the antagonist. All values are expressed as percentages of the corresponding controls. Each point and vertical bar represents a mean ± SE from 12–15 observations.

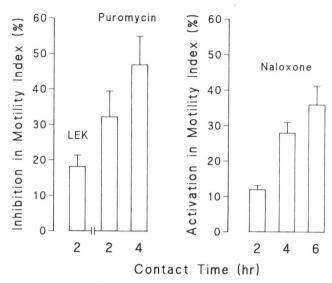

FIGURE 4. Changes in the motility index of human spermatozoa in the presence of exogenous leucine enkephalin (LEK, 100 μM), puromycin (100 μM), and naloxone (11 μM). The motility index was determined at 2, 4, or 6 hours after the pharmacological agent was added to the sperm sample. The degree of inhibition or activation of the motility index by each pharmacological agent was expressed as a percentage of the control value without the addition of the pharmacological agent to the sperm sample. Each point and vertical bar represents a mean ± SE from 6–14 observations. This figure is based on data reported in reference 23.

contact time of four hours. This decrease in motility index was due to decreases both in the percentage of motile cells and in the graded score for sperm motility.

The effects of two substance P antagonists, [D-Pro^2,D-Trp^{7,9}]–substance P (PT-SP) and [D-Arg,D-Trp^{7,9},Leu^{11}]–substance P (ATL-SP, spantide), were tested on human sperm motility. Both antagonists sustained the motility index at 100% or higher for four hours (FIGURES 2 and 3). In control samples, without antagonists, the motility index decreased from 100% to 70%. The percentage of motile cells, the graded score, and the motility index were higher in sperm samples treated with antagonists than in untreated samples for four hours. Concentrations of antagonists lower than 10^{-5} M maintained the motility index at a higher level than the corresponding controls.

Effects of Exogenous Enkephalins, Aminopeptidase Inhibitor, and Opiate Receptor Antagonist on Sperm Motility

Exogenous leucine enkephalin (100 μM) lowered the motility index of human sperm by 18% in two hours (FIGURE 4). Puromycin (100 μM), a strong inhibitor of aminopeptidase, caused a higher depression in the motility index (32%) than exogenous leucine enkephalin in two hours. Puromycin exhibited a sparing effect on endogenous enkephalins that depressed the motility index. Naloxone (11 μM), an opiate receptor antagonist, increased the motility index by 12%. The degree of this activation of the motility index by naloxone increased to 36% by increasing the

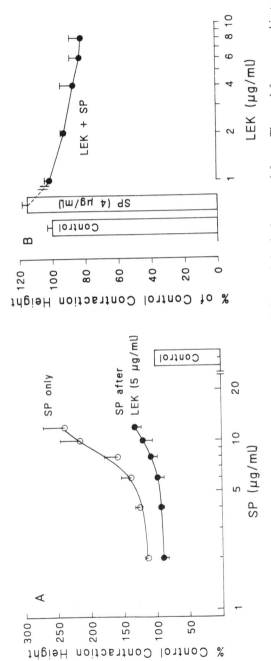

FIGURE 5. Effects of substance P (SP) and leucine enkephalin (LEK) on chemical transmission in the rat vas deferens. The vas deferens was subjected to electrical field stimulation at 7 pulses/min. All contraction heights were expressed as a percent of the control contraction height set at 100. Each point and vertical bar represents a mean ± SE from six observations. A: Concentration-response relationships for the facilitation of transmission by SP in the absence (top curve) and presence of LEK (5 μg/mL, lower curve). B: Concentration-response curves for the inhibition of chemical transmission by LEK. The preparation was challenged with SP (4 μg/mL). The facilitation of chemical transmission was antagonized by cumulatively increasing the concentration of LEK in the bath.

contact time to six hours. This means that naloxone antagonized the effects of endogenous enkephalins and other opiate peptides at an opiate receptor on spermatozoa.

Effects of Substance P and Enkephalins on the Electrically Stimulated Rat Vas Deferens

Exogenous substance P (2.0–20 μg/mL) increased the electrically stimulated contraction heights of the rat vas deferens. Increasing concentrations of substance P increased the contraction height (FIGURE 5A). Leucine enkephalin (5 μg/mL) lowered the concentration-response curve of substance P, indicating that it antagonized substance P in a noncompetitive manner. The contraction height elicited by

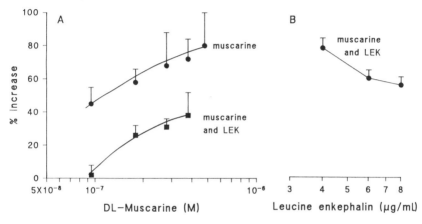

FIGURE 6. Influence of DL-muscarine and leucine enkephalin (LEK) on chemical transmission in the rat vas deferens that was subjected to field electrical stimulation (7 pulses/min). Each point is a mean ± SE from six values. The ordinate represents the percent increase in the contraction height over the control. A: Concentration-response curve for muscarine (6×10^{-8}– 7×10^{-7} M) alone (top curve) and for muscarine in the presence of LEK (10 μg/mL, lower curve). B: The chemical transmission was facilitated by a maximal dose of DL-muscarine (2.86×10^{-7} M). The height of contraction was reduced by adding cumulative doses of LEK in the presence of DL-muscarine.

substance P (4 μg/mL) was antagonized by leucine enkephalin (1.0–10 μg/mL) in a concentration-dependent manner (FIGURE 5B). Electrical stimulation released norepinephrine from the adrenergic nerve endings, causing contraction of the muscle. Thus, these observations indicate that substance P facilitates the adrenergic transmission, whereas enkephalins inhibit it.

Effects of Muscarine and Leucine Enkephalin on Adrenergic Transmission in the Rat Vas Deferens

Muscarine (10^{-7}–10^{-6} M) increased the electrically stimulated contraction heights of the rat vas deferens in a concentration-dependent manner (FIGURE 6A). The concentration-response curve was lowered by leucine enkephalin (10 μg/mL). The increased contraction height elicited by 2.86×10^{-7} M muscarine was lowered by leucine enkephalin (4–8 µg/mL) in a concentration-dependent manner (FIGURE 6B). The increase in contraction height elicited by muscarine was blocked by atropine (1 µM), but atropine did not affect the contraction heights elicited by electrical stimulation alone. These observations suggest that there are muscarinic receptors on the adrenergic nerves of the vas deferens and that cholinergic agonists facilitate adrenergic transmission in this tissue. The facilitation of adrenergic transmission by cholinergic agonists in the vas deferens was also antagonized by leucine enkephalin in a noncompetitive manner.

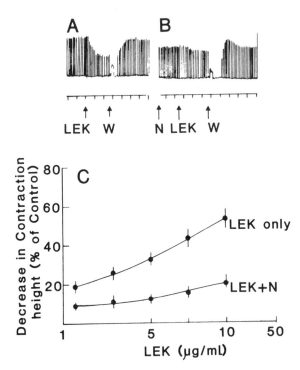

FIGURE 7. Effect of leucine enkephalin (LEK) and naloxone (N) on chemical transmission in the rat vas deferens that was subjected to electrical stimulation (7 pulses/min). Each point is a mean ± SE from six values. A: LEK (10 mg/mL) reduced contraction height (Δtension, 0.5 g) by about 50%, which was reversed by washing (W) the tissue. B: Naloxone (N, 60 nM) blocked the effect of LEK to inhibit chemical transmission. After washing (W), the tissue responded normally to electrical stimulation. C: Concentration-response curves of LEK alone (top curve) and of LEK in the presence of naloxone (N, 100 nM, lower curve). Naloxone lowered the whole concentration-response curve of LEK.

Effects of Leucine Enkephalin and Naloxone on the Rat Vas Deferens

Leucine enkephalin (10 µg/mL) decreased the contraction height (Δtension, 0.5 g) elicited by the stimulation of the rat vas deferens (FIGURE 7A). This effect was reversible by washing the tissue. Naloxone (100 nM) blocked the effect of leucine enkephalin on this tissue (FIGURE 7B). The decrease in the electrically induced contraction height of the rat vas deferens was dependent on the concentration of leucine enkephalin (FIGURE 7C). Naloxone (100 nM) lowered the whole concentration-response curve of leucine enkephalin, indicating noncompetitive antagonism. These observations indicate that leucine enkephalin down-regulates adrenergic transmission in the vas deferens.

DISCUSSION

The present study demonstrates that (a) substance P and enkephalins occur in human, bull, and rat spermatozoa, as well as in human seminal plasma and several accessory sex glands (prostate, seminal vesicles, and cauda epididymis); (b) they influence sperm motility in a concentration-dependent manner; and (c) they modify chemical transmission in the vas deferens.

The concentration of substance P (pg/mg protein) in seminal plasma was considerably higher than that reported for human peripheral plasma.[24] Similarly, the concentrations of enkephalins and β-endorphin were higher in seminal plasma than in peripheral plasma.[25] The levels of substance P and enkephalins in cauda epididymis, prostate, and seminal vesicles were higher than in peripheral plasma. These observations suggest that accessory sex glands are additional sources for these peptides. Developing mouse testicular germ cells were found to express a proenkephalin gene.[26]

Spermatozoa contain about equal levels of substance P and total opioid peptides, whereas seminal plasma contains higher levels of enkephalins than substance P. The prostate gland and cauda epididymis contain higher levels of substance P than enkephalins, whereas seminal vesicles contain higher levels of enkephalins than substance P. In human ejaculates, the early fractions contain secretions of the prostate gland, whereas later fractions contain secretions of the seminal vesicles. In human split ejaculates, the early fractions have a higher motility index than the later fractions. Prostatic secretions increase the motility of human sperm suspensions, whereas vesicle fluids decrease the sperm motility.[27] These observations agree with the effects of substance P and enkephalins on motility. Very low concentrations of substance P increased sperm motility,[28] whereas enkephalins decreased sperm motility. It can therefore be assumed that the ratio of the concentrations of substance P–like and enkephalin-like peptides is important for the motility and viability of ejaculated spermatozoa.

The ratio between substance P–like and enkephalin-like peptides may play a role in maintaining Ca^{++} homeostasis in ejaculated spermatozoa. Free Ca^{++} ions are required for several cellular functions. However, excess accumulation of free Ca^{++} is deleterious to all cells. Substance P increased Ca^{++} uptake in the nerve cell, whereas methionine enkephalin decreased Ca^{++} uptake to maintain the homeostasis of the cell and the release of acetylcholine.[1] It is possible that substance P has an activating influence, whereas enkephalins have a retarding effect on Ca^{++} influx into the sperm cell. The endogenous concentrations of substance P and enkephalins in spermatozoa and seminal plasma are well balanced to maintain Ca^{++} homeostasis and, therefore, sperm function. Alteration of these concentrations by the addition of exogenous substance P or enkephalins may disturb this homeostasis. Several observations support this conclusion: (a) aging human sperm for four hours increased the total Ca^{++} in sperm cells and decreased the motility index; (b) the decrease in the motility index was retarded by the Ca^{++} antagonist, verapamil, and by the Ca^{++} chelating agent, Na_2EDTA;[29] (c) exogenous leucine enkephalin decreased the motility index, whereas the leucine enkephalin antagonist, naloxone, prevented a fall in the motility index; (d) concentrations of substance P higher than 2.5×10^{-6} M depressed the motility index, whereas substance P antagonists maintained the motility index for four hours; (e) there were no significant differences between the molar concentrations of opioid peptides and substance P in spermatozoa. However, the concentration of enkephalins in seminal plasma was 45–47 times higher than that of substance P. This means that excess Ca^{++} uptake by spermatozoa was prevented by relatively high concentrations of enkephalins in seminal plasma. These observations suggest that substance P antagonists antagonized both the endogenous substance P in semen and the influx of extracellular Ca^{++} into spermatozoa and thereby prevented deleterious effects of excess intracellular Ca^{++} and maintained the motility index. Substance P may play other roles in the male genital system as well. It may play a role in the maturation of spermatozoa because it occurs in high concentrations in the epididymis, the site of sperm maturation.

Immunohistochemical studies of the vas deferens and seminal vesicles of several species showed the presence of nerve fibers containing substance P.[30] These techniques demonstrated the presence of met- and leu-enkephalin-containing fibers in the human prostate and seminal vesicles.[31] Rat testes,[32] prostates, and seminal vesicles were shown to contain β-endorphin-like peptides. All of these observations support the present findings of the occurrence of substance P and various opioid peptides in the male reproductive tract.

Substance P facilitated, whereas enkephalins inhibited adrenergic transmission in the rat vas deferens. Cholinergic agonists also facilitated adrenergic transmission in this tissue. The process of ejaculation can be divided into two distinct phases—an emission phase and an ejaculatory phase.[33] The emission phase consists of the movement of semen into the posterior urethra and the ejaculation phase involves the forceful expulsion of semen out of the penis. The vas deferens plays an important role in both phases. During the emission phase, there is active contraction of the vas deferens from the proximal to the distal end, which forces the contents toward the urethra. Human distal cauda epididymis and vas deferens have rich adrenergic innervation and large smooth muscle cells, whereas most of the epididymis has cholinergic innervation and small smooth muscle cells.[34] In the epididymis, continuous peristaltic contractions occur that move seminal fluid into the cauda and vas deferens. No peristalsis is present in the vas deferens. Contraction of the vas deferens smooth muscle leads to movement of the fluid into the posterior urethra. Adrenergic stimulation of the vas deferens is modulated by substance P and enkephalins. High levels of substance P secretions into the epididymal fluid may facilitate adrenergic stimulation of the vas deferens. Ejaculation is closely tied to emission. During the emission phase, pressure slowly builds up in the posterior urethra until it reaches a point at which rhythmic contractions of the periurethral and perineal musculature occur spontaneously, leading to the forceful expulsion of semen from the penis and resulting in an orgasmic experience.

The underlying mechanisms of erection and detumescence are not known. However, it is well accepted that erection is a vascular phenomenon and occurs after dilation of penile arteries. Vasodilation is brought about by two neuronal inputs— parasympathetic stimulation and adrenergic vasodilatory stimulation. These inputs act synergistically and are antagonized by vasoconstrictor adrenergic input. Enkephalins are known to inhibit both cholinergic and adrenergic chemical transmission. A question arises as to whether high levels of enkephalins in the later half of the ejaculates contribute to the termination of cholinergic and/or adrenergic vasodilatory stimuli to penile arteries and thereby detumescence.

SUMMARY AND CONCLUSIONS

The plexi of the male reproductive tract have components of both the autonomic and sensory nervous systems. Rat epididymis was found to be a rich source of substance P. Substance P levels in the epididymis were higher by about 2.8 and 19.3 times than those in the prostate and seminal vesicles, respectively. Seminal vesicles were found to be a rich source of enkephalins. They had about 2.9 and 2.6 times higher leucine enkephalin levels than epididymis and prostate, respectively. Human seminal plasma contained about 47 times higher levels of leucine enkephalin than substance P. Using the split ejaculate technique, it has been demonstrated that early fractions of the human ejaculate contain fluids from prostate (and possibly epididymis), whereas later fractions represent seminal vesicle secretions. A low exogenous concentration of substance P (400 nM) increased sperm motility, whereas leucine enkephalin (100 μM) depressed it. Substance P (1–10 μg/mL) and muscarinic agonists enhanced the adrenergic transmission of the rat vas deferens to electrical stimulation. Leucine enkephalin (1–10 μg/mL) depressed adrenergic transmission and antagonized the effects of substance P and muscarinic agonists. These studies suggest that substance P–like tachykinins may play a role in sperm maturation, in expulsion of fluid from the epididymis, and in initiation of motility, whereas leucine enkephalin–like peptides may contribute to the orgasmic experience and detumescence.

REFERENCES

1. SASTRY, B. V. R. & O. S. TAYEB. 1982. Regulation of acetylcholine release in the mouse cerebrum by methionine enkephalin and substance P. Adv. Biosci. **38:** 165–172.
2. SASTRY, B. V. R., V. E. JANSON, N. JAISWAL & O. S. TAYEB. 1983. Changes in enzymes of the cholinergic system and acetylcholine release in the cerebra of aging male Fischer rats. Pharmacology **26:** 61–72.
3. TAYEB, O. S. & B. V. R. SASTRY. 1987. Release of substance P, acetylcholine, and methionine enkephalin from mouse cerebral slices: effects of nicotine. *In* Substance P and Neurokinins. J. L. Henry, R. Couture, A. C. Cuello, G. Pelletier, R. Quirion & D. Regoli, Eds.: 350–352. Springer-Verlag. New York/Berlin.
4. SASTRY, B. V. R., L. K. OWENS & R. F. OCHILLO. 1990. Two furan analogs of muscarine as selective agonists at the presynaptic muscarinic receptors of the guinea pig longitudinal ileal muscle. Ann. N.Y. Acad. Sci. **604:** 566–568.
5. SASTRY, B. V. R., N. JAISWAL & O. S. TAYEB. 1986. Regulation of acetylcholine release from rodent cerebrum by presynaptic receptors, methionine enkephalin, and substance P. Adv. Behav. Biol. **30:** 1047–1056.
6. SASTRY, B. V. R. & O. S. TAYEB. 1988. Autoregulation of acetylcholine release: modulation by substance P and methionine enkephalin as a function of age. Regulat. Peptides **22:** 168.
7. SEGAWA, T., H. MURAKAMI, H. OGAWA & H. YAJIMA. 1977. Effect of enkephalin and substance P on sympathetic nerve transmission in mouse vas deferens. Jpn. J. Pharmacol. **28:** 13–19.
8. JAKISCH, J., M. GEPPERT, A. LUPP, H. Y. HUANG & P. ILLES. 1988. Types of opioid receptors modulating neurotransmitter release in discrete brain regions. *In* Regulatory Roles of Opioid Peptides. P. Illes & C. Farsang, Eds.: 240–258. Verlag Chemie. Weinheim, Federal Republic of Germany.
9. QUIRION, R. & T-V. DAM. 1985. Multiple tachykinin receptors. *In* Substance P Metabolism and Biological Actions. C. C. Jordon & P. Oehme, Eds.: 45–64. Taylor & Francis. London.
10. KONISHI, S., T. OKAMOTO & M. OTSUKA. 1985. Substance P as a neurotransmitter released from peripheral branches of primary afferent neurons producing slow synaptic excita-

tion in autonomic ganglion cells. *In* Substance P Metabolism and Biological Actions. C. C. Jordon & P. Oehme, Eds.: 121–136. Taylor & Francis. London.

11. NETTER, F. H. 1980. Nervous System. Vol. 1: 98. Ciba Collection of Medical Illustrations. Summit, New Jersey.

12. WEINER, N. & P. TAYLOR. 1985. Drugs acting at synaptic and neuroeffector junctional sites. *In* The Pharmacological Basis of Therapeutics. A. G. Gilman, L. S. Goodman, T. W. Rall & F. Murad, Eds.: 66–99. Macmillan Co. New York.

13. BISHOP, M. R., B. V. R. SASTRY, D. E. SCHMIDT & R. D. HARBISON. 1976. Occurrence of choline acetyltransferase and acetylcholine and other quaternary ammonium compounds in mammalian spermatozoa. Biochem. Pharmacol. **25:** 1617–1622.

14. SASTRY, B. V. R., V. E. JANSON & A. K. CHATURVEDI. 1981. Inhibition of human sperm motility by inhibitors of choline acetyltransferase. J. Pharmacol. Exp. Ther. **216:** 378–384.

15. SASTRY, B. V. R., S. L. BARNWELL, O. S. TAYEB, V. E. JANSON & L. K. OWENS. 1980. Occurrence of methionine enkephalin in human placental villus. Biochem. Pharmacol. **29:** 475–478.

16. SASTRY, B. V. R., O. S. TAYEB, S. L. BARNWELL, V. E. JANSON & L. K. OWENS. 1981. Peptides from human placenta: methionine enkephalin and substance P. Placenta Suppl. **3:** 327–337.

17. SASTRY, B. V. R., V. E. JANSON, L. K. OWENS & O. S. TAYEB. 1982. Enkephalin-like and substance P–like immunoreactivities of mammalian sperm and accessory sex glands. Biochem. Pharmacol. **31:** 3519–3522.

18. HENDERSON, G., J. HUGHES & R. W. KOSTERLITZ. 1978. *In vitro* release of leu- and met-enkephalin from the corpus striatum. Nature **271:** 677–679.

19. MILLER, R. J., K. J. CHANG, B. COOPER & P. CUATRECASAS. 1978. Radioimmunoassay and characterization of enkephalins in rat tissues. J. Biol. Chem. **253:** 531–538.

20. YANAIHARA, C. H., M. SATO, M. HIROHASHI, K. SAKAGAMI, T. YAMAMOTO, N. HASHIMOTO, N. YANAIHARA, K. ABE & T. KANEKO. 1976. Substance P radioimmunoassay using *N*-tyrosyl–substance P and demonstration of the presence of substance P–like immunoreactivities in human blood and porcine tissue extracts. Endocrinology (Japan) **23:** 457–463.

21. HENDERSON, G., J. HUGHES & R. W. KOSTERLITZ. 1972. A new example of morphine sensitive neuro-effector junction: adrenergic transmission in the mouse vas deferens. Br. J. Pharmacol. Chemother. **46:** 764–766.

22. SASTRY, B. V. R. & V. E. JANSON. 1983. Depression of human sperm motility by inhibition of enzymatic methylation. Biochem. Pharmacol. **32:** 1423–1432.

23. SASTRY, B. V. R. & V. E. JANSON. 1987. Opioid-like peptides in human semen and their effects on sperm motility. Ann. N.Y. Acad. Sci. **513:** 586–588.

24. PARRIS, W. C. V., J. R. KAMBAM, R. J. NAUKAM & B. V. R. SASTRY. 1990. Immunoreactive substance P is decreased in saliva of patients with chronic back pain syndromes. Anesth. Analg. **70:** 63–67.

25. FRAIOLI, F., A. FABBRI, L. GNESSI, L. SILNESTRONI, C. MORETTI, F. REDI & A. ISIDORI. 1984. Beta-endorphin, met-enkephalin, and calcitonin in human semen: evidence for a possible role in human sperm motility. Ann. N.Y. Acad. Sci. **438:** 365–369.

26. KILPATRICK, D. L. & C. F. MILLETTE. 1986. Expression of proenkephalin messenger RNA by mouse spermatogenic cells. Proc. Natl. Acad. Sci. U.S.A. **83:** 5015–5018.

27. ELIASSON, R., O. JOHNSEN & C. LINDHOLMER. 1974. Effects of seminal plasma on some functional properties of human spermatozoa. *In* Male Fertility and Sterility. R. E. Mancini & L. Martini, Eds.: 107–122. Academic Press. New York.

28. SASTRY, B. V. R. & V. E. JANSON. 1987. Substance P in human spermatozoa and modulation of sperm motility by substance P and its antagonists. *In* Substance P and Neurokinins. J. L. Henry, R. Couture, A. C. Cuello, G. Pelletier, R. Quirion & D. Regoli, Eds.: 179–181. Springer-Verlag. New York/Berlin.

29. JANSON, V. E. & B. V. R. SASTRY. 1985. Maintenance of human sperm motility by calcium antagonists. Pharmacologist **27:** 160.

30. STJERNQUIST, M., R. HÅKANSON, S. LEANDER, C. OWMAN, F. SUNDLER & R. UDDMAN. 1983. Immunohistochemical localization of substance P, vasoactive intestinal polypep-

tide, and gastrin-releasing peptide in vas deferens and seminal vesicle, and the effect of these and eight other neuropeptides on resting tension and neurally evoked contractile activity. Regulat. Peptides **7:** 67–86.

31. VAALASTI, A., H. TAINIO, M. PELTO-HUIKKO & A. HERVONEN. 1986. Light and electron microscope demonstration of VIP- and enkephalin-immunoreactive nerves in the human male genitourinary tract. Anat. Rec. **215:** 21–27.

32. BARDIN, C. W., C. SHAHA, J. MATHER, Y. SALOMON, A. N. MARGIORIS, A. S. LIOTTA, I. GERENDAI, C. L. CHEN & D. T. KRIEGER. 1984. Identification and possible function of pro-opiomelanocortin-derived peptides in the testis. Ann. N.Y. Acad. Sci. **438:** 346–363.

33. HAMILTON, D. W. 1982. Erection, ejaculation, and examination of the ejaculate. *In* Basic Reproductive Medicine. Volume 2: Reproductive Function in Men. D. Hamilton & F. Naftolin, Eds.: 291–310. MIT Press. Cambridge, Massachusetts.

34. BAUMBARTEN, H. G., A. F. HOLSTEIN & E. ROSENGREY. 1971. Arrangement, ultrastructure, and adrenergic innervation of smooth musculature of the ductili efferentes, ductus epididymis, and ductus deferens of man. Z. Zellforsch. Mikrosk. Anat. **120:** 37–79.

[125]I–Substance P Binding Sites in Rat Spinal Cord in a Chronic Constriction Injury and following Dorsal Rhizotomy[a]

L. M. AANONSEN AND V. S. SEYBOLD

Department of Biology
Macalester College
St. Paul, Minnesota 55105
and
Department of Cell Biology and Neuroanatomy
University of Minnesota
Minneapolis, Minnesota 55455

A chronic constriction injury (CCI) of the sciatic nerve has been characterized in rats that may represent a model of neuropathic pain disorders in humans.[1] In addition to hyperalgesic responses to noxious thermal and chemical stimuli, depletion of substance P (SP)–immunoreactivity has been observed in these rats on the nerve-ligated side of the spinal cord.[2] The purpose of the present study was to determine the effects of CCI on SP receptor binding and to compare the results with those observed after multiple, unilateral dorsal rhizotomy at comparable levels.

For the CCI experiments, a unilateral mononeuropathy was induced in male Sprague-Dawley rats (250–300 g) according to the method described previously.[1] Briefly, the rat was anesthetized, the common sciatic nerve on the left side of the animal was exposed, and consecutive loose ligatures (4) were tied around the nerve. Sham-surgery was performed on the right side of each of these rats. The animals were allowed to survive for 2, 5, 10, and 20 days after surgery ($n = 8$ rats/group). To determine whether the surgery alone had an effect, rats were sham-operated on the left side (no surgery on the right side) and were allowed to survive for 10 days (4 rats) and 20 days (6 rats). At the end of the survival periods, the rats were anesthetized and perfused with a buffer and spinal segment L4 was removed and sectioned (10 μm) on a cryostat. Responses to a noxious thermal stimulus were tested on sham and experimental animals on the day of sacrifice. The thermal stimulus was generated by a radiant heat source beneath a glass floor in a plastic cage.[1] The heat source was aimed at the proximal half of the plantar hindpaw and then the latency to withdraw the paw was noted. The latency score was computed by subtracting the average latency of the control (five measurements) from the average latency of the nerve-injured side. A significant decrease in paw withdrawal latency was noted on the nerve-injured side when compared to the control side at 5 and 10 days, but not at 20 days after sciatic ligation.

For the dorsal rhizotomy experiments, male Sprague-Dawley rats (200–250 g) were anesthetized and a laminectomy was performed to expose the L1–S1 dorsal roots on the left side of the spinal cord. These roots were tied and cut on the side of the ligature proximal to the dorsal root ganglia. The musculature and skin were closed in layers. Control animals received no surgery. The animals were allowed to

[a]This work was supported by USPHS Grant Nos. DA05309 and NS17702.

CCI

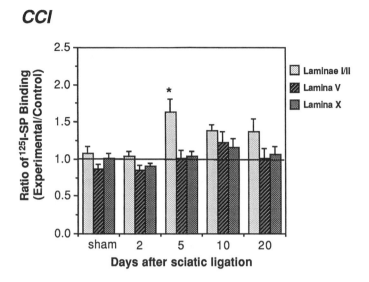

Dorsal Rhizotomy

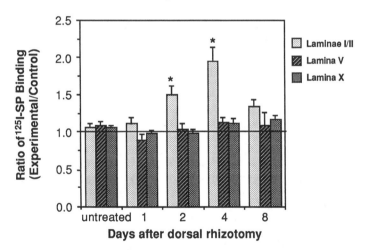

FIGURE 1. Ratio of SP binding in laminae I/II, V, and X of the rat spinal cord. The graphs represent the ratios of the grain densities (mean ± SEM) obtained from three areas of the spinal cord. Control values reflect data ipsilateral to sham-surgery (CCI) or intact dorsal roots (dorsal rhizotomy). Experimental values reflect data ipsilateral to sciatic ligation or multiple, unilateral dorsal rhizotomy. An asterisk represents one-way ANOVA with Dunnett's post-hoc test, $P < 0.05$.

survive for 1, 2, 4, and 8 days after surgery (n = 8 rats/group). The rats were perfused as described earlier. The extent of the dorsal rhizotomies was confirmed and spinal segment L4 was removed and sectioned on a cryostat (10 μm).

The binding protocol described by Charlton and Helke[3] was used in these experiments with minor modifications. ^{125}I–Bolton Hunter substance P (^{125}I-SP; 2000 Ci/mmol, Amersham) was used at a concentration of 50 pM in all ligand binding experiments. Adjacent sections were incubated in the presence of 0.1 μM SP to determine nonspecific binding. Autoradiograms were prepared using the technique first described by Young and Kuhar.[4] Emulsion-coated coverslips were apposed to the slide-mounted tissue sections and were stored desiccated in light-tight boxes for 9 days. Quantitative measurements of grain densities were determined using image processing and analysis programs for the Macintosh II (QuickCapture, Data Translation, and Image 1.13, W. Rasband, NIH). Nonspecific binding was found to be <5% of the total grain density in all areas measured. Data were obtained from an observer who was blinded to the sample treatment.

TABLE 1. Summary of Dissociation Constants and B_{max} Values for ^{125}I-SP in Laminae I/II of Rat Spinal Cord[a]

	CCI		Rhizotomy	
	Control	Experimental	Control	Experimental
K_D[b]	122.7 ± 20.1	45.3 ± 3.4[c]	183.4 ± 20.9	125.6 ± 18.1[c]
B_{max}[b] (fmol/mg protein)	365.4 ± 55.1	412.7 ± 30.6	329.8 ± 22.9	486.5 ± 64.2[c]

[a]Grain densities for Scatchard analysis were quantified in laminae I/II on control and experimental sides of the spinal cord. Scatchard analysis was performed using nonlinear regression analysis of the data (McPherson version of LIGAND). The spinal cords used for statistical analysis (N = 3) were selected based on their lack of variability as determined in Scatchard analysis (correlation coefficient > 0.85).
[b]Values represent the mean ± SEM (N = 3).
[c]Student's unpaired t test, P < 0.05.

The analysis of the autoradiograms showed that CCI resulted in an increased density of silver grains in laminae I/II at 5 days postsurgery on the side ipsilateral to the injury (FIGURE 1). Scatchard analysis by autoradiography revealed that, in laminae I/II, the K_D for ^{125}I-SP was lower on the side ipsilateral to the CCI with no change in B_{max} (TABLE 1). Bennett et al.[2] reported a slight depletion of SP-immunoreactivity in laminae I/II in this model at 5 days and a more pronounced depletion at 10 and 20 days after sciatic ligation. The time course for the decrease in ^{125}I-SP binding in laminae I/II in the present study is consistent with the changes in SP-immunoreactivity.

In the dorsal rhizotomy experiments, increased grain density was observed in laminae I/II on the side ipsilateral to the lesion at 2 and 4 days postsurgery (FIGURE 1). By Scatchard analysis, this was shown to reflect a decrease in K_D and an increase in B_{max} (TABLE 1). Because a decrease in binding in the dorsal horn was not apparent after dorsal rhizotomy, it is not likely that receptors for SP are present on terminals of primary afferent neurons. When the results of the CCI experiments are interpreted in the context of the rhizotomy experiments, the data suggest that SP release is decreased in this model of neuropathic pain.

REFERENCES

1. BENNETT, G. J. & Y-K. XIE. 1988. Pain **33:** 87–107.
2. BENNETT, G. J., *et al.* 1989. *In* Processing of Sensory Information in the Superficial Dorsal Horn of the Spinal Cord. F. Cervero, G. J. Bennett & P. M. Headley, Eds. Plenum. New York.
3. CHARLTON, C. G. & C. J. HELKE. 1985. J. Neurosci. **5:** 1293–1299.
4. YOUNG, W. S. & M. J. KUHAR. 1979. Brain Res. **20:** 246–254.

NK-1 Receptors and Vascular Permeability in Rat Airways

L. ABELLI,[a] F. NAPPI,[a] C. A. MAGGI,[b] P. ROVERO,[c]
M. ASTOLFI,[a] D. REGOLI,[d] G. DRAPEAU,[d]
AND A. GIACHETTI[b]

[a]Department of Pharmacology
Menarini Ricerche Sud S.p.A.
00040 Pomezia, Italy

[b]Department of Pharmacology
[c]Department of Chemistry
Menarini Industrie Farmaceutiche Riunite
50131 Firenze, Italy

[d]Department of Physiology and Pharmacology
University of Sherbrooke Medical School
Sherbrooke, Canada J1H 5N4

The ability of synthetic tachykinin analogues to increase vascular permeability in the tracheobronchial region of urethane (1.2 g/kg sc)–anesthetized male Wistar rats was investigated in order to characterize the tachykinin receptor subtype(s) involved.

Plasma protein extravasation was evaluated by means of the Evan's Blue (20 mg/kg iv) leakage technique[1,2] at 5 minutes after intravenous administration of the test substances.

The NK-1 selective agonists,[3,4] namely, [β-Ala^4,Sar^9]SP(4–11) sulfone and [pGlu^6,Pro^9]SP(6–11), were dose-dependently effective (0.037–3.7 nmol/kg), whereas the NK-2 ([β-Ala^8]NKA(4–10) and [Nle^{10}]NKA(4–10)) and NK-3 ([MePhe^7]NKB) selective agonists[3,5] were inactive (TABLE 1). These findings provide evidence that the response of the airways to intravenous tachykinins is exclusively mediated by the NK-1 receptor subtype.

The response to the NK-1 agonist, [β-Ala^4,Sar^9]SP(4–11) sulfone, a compound devoid of mast cell–degranulating activity, was not modified by pretreatment with BW 755C (188 μmol/kg iv, 5 min before), whereas the effect of an equimolar dose (3.7 nmol/kg iv) of substance P (SP) was dose-dependently inhibited (up to 50%) by the dual cyclooxygenase and lipoxygenase inhibitor (56–188 μmol/kg).

The involvement of LTC$_4$ and LTD$_4$ in the response to SP was ruled out by the ineffectiveness of the leukotriene antagonist, FPL 55712 (8.9 μmol/kg iv, 2 min before), and of the inhibitor of leukotriene synthesis, U-60257B (43.2 μmol/kg iv, 8 min before). Conversely, the response to SP of rats pretreated subcutaneously with the mast cell–degranulating compound 48/80 (5 mg/kg daily for 3 days) was reduced by 30% ($n = 12$ rats per group, $P < 0.05$).

In conclusion, the effect of SP on vascular permeability appears to be mediated by a receptor-coupled action on NK-1 sites, for which SP has preferential affinity, and through the release of endogenous prostanoids. The latter mechanism appears to be activated by the N-terminal basic residues of SP, which are responsible for the mast cell–degranulating activity of the neuropeptide.[6]

TABLE 1. Effect of Synthetic Tachykinin Analogues on Plasma Protein Extravasation in the Tracheobronchial Region of Urethane-anesthetized Rats[a]

Compound	Dose (nmol/kg iv)	Evan's Blue Content (ng/mg of wet tissue weight)	
		Caudal Trachea	Main Bronchi
vehicle	—	12 ± 1	12 ± 1
[β-Ala^4,Sar^9]SP(4–11) sulfone	0.037	15 ± 2	15 ± 3
	0.11	20 ± 2^b	21 ± 2^b
	0.37	64 ± 8^b	62 ± 7^b
	1.11	114 ± 7^b	75 ± 4^b
	3.70	113 ± 6^b	99 ± 7^b
[pGlu^6,Pro^9]SP(6–11)	0.037	12 ± 1	12 ± 1
	0.11	13 ± 2	13 ± 3
	0.37	22 ± 5^b	24 ± 4^b
	1.11	65 ± 12^b	75 ± 10^b
	3.70	100 ± 10^b	65 ± 7^b
[β-Ala^8]NKA(4–10)	0.11	11 ± 3	12 ± 1
	0.37	12 ± 1	12 ± 2
	1.11	13 ± 2	13 ± 1
	3.70	14 ± 2	14 ± 1
[Nle^{10}]NKA(4–10)	0.11	12 ± 2	12 ± 1
	0.37	16 ± 2	9 ± 2
	1.11	13 ± 3	9 ± 3
	3.70	9 ± 3	12 ± 2
[MePhe^7]NKB	0.11	11 ± 2	11 ± 2
	0.37	11 ± 2	12 ± 1
	1.11	9 ± 2	11 ± 2
	3.70	16 ± 3	12 ± 1

[a]Data are means $\pm$ SEM; n = 6–10 animals per group.
[b]Significantly different from control group, $P < 0.05$.

REFERENCES

1. SARIA, A. & J. M. LUNDBERG. 1983. Evan's blue fluorescence: quantitative and morphological evaluation of vascular permeability in animal tissues. J. Neurosci. Methods **8:** 41–49.
2. ABELLI, L., V. SOMMA, C. A. MAGGI, D. REGOLI, M. ASTOLFI, M. PARLANI, P. ROVERO, B. CONTE & A. MELI. 1989. Effects of tachykinins and selective tachykinin receptor agonists on vascular permeability in the rat lower urinary tract: evidence for the involvement of NK-1 receptors. J. Auton. Pharmacol. **9:** 253–263.
3. DRAPEAU, G., P. D'ORLEANS-JUSTE, S. DION, N-E. RHALEB, N. ROUISSI & D. REGOLI. 1987. Selective agonists for substance P and neurokinin receptors. Neuropeptides **10:** 43.
4. WORMSER, U., R. LAUFER, Y. HART, M. CHOREV, C. GILON & Z. SELINGER. 1986. Highly selective agonists for substance P receptor subtypes. EMBO J. **5:** 2805.
5. MAGGI, C. A., S. GIULIANI, L. BALLATI, P. ROVERO, L. ABELLI, S. MANZINI, A. GIACHETTI & A. MELI. 1990. *In vivo* pharmacology of [β-Ala^8]neurokinin A(4–10), a selective NK-2 tachykinin receptor agonist. Eur. J. Pharmacol. **177:** 81–86.
6. DEVILLIER, P., D. REGOLI, A. ASSERAF, B. DESCOURS, J. MARSAC & M. RENOUX. 1986. Histamine release and local responses of rat and human skin to substance P and other mammalian tachykinins. Pharmacology **32:** 340–347.

Activation of Primary Afferents in the Rabbit Ear by Noxious Heat[a]

RAINER AMANN, JOSEF DONNERER,
AND FRED LEMBECK

Department of Experimental and Clinical Pharmacology
University of Graz
A-8010 Graz, Austria

Several "natural" stimuli have been suggested to activate the afferent as well as the peripheral function of capsaicin-sensitive afferent neurons. In the skin, capsaicin-sensitive fibers contribute to the perception of increased temperature as well as to local tissue reaction after thermal injury.[1,2] On the other hand, a moderate decrease of skin temperature has been reported to block excitability of capsaicin-sensitive fibers.[3]

The aim of the present study was to determine the effects of low (18 °C) temperature and of noxious heat on excitation and peripheral neuropeptide release of primary afferents. Ruthenium Red (RR), which has been shown to inhibit selectively capsaicin-induced stimulation of afferents,[4,5] was used to further characterize the effect of noxious heat.

Experiments were performed in the isolated perfused rabbit ear with intact neuronal connection as described previously.[6] In this preparation, noxious heat, bradykinin (BK), and capsaicin stimulate exclusively C-polymodal nociceptors.[7] Stimulation produces a dose-dependent depressor reflex, which can be used to determine stimulus intensity. Additionally, this preparation allows the determination of peripheral neuropeptide release from primary afferents by quantification of substance P–like immunoreactivity (SP-IR) in the effluate.

EFFECT OF LOW TEMPERATURE PERFUSION

At 18 °C, neither 10 μM capsaicin nor 60 mM K^+ evoked any detectable release of SP-IR ($N = 4$, each). At this temperature, the excitatory effect of capsaicin was nearly abolished. In only 2 out of 10 preparations, intra-arterial injection of 30 nmol capsaicin produced a depressor reflex (for values at 37 °C, see TABLE 2 later). However, 90 nmol capsaicin elicited a response in 4 out of 10 animals.

EFFECT OF NOXIOUS HEAT

Release Experiments

Capsaicin, an increase of the temperature of the perfusate to 50 °C (10 min), and 60 mM K^+ produced a Ca^{2+}-dependent release of SP-IR (TABLE 1). RR (20 μM) did

[a] This work was supported by the Austrian Scientific Research Funds (No. 7676).

TABLE 1. Evoked Release of SP-IR[a]

	Total Evoked Release (fmol SP-IR)		
Stimulus	Control	20 μM RR	Ca^{2+}-free
50 °C, 10 min	82 ± 9	10 ± 2[b]	< 2[b]
60 mM K$^+$, 5 min	58 ± 5	60 ± 3[b]	< 2[b]
10 μM capsaicin, 5 min	54 ± 6	< 2[b]	5 ± 2[b]

[a]Evoked release of SP-IR in the effluate of the isolated perfused rabbit ear. The Ca^{2+}-free perfusate contained 3 mM ethylene glycol bis(aminoethylether)-tetra-acetate (EGTA). Mean ± SEM of 4–8 experiments.
[b]$p < 0.05$ versus control.

not affect the K$^+$-evoked release, but it did inhibit that evoked by capsaicin and heat stimulation.

Depressor Reflex

Injection of capsaicin or BK into the central artery of the vascularly separated ear, as well as a sudden increase of the temperature of the skin to 53 °C for 1 min, elicited a reproducible depressor reflex. In the presence of RR, the effect of capsaicin was abolished and that of heat stimulation was reduced. This inhibitory action of RR was also observed in a Ca^{2+}-free perfusate. On the other hand, RR did not inhibit the BK-elicited depressor reflex (TABLE 2).

CONCLUSIONS

The results indicate that, in the rabbit ear, low temperature causes nonselective blockade of the peripheral and afferent function of capsaicin-sensitive fibers. Noxious heat causes peripheral neuropeptide release and excitation of afferents via an RR-sensitive mechanism. This may indicate that heat stimulates afferents, directly or indirectly, via a similar mechanism as capsaicin.

TABLE 2. Capsaicin-induced Excitation[a]

	Depressor Reflex (mmHg)				
Stimulus	Control	RR (20 μM)	Recovery 60 min	Ca^{2+}-free	Ca^{2+}-free plus RR
53 °C, 1 min	23 ± 1	5 ± 4[b]	6 ± 4[b]	14 ± 3	2 ± 1[b]
0.2 nmol BK	10 ± 2	9 ± 4	—	—	—
1.0 nmol BK	25 ± 3	28 ± 3	—	—	—
30 nmol capsaicin	24 ± 3	0[b]	20 ± 2	32 ± 4	0[b]

[a]These data were gathered from isolated perfused rabbit ear with intact neuronal connection. Depressor reflex was elicited by heat application to the skin of the ear or by injection of bradykinin or capsaicin into the central ear artery. The Ca^{2+}-free perfusate contained 3 mM EGTA. Mean ± SEM of at least six experiments.
[b]$p < 0.05$ versus the corresponding control value.

REFERENCES

1. SARIA, A. 1984. Br. J. Pharmacol. **82:** 217–222.
2. HELME, R. D., G. M. KOSCHORKE & M. ZIMMERMANN. 1986. Neurosci. Lett. **63:** 295–299.
3. SZOLCSANYI, J. 1977. J. Physiol. (Paris) **73:** 251–259.
4. AMANN, R. & F. LEMBECK. 1989. Eur. J. Pharmacol. **161:** 227–229.
5. MAGGI, C. A., R. PATACCHINI, P. SANTICIOLI, E. DEL BIANCO, P. GEPPETTI & A. MELI. 1989. Eur. J. Pharmacol. **170:** 167–177.
6. AMANN, R., J. DONNERER & F. LEMBECK. 1989. Neuroscience **32:** 255–259.
7. SZOLCSANYI, J. 1987. J. Physiol. **388:** 9–23.

Capsaicin-induced Desensitization in Rat and Rabbit[a]

RAINER AMANN AND FRED LEMBECK

Department of Experimental and Clinical Pharmacology
University of Graz
A-8010 Graz, Austria

Capsaicin is known to produce "desensitization" of primary afferent C/A-delta fibers. This term has been used for a number of changes in neuronal function and morphology.[1] Investigations of the mechanisms of the early stage of desensitization, which has been called the "sensory neuron blocking stage",[1] have produced unequivocal results. Studies in rats have suggested that capsaicin-induced accumulation of intraneuronal calcium[2] or desensitization of a capsaicin receptor[3] can reduce the responsiveness of primary afferent neurons to further stimulation. On the other hand, studies in rabbits have shown that "desensitization" is caused by depletion of a pool of releasable peptides.[4] Because, in rabbits, in contrast to rats, capsaicin does not induce degeneration of primary afferents,[5] there may be different mechanisms in both species with regard to the development of desensitization.

METHODS AND RESULTS

In the rat, capsaicin-evoked release of calcitonin gene–related peptide–like immunoreactivity (CGRP-IR) was determined in the superfused isolated urinary bladder as described previously.[6] In the rabbit, stimulation of peripheral afferent terminals was evaluated in the iris sphincter muscle *in vitro*.[4] In this preparation, capsaicin-induced and bradykinin (BK)–induced contractions were caused by neuropeptide release from primary afferent terminals.[4] "Desensitization" was evaluated by determining the effect of capsaicin (5 min contact time) in tissues that had been preexposed (5 min contact time, 60 min before) to different concentrations of capsaicin.

In the rat, capsaicin was about 30-fold more potent in stimulating neuropeptide release than in the rabbit (FIGURE 1) and 400-fold more potent in producing desensitization (FIGURE 2). Already, a concentration of capsaicin that was threshold for release caused desensitization. Both 0.1 and 0.3 μM capsaicin were more effective in preventing capsaicin-evoked release than K^+-evoked release (FIGURE 2). Desensitization by 0.3 μM capsaicin was prevented when Ca^{2+} was omitted from the superfusate during the preexposure period ($N = 6$) or when experiments were performed at 18 °C ($N = 8$). In the rabbit iris, desensitization could only be obtained when tissues were preexposed to concentrations of capsaicin that produced maximal contractions (24–56 μM); no selective desensitization could be demonstrated because BK-induced contractions were inhibited to a similar degree as those produced by capsaicin (FIGURE 2).

These results suggest that, in the rat, low concentrations of capsaicin produce selective, temperature-dependent, and Ca^{2+}-dependent desensitization of neuropep-

[a]This work was supported by the Austrian Scientific Research Funds (No. 7676).

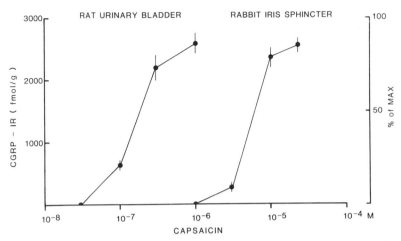

FIGURE 1. Dose-dependent stimulation of peripheral afferent terminals by capsaicin in rat and rabbit. Left: Capsaicin-evoked release of CGRP-IR in the superfused isolated rat urinary bladder. Right: Capsaicin-evoked contractions (expressed as the % of contraction produced by 10^{-4} M carbachol) in the rabbit iris sphincter *in vitro*. Means $\pm$ SEM; $N = 6$–10. The EC_{50} values were 0.157 μM (95% confidence interval: 0.056–0.417) and 5.3 μM (4.3–6.4) in the rat and rabbit, respectively.

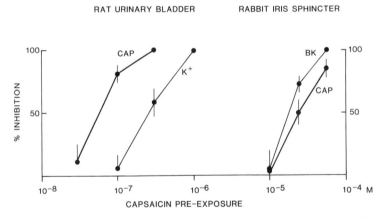

FIGURE 2. Capsaicin-induced desensitization in the rat (left) and rabbit (right). Left: Percent inhibition of the capsaicin (0.1 μM)– and K$^+$ (60 mM)–evoked release in the isolated urinary bladder after preexposure to capsaicin. Under control conditions (preexposure to vehicle), 0.1 μM capsaicin and 60 mM K$^+$ released 660 $\pm$ 76 ($N = 10$) and 602 $\pm$ 110 ($N = 8$) fmol CGRP-IR/g. The IC_{50} to inhibit the capsaicin-evoked release was 0.065 μM (0.04–0.092). The K$^+$-evoked release was significantly ($p < 0.05$) less attenuated than that evoked by capsaicin. Right: Effect of capsaicin preexposure on capsaicin (10 μM)– and BK (100 nM)–induced contractions of the rabbit iris sphincter. The control values were 79 $\pm$ 2.8% ($N = 5$) and 52 $\pm$ 4% ($N = 7$) of the carbachol maximum for capsaicin and BK, respectively. The IC_{50} of capsaicin was 25.2 μM (9.8–65.9), which is about 400-fold higher than the value obtained in the rat.

tide release. In view of this selectivity, intracellular accumulation of Ca^{2+} or depletion of releasable peptide is not likely to account for the desensitization to low doses of capsaicin in the rat. The rabbit is far less sensitive to the desensitizing effect of capsaicin; the present results are consistent with the view that, in this species, desensitization is due to depletion of releasable peptide pools.

REFERENCES

1. SZOLCSANYI, J. 1985. *In* Tachykinin Antagonists. R. Håkanson & F. Sundler, Eds.: 45–54. Elsevier. Amsterdam/New York.
2. MAGGI, C. A., P. SANTICIOLI, P. GEPPETTI, M. PARLANI, M. ASTOLFI, E. DEL BIANCO, R. PATACCHINI, S. GIULIANI & A. MELI. 1989. Gen. Pharmacol. **20**(4): 445–456.
3. DRAY, A., M. W. HANKINS & J. C. YEATS. 1989. Neuroscience **31**(2): 479–483.
4. HÅKANSON, R., B. BEDING, R. EKMAN, M. HEILIG, C. WAHLESTEDT & F. SUNDLER. 1987. Neuroscience **21**(3): 943–950.
5. LYNN, B. & J. SHAKHANBEH. 1988. Neuroscience **24**(3): 769–775.
6. AMANN, R., G. SKOFITSCH & F. LEMBECK. 1988. Naunyn-Schmiedeberg's Arch. Pharmacol. **338**: 407–410.

Substance P Is Distributed between Somatotrophs and Thyrotrophs in a Sexually Dimorphic Manner in Rat[a]

ELAINE R. BROWN,[b] KEVIN A. ROTH,[c]
AND JAMES E. KRAUSE[b,d]

bDepartment of Anatomy and Neurobiology
cDepartment of Pathology
Washington University School of Medicine
St. Louis, Missouri 63110

Substance P (SP) immunoreactivity has been detected by radioimmunoassay in the rat anterior pituitary (AP) where it is differentially regulated by gonadal steroids. Androgens increase and estrogens decrease pituitary SP levels, causing males to have a fivefold higher AP SP content than females.[1-4] These steroid-induced changes in SP content result, at least in part, from androgens increasing and estrogens decreasing SP-encoding mRNAs in the AP.[4] Because steroid-regulated AP SP may be acting locally to affect pituitary hormone secretion, it would be beneficial to know which of the AP cell types express, regulate, and potentially secrete SP. Although it has been difficult to detect SP immunohistochemically in the pituitary, we have used a sensitive immunogold silver-enhancement staining technique to detect SP-immunoreactive (SP-ir) cells in pituitary sections from adult male and female rats. The present studies used this technique to identify SP-ir cells, in combination with immunofluorescence to identify the different pituitary cell populations, in order to determine the pituitary hormones with which SP colocalizes.

Adult male and female Sprague-Dawley rats (200–300 g) were perfused with cold Bouin's fixative and pituitaries were removed and placed in 10% sucrose at 4 °C. Frozen sections (10 μm) were thaw-mounted onto gelatin-coated slides and were prepared for SP immunohistochemistry as previously described[5] using a rabbit SP-specific antiserum, R-5.[6] The SP antibody was detected with a gold-labeled anti-rabbit serum followed by silver-enhancement development. Specificity was confirmed when no staining was seen when 1 μM SP was added to the primary incubation. Because the silver intensification procedure destroys the antigenicity of the initial primary antibody,[7] multiple labeling studies could be done using other rabbit antisera against the different pituitary hormones, as well as a monkey anti–growth hormone (GH) antiserum. (All pituitary hormone antisera were provided by the National Hormone and Pituitary Program.) Pituitary hormones were then detected by immunofluorescence with fluoresceinated anti-monkey and Texas Red–conjugated anti-rabbit sera.

Immunohistochemical staining for SP revealed a number of SP-ir cells in the AP (FIGURE 1A) and some SP-ir fibers in both the anterior and posterior pituitary. Comparisons of pituitaries from males and females revealed that males had approximately fourfold more SP-ir cells in the AP than did females, corroborating the

[a]This work was supported in part by a grant from the Markey Foundation (to K. A. Roth) and by a Washington University–Monsanto grant (to J. E. Krause).
[d]To whom all correspondence should be addressed.

previously reported sexual dimorphism in AP SP content.[1-4] Colocalization studies revealed that the vast majority (98%) of the SP-ir cells in the male AP were also immunoreactive for GH. These SP-ir cells represented about 27% of the entire somatotroph population in the male pituitary, whereas only 6% of the GH cells in the female contained SP immunoreactivity (FIGURES 1A, 1B, and 2). An additional population of SP-ir cells that was more prevalent in the female than in the male AP colocalized with thyroid stimulating hormone (TSH; FIGURES 1A, 1C, and 2). SP did not appear to colocalize with prolactin, gonadotropins, or corticotropin.

To assess which of the SP-ir AP cell populations reduce SP content in response to estrogen treatment, female rats were ovariectomized (OX) and were treated with either 2 μg of estradiol benzoate (EB) or oil vehicle by daily subcutaneous injection for six days following surgery. Rats were then perfused and pituitaries were processed for SP and pituitary hormone immunohistochemistry. Pituitaries from oil-

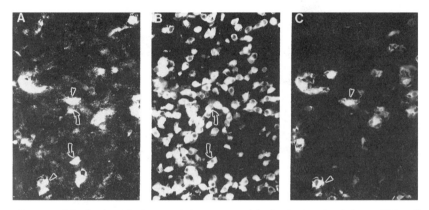

FIGURE 1. Distribution of substance P immunoreactivity in the female pituitary. SP-ir cells were identified in pituitary sections from a normal cycling female with an SP-specific antiserum (R-5), which was detected by immunogold with silver-enhancement. SP-ir cells were visualized by reflected-light polarization (A). Identical fields from multiple labeling studies using anti-GH (B) and anti-TSH (C) antisera, detected by immunofluorescence, reveal that SP is found in both somatotrophs and thyrotrophs in the female. Arrowheads designate SP-ir cells colocalizing with TSH and arrows indicate SP-ir cells colocalizing with GH. Magnification of original photographs: ×400. (However, the figure was reduced by 50%.)

treated OX rats showed a fourfold increase in the total number of SP-ir cells compared to pituitaries from either normal cycling females or EB-treated OX rats. This difference represents an increase in the SP-expressing somatotroph population in the oil-treated OX group (FIGURE 2). Estrogen replacement diminished the OX-induced increase in the percentage of SP-ir GH cells by 80%. There was no apparent effect of OX or EB treatment on the SP-ir thyrotroph population (FIGURE 2). These results imply that the estrogen-induced decrease in pituitary SP mRNA expression and peptide content[1-4] occurs in a subpopulation of somatotrophs.

We have demonstrated by immunohistochemical analysis that there is a sex-dependent differential distribution of SP in the pituitary. Males have a greater percentage of SP-ir somatotrophs, yet females, regardless of steroid status, have more SP-ir thyrotrophs than do males. The significance of this sexual dimorphism is not yet understood. However, it is likely that the sex difference in AP SP content

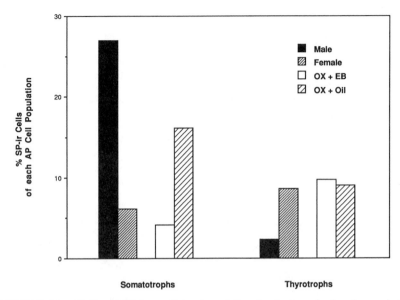

FIGURE 2. Quantitation of SP-ir somatotrophs and thyrotrophs in male, female, ovariecto-mized (OX) oil-treated, and OX estrogen-treated rats. SP colocalization was determined as described in the text. Ten or more random fields (×500) were counted from immunohistochem-ically stained pituitary sections from adult male, cycling female, OX oil-treated, and OX EB-treated rats. Immunogold-labeled SP-ir cells as well as fluorescently labeled GH- and TSH-ir cells were counted and the percentage of double-labeled cells of each of the GH and TSH cell populations was determined and averaged over all fields counted. Males had a larger proportion of SP-ir somatotrophs than did females, whereas females had more SP-ir thyro-trophs than did males. OX resulted in an increase in the SP-ir somatotroph population, which was reversed with EB replacement, but there were no apparent effects on the number of SP-ir thyrotrophs with OX or EB treatment. Because the somatotrophs were much more abundant than thyrotrophs, these data do not reveal the fact that female, oil-treated OX, and EB-treated OX rats actually had more SP-ir somatotrophs than SP-ir thyrotrophs.

results, at least in part, from estradiol suppressing SP expression in a subpopulation of somatotrophs in the female because estrogen replacement reverses the effect of an OX-induced increase in the SP-ir somatotroph population. The localization of estrogen-regulated SP to GH-secreting cells in the AP, as well as the identification of a subpopulation of SP-ir thyrotrophs, extends the basis by which the functional significance of SP in pituitary physiology can be addressed.

REFERENCES

1. YOSHIKAWA, K. & J. S. HONG. 1983. Sex-related difference in substance P level in rat anterior pituitary: a model of neonatal imprinting by testosterone. Brain Res. **273:** 362–365.

2. COSLOVSKY, R., R. W. EVANS, S. E. LEEMAN, L. E. BRAVERMAN & N. ARONIN. 1984. The effects of gonadal steroids on the content of substance P in the rat anterior pituitary. Endocrinology **115:** 2285–2289.

3. DE PALATIS, L. R., O. KHORRAM & S. M. MCCANN. 1985. Age-, sex-, and gonadal steroid–related changes in immunoreactive substance P in the rat anterior pituitary gland. Endocrinology **117:** 1368–1373.

4. BROWN, E. R., R. E. HARLAN & J. E. KRAUSE. 1990. Gonadal steroid regulation of substance P (SP) and SP-encoding messenger ribonucleic acids in the rat anterior pituitary and hypothalamus. Endocrinology **126:** 330–340.

5. BROWN, E. R., K. A. ROTH & J. E. KRAUSE. 1991. The sexually dimorphic distribution of substance P in specific anterior pituitary cell populations. Proc. Natl. Acad. Sci. U.S.A. **88:** 1222–1226.

6. KRAUSE, J. E., A. J. REINER, J. P. ADVIS & J. F. MCKELVY. 1984. *In vivo* biosynthesis of [^{35}S] and [^{3}H] substance P in the striatum of the rat and their axonal transport to the substantia nigra. J. Neurosci. **4:** 775–785.

7. ROTH, K. A., J. HERTZ & J. I. GORDON. 1990. Mapping enteroendocrine cell populations in transgenic mice reveals an unexpected degree of complexity in cellular differentiation within the gastrointestinal tract. J. Cell Biol. **110:** 1791–1801.

^{125}I-Iodohistidyl^1–Neurokinin A Binds Specifically to a 43-kDa and an 86-kDa Protein in Crude Membranes from Hamster Urinary Bladder

S. H. BUCK,[a] S. A. SHATZER,[a]
P. L. M. van GIERSBERGEN,[a,b] AND B. O. FANGER[a]

[a]Marion Merrell Dow Research Institute
Cincinnati, Ohio 45215

[b]Department of Pharmacology and Cell Biophysics
University of Cincinnati College of Medicine
Cincinnati, Ohio 45267

INTRODUCTION

A photoreactive analogue of substance P (SP) has been used to visualize a rat-brain, specific SP binding protein with a molecular weight of 46,000 Da.[1] In agreement with this finding, ^{3}H-SP has been covalently bound to a 46-kDa protein by the cross-linking reagent, disuccinimidyl suberate (DSS), in rat brain membranes.[2] Solubilization of ^{3}H-SP binding proteins from bovine brain stem and subsequent gel filtration analysis have indicated specific ^{3}H-SP binding to a protein with a molecular weight of 55,000–60,000.[3] DSS has also been used to reveal specific binding proteins for iodinated SP with molecular weights of 58,000 and 33,000 Da in human lymphoblast cell membranes.[4] We have used the membrane-impermeable cross-linking reagent, bis(sulfosuccinimidyl) suberate (BS^3), to examine the binding proteins for iodinated neurokinin A (^{125}I-NKA) in hamster urinary bladder (HUB), a tissue enriched in NK$_2$ receptors.[5]

METHODS

Crude membranes from HUB were prepared and incubated as previously described,[6,7] except that 25 mg tissue (approximately 625 μg protein) was used along with 1 nM ^{125}I-NKA. After 2 h, the membranes were centrifuged and the pellet was resuspended in 0.5 mL of ice-cold 50 mM phosphate-buffered saline (pH 8.0) containing 5 mM BS^3. After 15 min, the cross-linking reaction was quenched with 200 mM glycine and the membranes were pelleted as before. The pellets were dissolved in Laemmli sample buffer [with or without 100 mM dithiothreitol (DTT)] and proteins were separated by electrophoresis on SDS-PAGE gels.[8] The gels were then fixed, dried, and autoradiographed on Kodak XAR-2 film.

RESULTS AND DISCUSSION

Experiments revealed that affinity cross-linking was optimal using 5 mM BS^3 compared to 1 mM BS^3 or 1 mM or 5 mM DSS. The ligand labeled a 43-kDa band

and an 86-kDa band. Essentially all of the cross-linking to both bands was inhibited by 1 μM unlabeled NKA and the IC_{50} for NKA was determined to be approximately 1 nM for both bands (FIGURE 1). The binding was specific because it was not inhibited to any extent by 30 nM SP, senktide, bombesin, bradykinin, α-MSH, somatostatin, or VIP and it was only partially inhibited by 30 nM neurokinin B (FIGURE 1). The rank-order potency pattern of NKA > NKB > SP/senktide is consistent with binding to an NK_2 receptor.[6,7]

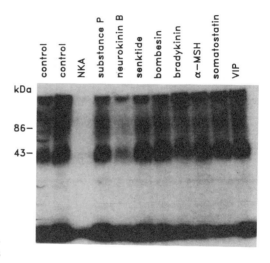

FIGURE 1. Specificity of cross-linking of ^{125}I-NKA in HUB membranes (top panel) and competition by increasing concentrations of NKA (bottom panel). Top panel = + 100 mM DTT; bottom panel = − 100 mM DTT. All peptides in the experiment depicted in the top panel were at 30 nM concentration.

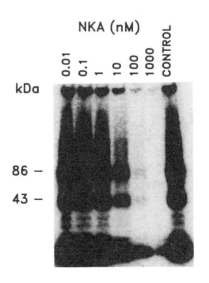

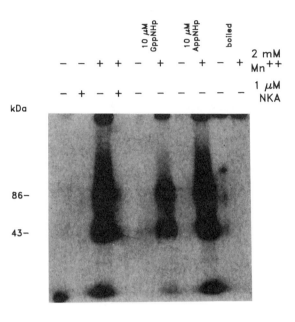

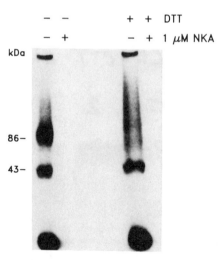

FIGURE 2. Effects of Mn^{++}, guanine nucleotide, adenine nucleotide, and boiling of tissue on cross-linking of ^{125}I-NKA in HUB membranes (top panel) and of reduction of disulfide bonds by 100 mM DTT (bottom panel).

The affinity cross-linking of ^{125}I-NKA to both bands was markedly enhanced by Mn^{++} and was partially inhibited by 10 μM GppNHp, but not by AppNHp (FIGURE 2). This is consistent with results obtained in HUB membranes using standard ligand binding assays.[7,9] Prior boiling of the HUB membranes abolished all of the specific binding of ^{125}I-NKA in both bands, suggesting that they are membrane proteins (FIGURE 2). When the SDS-PAGE gels were run in the presence of 100 mM DTT, the labeling of the 86-kDa band disappeared completely (FIGURE 2). Other experiments in which the individual labeled protein bands were cut from the gels and reduced with 2-mercaptoethanol revealed that the radioactivity in the 86-kDa band migrated to the 43-kDa band.

These results suggest that the HUB NK_2 receptor is a 43-kDa protein that is normally linked to another protein of approximately the same molecular weight, perhaps forming receptor homodimers. It is interesting to note that this 43-kDa molecular weight is identical to the molecular weight of the bovine stomach NK_2 receptor that has been cloned and expressed in oocytes.[10] Furthermore, it is noteworthy that BS^3 does not penetrate into hydrophobic membrane regions,[11] suggesting that the N-terminal portion of ^{125}I-NKA (which contains the most reactive moieties) is also outside of these regions when the ligand is bound to receptor. Additional research is necessary to determine if the HUB NK_2 receptor is identical to the bovine stomach receptor and to determine the significance of the 86-kDa protein band that is also labeled by affinity cross-linking with ^{125}I-NKA.

REFERENCES

1. DAM, T-V., E. ESCHER & R. QUIRION. 1987. Biochem. Biophys. Res. Commun. **149:** 297–303.
2. NAKATA, Y., C. HIRAOKA & T. SEGAWA. 1988. Eur. J. Pharmacol. **152:** 171–174.
3. NAKATA, Y., H. TANAKA, Y. MORISHIMA & T. SEGAWA. 1988. J. Neurochem. **50:** 522–527.
4. PAYAN, D. G., J. P. MCGILLIS & M. L. ORGANIST. 1986. J. Biol. Chem. **261:** 14321–14329.
5. BUCK, S. H., B. O. FANGER & P. L. M. VAN GIERSBERGEN. 1991. Ann. N.Y. Acad. Sci. This volume.
6. BURCHER, E., S. H. BUCK, W. LOVENBERG & T. L. O'DONOHUE. 1986. J. Pharmacol. Exp. Ther. **236:** 819–831.
7. BUCK, S. H. & S. A. SHATZER. 1988. Life Sci. **42:** 2701–2708.
8. LAEMMLI, U. K. 1970. Nature **227:** 680–685.
9. VAN GIERSBERGEN, P. L. M., S. A. SHATZER, A. K. HENDERSON, J. LAI, S. NAKANISHI, H. I. YAMAMURA & S. H. BUCK. 1991. Proc. Natl. Acad. Sci. U.S.A. **88:** 1661–1665.
10. MASU, Y., K. NAKAYAMA, H. TAMAKI, Y. HARADA, M. KUNO & S. NAKANISHI. 1987. Nature **329:** 836–838.
11. STAROS, J. K. 1982. Biochemistry **21:** 3950–3955.

Multiple Neurokinin Receptor Subtypes Are Present in the Colon of the Cat and Rat

FULL-YOUNG CHANG, DOUGLAS SHARP,
AND ANN OUYANG[a]

Department of Medicine
University of Pennsylvania
Philadelphia, Pennsylvania 19104-6144

Substance P (SP), neurokinin A (NKA), and neurokinin B are members of the neurokinin family that act with relative specificity at NK1, NK2, and NK3 receptors, respectively. The receptor subtype distributions in cat and rat colon muscle are unknown. The aims of this study have been to determine the types and sites of neurokinin receptors in the proximal colon of the cat and rat using the specific NK1 receptor agonist, [pGlu^6,Pro^9]–substance P$_{6-11}$ (septide), and the NK3 receptor agonist, succinyl-[Asp^6,MePhe^8]–substance P$_{6-11}$ (senktide).

METHODS

Segments of proximal colon were removed from anesthetized adult cats and rats and were stripped of mucosa. Circular muscle strips were mounted in glass chambers in Krebs (37 °C) oxygenated with 95% O_2. After equilibration, the strips were stretched to L_0 as determined using 10^{-4} M bethanechol. Isometric contractions were studied using increasing doses of SP, NKA, septide, and senktide for dose responses and tachyphylaxis studies and with pretreatment of 10^{-5} M atropine and 10^{-5} M tetrodotoxin (TTX) to examine the sites of action. Responses were normalized as a percent of the bethanechol response in the same tissue. Results are expressed as means ± SEM.

RESULTS

Cat

SP, septide, and NKA resulted in contractile responses with ED$_{50}$ values of 2.5 × 10^{-7}, 2.2 × 10^{-8}, and 6 × 10^{-8} M, respectively (FIGURE 1). Senktide had no effect. The response to SP was significantly blocked by previous exposure to septide. Septide was also blocked by SP, NKA, or septide itself. Senktide did not block the subsequent response to septide. The response to NKA was blocked by previous exposure to septide only at a lower dose. Atropine reduced the response to 10^{-6} M SP and NKA (8.6 ± 4.8% and 59.4 ± 9.2% of control, respectively) ($p < 0.02$). However, TTX did not block the response to 10^{-6} M NKA (64.3 ± 46.0% of control).

---

[a]To whom all correspondence should be addressed.

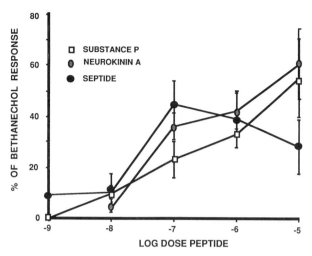

FIGURE 1. Cat colon response to SP, septide, and NKA. Senktide, a specific NK3 receptor agonist, had no effect.

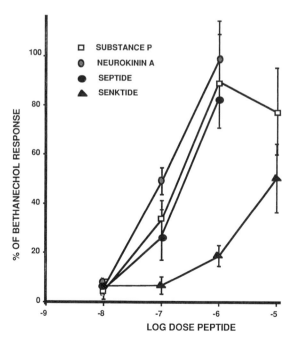

FIGURE 2. Rat colon response to septide, SP, NKA, and senktide.

Rat

SP, septide, NKA, and senktide caused contractile responses of the proximal colon. The ED_{50} values of SP, septide, NKA, and senktide were 5.6×10^{-7}, 2×10^{-7}, 2×10^{-7}, and 2×10^{-6} M, respectively (FIGURE 2). Atropine partially blocked the responses to 10^{-6} M SP, 10^{-6} M NKA, and 10^{-5} M senktide to $51.5 \pm 9.5\%$, $45.1 \pm 10.5\%$, and $52.6 \pm 11.7\%$ of control, respectively ($p < 0.05$). TTX did not block the responses of SP or NKA at 10^{-6} M, but did inhibit the response to 10^{-6} M septide and 10^{-5} M senktide ($56.1 \pm 12.4\%$ and $40.8 \pm 10.6\%$ of control, $p < 0.05$).

DISCUSSION

Cat

The response to septide implies that there are NK1 receptors in the cat proximal colon. Cross-tachyphylaxis between SP and septide suggests that SP acts via the NK1 receptor. Inhibition by septide of the response to NKA at lower doses indicates that NKA acts via both NK1 and another receptor. The lack of response to senktide and the failure of tachyphylaxis of the response to NKA after senktide suggest that this additional receptor is an NK2 receptor. Both NK1 and NK2 responses are partly mediated via cholinergic nerves. The failure of TTX to inhibit the NKA responses to the same degree as atropine suggests that NKA also acts via a neural inhibitory pathway and on smooth muscle cells.

Rat

The responses to septide and senktide suggest that both NK1 and NK3 receptors are present. The NK3 receptors are probably on cholinergic postganglionic nerves, whereas NK1 receptors appear to be on noncholinergic nerves. The failure of TTX to block the responses to NKA suggests an additional inhibitory neural pathway involving NK2 receptors.

CONCLUSIONS

This study demonstrates the presence of multiple neurokinin receptors in the proximal colon of the cat and rat.

REFERENCES

1. LAUFER, R., C. GILON, M. CHOREV & Z. SELINGER. 1988. Desensitization with a selective agonist discriminates between multiple tachykinin receptors. J. Pharmacol. Exp. Ther. **245:** 639–643.
2. ROTHSTEIN, R. D., E. JOHNSON & A. OUYANG. 1989. Substance P: mechanism of action and receptor distribution at the feline ileocecal sphincter region. Am. J. Physiol. **257:** G447–G453.
3. BURCHER, E. 1989. The study of tachykinin receptors. Clin. Exp. Pharmacol. Physiol. **16:** 539–543.

Comparative Autoradiographic Distribution of [125I]–Neuropeptide Gamma and [125I]–Neurokinin A Binding Sites in Guinea Pig Brain

THAN-VINH DAM,[a] YASUO TAKEDA,[b]
JAMES E. KRAUSE,[b] AND RÉMI QUIRION[a]

[a]Douglas Hospital Research Center
and
Department of Psychiatry
McGill University
Verdun, Québec, Canada H4H 1R3

[b]Department of Anatomy and Neurobiology
Washington University School of Medicine
St. Louis, Missouri 63110

Mammalian tachykinins are derived from the preprotachykinin I and II genes (PPT-I and PPT-II), which are two different, but related genes.[1,2] Substance P (SP), neurokinin A (NKA), and the NKA-derived peptides, neuropeptide K (NPK), neuropeptide γ (NPγ), and NKA(3–10), are encoded by mRNAs resulting from the PPT-I gene transcription,[3–5] whereas neurokinin B (NKB) is derived from the PPT-II gene.[6,7] The RNA transcribed from the PPT-I gene is alternatively spliced to yield three different mRNAs encoding the α, β, and γ PPT precursors.[1–5] NPγ is exclusively derived from γ-PPT mRNA.[2,8] Moreover, the proportion of γ-PPT mRNA in the rat central nervous system (CNS) represents up to 80% of the total PPT-I-derived mRNAs,[2] and NPγ, the N-terminal extended form of NKA, comprises significant amounts of neurokinin (NK) immunoreactivity in the rat CNS and periphery.[9] Our previous study has shown that NPγ and NKA bind to NK-2 receptors in the rat CNS.[10] We have now compared the autoradiographic distribution of NK-2 receptors in rat and guinea pig brains using [125I]-NPγ and 2-[125I]-iodohistidyl[1]-NKA.

MATERIALS AND METHODS

Male Sprague-Dawley (225 g) rat and Hartley (350 g) guinea pig brain sections were prepared as described earlier.[10] Tissue sections were incubated with 25 pM [125I]-NPγ (1000 Ci/mmol) or 50 pM [125I]-NKA (2200 Ci/mmol, Amersham, Montréal, Québec) in a buffer that included various enzyme inhibitors[10–12] in order to ensure the stability of the ligands. Specific binding was determined as the difference in binding observed in the presence and absence of 1 μM NPγ or NKA.[10] At the end of the incubation, sections were (i) washed, (ii) apposed to sensitive films (Hyperfilm, Amersham), and (iii) developed, after appropriate exposure, as described before.[10,12]

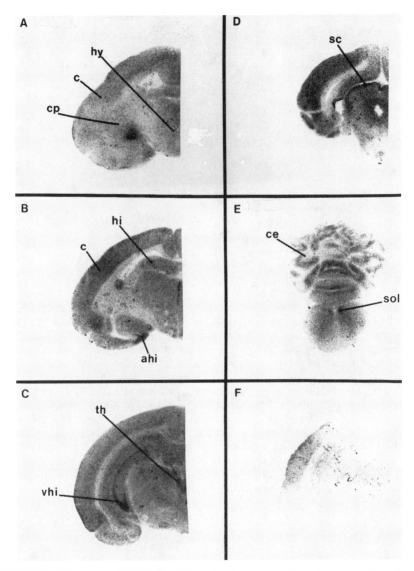

FIGURE 1. Distribution of [^{125}I]-NPγ binding sites in coronal guinea pig brain sections. High densities of sites are present in the stratum radiatum of the hippocampus (C), the amygdalo-hippocampal area (B), the superior colliculus (D), and the nucleus tractus solitarius (E). Low to moderate densities of [^{125}]-NPγ binding sites are seen in the frontal cortex (A,B), certain midline thalamic nuclei (C), and the cerebellum (E). (F): Section incubated in the presence of 1 μM NPγ. Abbreviations: ahi, amygdalo-hippocampal area; c, cortex; ce, cerebellum; cp, caudate putamen; hi, hippocampus; hy, hypothalamus; sc, superior colliculus; sol, nucleus tractus solitarius; th, thalamus; vhi, ventral hippocampus.

RESULTS AND DISCUSSION

As shown in FIGURE 1, the distribution of [^{125}I]-NPγ binding sites is very discrete in guinea pig brain. Only the stratum radiatum of the hippocampus (FIGURE 1C), the amygdalo-hippocampal area (FIGURE 1B), the superior colliculus (FIGURE 1D), and

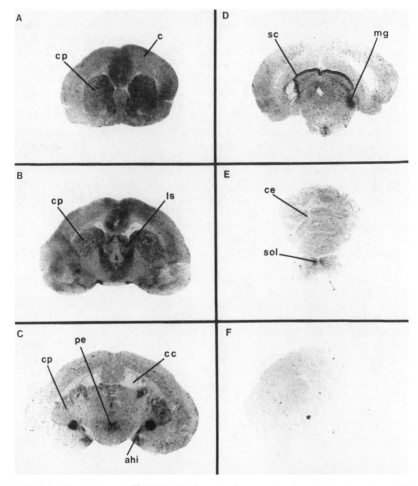

FIGURE 2. Distribution of [^{125}I]-NKA binding sites in coronal guinea pig brain sections. High densities of sites are present in the entorhinal cortex (A,B), the striatum (A,B), certain amygdaloid nuclei (C), the amygdalo-hippocampal area (C), the superior colliculus (D), and the medial geniculate nucleus (D). Moderate densities of sites are seen in different hypothalamic nuclei (B,C) and in the nucleus tractus solitarius (E). The cerebellum contains only low densities of [^{125}I]-NKA sites (E), whereas the corpus callosum is devoid of labeling (C). (F): Section incubated in the presence of 1 μM NKA. Abbreviations: ahi, amygdalo-hippocampal area; c, cortex; cc, corpus callosum; ce, cerebellum; cp, caudate putamen; ls, lateral septum; mg, medial geniculate nucleus; pe, periventricular nucleus of the hypothalamus; sc, superior colliculus; sol, nucleus tractus solitarius.

the nucleus tractus solitarius (FIGURE 1E) are highly enriched with $[^{125}I]$-NPγ sites. Regions containing low to moderate densities of $[^{125}I]$-NPγ binding sites include the frontal cortex (FIGURES 1A and 1B), certain midline thalamic nuclei (FIGURE 1C), and the cerebellum, especially in lobules 9 and 10 (FIGURE 1E). Mesencephalic areas are not enriched with $[^{125}I]$-NPγ sites (FIGURES 1C and 1D).

The distribution of $[^{125}I]$-NKA binding sites in guinea pig brain is shown in FIGURE 2. Binding is mostly concentrated in the entorhinal cortex (FIGURES 2A and 2B), with the caudal cortical areas containing only few $[^{125}I]$-NKA binding sites (FIGURES 2C and 2D). High levels of $[^{125}I]$-NKA sites are also observed in the rostral striatum (FIGURES 2A and 2B), certain amygdaloid nuclei (FIGURE 2C), the amygdalo-hippocampal area (FIGURE 2C), the superior colliculus (FIGURE 2D), and the medial geniculate nucleus (FIGURE 2D). Moderate densities of $[^{125}I]$-NKA binding sites are seen in different hypothalamic nuclei (FIGURES 2B and 2C) and in the nucleus tractus solitarius (FIGURE 2E). The cerebellum contains only low densities of $[^{125}I]$-NKA sites (FIGURE 2E), whereas mesencephalic areas and the corpus callosum are devoid of labeling (FIGURE 2C).

We have previously shown that the labeling patterns of $[^{125}I]$-NPγ and $[^{125}I]$-NKA are very similar in the rat brain.[10] In this species, these two ligands bind to a very discrete population of sites that are mostly concentrated in the external plexiform layer of the olfactory bulb, the prefrontal cortex, the lateral septum, certain hippocampal laminae and thalamic nuclei, and the amygdalo-hippocampal area.[10] Globally, it also appears that these two ligands bind to a similar population of sites (possibly of the NK-2 type) in the guinea pig brain. However, certain differences are seen both in relation to the distribution of labeling in these two species and in regard to labeling profiles of $[^{125}I]$-NPγ and $[^{125}I]$-NKA in guinea pig brain. For example, whereas various laminae of the rat hippocampus are enriched with $[^{125}I]$-NPγ sites (stratum radiatum = pyramidal layer > molecular layer > granular layer of the dentate gyrus),[10] only the stratum radiatum is enriched with $[^{125}I]$-NPγ sites in the guinea pig CNS (FIGURE 1C).

Moreover, it appears that $[^{125}I]$-NKA binding sites are more abundant than $[^{125}I]$-NPγ sites in the guinea pig brain (FIGURES 1 and 2). This may be related to the relatively better selectivity (although not absolute) of $[^{125}I]$-NPγ for NK-2 sites.[10] However, more definite conclusions in that regard will have to await the development of highly selective radioligands, possibly based on recently characterized NK-2 receptor subtype antagonists.[13,14] Finally, it should also be added that, whereas γ-PPT mRNA (encoding the NPγ precursor) is most abundant in rat brain,[2] β-PPT mRNA is predominant in bovine as well as human tissues.[2,4,8] Thus, the relative importance of NPγ as an NK endogenous ligand may be species-dependent; the nature of the most abundant PPT mRNA in guinea pig brain remains to be established.

REFERENCES

1. NAKANISHI, S. 1987. Physiol. Rev. **67:** 1117–1142.
2. KRAUSE, J. E., M. R. MCDONALD & Y. TAKEDA. 1989. BioEssays **10:** 62–69.
3. NAWA, H., T. HIROSE, H. TAKASHIMA, S. INAYAMA & S. NAKANISHI. 1983. Nature (London) **306:** 32–36.
4. NAWA, H., H. KOTANI & S. NAKANISHI. 1984. Nature (London) **312:** 729–734.
5. KRAUSE, J. E., J. M. CHIRGWIN, M. S. CARTER, Z. S. XU & A. D. HERSHEY. 1987. Proc. Natl. Acad. Sci. U.S.A. **84:** 881–885.
6. KOTANI, H., M. HOSHIMARU, H. NAWA & S. NAKANISHI. 1986. Proc. Natl. Acad. Sci. U.S.A. **83:** 7074–7078.

7. BONNER, T. I., H-U. AFFOLTER, A. C. YOUNG & W. S. YOUNG. 1987. Mol. Brain Res. **2:** 243–249.
8. HELKE, C. J., J. E. KRAUSE, P. W. MANTYH, R. COUTURE & M. J. BANNON. 1990. FASEB J. **4:** 1606–1615.
9. TAKEDA, Y., J. TAKEDA, B. M. SMART & J. E. KRAUSE. 1990. Regulat. Peptides **28:** 323–333.
10. DAM, T-V., Y. TAKEDA, J. E. KRAUSE, E. ESCHER & R. QUIRION. 1990. Proc. Natl. Acad. Sci. U.S.A. **87:** 246–250.
11. QUIRION, R. & T-V. DAM. 1988. Regulat. Peptides **22:** 18–25.
12. DAM, T-V., E. ESCHER & R. QUIRION. 1988. Brain Res. **453:** 372–376.
13. BUCK, S. H., B. O. FANGER & P. L. M. VAN GIERSBERGEN. 1991. Ann. N.Y. Acad. Sci. This volume.
14. MAGGI, C. A., R. PATACCHINI, M. ASTOLFI, P. ROVERO, S. GIULIANI & A. GIACHETTI. 1991. Ann. N.Y. Acad. Sci. This volume.

Substance P–containing and Calcitonin Gene–related Peptide–containing Neurons in the Human Trigeminal Ganglion

Immunohistochemical Detection, Morphometric Characterization, and Coexistence of Peptides

M. DEL FIACCO, G. DIAZ, A. FLORIS, AND M. QUARTU

Department of Cytomorphology
University of Cagliari
09124 Cagliari, Italy

The neuropeptides, substance P (SP) and calcitonin gene–related peptide (CGRP), have been localized in primary sensory trigeminal neurons in laboratory animals.[1,2] Coexistence of peptides has also been extensively demonstrated.[3] We have recently described the presence and morphometric characteristics of SP-like immunoreactive (SPI) neurons in the human trigeminal ganglion.[4] This work provides further data on the SPI neuronal elements, analyzes the CGRP-like immunoreactive (CGRPI) neuronal population, and shows coexistence of peptides in human primary trigeminal neurons.

Specimens obtained within 40 h postmortem from subjects at life stages ranging from 21 weeks of gestation to 67 years were processed by the indirect immunofluorescence technique using a monoclonal rat anti-SP antibody[5] and a rabbit anti-CGRP antiserum (Peninsula RAS-6009-N). Morphometric analysis and the percent frequency calculation were performed as previously described.[4] Both primary antisera stained the cytoplasmic compartment of neuronal perikarya, beaded and nonbeaded fibers of various caliber, and pericellular basketlike varicose filaments (FIGURE 1). Perikarya and nerve fibers immunoreactive to both neuropeptides were observed at all examined ages, whereas pericellular basketlike structures were only detected at fetal (FIGURE 1, panels I and J), preterm neonatal, and (more rarely) full-term neonatal life stages. As previously reported,[5] SPI perikarya could be classified as showing high-density and low-density immunoreactivity at neonatal and adult stages, whereas such discrimination was less perceptible in fetal tissue. CGRPI cell bodies showed a wider range of fluorescent granule density. In addition, some of them were characterized by an intensely fluorescent perinuclear thickening of immunoreactive material.

Double immunostaining revealed the coexistence of peptides in many cells, although several perikarya were found to contain only either SP or CGRP (FIGURE 1, panels K and L). Values of the percent frequency of labeled perikarya varied with age, being slightly higher at perinatal stages compared to adult life both for SP (full-term newborn: 23.64 ± 3% confidence limit; adult: 17.73 ± 2%) and CGRP (fetus 21 weeks: 17.73 ± 1.3%; preterm newborn: 48.58 ± 3.2%; adult: 45.12 ± 2.3%).

As to the size of cell bodies, both SPI and CGRPI neuronal populations appeared heterogeneous: although most of them were small and medium sized (less

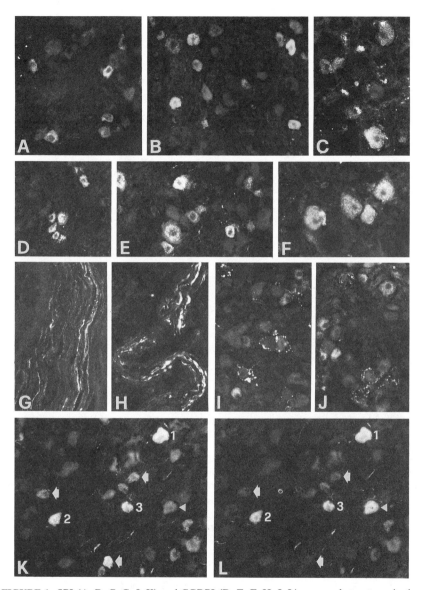

FIGURE 1. SPI (A, B, C, G, I, K) and CGRPI (D, E, F, H, J, L) neuronal structures in the trigeminal ganglion from fetus (D, I, J), preterm newborn (A, E), 1-h-old to 10-day-old full-term newborns (B, G, H, K, L), and 67-year-old adult (C, F). High and low density SPI perikarya are easily distinguishable in C and K. Some CGRPI neurons show perinuclear thickenings of immunoreactive material (D, E, F). Both SPI (G) and CGRPI (H) fibers vary in caliber and in the presence of varicosities. SPI (I) and CGRPI (J) pericellular basketlike varicose filaments are frequently found around nonimmunoreactive cell bodies in fetal tissue. SP (K) and CGRP (L) double immunostaining on the same tissue section shows the coexistence of peptides (numbers); some perikarya containing either SP or CGRP are indicated by arrows and triangles, respectively. A, B, C, E, F, H, K, L: ×210; D, I, J: ×205; G: ×215. (However, the figure has been reduced to 55%.)

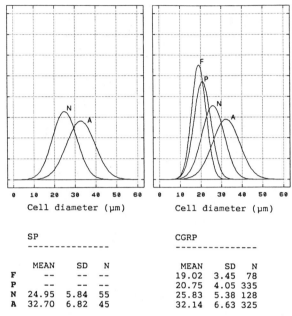

	SP		
	MEAN	SD	N
F	--	--	--
P	--	--	--
N	24.95	5.84	55
A	32.70	6.82	45

	CGRP		
	MEAN	SD	N
F	19.02	3.45	78
P	20.75	4.05	335
N	25.83	5.38	128
A	32.14	6.63	325

FIGURE 2. Normal distribution of diameters of SPI and CGRPI neuronal cell bodies at different life stages: F, fetus; P, preterm newborn; N, newborn; A, adult. The increase of average cell sizes, related to subject age, is accompanied by an increase of standard deviations. The coincidence of the left distribution tails points to a minimum cell size common to all samples.

than 35 μm in diameter), perikarya measuring up to 55 μm for SP and up to 52 μm for CGRP were detected in adult tissue. FIGURE 2 reports the normal distributions of diameters of SPI and CGRPI perikarya at different life stages.

The results obtained allow us to extend to man the functional implications of SP and CGRP as neuroactive substances in primary sensory trigeminal neurons. The transient appearance of pericellular terminal-like elements suggests additional functional roles for both peptides in the ganglion at early stages of ontogenesis.

REFERENCES

1. HÖKFELT, T., J. O. KELLERTH, G. NILSSON & B. PERNOW. 1975. Science **190:** 889–890.
2. ROSENFELD, M. G., J-J. MERMOD, S. G. AMARA, L. W. SWANSON, P. E. SAWCHENKO, J. RIVIER, W. W. VALE & R. M. EVANS. 1983. Nature **304:** 129–135.
3. LEE, Y., Y. KAWAI, S. SHIOSAKA, K. TAKAMI, H. KIYAMA, S. GIRGIS, I. MACINTYRE, P. C. EMSON & M. TOHYAMA. 1985. Brain Res. **330:** 194–196.
4. DEL FIACCO, M., M. QUARTU, A. FLORIS & G. DIAZ. 1990. Neurosci. Lett. **110:** 16–21.
5. CUELLO, A. C., G. GALFRÈ & C. MILSTEIN. 1979. Proc. Natl. Acad. Sci. U.S.A. **76:** 3532–3536.

An Examination of the Proposed Functional Interaction of Substance P and 5-HT in the Guinea Pig Ileum

ALYSON J. FOX AND IAN K. M. MORTON

Pharmacology Group
Division of Biomedical Sciences
King's College London
London SW3 6LX, United Kingdom

INTRODUCTION

Gaddum and Picarelli[1] showed that 5-HT can contract the guinea pig ileum via the "D" receptor located on the longitudinal smooth muscle and via the "M" receptor present on cholinergic neurons, now referred to as 5-HT_2 and 5-HT_3 receptors, respectively. Similarly, substance P (SP) and other tachykinins can contract this preparation both directly via smooth muscle NK-1 receptors and indirectly via NK-3 receptor–mediated ACh release.[2] It has been suggested that SP release mediates the neuronal actions of 5-HT.[3,4] Buchheit *et al.*[4] proposed that, at low 5-HT concentrations, activation of a non-5-HT_3 receptor (which may be identical to the newly described 5-HT_4 receptor[5]) releases SP, which in turn liberates ACh to cause contraction. At higher 5-HT concentrations, it was suggested that 5-HT_3 receptor activation liberates SP, which then causes direct contraction of the smooth muscle. This proposed scheme is summarized in FIGURE 1, which also illustrates how neurokinin NK-1 and NK-3 receptors may be expected to be involved. Here, we reexamine the aforementioned proposal that SP is involved in the contractile action of 5-HT.

METHODS

The effects of the selective NK-1 receptor antagonist, GR71251,[6] and desensitization with the selective NK-3 receptor agonist, senktide,[7] were tested against contractile responses of longitudinal muscle–myenteric plexus (LMMP) preparations to 5-HT. Preliminary experiments showed that GR71251 competitively antagonized responses to the selective NK-1 receptor agonist, substance P methyl ester (SPOME), giving a pK_B estimate of 7.63 ± 0.14 (SEM). Desensitization with senktide was found to be best achieved through the continued presence of the agonist (30 nM) in the bathing fluid; this protocol abolished subsequent responses to senktide, whereas responses to SPOME and carbachol were unaffected. Experiments were also performed to test the ability of senktide to release [^{3}H]-ACh using the methodology previously described.[8]

To test the effects of these ligands on responses to 5-HT, matched preparations received 5-HT (10 nM–30 μM) either alone or in the presence of GR71251 (3 μM) added 5 min prior to each 5-HT application or after desensitization with senktide (or with a combination of the two treatments). Additional experiments were also

385

performed in which preparations received 5-HT alone or after a 1-h incubation with capsaicin (1 μM) or in the presence of a combination of peptidase inhibitors [phosphoramidon (1 μM), captopril (1 μM), and bestatin (100 μM)]. In all experiments, 5-HT doses were applied in a fully randomized order using a 15-min dose cycle.

RESULTS AND DISCUSSION

We have previously shown that $5-HT_3$ receptor activation leads to [^{3}H]-ACh release[8] and, here, the selective NK-3 receptor agonist, senktide, also produced concentration-related increases in [^{3}H]-ACh release that matched its contractile activity (pD_2 estimates: 8.80 ± 0.07 for release, $n = 8$; 8.16 ± 0.10 for contraction,

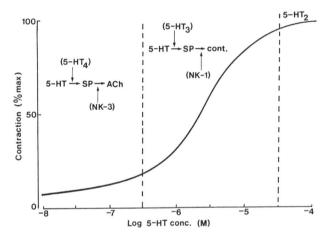

FIGURE 1. Summary of the proposal by Buchheit *et al.*[4] for the involvement of SP release in the contractile action of 5-HT in the guinea pig ileum. The predicted contributions of NK-1 and NK-3 receptors are indicated.

$n = 8$). If SP were involved in the responses to 5-HT as proposed by Buchheit *et al.*,[4] it would be expected that NK-1 and NK-3 receptor blockade would produce shifts in the 5-HT concentration-response curve (see FIGURE 1). However, from FIGURE 2, it can be seen that neither the NK-1 receptor antagonist, GR71251, nor desensitization with senktide, either alone or in combination, inhibits responses to 5-HT. In fact, senktide desensitization appears to potentiate 5-HT-evoked contractions, the reason for which is unclear, although it could possibly be due to desensitization of prejunctional inhibitory muscarinic receptors[9] by the continued senktide-evoked ACh release. Capsaicin was without effect here on responses to 5-HT and a combination of peptidase inhibitors did not potentiate 5-HT-evoked contractions, as might be expected to occur if these were mediated through the release of SP. Taken together, these results indicate that the contractile activity of 5-HT in the guinea pig ileum is not mediated through the release of SP or another neurokinin.

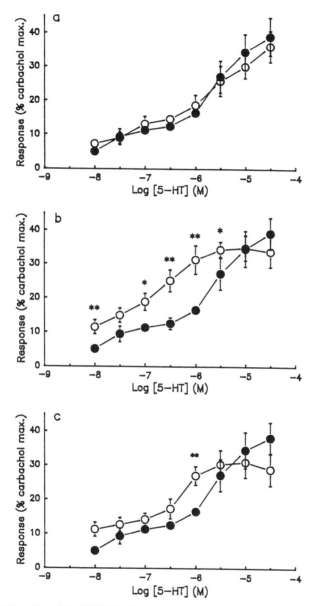

FIGURE 2. The effect of (a) GR71251, (b) desensitization with senktide, and (c) a combination of the two treatments on contractile responses to 5-HT. Symbols indicate concurrent control responses (●) or responses in the presence of neurokinin receptor blockade (○). Each point is the mean ± SEM from 8–10 preparations. Significant differences between test and control are indicated by ∗ ($P < 0.05$) and ∗∗ ($P < 0.01$).

REFERENCES

1. GADDUM, J. H. & Z. P. PICARELLI. 1957. Two kinds of tryptamine receptors. Br. J. Pharmacol. Chemother. **12:** 323–328.
2. LAUFER, R., U. WORMSER, Z. FRIEDMAN, C. GILON, M. CHOREV & Z. SELINGER. 1985. Neurokinin B is a preferred agonist for a neuronal substance P receptor and its action is antagonized by enkephalin. Proc. Natl. Acad. Sci. U.S.A. **82:** 7444–7448.
3. CHAHL, L. 1983. Substance P mediates atropine-sensitive response of guinea pig ileum to serotonin. Eur. J. Pharmacol. **87:** 485–489.
4. BUCHHEIT, K. H., G. ENGEL, E. MUTSCHLER & B. RICHARDSON. 1985. Study of the contractile effect of 5-hydroxytryptamine (5-HT) in the isolated longitudinal smooth muscle strip from guinea pig ileum. Naunyn-Schmiedeberg's Arch. Pharmacol. **329:** 36–41.
5. CLARKE, D. E., D. A. CRAIG & J. R. FOZARD. 1989. The 5-HT$_4$ receptor: naughty but nice. Trends Pharmacol. Sci. **10:** 485–489.
6. WARD, P., G. B. EWAN, C. C. JORDAN, S. J. IRELAND, R. M. HAGAN & J. R. BROWN. 1990. Potent and highly selective neurokinin (NK-1) antagonists. J. Med. Chem. **33:** 1848–1851.
7. WORMSER, U., R. LAUFER, Y. HART, M. CHOREV, C. GILON & Z. SELINGER. 1986. Highly selective ligands for substance P receptor subtypes. EMBO J. **5:** 2805–2808.
8. FOX, A. J. & I. K. M. MORTON. 1990. An examination of the 5-HT$_3$ receptor mediating contraction and evoked [^{3}H]-ACh release in the guinea pig ileum. Br. J. Pharmacol. **101:** 553–558.
9. KILBINGER, H. & I. WESSLER. 1980. Inhibition by acetylcholine of the stimulation-evoked release of [^{3}H]-acetylcholine from the guinea pig myenteric plexus. Neuroscience **5:** 93–112.

Molecular Cloning of the Human Neurokinin-2 Receptor cDNA by Polymerase Chain Reaction and Isolation of the Gene[a]

NORMA P. GERARD[b,c] AND CRAIG GERARD[d,e]

[b]*Department of Medicine*
Beth Israel Hospital
[d]*Department of Pediatrics*
Children's Hospital
and
Ina Sue Perlmutter Laboratory at Children's Hospital
and
Thorndike Laboratory of Harvard Medical School
Boston, Massachusetts 02215

Neurokinin A (substance K) is a peptide neurotransmitter of the tachykinin family with potential as a major mediator in human airway and gastrointestinal tissues.[1,2] Neurokinin A acts via a receptor (the NK-2 receptor) that is believed to be localized on smooth muscle cells and pharmacologically coupled to a GTP-binding protein.[3]

To characterize the human NK-2 receptor, we prepared a partial cDNA from human tracheal RNA using the polymerase chain reaction with oligonucleotide primers derived from the bovine NK-2 receptor cDNA sequence.[4] This partial human NK-2 receptor cDNA was used to screen a human genomic DNA library and yielded a clone, NGNK-2, of approximately 20 kilobase pairs. Analysis of NGNK-2 indicates that it contains the entire coding sequence of the NK-2 receptor as well as 5' and 3' flanking sequences. The gene is organized with five exons interrupted by four introns. We determined the complete sequence of the exons and the intron/exon junctions, as well as the transcription initiation site at nucleotide -222 and the 3' polyadenylation signal at nucleotide 1530. Sequence analysis of exons 1 and 5, where major differences occur between the human and animal species, provided information for PCR primers that allowed us to prepare full-length cDNA for the human NK-2 receptor. The protein predicted from the gene sequence is extended by 14 amino acids at the C-terminus compared to the bovine molecule and by 9 residues compared to the rat molecule (FIGURE 1). The seven membrane-spanning regions are encoded by exons 1–4 and none are interrupted by introns. These regions are highly conserved among the species studied, suggesting stringent evolutionary control over these molecules.

[a]This work was supported in part by NIH Grant No. HL41587.
[c]N. P. Gerard is the recipient of NIH Research Career Development Award No. HL01777.
[e]C. Gerard is the recipient of a Faculty Scholars Award from R. J. R. Nabisco.

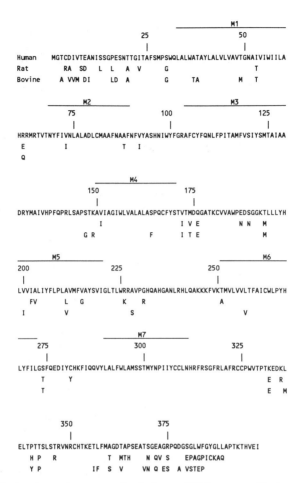

FIGURE 1. Deduced protein sequence for the human NK-2 receptor. The human sequence is presented continuously with rat and bovine substitutions indicated below. Two potential glycosylation sites are indicated in the amino terminal region by triangles. M1 through M7 indicate each of the seven hydrophobic regions characteristic of the G protein–coupled receptors of the rhodopsin superfamily. Significant variations at the amino and carboxyl termini are apparent.

REFERENCES

1. MAGGIO, J. E. 1988. Annu. Rev. Neurosci. **11**: 13–28.
2. HUA, X-Y., E. THEODORSSON-NORHEIM, E. BRODIN, J. M. LUNDBERG & T. HÖKFELT. 1985. Regulat. Peptides **13**: 1–19.
3. DOHLMAN, H. G., M. G. CARON & R. J. LEFKOWITZ. 1987. Biochemistry **26**: 2557–2664.
4. MASU, Y., K. NAKAYAMA, H. TAMAKI, Y. HARADA, M. KUNO & S. NAKANISHI. 1987. Nature **329**: 836–838.

Regulation of Preprotachykinin Gene Expression by Nerve Growth Factor

C. A. GILCHRIST, C. MORRISON, AND A. J. HARMAR

MRC Brain Metabolism Unit
Royal Edinburgh Hospital
Edinburgh EH10 5HF, Scotland, United Kingdom

We have shown previously[1] that, in cultures of adult rat sensory neurons, expression of the preprotachykinin (PPT) and calcitonin/CGRP genes is regulated by nerve growth factor (NGF). To investigate the mechanism by which NGF regulates PPT gene expression, we have transfected the NGF-sensitive PC12 cell line with a series of plasmids containing parts of the promoter region of the PPT gene linked to the reporter gene, chloramphenicol acetyltransferase (CAT).

The prototype plasmid (pBX.cat) was constructed by inserting 1.84 kb of the 5′ flanking sequence from the bovine PPT gene (gift from S. Nakanishi[2]) into plasmid pBLCAT2[3] in place of the thymidine kinase promoter. A series of deletion subclones was also created (FIGURE 1). Then, pBX.cat (5 μg) or related plasmids were transfected into PC12 cells by electroporation. After growth of the cells in the presence or absence of NGF for two days, cells were harvested and extracts were assayed for CAT activity (FIGURE 1).

NGF induced a 2-fold increase in the expression of CAT in PC12 cells transfected with pBX.cat, indicating that there are NGF-responsive sequences within 1.84 kb of the transcriptional start site of the PPT gene. Two regions of the PPT gene—0.58 kb to 0.85 kb and 1.42 kb to 1.67 kb upstream of the transcription start site—appeared to mediate NGF responsiveness (compare pPST.cat with pEV.cat and pSSP14delX with pS.cat).

To investigate one of the putative NGF-responsive elements, we subcloned a 265-bp fragment that contained the more proximal element (−850 bp to −585 bp) into the vector pBLCAT2, upstream of the thymidine kinase promoter (pEV-PST.cat). The fragment conferred NGF inducibility (1.5-fold) upon the promoter (FIGURE 2).

Several regions of the PPT promoter appeared to play a role in determining the level of expression of CAT in transfected cells. Three regions (−1.67 kb to −1.42 kb, −0.85 kb to −0.58 kb, and −0.58 kb to −85 bp) increased the expression of CAT in transfected cells. Deletion of sequences between −1.42 kb and −0.85 kb resulted in enhanced expression of CAT, suggesting the presence of a negative control element.

Because PC12 cells do not express the PPT gene endogenously, we investigated the importance of these putative control regions in F11 cells, a neuroblastoma × glioma hybrid cell line that, although not responsive to NGF, produces substance P at low levels.[4] The basal level of expression of CAT was 4-fold to 6-fold higher in transfected F11 cells than in PC12 cells. However, the relative expression of different PPT-CAT constructs was similar in the two cell lines, suggesting that the factors regulating basal gene expression are similar.

We conclude that the regulation of PPT gene expression by NGF is mediated, at least in part, at the level of gene transcription. Two regions of the PPT gene (−0.85 kb to −0.58 kb and −1.67 kb to −1.42 kb) may mediate NGF responsiveness. The

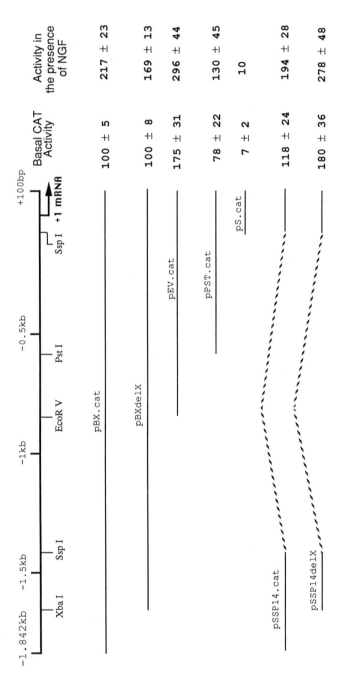

FIGURE 1. Mapping of NGF-responsive sequences in the 5′ region of the PPT gene. The region of PPT DNA (1.9 kb) used to create the PPT-CAT constructs is shown at the top. It includes the site of PPT mRNA initiation (+1). For each construct, the basal level of CAT expression and the activity in the presence of NGF are shown. CAT activity is expressed relative to pBX.cat in the absence of NGF (100%).

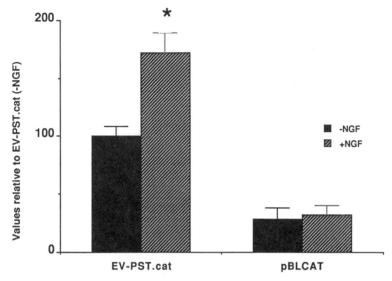

FIGURE 2. A 265-bp PPT fragment confers enhancer activity and NGF responsiveness upon a heterologous promoter. The 265-bp fragment, EcoRV (−850 bp) to Pst1 (−585 bp), was subcloned into pBLCAT2, upstream of the thymidine kinase promoter, to create pEV-PST.cat and the level of CAT expression was measured in the presence or absence of NGF. CAT activity was normalized to the levels observed in cells transfected with pEV-PST.cat in the absence of NGF. A significant difference is indicated by the asterisk.

first of these sequences confers NGF inducibility and increased basal transcription on the thymidine kinase promoter.

REFERENCES

1. LINDSAY, R. M. & A. J. HARMAR. 1989. Nature **337:** 362–364.
2. NAWA, H., H. KOTANI & S. NAKANISHI. 1984. Nature **312:** 729–734.
3. LUCKOW, B. & G. SCHÜTZ. 1987. Nucleic Acids Res. **15:** 5490.
4. FRANCEL, P. C., K. HARRIS, M. SMITH, M. C. FISHMAN, G. DAWSON & R. J. MILLER. 1987. J. Neurochem. **48:** 1624–1631.

Modulation of Endogenous Levels of Substance P in Rat CNS Tissues by N,N-Diethyldithiocarbamate

JAMES P. GILLIGAN,[a] SUSAN J. LOVATO,[a]
AND ARCO Y. JENG[b]

[a] Unigene Laboratories
Fairfield, New Jersey 07004

[b] Research Department
Pharmaceuticals Division
CIBA-GEIGY Corporation
Summit, New Jersey 07901

INTRODUCTION

α-Amidating enzyme (αAE) is a Cu^{2+}- and ascorbate-requiring enzyme that converts glycine-extended prohormones to mature, biologically active hormones.[1] This posttranslational processing enzyme has been purified from several sources including bovine pituitary[2] and rat medullary thyroid carcinoma (MTC) tissues.[3] However, the modulation of αAE activity *in vivo* is not well understood. Mains *et al.* reported that chronic administration of a Cu^{2+}-chelating agent, N,N-diethyldithiocarbamate (DDC), or its disulfide dimer, disulfiram (Antabuse), decreased the α-amidation of pituitary α-melanotropin and the joining peptide of proadrenocorticotropic hormone in rats.[4] In this communication, we examined whether or not DDC treatment would inhibit the α-amidation of glycine-extended substance P (SP-Gly), a peptide shown to have a high affinity for αAE,[5] in the rat central nervous system.

METHODS

Sprague-Dawley rats were placed on a dosing regimen consisting of two subcutaneous injections of DDC (in phosphate-buffered saline and 0.1% Tween-80) daily for three days. Four hours after the last injection, rats were anesthetized with ether and decapitated and then the hypothalamus, substantia nigra, and spinal cord were removed. The tissues were homogenized in 0.5 mL of 100 mM HCl and centrifuged. The supernatants were neutralized and lyophilized prior to analysis of SP by an SP-specific RIA.[6] The antibodies used in this assay recognized SP with an affinity that was 10,000-fold greater than that of SP-Gly. Conditions were developed to convert SP-Gly to the α-amidated hormone using exogenous αAE purified from rat MTC tissues. SP-Gly levels were determined by subtracting immunoreactive SP values obtained in samples not treated with αAE from SP levels detected in duplicate samples reacted with this enzyme.[6] Protein content was measured according to the method of Bradford.[7]

TABLE 1. Modulation of Endogenous Substance P Levels by DDC[a]

Tissue	Control pmol/mg	Control pmol/tissue	100 mg DDC/kg pmol/mg	100 mg DDC/kg pmol/tissue	250 mg DDC/kg pmol/mg	250 mg DDC/kg pmol/tissue
hypothalamus	9.0 ± 0.8	11 ± 1	8.2 ± 0.9	7.6 ± 0.9	6.7 ± 0.7	6.7 ± 0.8
spinal cord	5.7 ± 0.7	30 ± 4	5.4 ± 0.4	29 ± 1	3.9 ± 0.5	22 ± 3
substantia nigra	20 ± 3	22 ± 4	16 ± 1	16 ± 1	17 ± 1	13 ± 1

[a]DDC in phosphate-buffered saline and 0.1% Tween-80 was injected subcutaneously in rats twice daily at the dose indicated for three days. The contents of SP in each tissue were determined by RIA and are expressed in pmol/mg protein or pmol/tissue (mean ± SE, $n = 4$).

TABLE 2. Effects of αAE on SP Levels in Rats Treated with DDC[a]

Tissue	Control −αAE	Control +αAE	DDC-treated −αAE	DDC-treated +αAE
hypothalamus	16 ± 1 (6)	21 ± 2 (6)	12 ± 1 (5)	18 ± 2 (5)
spinal cord	5.2 ± 0.6 (6)	5.6 ± 0.5 (6)	4.0 ± 0.9 (5)	6.7 ± 1.1 (5)
substantia nigra	16 ± 1 (6)	18 ± 2 (6)	9 ± 2 (5)	17 ± 2 (5)

[a]SP levels are expressed in pmol/mg protein [mean ± SE (n)]. Rats were treated with 250 mg DDC/kg or vehicle twice daily for three days. Samples were pretreated with or without 25 ng of αAE, 1 μM Cu^{2+}, 3 mM ascorbate, and 100 μg of catalase/mL for 30 min at 37 °C.[6]

RESULTS AND DISCUSSION

DDC inhibited αAE *in vitro* with an IC_{50} value of 200 nM (results not shown). In rats treated with 250 mg DDC/kg twice daily for three days, SP levels in the hypothalamus, spinal cord, and substantia nigra were shown to decrease by 39%, 27%, and 41%, respectively, when compared to controls (TABLE 1). These decreases in SP levels could result from either a decrease in peptide synthesis or an accumulation of nonimmunoreactive SP-Gly as a result of αAE inhibition by DDC. To differentiate between these two possibilities, duplicate samples were incubated with exogenous αAE and cofactors to assess SP-Gly levels. The results presented in TABLE 2 demonstrate that, following treatment of these samples with αAE, CNS immunoreactive SP levels were indistinguishable from control values, indicating that the observed decreases in immunoreactive SP levels from drug-treated animals were in fact due to the accumulation of SP-Gly. The levels of biologically inactive SP-Gly were found to increase from less than 10% in controls to 33–47% in rats treated with DDC. Thus, inhibitors of αAE may provide a useful tool for studying the *in vivo* regulation of SP.

REFERENCES

1. MAINS, R. E., *et al.* 1987. Ann. N.Y. Acad. Sci. **493:** 278–291.
2. MURTHY, A. S. N., *et al.* 1986. J. Biol. Chem. **261:** 1815–1822.
3. GILLIGAN, J. P., *et al.* 1989. Endocrinology **124:** 2729–2736.
4. MAINS, R. E., *et al.* 1986. J. Biol. Chem. **261:** 11938–11941.
5. TAMBURINI, P. P., *et al.* 1988. Arch. Biochem. Biophys. **267:** 623–631.
6. JENG, A. Y., *et al.* 1990. Anal. Biochem. **185:** 213–219.
7. BRADFORD, M. M. 1976. Anal. Biochem. **72:** 248–254.

Evidence Supporting a Mitogenic Role for Substance P in Amphibian Limb Regeneration

Involvement of the Inositol Phospholipid Signaling Pathway

MORTON GLOBUS, MICHAEL J. SMITH,
AND SWANI VETHAMANY-GLOBUS

Department of Biology
University of Waterloo
Waterloo, Ontario, Canada N2L 3G1

The widely distributed neural peptide, substance P (SP), evokes a variety of biological responses;[1] however, its diverse roles have not been fully elucidated. In 1983, we raised the possibility for the first time that SP may function as a mitogenic (neurotrophic) agent of the nerve during newt forelimb regeneration.[2] The essential trophic function of nerves in this process is the promotion of mitosis in the blastema cells of the regenerate;[3,4] however, resolution of the neurally derived proliferative signals involved has not been accomplished.

Several pieces of evidence have suggested that SP is a strong candidate for a mitogenic role. First, the immunocytochemical localization of SP in neuronal perikarya of sensory ganglia[5] (FIGURE 1) was consistent with the localization of neurotrophic activity reported during limb regeneration.[3,4] Second, we detected SP at its presumed site of action in the limb regenerate (FIGURE 1) by immunohistochemical staining and by RIA.[5] Third, SP immunofluorescence in the regenerate gradually diminished following denervation of the limb.[6] Fourth, SP was mitogenic at extremely low concentrations (10 pg/mL) in cultured limb blastemas.[2] Finally, the mitogenic influence of intact nerves was suppressed in a dose-responsive manner when sensory ganglia, cocultured transfilter to the blastema, were treated with increasing concentrations of SP antiserum in the culture medium.[2] Confirmatory reports have since appeared in the literature showing that SP is mitogenic in mammalian connective tissue cells[7] and in regenerating planarians.[8]

We have recently investigated the possibility that transduction of mitogenic signals across blastema cell membranes may be mediated by the inositol phospholipid signaling pathway. Agonist-stimulated hydrolysis of phosphatidylinositol 4,5-bisphosphate is known to generate the intracellular second messengers, inositol 1,4,5-triphosphate and 1,2-diacylglycerol, which are both known to influence events leading to mitosis in many systems.[9,10] We have measured a rapid dose-dependent reduction of inositol phospholipids and an accumulation of radiolabeled inositol phosphates in the newt forelimb blastema in response to stimulation by SP and related tachykinins.[11] As seen in the left half of FIGURE 2, this effect was abolished when the blastema fragments were treated with neomycin,[11] a known inhibitor of inositol phospholipid turnover. Furthermore, SP stimulated the incorporation of [^{3}H]-thymidine into DNA of blastemal mesenchyme cells (right half of FIGURE 2) and this effect was also suppressed by neomycin at a dose corresponding to that

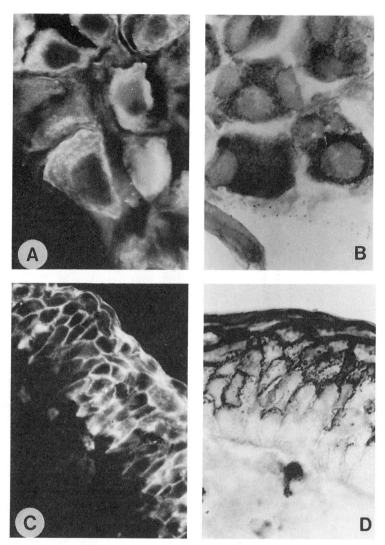

FIGURE 1. Immunofluorescence micrograph of an adult newt sensory ganglion (A) showing intense substance P (SP) immunoreactivity in the perikarya. Staining was abolished (not seen here) by preincubation of the antibody with SP. Peroxidase-antiperoxidase staining of sensory ganglia is seen in panel B. Substance P immunoreactivity is demonstrated in the epidermis of the limb regeneration blastema, as seen by immunofluorescence (C) and peroxidase-antiperoxidase staining (D).

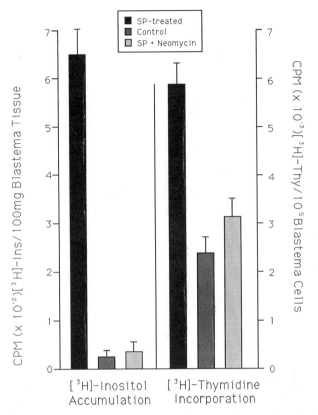

FIGURE 2. Left: [³H]-Inositol accumulation. Mesenchymal fragments of newt forelimb regeneration blastemas were prelabeled with myo-2-[³H]-inositol and then they were washed and exposed to 1 μM SP in the presence of lithium. Labeled inositol phosphates and inositol phospholipids extracted from the tissues were resolved using anion exchange and thin layer chromatography, respectively. Right: DNA synthetic activity in cultured blastema cells[4,12,13] was assessed by incorporation of [³H]-thymidine into the DNA.

required to inhibit inositol phosphate accumulation.[11] These results strongly suggest that one mechanism by which SP and perhaps other putative neurotrophic factors mediate their effect(s) on the blastema during the proliferative phase of limb regeneration is by stimulating the inositol phospholipid signaling pathway.

REFERENCES

1. LEEMAN, S. E. 1982. Recent Prog. Horm. Res. **38:** 93–132.
2. GLOBUS, M., S. VETHAMANY-GLOBUS, A. KESIK & G. MILTON. 1983. *In* Limb Development and Regeneration. J. F. Fallon & A. I. Caplan, Eds.: 513–524. Alan R. Liss. New York.
3. SINGER, M. 1974. Ann. N.Y. Acad. Sci. **228:** 308–322.
4. GLOBUS, M. & S. VETHAMANY-GLOBUS. 1977. Dev. Biol. **56:** 316–328.
5. GLOBUS, M. & P. ALLES. 1990. J. Exp. Zool. **254:** 165–176.

6. GLOBUS, M. & G. MICHENER. Manuscript in preparation.
7. NILSSON, J., A. M. VON EULER & C-J. DALSGAARD. 1985. Nature **315:** 61–63.
8. SALO, E. & T. BAGUNA. 1986. J. Exp. Zool. **237:** 129–135.
9. BERRIDGE, M. & R. F. IRVINE. 1984. Nature **312:** 315–321.
10. WHITMAN, M. & L. CANTLEY. 1988. Biochim. Biophys. Acta **948:** 327–344.
11. SMITH, M. J. & M. GLOBUS. Manuscript in preparation.
12. VETHAMANY, S. 1970. Ph.D. thesis. University of Toronto, Canada.
13. SMITH, M. J. & M. GLOBUS. 1989. In Vitro **25**(9): 849–856.

Evidence for Two Types of Tachykinin Receptors on Cholinergic Neurons of the Guinea Pig Ileum Myenteric Plexus[a]

S. GUARD,[b,c] A. T. McKNIGHT,[c,d] K. J. WATLING,[c,d]
AND S. P. WATSON[b]

[b]University Department of Pharmacology
Oxford, United Kingdom

[d]Merck Sharp & Dohme Research Laboratories
Neuroscience Research Center
Harlow, Essex, United Kingdom

In previous studies of tachykinin-induced [³H]-acetylcholine ([³H]-ACh) release from the guinea pig ileum myenteric plexus, the effects of the naturally occurring tachykinins have been investigated.[1-3] In the present study, we have used the NK_1-receptor-selective and the NK_3-receptor-selective agonists, substance P methyl ester (SPOMe) and succinyl-[Asp^6,$MePhe^8$]-SP(6–11) (senktide), respectively, to examine the possible involvement of different tachykinin receptor types in tachykinin-evoked release of ACh from guinea pig ileum myenteric plexus neurons.

Guinea pig ileum longitudinal muscle–myenteric plexus strips were set up in 3-mL silanized organ baths and were left to equilibrate for 30 min in Krebs solution, pH 7.4 at 37 °C, gassed with 95% O_2/5% CO_2. During this period, the strips were washed by overflow perfusion (0.5 mL/min). At the end of the equilibration period, perfusion was stopped and the strips were incubated with 0.1 μM [³H]-choline for 30 min. During this time, the strips were stimulated electrically at supramaximal voltage with square wave pulses of 1 ms duration, 0.5 Hz, by means of two platinum electrodes positioned at the top and bottom of the organ bath. The strips were then washed by overflow perfusion with Krebs solution containing 10 μM hemicholinium-3 to inhibit the reuptake of [³H]-choline. After an initial washout period of 30 min at 2 mL/min and a further 60-min washout at 1 mL/min, the perfusate was collected in 4-min fractions. Agonists were applied for 3 min, with antagonists or ion channel blockers being added to the perfusion medium 10 min before the stimulation with agonists. Following a 40-min washout of the agonists, the tissues were stimulated electrically at 0.2 Hz, 1 ms duration for 2 min as a control for tissue integrity. For experiments with zero calcium, the Krebs solution was replaced (after the 90-min washout period) with Krebs solution containing zero calcium/5 mM EGTA. Agonists were made up in this zero calcium solution and were perfused for 3 min as previously described. Tritium content of the samples was determined by liquid scintillation spectrometry. The amount of radioactivity in each sample was expressed as a fraction of the radioactivity present in the strip at the start of the respective collection period (i.e., fractional release).

The NK_3-selective agonist, senktide, and the NK_1-selective agonist, SPOMe, both

[a]This work was supported by the MRC and by an SERC "CASE" award to S. Guard.

[c]Present address: Parke-Davis Neuroscience Research Center, Addenbrookes Hospital Site, Hills Road, Cambridge CB2 2QB, United Kingdom.

produced a concentration-dependent increase in spontaneous [³H]-ACh release above basal levels. The maximal effect of senktide, as determined by the peak response above basal, was between 10-fold and 18-fold, with an EC_{50} of 2.4 nM (basal = 8320 ± 814 dpm; in the presence of 30 nM senktide = 98,050 ± 9035 dpm; n = 9). In contrast, the peak response to SPOMe was between 2-fold and 3.5-fold above basal, with an EC_{50} of 11.3 nM (basal = 11,902 ± 1651 dpm; in the presence of 100 nM SPOMe = 36,363 ± 692 dpm; n = 8). This can be compared with the peak release of [³H]-ACh elicited by electrical stimulation, which was 4.25 ± 0.27–fold

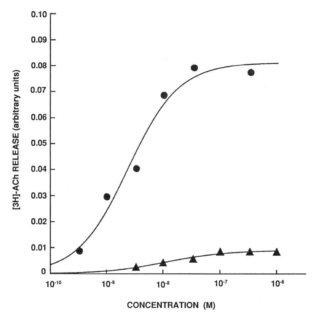

FIGURE 1. The effect of senktide (circles) and SPOMe (triangles) on spontaneous [³H]-ACh release from guinea pig ileum longitudinal muscle–myenteric plexus strips. Guinea pig ileum strips were incubated for 30 min with [³H]-choline (during which time the tissues were field-stimulated at 0.05 Hz, 1 ms duration), followed by a 30-min washout period (in the presence of 10 μM hemicholinium-3). Then, they were stimulated for 3 min with senktide or SPOMe. [³H]-ACh release is expressed as the increase in spontaneous release above basal (taken as the area under the curves minus the basal area). Each point represents the mean of 2–7 separate determinations.

above basal (n = 28). The absolute amount of [³H]-ACh released by senktide (as determined by the area under the curves) was approximately 10 times greater than that released by SPOMe (FIGURE 1).

Both senktide- and SPOMe-induced increases in [³H]-ACh release were completely blocked by 0.3 μM tetrodotoxin (TTX). The senktide-induced contraction was completely blocked by TTX, whereas SPOMe-induced contractions were not affected. Senktide-evoked [³H]-ACh release and SPOMe-evoked [³H]-ACh release were also calcium-dependent because removal of extracellular calcium completely blocked the release of [³H]-ACh. As expected, in the absence of extracellular calcium, contractile responses to both senktide and SPOMe were completely blocked.

(a)

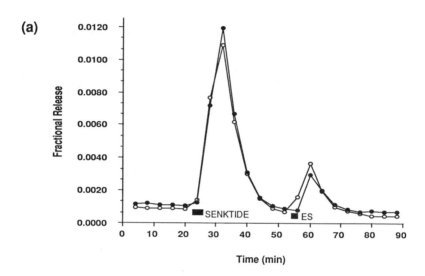

(h)

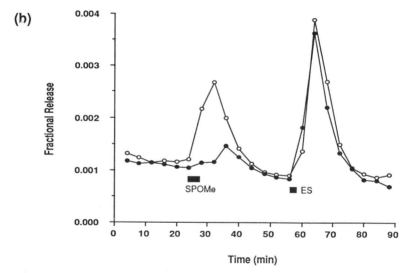

FIGURE 2. Effect of [D-Pro^4,D-Trp^{7,9,10}]-SP(4–11) (10 μM) on senktide- and SPOMe-induced [^{3}H]-ACh release from guinea pig ileum longitudinal muscle–myenteric plexus strips. Guinea pig ileum strips were stimulated for 3 min by (a) 3 nM senktide or (b) 10 nM SPOMe in the presence (closed symbols) or absence (open symbols) of [D-Pro^4,D-Trp^{7,9,10}]-SP(4–11) (10 μM). Approximately 30 min later, tissues were stimulated electrically (ES) for 2 min at 0.2 Hz, 1 ms duration. Each point represents the mean fractional release/4-min period from three separate experiments.

The NK_1/NK_2 tachykinin receptor antagonist, [D-Pro^4,D-Trp^{7,9,10}]-SP(4–11) (10 μM), had no significant effect on senktide-evoked [^{3}H]-ACh release (FIGURE 2) or on the associated contraction. In contrast, the SPOMe-evoked increase in [^{3}H]-ACh release was markedly reduced (control area = 0.0048 compared with 0.0009 in the presence of 10 μM [D-Pro^4,D-Trp^{7,9,10}]-SP(4–11); $P < 0.05$; $n = 3$). Furthermore, this concentration of antagonist significantly reduced SPOMe-induced contractions.

These data provide evidence for the existence of both NK_1 and NK_3 receptors on cholinergic neurons of the guinea pig ileum myenteric plexus, with NK_3-receptor agonists, such as senktide, being capable of releasing approximately 10-fold more ACh than the NK_1-receptor agonist, SPOMe. The elucidation of the relative contributions of neuronal NK_1 and NK_3 tachykinin receptors to the effects of tachykinins in the peristaltic reflex of the guinea pig ileum must await the advent of potent and selective NK_1 and NK_3 tachykinin receptor antagonists.

REFERENCES

1. FOSBRAEY, P., R. L. FEATHERSTONE & I. K. M. MORTON. 1984. Naunyn-Schmiedeberg's Arch. Pharmacol. **326:** 111–115.
2. FEATHERSTONE, R. L., P. FOSBRAEY & I. K. M. MORTON. 1986. Br. J. Pharmacol. **87:** 73–78.
3. KILBINGER, H., P. STAUß, I. ERLHOF & P. HOLZER. 1986. Naunyn-Schmiedeberg's Arch. Pharmacol. **334:** 181–187.

Novel Ligands Confirm NK-1 Receptor–mediated Modulation of Neurotransmission in the Guinea Pig Vas Deferens Preparation

JUDITH M. HALL AND IAN K. M. MORTON

Pharmacology Group
Biomedical Sciences Division
King's College London
London SW3 6LX, United Kingdom

Contractile responses to sympathetic electrical field stimulation of the guinea pig vas deferens preparation are potentiated by tachykinins, although the subtype of the neurokinin receptor involved is uncertain. In particular, activities of earlier agonist ligands suggested receptors to be predominantly of the NK-1 subtype,[1,2] whereas one of the original neurokinin receptor antagonists, [D-Arg^1,D-Pro^2,D-Trp^{7,9},Leu^{11}]-SP$_{(1-11)}$, showed agonist preferences that may indicate a mixed NK-1 and NK-2 neurokinin receptor population (see references 2 and 3). New selective and stable neurokinin receptor agonist[4] and antagonist[5,6] ligands have been used here to reinvestigate this apparent paradox and to fully characterize the neurokinin receptor population in the guinea pig vas deferens.

MATERIALS AND METHODS

The use of the preparation has been described elsewhere.[2,7] Briefly, vasa were field-stimulated with five pulses at 20 Hz at a 1-ms pulse width every 20 s and potentiation was estimated in terms of the increased force of twitch responses normalized in terms of potentiation by substance P (1 μM). Agonists were assayed using a fully randomized serial block design and activities were compared at the level of 100% potentiation, with relative activities expressed relative to substance P within the same preparations. Neurokinin receptor antagonists (0.32–32 μM; 7-min incubation) were tested on full agonist cumulative concentration-response curves. Experiments were carried out at 37 °C in Krebs solution containing atropine, mepyramine (1 μM), and hexamethonium (10 μM), along with cimetidine (1 μM) in antagonist experiments. Antagonist activities are expressed as pK_B estimates. The following neurokinin ligands were used: the novel highly selective NK-1 antagonist,[6] GR71251 ([D-Pro^9(Spiro-γ-lactam)Leu^{10},Trp^{11}]-SP$_{(1-11)}$; Glaxo Group Research); the selective NK-2 antagonist,[5] L659 877 [cyclo(Gln,Trp,Phe,Gly,Leu,Met), Cambridge Research Biochemicals]; the mammalian neurokinins, substance P (SP), neurokinin A (NKA), and neurokinin B (NKB) (all Peninsula Laboratories Europe); the novel selective NK-1 agonist,[4] GR73632 (δ-aminovaleryl-[L-Pro^9,N-MeLeu^{10}]-SP$_{(7-11)}$) (Glaxo Group Research); the NK-2 agonist,[4] GR64349 ([Lys^3,Gly^8-R-γ-lactam-Leu^9]-NKA$_{(3-10)}$) (Glaxo Group Research); and the established selective NK-3 agonist,[8] senktide (Succ-[Asp^6,N-MePhe^8]-SP$_{(6-11)}$) (Peninsula Laboratories Europe).

RESULTS AND DISCUSSION

TABLE 1 shows the EC_{50} estimates and the relative activities for several tachykinins. Overall, these results suggest a predominant NK-1 receptor population, particularly in view of the very high activity of GR73632. Although not precluding an NK-2 contribution, it should be noted that the NK-2 selective agonist, GR64349, was active only at the highest concentration (10 μM) tested. Because senktide was inactive, NK-3 receptors were not involved.

The NK-1 selective antagonist, GR71251, gave indistinguishable pK_B estimates against GR73632 and GR64349 (also shown in TABLE 1), with an overall pK_B value similar to that obtained in other NK-1 systems.[6,7] The NK-2 selective antagonist, L659 877, gave somewhat variable degrees of antagonism, but with pK_B estimates that were inconsistent with an interaction with an NK-2 receptor population.[5]

TABLE 1. Agonist and Antagonist Activities in the Guinea Pig Vas Deferens[a]

Agonist	Subtype Selectivity	Activity (μM)	Confidence Limits (95%)	Relative Activity	Affinity of GR71251	
					pK_B	SEM
substance P		0.6	(0.5–0.9)	1.00	—	—
neurokinin A		1.3	(0.6–2.6)	0.56	—	—
neurokinin B		2.00	(1.2–3.4)	0.36	—	—
GR73632	NK-1	0.002	(0.001–0.003)	120.0	7.65[c]	0.25
GR64349[b]	NK-2	2.6	(2.0–3.2)	0.05	7.43[c]	0.22
senktide	NK-3	> 30.0	—	< 0.03	—	—

[a]Values shown are for $n = 4$ for senktide and $n \geq 8$ for all other estimates.
[b]Inactive at ≤ 1 μM, but with marked activity at ≥ 10 μM.
[c]Not significantly different, $P > 0.05$.

We conclude that the field-stimulated guinea pig vas deferens preparation serves as a useful model to study tachykinin actions through the interaction with a pure NK-1 receptor population subserving neuromodulation of sympathetic transmission.

REFERENCES

1. WATSON, S. P., B. E. B. SANDBERG, M. R. HANLEY & L. L. IVERSEN. 1983. Tissue selectivity of substance P alkyl esters: suggesting multiple receptors. Eur. J. Pharmacol. 87: 77–84.
2. HALL, J. M., A. J. FOX & I. K. M. MORTON. 1987. Characterization of tachykinin receptors in the vas deferens of the guinea pig. Br. J. Pharmacol. 91: 475P.
3. BAILEY, S. J., R. L. FEATHERSTONE, C. C. JORDAN & I. K. M. MORTON. 1986. An examination of the pharmacology of two substance P antagonists and evidence for tachykinin receptor subtypes. Br. J. Pharmacol. 87: 79–85.
4. HAGAN, R. M., S. J. IRELAND, C. C. JORDAN, F. BAILEY, M. STEPHENS-SMITH, M. DEAL & P. WARD. 1990. Novel, potent, and selective agonists of NK_1 and NK_2 receptors. Br. J. Pharmacol. 98: 717P.
5. MCKNIGHT, A. T., J. J. MAGUIRE, B. J. WILLIAMS, A. C. FOSTER, R. TRIDGETT & L. L. IVERSEN. 1988. Pharmacological specificity of synthetic peptides as antagonists of tachykinin receptors. Regulat. Peptides 21: 127.

6. WARD, P., G. B. EWAN, C. C. JORDAN, S. J. IRELAND, R. M. HAGAN & J. R. BROWN. 1990. Potent and highly selective neurokinin (NK-1) antagonists. J. Med. Chem. **33:** 1848–1851.
7. HALL, J. M. & I. K. M. MORTON. 1991. Novel selective agonists and antagonists confirm neurokinin NK_1 receptors in guinea-pig vas deferens. Br. J. Pharmacol. **102:** 511–517.
8. WORMSER, U., R. LAUFER, Y. HART, M. CHOREV, C. GILON & Z. SELINGER. 1986. Highly selective agonists for substance P receptor subtypes. EMBO J. **5:** 2805–2808.

Effects of Substance P and SP(1–7) on Dopamine Release from Rat Substantia Nigra

MICHAEL E. HALL, CRAIG NOCKELS,
AND JOHN M. STEWART

Department of Biochemistry
University of Colorado School of Medicine
Denver, Colorado 80262

The generally accepted view on central actions of substance P (SP) is that they, like those in the periphery, are mediated by receptors that recognize primarily the carboxy-terminal part that is similar to the C-terminal sequences of other tachykinins. Enzymes that cleave SP in this region, especially endopeptidase 3.4.24.11 (EP 24.11), are considered to be solely degrading enzymes that inactivate SP. However, extensive research has demonstrated that certain amino-terminal SP fragments, which lack tachykinin-like activity on smooth muscle and which should be biologically inactive, can reproduce many of the central effects of exogenous SP. Similarly, C-terminal fragments fail to mimic many central effects of SP; in some cases, they exert effects opposite to those of SP.[1] Inhibition of enzymatic "degradation" of SP (by phosphoramidon, which blocks EP 24.11), which should prolong its action, actually blocks some central effects of exogenous SP.[2,3] We have examined the effects of SP and SP(1–7) (an N-terminal fragment produced from SP by EP 24.11) on the release of dopamine (DA) from substantia nigra (SN) slices.

Reubi *et al.*[4] and Starr *et al.*[5] reported that exogenous SP enhances spontaneous release of ^{3}H-DA from SN slices. We have replicated this result and have further demonstrated that SP(1–7) shows a similar effect in this system.

Substantiae nigrae were rapidly dissected from brains of freshly killed male Sprague-Dawley rats and were incubated in modified Krebs bicarbonate buffer (MKB) containing 10 μCi of ^{3}H-DA at 37 °C for 15 min. All buffers were oxygenated by continuous bubbling with 98% O_2/2% CO_2. Tissue was washed twice in MKB buffer and then transferred to a nylon mesh screen in an open chamber where it was superfused (1 mL/min) with MKB buffer at 37 °C. After a 30-min washout, superfusate was collected in 1-min periods for the next 10 minutes. During the fifth and sixth minutes of collection (sample nos. 5 and 6), tissue was superfused with buffer from a separate reservoir containing SP, SP(1–7), or no added peptide. Aliquots (0.5 mL) of each sample were measured for ^{3}H-DA content by liquid scintillation counting. At the end of the 10-min collection period, the tissue was dissolved in hyamine hydroxide and was counted to determine the total ^{3}H-DA remaining in the tissue. The ^{3}H-DA released in each fraction was expressed as a percent of the total radioactivity in the tissue at the time that the fraction was collected. Data were subjected to analysis of variance; post-hoc comparisons of group means were performed using Duncan's Multiple Range Test. Fraction nos. 5 and 6 were analyzed separately.

During the initial collection periods, approximately 0.4% of the total tissue ^{3}H-DA was released per minute. When tissue was superfused with SP (10^{-6} M), the release increased to about 0.6%/min (FIGURE 1), consistent with results of previous

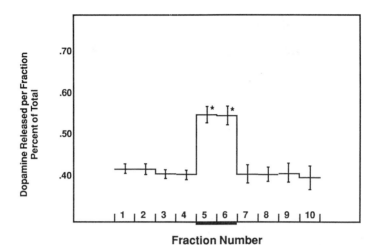

FIGURE 1. Release of ^{3}H-DA from substantia nigra slices evoked by SP. Efflux is expressed as the mean ($\pm$SEM; $n = 6$) percent of the total tissue ^{3}H released during each of the ten 1-minute collection periods. The black bar indicates the presence of SP (10^{-6} M). An asterisk indicates $p < 0.01$ compared to buffer control.

investigators.[4,5] When tissue was superfused with SP(1–7) at 10^{-6} M, the release also increased to 0.6%/min (FIGURE 2). There was no increase in ^{3}H-DA release during fraction nos. 5 and 6 in control superfusions.

A strong seasonal variation in the peptide-evoked release of ^{3}H-DA from SN slices was observed. SP and SP(1–7) reliably enhanced DA release only during the

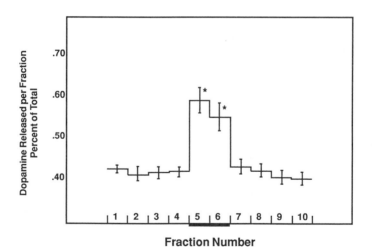

FIGURE 2. Release of ^{3}H-DA from substantia nigra slices evoked by SP(1–7). Efflux is expressed as the mean ($\pm$SEM; $n = 6$) percent of the total tissue ^{3}H released during each of the ten 1-minute collection periods. The black bar indicates the presence of SP(1–7) (10^{-6} M). An asterisk indicates $p < 0.01$ compared to buffer control.

summer and autumn. During the rest of the year, neither peptide consistently enhanced ^{3}H-DA release. A similar seasonal effect has been observed elsewhere (M. Starr, personal communication).

The result that SP(1–7) is equipotent with SP in enhancing spontaneous ^{3}H-DA release adds further support to the hypothesis that such N-terminal metabolites of SP play a role in mediating a set of the central effects of SP. The growing body of data now includes evidence of SP(1–7)-specific binding sites in rat brain[6] and demonstrates that other receptors, in addition to the accepted NK-A, -B, and -C types, must be considered in order to understand fully the central actions of the tachykinins.

REFERENCES

1. HALL, M. & J. STEWART. 1984. Peptides **5:** 85–89.
2. HALL, M., F. MILEY & J. STEWART. 1989. Peptides **10:** 895–901.
3. IGWE, O., X. SUN, C. SCHAMBER & A. LARSON. 1989. Neurosci. Abstr. **15:** 838.
4. REUBI, J., P. EMSON, T. JESSEL & L. IVERSEN. 1978. Naunyn-Schmiedeberg's Arch. Pharmacol. **304:** 271–275.
5. STARR, M., T. JAMES, G. COLLINGRIDGE & J. DAVIES. 1982. *In* Current Status of Centrally-Acting Peptides. B. Dhawan, Ed.: 157–164. Pergamon. Elmsford, New York.
6. HALL, M., *et al.* To be published.

Characterization of Substance P Receptors in Human Astrocytoma Cells

C. L. JOHNSON,[a] C. G. JOHNSON,[a] K. A. STAUDERMAN,[b]
AND S. H. BUCK[b]

[a]Department of Pharmacology and Cell Biophysics
University of Cincinnati
Cincinnati, Ohio 45267

[b]Marion Merrell Dow Research Institute
Cincinnati, Ohio 45215

INTRODUCTION

Previous studies have demonstrated the presence of substance P (SP) binding sites on primary cultures of astrocytes.[1] We employed the human glioma-derived cell line UC11MG to examine the characteristics and functional significance of this receptor. The UC11 line exhibits properties typically associated with astrocytes, including strong expression of glial fibrillary acidic protein, S-100 protein, and glutamine synthetase.[2,3] It is generally accepted that astrocytes play a major role in CNS homeostasis by removing excess K^+ and neurotransmitters such as glutamate from the neuronal environment.

RECEPTOR BINDING STUDIES

The binding constants for $[^3H]$-$[Sar^9,Met(O_2)^{11}]$–substance P (SarSP) on intact UC11 cells at 4 °C are summarized in TABLE 1. The binding site densities listed in the table correspond to more than 150,000 sites/cell. Structure activity studies with several SP analogues indicated that the binding site was of the NK1 subtype (TABLE 2).

INOSITOLPHOSPHATE FORMATION

SP (10^{-7} M) induced a transient increase in IP_3 formation. HPLC analysis indicated that 1,4,5-IP_3 formation peaked at $\approx 15''$ (> 20-fold increase above basal) and then decreased to near zero by $60''$. Using 10^{-7} M SP and a $20''$ assay for IP_3, the IC_{50} for the SP antagonist, spantide, was 160 nM ($N = 3$). SP induced linear IP_1 formation for more than $90'$. The ED_{50} for IP_1 formation by six SP analogues correlated ($r = 0.975$) with the IC_{50} in competition binding assays (TABLE 2).

POTASSIUM TRANSPORT

$^{86}Rb^+$ uptake was linear for $60'$. Ouabain (10^{-4} M) induced an inhibition of $^{86}Rb^+$ uptake of $25.3 \pm 1.8\%$; $Na^+/K^+/Cl^-$ cotransport inhibitors (10^{-3} M furosemide or 10^{-4}

410

TABLE 1. Characterization of Substance P Binding in UC11 Cells[a]

Type of Binding Assay	Binding Constants	Maximum Binding (fmol/mg protein)
saturation assay ($N = 3$)	$K_D = 447 \pm 103$ pM	862 ± 93
competition assay ($N = 3$)	$K_D = 491 \pm 48$ pM	912 ± 67
kinetic assay	$k_1 = 1.87 \times 10^7$ M^{-1} min^{-1}	
	$k_{-1} = 0.0048$ min^{-1}	—
	$K_D = 257$ pM	

[a]All binding assays were conducted at 4 °C on confluent UC11 cells on 24-well plastic culture plates. Saturation assays were conducted with eight concentrations of [^{3}H]-[Sar^9,Met(O$_2$)^{11}]–substance P (SarSP) in the range of 50 to 3000 pM. Nonspecific binding was measured in the presence of 100 nM substance P. Competition assays were conducted with seven concentrations of unlabeled SarSP in the range of 0.1 to 100 nM. Saturation and competition assay times were three hours. The binding data were analyzed with the LIGAND program. Kinetic experiments were conducted with six different ligand concentrations, with 24 data points collected for each concentration over the time range of 0 to 240 minutes. The kinetic data were fit to an equation of the form, $B_e(1 - e^{-k_{obs}t})$, and the k_{obs} values were plotted against the free ligand concentration to yield values for k_1 and k_{-1}.

M bumetanide) inhibited by $45.8 \pm 4.2\%$ and a combination of ouabain and cotransport inhibitor reduced uptake by $78.6 \pm 4.0\%$ ($N = 5$). SP (10^{-7} M) stimulated ^{86}Rb$^+$ uptake as follows: under control conditions, $96 \pm 16\%$ above basal; in presence of ouabain, $103 \pm 23\%$; in presence of cotransport inhibitors, $43 \pm 8\%$; in presence of ouabain and cotransport inhibitors, $5 \pm 4\%$. These results suggest that SP-stimulated ^{86}Rb$^+$ uptake is primarily mediated by the cotransport system, but, in the presence of cotransport inhibitors, the Na$^+$,K$^+$-ATPase can partially support SP-stimulated transport. SP (10^{-7} M) also stimulated ^{86}Rb$^+$ release from preloaded cells by $62 \pm 20\%$ ($N = 3$) at 20'.

TABLE 2. Structure Activity Studies for Several Substance P Analogues in Competition Binding Assays and IP$_1$ Formation[a]

Compound	Binding Assays IC$_{50}$ (nM)	IP$_1$ Assays ED$_{50}$ (nM)
SP	1.18 ± 0.12 ($N = 3$)	2.89 ± 0.43 ($N = 14$)
[Sar^9,Met(O$_2$)^{11}]-SP	1.47 ± 0.23 ($N = 3$)	3.58 ± 0.73 ($N = 4$)
SP-OMe	48 ($N = 1$)	24 ± 4 ($N = 2$)
NKA	231 ± 10 ($N = 3$)	76.0 ± 16.4 ($N = 4$)
Kassinin	442 ± 91 ($N = 3$)	120 ± 6 ($N = 2$)
SP(5–11)	163 ($N = 1$)	160 ± 64 ($N = 2$)
[Pro^7]-NKB	$> 30,000$ ($N = 1$)	$> 30,000$ ($N = 1$)

[a]Competition binding assays were conducted in triplicate with a [^{3}H]-SarSP concentration of 0.3 to 1.2 nM for three hours at 4 °C. IP$_1$ assays were conducted in triplicate for 60' at room temperature. Each ligand was tested at seven concentrations at half log unit increments approximately centered on the IC$_{50}$ or ED$_{50}$ values. The data were fit to a four-parameter logistic function to obtain the IC$_{50}$ or ED$_{50}$ value. All ligands except SP-OMe and [Pro^7]-NKB appeared to be full agonists on IP$_1$ formation. SP-OMe had an intrinsic activity of approximately 58% relative to SP. [Pro^7]-NKB produced a less than 50% increase in IP$_1$ formation at the highest concentration that could be tested (30 μM).

GLUTAMATE TRANSPORT

UC11 cells accumulated [^{3}H]-glutamate by a saturable process that was strongly dependent on temperature and extracellular Na$^+$ and Cl$^-$. Under control conditions, the K_m for glutamate was 130–136 μM and the V_{max} was 80–106 nmoles/30′/mg protein ($N = 2$). SP (10^{-7} M) induced a 34.4 ± 1.4% ($N = 9$) decrease in glutamate uptake. The inhibitory effect of SP was entirely due to a decrease in V_{max}. In cells prelabeled with [^{3}H]-glutamate, SP stimulated the release of the neurotransmitter (53.8 ± 10.8%, $N = 9$). K$^+$-induced depolarization (isosmotic) did not induce glutamate release. Glutamate release did not appear to be related to SP-induced mobilization of intracellular Ca^{2+} because release still occurred after use of an EGTA-ionomycin depletion protocol.

CONCLUSIONS

The UC11 cell line exhibits a high density of SP binding sites that appear to be of the NK1 subtype. These receptors cause a marked stimulation of inositolphosphate formation and also influence both glutamate and K$^+$ transport.

REFERENCES

1. TORRENS, Y., M. C. DAGUET DE MONTETY, M. EL ETR, J. C. BEAUJOUAN & J. GLOWINSKI. 1989. J. Neurochem. **52:** 1913–1918.
2. LIWNICZ, B. H., G. ARCHER, S. W. SOUKUP & R. G. LIWNICZ. 1986. J. Neuro-Oncol. **3:** 373–385.
3. LOMNETH, R., G. BKAILY, N. SPERELAKIS, B. H. LIWNICZ & E. GRUENSTEIN. 1989. Brain Res. **486:** 95–107.

The Role of Substance P in Regulation of Blood Pressure and Hypertension

JUAN CHEN, JIAN-PING GAO, CHENG-TAO XU,
GUO-QING ZHU, AND YAN LIU

Peking Union Medical College
Beijing, China 100005

Substance P (SP) plays an important role in the central and peripheral nervous regulation of blood pressure. It has been demonstrated that the cell bodies of SP-containing neurons, which have direct projections to the intermediolateral cell column (IML) of the spinal cord, are located in the rostral ventrolateral medulla (RVM),[1] a vasomotor center. The mechanism of SP in the regulation of blood pressure and hypertension was investigated in anesthetized Wistar rats, spontaneously hypertensive rats (SHR), and age-matched Wistar-Kyoto (WKY) rats. Our findings were as follows: First, stimulation of the RVM by application of 20 μg of physostigmine (PHY) or 5 μL of 40 mM/L kainic acid (KA) produced an increase in mean blood pressure (MAP) near 60 mmHg. This was accompanied by a release of SP from the spinal cord: the SP-like immunoreactivity (SPLI) of spinal perfusate rose by 0.76-fold as compared with control. Intrathecal injection of capsaicin (6.5, 12.5, 25, 50 μg) to release SP from the spinal cord induced dose-dependent pressor responses. However, all of these pressor responses were blocked by 5–10 μg of the SP antagonist, D-Pro^2,D-Phe^7,D-Trp^9-SP (D-SP), or by 10 μL of 1:5 SP antiserum given intrathecally. In addition, the pressor response of PHY was inhibited by application of 5 μg of atropine to the RVM. Second, a 3-fold increase in plasma noradrenaline (NA) and a 1.9-fold increase in adrenaline (AD) were observed at the peak of the pressor response evoked by application of KA to the RVM. The levels of plasma NA and AD were reversed, whereas the pressor response caused by KA was abolished completely by intrathecal administration of 10 μg of D-SP. Third, the SPLI of the RVM and IML in both SHR and renal artery hypertensive rats (induced by application of a constricting clip on the left renal artery) was elevated dramatically in comparison with the SPLI of WKY and sham-operated rats, respectively (TABLE 1). The MAP was lowered to normal levels in both SHR and renal hypertensive rats (RHR) when 5 μg of D-SP was given intrathecally.

These results suggest that the excitation resulted either from PHY stimulating the muscarinic receptor indirectly and then activating the SP neurons or from KA directly by provoking the RVM to produce a release of SP from the spinal cord; that is, the pressor response evoked by activation of the RVM may be mediated by an SP-containing bulbospinal pathway, with SP transmitting excitatory information to the peripheral vasculature via the spinal sympathetic adrenal medulla system, which plays an important role in maintaining vasomotor tone. The unusual elevation of SP content of the RVM and IML in SHR and RHR rats might partly account for their high levels of sympathoadrenal activity and high blood pressure.

In an additional series of experiments, the levels of plasma SPLI and catecholamine were measured in patients and rats with hypertension. The experimental data showed the following results: First, in patients with primary hypertension, the levels of plasma SPLI were significantly lower, but the concentrations of plasma NA and AD were higher than those in normotensive subjects (TABLE 2). However, the levels

TABLE 1. The Levels of MAP, Plasma NA, Plasma AD, and SPLI in Normotensive Subjects and Patients with Primary Hypertension ($X \pm$ SE)

Group	MAP (mmHg)	NA (pg/mL)	AD (pg/mL)	SPLI (pmol/mL)
normal subjects ($n = 36$)	94.2 ± 1.6	222.5 ± 12.4	87.8 ± 8.1	498.4 ± 59.8
hypertension ($n = 27$)	125.9 ± 3.0^a	459.4 ± 49.8^b	352.5 ± 66.3^a	223.2 ± 28^a

[a] $p < 0.01$ compared with normal subjects.
[b] $p < 0.05$ compared with normal subjects.

TABLE 2. The Levels of MAP and SPLI in the RVM and IML of Different Rat Strains ($X \pm$ SE)

		SPLI (pmol/10 mg wet weight)	
Strains	MAP (mmHg)	RVM	IML
SHR	167.8 ± 4.4^a	2.33 ± 0.25^b	1.37 ± 0.15^a
	($n = 16$)	($n = 4$)	($n = 10$)
WKY	91.6 ± 2.7	1.87 ± 0.22	0.64 ± 0.05
	($n = 18$)	($n = 7$)	($n = 10$)
RHR	167.3 ± 5.5^c	2.46 ± 0.16^c	1.76 ± 0.12^d
	($n = 15$)	($n = 5$)	($n = 6$)
sham-operated	73.6 ± 3.0	1.77 ± 0.30	1.18 ± 0.22
	($n = 19$)	($n = 8$)	($n = 7$)

[a] $p < 0.01$ compared with WKY strains.
[b] $p < 0.05$ compared with WKY strains.
[c] $p < 0.05$ compared with sham-operated strains.
[d] $p < 0.01$ compared with sham-operated strains.

of plasma SPLI increased and the concentration of plasma catecholamine decreased after antihypertensive drug treatment. Moreover, the magnitude of plasma SPLI elevation in patients with hypertension was markedly related to the depressor efficiency. Second, in comparison with WKY rats, SHR rats had significantly lower plasma SPLI levels.

It has been suggested that SP in plasma has not only a vasodilating effect, but also a suppressing effect on the synthesis and release of catecholamine from adrenal medulla.[2] Therefore, these data imply that plasma SP may be involved in the pathogenesis of hypertension.

REFERENCES

1. HELKE, C. J., J. J. NEIL, V. J. MASSARI & A. D. LOEWY. 1982. Substance P neurons project from the ventral medulla to the intermedio-lateral cell column and ventral horn in the rat. Brain Res. **243:** 147–152.
2. ROLE, L. W., S. E. LEEMAN & R. L. PERLMAN. 1981. Somatostatin and substance P inhibit catecholamine secretion from isolated cells of guinea pig adrenal medulla. Neuroscience **6:** 1813–1821.

Modulation of Sialyl-Glycoconjugate Secretion in Cultures of Immortalized Lymphocytes by Treatment with Substance P and Interleukin-2

A. KAGE, U. SIEBERT, S. ROGOWSKI, AND E. KÖTTGEN

Institut für Klinische Chemie und Biochemie
Universitätsklinikum Rudolf Virchow
D-1000 Berlin 19, Federal Republic of Germany

The attachment of carbohydrates on polypeptide chains is an important posttranslational modification. Carbohydrate chains on the surface of eukaryotic cells are involved in the interaction of cells with their environment by specific binding to carbohydrate-recognizing molecules, the lectins. These interactions are responsible for phenomena like cytotoxicity and homing.[1] The binding of lectins to surface carbohydrates can lead to specific cellular responses. The stimulation of T lymphocytes by the lectin phytohemagglutinin, for example, results in increased phosphoinositol turnover. The glycosylation pattern of cells is under continuous regulatory control and can be altered by physiological and pharmacological factors. This results in the modulation of the lectin-carbohydrate binding and therefore influences the cellular response to lectins.

A very common terminal oligosaccharide structure found at glycoproteins on the surface of cells is galactose β-glycoside bound to N-acetylglucosamine (Gal-β1-4GlcNAc-). β-Galactoside-binding lectins, which are found in all vertebrates, bind preferentially to this oligosaccharide structure.[2] A very common modification found in these oligosaccharides is the substitution with sialic acid at position 6 of the galactose, which leads to a decrease of affinity of the β-galactoside-binding lectins. Substitution of the galactose at position 2 or 3 does not interfere with this binding.

The aim of our study was to investigate the influence of substance P (SP) and recombinant interleukin-2 (rIL-2) on the expression of 2′,6′-sialylgalactose on glycoproteins produced by cultured lymphocytes.

IM-9 cells and H9 lymphocytes were cultured in the presence or absence of rIL-2 (2.5 or 50 U/mL, Boehringer, Federal Republic of Germany). Substance P (Bachem, Federal Republic of Germany) was added at hourly intervals to a final concentration of 1 μg/mL. At the times indicated in FIGURES 1a and 1b, supernatants were collected. The total glycosylation pattern was quantitated using a new test, the lectin binding inhibition assay (lectin-BIA), which enables the characterization of the glycosylation pattern. In this assay, the unknown carbohydrate moieties of the glycoproteins from the sample and from glycoproteins immobilized on microtiter plates compete for binding to a biotinylated lectin with known binding specificity. The amount of solid-phase bound lectin is quantified by a colorimetric reaction after incubation with streptavidin-coupled peroxidase.[3] We used the biotinylated lectin from *Sambucus nigra* agglutinin (SNA) (Boehringer, Federal Republic of Germany), which has a high specificity for 2′,6′-sialylated oligosaccharides. For standardization of the SNA-BIA, different concentrations of 2′,6′-sialyl-lactose were used. 2′,3′-Sialyl-

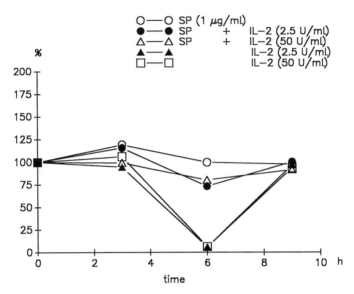

FIGURE 1a. *Sambucus nigra* agglutinin binding inhibition activity is determined in supernatant of IM-9 cells. Values are given as the percentage of the *Sambucus nigra* agglutinin binding inhibition activity of untreated cells (normalized to 100%).

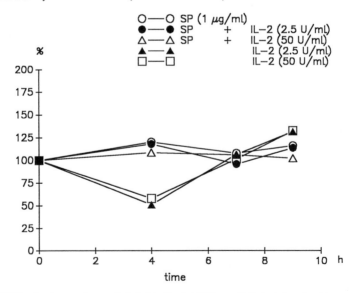

FIGURE 1b. *Sambucus nigra* agglutinin binding inhibition activity is determined in supernatant of H9 cells. Values are given as the percentage of the *Sambucus nigra* agglutinin binding inhibition activity of untreated cells (normalized to 100%).

lactose showed less than 5% binding inhibition activity for *Sambucus nigra* agglutinin (data not shown).

The results obtained show that incubation of both IM-9 and H9 cells with rIL-2 reduced the secretion of binding inhibition activity for *Sambucus nigra* agglutinin. This indicates a reduced concentration of glycoconjugates with terminal 2',6'-sialylgalactose residues. This effect occurs in both cell lines: reduced binding inhibition activity is found in IM-9 cells after six hours and in H9 cells after four hours. Three hours after the minimum of binding inhibition activity is observed, the starting values are found again in both cell lines. All samples obtained from cultures treated with SP showed no difference in *Sambucus nigra* agglutinin binding inhibition activity.

These results indicate an antagonistic modulation of the *Sambucus nigra* agglutinin binding inhibition by SP and rIL-2. This could be caused by an antagonistic regulation of the activity of 2',6'-sialyltransferase, which is necessary for the synthesis of the sialic acid–derivatized galactosyl residues, or by an antagonistic regulatory effect of SP and rIL-2 on the sialidase activity, which is involved in degradation of these oligosaccharides. Both mechanisms will eventually lead to a modified affinity to the β-galactoside-binding lectin. The pathobiochemical significance and the molecular basis for these findings remain to be studied.

REFERENCES

1. CAMERON, D. J. & W. H. CHURCHILL. 1982. Specificity of macrophage mediated cytotoxicity: role of target cell sialic acid. Jpn. J. Exp. Med. **52:** 9–16.
2. BARONDES, S. H., M. A. GITT, H. LEFFLER & D. N. W. COOPER. 1988. Multiple soluble vertebrate galactoside-binding lectins. Biochimie **70:** 1627–1632.
3. KAGE, A., D. WEITZEL & E. KÖTTGEN. 1989. Quantitative characterization of oligosaccharide structure of glycoconjugates using enzyme labeled lectins. *In* Proceedings of the Tenth International Symposium on Glycoconjugates (Jerusalem), p. 413–414.

Effects of Serotonin and Opioid Agonists on Tachyphylaxis to SP-induced Vasodilatation

ZEINAB KHALIL AND ROBERT D. HELME

National Research Institute of Gerontology and Geriatric Medicine
North West Hospital
Parkville, Victoria 3052, Australia

INTRODUCTION

The role of substance P (SP), serotonin, and opioids in modulating pain transmission has been well established. SP is the major putative mediator that is released from peripheral and central terminals of primary afferents to modulate pain and inflammation. Associated with the increased nociceptive input from peripheral tissue damage, there is a diffuse release of serotonin within the spinal cord.[1] The effect of this centrally released serotonin on the peripheral inflammatory response has not been investigated. Conversely, the role of opioid peptides in reducing inflammation and pain has been attributed to inhibition of SP release from primary afferents.[2] The role of opioids in modulating the inflammatory response to SP after its release has also not been investigated. The present study was designed to examine the possibility that a peripheral inflammatory vasodilatation response to SP, manifested as altered local blood flow, could be modulated by a centrally acting serotonin agonist (5-methoxy dimethyltryptamine, 5-MeODMT) or by a peripherally administered δ opioid agonist (DSLET).

METHODS

Suction blisters were induced on the anesthetized rat hind footpad, the surface epithelium was removed, and a perfusion chamber was fixed over the blister base. Local blood flow was measured using a laser Doppler flow meter.[3] The protocol consisted of a (15–20)-min equilibration period followed by a 10-min prestimulation period with Ringer's solution (R). 5-MeODMT (0.5, 1, 2 mg/kg) or vehicle was then injected intraperitoneally followed by 10 min of (R); in another group of rats, DSLET (0.1, 1, 10 μM) was perfused locally over the blister base for 10 min. SP was then perfused at 1 μM concentration either alone (in the case of 5-MeODMT) or together with DSLET. In one experiment, naloxone (1 mg/kg) was injected intravenously after the initial prestimulation period. The action of each substance was also examined in rats pretreated as neonates with 50 mg/kg capsaicin.

RESULTS AND DISCUSSION

Perfusion of SP induced an increased blood flow within 30 s and attained a maximum response at 3–5 min. Tachyphylaxis ensued within 10–15 min despite

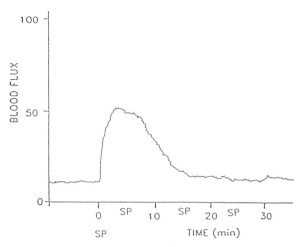

FIGURE 1A. An actual tracing of a typical record of the change in blood flow in response to SP (1 μM) perfused over the blister base for 30 min. The output from the laser Doppler flow meter has arbitrary units of relative blood flow (blood flux).

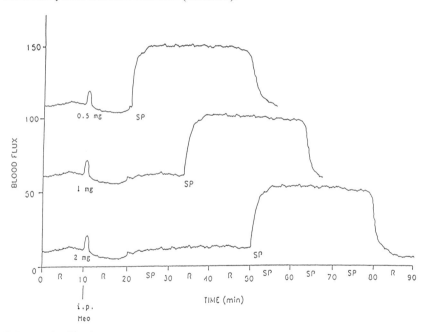

FIGURE 1B. The dose-response effect of 5-MeODMT (Meo) was studied using three (0.5, 1, and 2 mg/kg) concentrations. All three doses induced an initial inhibitory period during which SP was incapable of inducing any increased blood flow; this was followed by an excitatory period where the increased blood flow in response to SP was maintained. A dose-response effect was obtained by comparing the results of the early inhibitory period. Whereas 0.5 mg/kg of 5-MeODMT induced an inhibitory period that lasted for about 10 min, 1 mg/kg induced a longer inhibitory effect that lasted for 20 min as compared to a 35-min inhibition induced by 2 mg/kg of 5-MeODMT. It should be noted that the duration of the early inhibitory period following each dose of 5-MeODMT was determined by performing a number of experiments where SP was perfused at different time points. When no response was obtained, SP perfusion was ceased after 10 min to avoid receptor desensitization.

continuous SP perfusion (FIGURE 1A). 5-MeODMT or DSLET did not alter basal blood flow, but they each exerted significant modulatory effects on the increased blood flow in response to SP. 5-MeODMT induced (i) an early (dose-dependent) inhibitory effect during which SP could not induce any increased blood flow and (ii) a late enhancing effect where the increase in blood flow in response to SP was sustained (FIGURE 1B). Local perfusion of 5-MeODMT (1 μM) over the blister base did not alter the increased blood flow in response to subsequent or simultaneous perfusion of SP, suggesting that the modulatory effects of ip 5-MeODMT were not mediated via a peripheral mechanism. The underlying mechanism of action probably involves activation of specific receptors on capsaicin-sensitive sensory fibers because the modulatory effects were absent in capsaicin-pretreated rats.

The increased blood flow in response to SP was inhibited by DSLET in a dose-dependent manner. Significant inhibitory effects were observed using measures of the surface area under the response curve and the duration of the response, but these effects were significant only at the highest concentration of DSLET used when measuring the maximum blood flow attained (TABLE 1); this may reflect an acceleration of the tachyphylaxis to SP by DSLET. The ability of DSLET to inhibit the increased blood flow in response to SP was reversed by naloxone pretreatment and

TABLE 1. Significant Inhibitory Effects of DSLET on the Dilatation Response to SP[a]

	Area (cm^2)	Duration (min)	Maximum Height (cm)
SP	26.2 ± 3.6	13.3 ± 1.9	5.5 ± 0.7
SP + DSLET (0.1 μM)	19.2 ± 2.9*	10.2 ± 1.5*	5.2 ± 0.5
SP + DSLET (1 μM)	16.7 ± 3.4*	7.8 ± 0.96*	4.9 ± 0.6
SP + DSLET (10 μM)	11.5 ± 2.0*	5.6 ± 0.9*	4.1 ± 0.5*

[a]The significant (*) inhibitory effects of 0.1, 1, and 10 μM DSLET on the dilatation response to SP were obtained using measurements of the surface area under the response curve (cm^2) and the duration of the response [time taken for complete desensitization to occur (min)]. The use of the maximum height (cm) as a measure of the response, though, only showed a significant inhibitory effect with the highest (10 μM) concentration of DSLET tested.

was significantly less in capsaicin-pretreated rats, suggesting that these modulatory effects were mediated via activation of specific opioid receptors located on unmyelinated afferent sensory fibers.

CONCLUSIONS

The present study supports the hypothesis that centrally released serotonin may modulate a peripheral inflammatory response to SP. The early inhibitory effect could result in reduced transmission of nociceptive input and the late sustained inflammatory response could lead to resolution of inflammation and to acceleration of the healing process. In addition, our data raise the possibility that opioids could inhibit the inflammatory response to SP by accelerating tachyphylaxis. Although it could be argued that circulating endogenous opioids are unlikely to reach high enough concentrations in the blood to activate such peripheral mechanisms physiologically, the present findings could have clinical implications as peripherally administered opioids may inhibit a protective neurogenic inflammatory response.

REFERENCES

1. WEIL-FUGAZZA, J., F. GODEFROY & D. LE BARS. 1984. Increase in 5-HT synthesis in the dorsal part of the spinal cord, induced by a nociceptive stimulus: blockade by morphine. Brain Res. **297:** 247–264.
2. LEMBECK, F. & J. DONNERER. 1985. Opioid control of the function of primary afferent substance P fibres. Eur. J. Pharmacol. **114:** 241–246.
3. KHALIL, Z. & R. D. HELME. 1990. Serotonin modulates SP-induced plasma extravasation and vasodilatation in rat skin by an action through capsaicin primary afferent nerves. Brain Res. **527:** 292–298.

Allosteric Interaction of Heparin with NK-1 Receptors in Rat Striatal Membranes

GABRIELE ANDREA KNAUS, HANS-GÜNTHER KNAUS,
AND ALOIS SARIA[a]

Neurochemistry Unit
Department of Psychiatry
University Hospital Innsbruck
A-6020 Innsbruck, Austria

INTRODUCTION

It is widely accepted that binding of labeled substance P to central or peripheral neurokinin receptors is regulated by tachykinins, cations, and nonhydrolyzable guanine nucleotides. Both the cations and the guanine nucleotides exhibit no effect when tested in functional neurokinin receptor assays; that is, substance P induces contraction of the isolated guinea pig ileum. In this study, we introduce heparin as a compound interacting with substance P receptors in a complex allosteric manner.

RESULTS AND DISCUSSION

Binding studies with [^{125}I]BH-SP and rat striatal membranes were performed as described in reference 1. Naturally occurring, high molecular weight heparin (here referred to as heparin) interacts with specific [^{125}I]BH-SP binding to rat striatal membranes in a biphasic, bell-shaped dose-response curve. Low molecular weight (LMW) heparin and de-N-sulfated heparin lack the stimulatory component (FIGURE 1A). Heparin ($< 8 \mu g/mL$) stimulates specific [^{125}I]BH-SP binding up to 184 ± 23.4% of control binding. To assess these findings in more detail, equilibrium saturation and kinetic studies were carried out. Stimulation of [^{125}I]BH-SP binding at low heparin concentrations (5 $\mu g/mL$) can be attributed to a decrease of the apparent K_D of the high affinity [^{125}I]BH-SP binding site (FIGURE 1B), which is due to a fourfold increase of the association rate constant (FIGURE 1C), whereas the dissociation kinetic parameters remain unchanged (FIGURE 1D). Higher heparin concentrations (100 $\mu g/mL$) as well as the presence of 10 μM GTP-γ-S induce their inhibitory effects by suppressing the association reaction and increasing the dissociation velocity (FIGURE 1D). The corresponding K_D or B_{max} values and the kinetic rate constants are given in the legend to FIGURE 1.

Thus, heparin fulfills the criteria to define a novel binding domain on neurokinin-1 receptors different from those labeled by the tachykinins. The main characteristics of heparin when acting on neurokinin receptors are as follows:

(1) dose-dependent conversion of neurokinin-1 receptors to states of different affinities for [^{125}I]BH-SP, which are reflected by altering the equilibrium binding parameters;

---

[a] To whom all correspondence should be addressed.

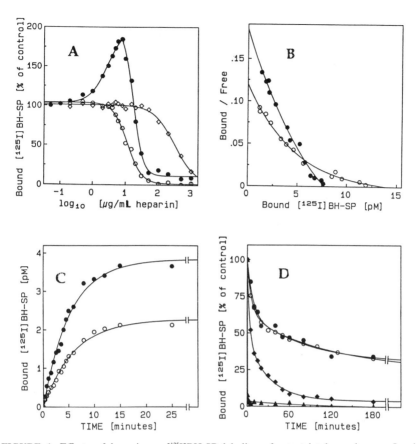

FIGURE 1. Effects of heparin on [^{125}I]BH-SP labeling of rat striatal membranes. In all experiments, a rat striatal membrane protein concentration of 0.296–0.434 mg/mL was incubated with 29.7–46.8 pM [^{125}I]BH-SP. (A) Dose-response curves in the presence of increasing concentrations of heparin (●), LMW heparin (○), and de-*N*-sulfated heparin (◇) are shown. The following equilibrium binding parameters were obtained: (●) IC$_{50}$ I = 2.81 ± 0.14 µg/mL, n_H = 1.63 ± 0.22, maximal stimulation up to 184 ± 23%; IC$_{50}$ II = 16.98 ± 2.54 µg/mL, n_H = 3.01 ± 1.24; (○) IC$_{50}$ = 11.2 ± 4.56 µg/mL, n_H = 2.04 ± 0.43; (◇) IC$_{50}$ = 309 ± 76 µg/mL, n_H = 1.33 ± 0.19. (B) Saturation isotherms for neurokinin-1 receptors. Rat striatal membrane protein was incubated with [^{125}I]BH-SP (11.89–5001 pM) in the absence (○) and presence (●) of 5 µg/mL heparin. The following equilibrium binding constants were obtained: (○) K_D1 = 69.3 ± 32.4 pM, B_{max}1 = 7.42 ± 2.3 pM (corresponds to 24.01 ± 7.44 fmoles/mg protein); K_D2 = 281 ± 74.3 pM, B_{max}2 = 5.51 ± 2.34 pM (corresponds to 18.30 ± 7.77 fmoles/mg protein); (●) K_D = 42.3 ± 16.4 pM, B_{max} = 7.78 ± 1.34 pM (corresponds to 25.84 ± 4.45 fmoles/mg protein). (C) Association kinetics: Rat striatal membrane protein was incubated with [^{125}I]BH-SP for the indicated times. At equilibrium, the specifically bound ligand was 2.28 pM in the absence (○) and 3.84 pM in the presence (●) of 5 µg/mL heparin. The following association rate constants were measured: control, K_{obs} = 0.164 ± 0.08 min^{-1} (k_{+1} = 0.00076 ± 0.00009 min^{-1} pM^{-1}); presence of 5 µg/mL heparin, K_{obs} = 0.188 ± 0.11 min^{-1} (k_{+1} = 0.0034 ± 0.0011 min^{-1} pM^{-1}). (D) Dissociation kinetics: Membrane protein was labeled with [^{125}I]BH-SP for 25 minutes at 22 °C. The specifically bound ligand at equilibrium was 1.87 ± 0.53 pM. At the times indicated, dissociation was initiated by addition of 300 nM unlabeled substance P (○, K_{-1}I = 0.178 ± 0.06 min^{-1}; K_{-1}II = 0.013 ± 0.006 min^{-1}), 300 nM substance P and 5 µg/mL heparin (●, K_{-1}I = 0.154 ± 0.09 min^{-1}; K_{-1}II = 0.009 ± 0.004 min^{-1}), 300 nM substance P and 100 µg/mL heparin (◆, K_{-1}I = 0.314 ± 0.07 min^{-1}; K_{-1}II = 0.032 ± 0.007 min^{-1}), or 300 nM substance P and 10 µM GTP-γ-S (▲, K_{-1}I = 6.09 ± 3.4 min^{-1}; K_{-1}II = 0.012 ± 0.007 min^{-1}).

(2) increase of the association velocity at low concentrations and acceleration of the dissociation rates of [^{125}I]BH-SP in double-chase experiments, indicating both positive and negative heterotropic allosteric interactions;

(3) the size (LMW heparin lacks the stimulation) and the sulfate moieties (de-N-sulfated heparin is much less active, suggesting the importance of the N-sulfate groups) suffice the interaction with neurokinin receptors;

(4) selective action on neurokinin receptors as demonstrated by the inability to alter the labeling of other radioligands that are markers for dopamine, serotonin, opiate, benzodiazepine, α_1- and β_2-adrenoreceptors, etc. (results not shown); therefore, the effects of the highly charged polyanion heparin could not be explained by general, nonspecific membrane perturbation;

(5) a direct interaction of heparin with the positively charged SP seems unlikely because heparin-sepharose failed to adsorb labeled SP even at very low ionic strengths (FIGURE 2);

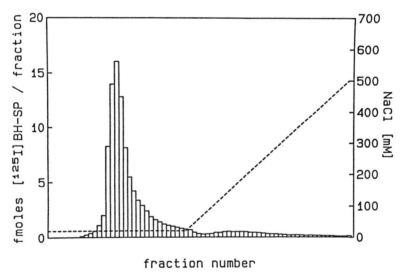

FIGURE 2. Chromatography profile of [^{125}I]BH-SP on heparin-sepharose Cl6B. The dashed line indicates a linear NaCl gradient.

(6) we postulate an intracellular mode of action (like the guanine nucleotides): both compounds allosterically interact with [^{125}I]BH-SP labeling, are highly charged, and are therefore not able to cross intact plasma membranes; they display no effect when tested in functional assays. A similar behavior of heparin on intracellularly located targets has previously been described (references 2 and 3).

Hence, heparin can be regarded as a useful tool to further assess functional and structural parameters of neurokinin receptors and may serve as a prototype in the design of specific, nonpeptidergic drugs that would exhibit selective effects on binding and regulation of tachykinin receptors.

REFERENCES

1. HUMPEL, C. H., G. A. KNAUS, B. AUER, H-G. KNAUS, C. HARING, E. THEODORSSON & A. SARIA. 1990. Synapse **6:** 1–9.
2. GHOSH, T. K., P. S. EIS, J. M. MULLANEY, C. L. EBERT & D. L. GILL. 1988. J. Biol. Chem. **263:** 11075–11079.
3. BENOVIC, J. L., W. C. STONE, M. G. CARON & R. J. LEFKOWITZ. 1989. J. Biol. Chem. **264:** 6707–6710.

Cloning, Expression of the Human Substance K Receptor, and Analysis of Its Role in Mitogenesis

CURT CYR,[a] VICTORIA SOUTH,[b] ALAN SALTZMAN,[b]
S. FELDER,[b] GEORGE A. RICCA,[b] MICHAEL JAYE,[b]
KAY HUEBNER,[c] JAKOB KAGAN,[c] CARLO M. CROCE,[c]
JOSEPH SCHLESSINGER,[a] AND RICHARD M. KRIS[a,d]

[a]Department of Pharmacology
New York University School of Medicine
New York, New York 10016

[b]Rorer Biotechnology, Incorporated
King of Prussia, Pennsylvania 19406

[c]Fels Institute for Cancer Research and Molecular Biology
Temple University School of Medicine
Philadelphia, Pennsylvania 19140

Substance K is a member of the tachykinin family of peptides, all of which contain a C-terminal sequence of Phe-X-Gly-Leu-Met-NH_2. There are three members of this family: substance P, substance K, and neuromedin K. Substance P has been most widely studied; however, since their discovery in 1983, substance K and neuromedin K have received much attention.[1-5] The human substance K (SK) receptor was cloned from a human jejunal cDNA library. The primary structure of the SK receptor consisted of 398 amino acids, including seven putative transmembrane regions (FIGURE 1). The gene for the human SK receptor was localized to the chromosome region, 10p13 to 10q23, by analysis of its segregation pattern in rodent-human hybrids, a region in which the human alpha-2 adrenergic receptor was also mapped.

The human SK receptor was expressed in transfected NIH-3T3 cells lacking endogenous SK receptors. Scatchard analysis of ^{125}I-labeled substance K binding indicated approximately 100,000 receptors per cell with a single dissociation constant (K_d) of 12 nM. Covalent cross-linking experiments utilizing ^{125}I-SK and three different chemical cross-linking reagents (DSS, DST, or EDC) demonstrated an apparent molecular weight of 45 kilodaltons, consistent with little or no N-linked glycosylation. Signal transduction events were measured following the binding of SK to the cell lines expressing the SK receptor. There was a rapid increase in the production of total inositol phosphates and in the release of Ca^{++} from internal stores (FIGURE 2). Also, the release of prostaglandin E_2 was stimulated by the binding of SK to its receptor, suggesting the activation of phospholipase A_2. Growth of the cells transfected with the human SK receptor was stimulated by the addition of SK to the medium to a level similar to 10% serum. Therefore, the human substance K receptor can function as a growth factor receptor when expressed in mouse 3T3 cells.

[d]To whom all correspondence should be addressed.

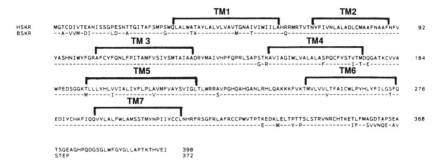

FIGURE 1. Comparison of the amino acid sequences of human and bovine substance K receptors. The human sequence is shown on top and the bovine sequence is shown on the bottom. The putative transmembrane regions are denoted above the sequences. Identical sequences are indicated by a dashed line.

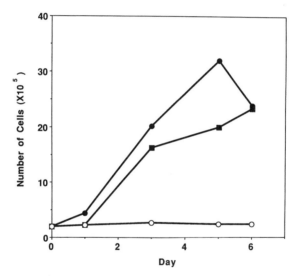

FIGURE 2. Measurements of Ca^{++} release induced by substance K. The intracellular free $[Ca^{++}]_i$ in HSKR-1 cells was measured using the Fura-2 fluorescence ratio. The cells were starved at 80% confluence with no serum for six hours. The cells were stimulated at time 0 with 20 μM substance K (■), 200 nM substance K (●), or 20 μM substance P (○).

REFERENCES

1. CHANG, M. M., S. E. LEEMAN & H. D. NIALL. 1971. Nature (London) New Biol. **232:** 86–87.
2. KANGAWA, K., N. MINAMINO, A. FUKUDA & H. MATSUO. 1983. Biochem. Biophys. Res. Commun. **114:** 533–540.
3. KIMURA, S., M. OKADA, Y. SUGITA, I. KANAZAWA & E. MUNEKATA. 1983. Proc. Jpn. Acad. **B59:** 101–104.
4. MAGGIO, J. E., B. E. B. SANDBERG, C. V. BRADLEY, L. L. IVERSON, S. SANTIKARN, B. H. WILLIAMS, J. C. HUNTER & M. R. HANLEY. 1983. *In* Substance P, p. 20–23. Boole Press.
5. TATEMOTO, K., J. M. LUNDBERG, H. JORNVALL & V. MUTT. 1985. Biochem. Biophys. Res. Commun. **128:** 947–953.

Substance P Is Present in Cholinergic Paravertebral Sympathetic Neurons Innervating Exocrine Sweat Glands[a]

B. LINDH,[b,c] M. PELTO-HUIKKO,[c] A. HÆGERSTRAND,[b]
M. SCHALLING,[c] J. M. LUNDBERG,[d] AND T. HÖKFELT[c]

[b]Department of Anatomy
[c]Department of Histology and Neurobiology
[d]Department of Pharmacology
Karolinska Institute
S-104 01 Stockholm, Sweden

The majority of the neurons in paravertebral sympathetic ganglia of the cat are noradrenergic. However, a population of ganglion cells innervating exocrine sweat glands in the footpads and blood vessels in the skeletal muscle are in all probability cholinergic. In an early immunohistochemical study, it was shown that these cholinergic sympathetic neurons contain immunoreactivity to vasoactive intestinal polypeptide (VIP).[1] Two types of VIP-positive cells could be distinguished: one type with strong immunofluorescence often clustered in groups and a second type with scattered cells and weak fluorescence.[1] Peptide histidine isoleucine (PHI), which is expressed in the same precursor gene as VIP, is present in these cells as well. Recently, it was demonstrated that the scattered VIP-positive cells also contain immunoreactivity to calcitonin gene–related peptide (CGRP).[2] Retrograde axonal tracing experiments have indicated that the scattered cell population provides an important input to exocrine sweat glands.[3]

When the exocrine sweat gland innervation of the cat was further analyzed, a total overlap of nerve fibers containing VIP–, CGRP–, and substance P (SP)–like immunoreactivity (LI) was observed. Although we were unable to demonstrate SP-positive cell bodies in untreated paravertebral sympathetic ganglia, these findings suggested that the scattered cell population contained SP, in addition to VIP, PHI, and CGRP. These suggestions were corroborated when ganglia were kept for 24 h in cell culture medium prior to fixation.[4] Thus, SP-positive neurons were demonstrated in ganglia maintained in cell culture medium, and double staining revealed that these cells were of the scattered type and also contained immunoreactivity to VIP and CGRP.

In another set of experiments, a synthetic oligonucleotide probe, complementary to a sequence of the rat β-preprotachykinin (β-PPT),[5] coding for part of the mature SP molecule was used to localize, by *in situ* hybridization, SP mRNA to individual paravertebral sympathetic ganglion cells of the cat (FIGURE 1). The labeled cells were scattered throughout the ganglia and did not form any distinct groups. Subsequent immunohistochemical processing of the hybridized sections revealed that the cells labeled with the β-PPT probe contained CGRP-LI, but lacked

[a]This study was supported by grants from the Karolinska Institute and the Swedish Medical Research Council (Nos. 12x-5189, 04x-2887, 04x-7126, 14x-6554) and Stiftelsen Lars Hiertas Minne and Tore Nilsons Fond för Medicinsk Forskning.

immunoreactivity to the catecholamine-synthesizing enzyme, tyrosine hydroxylase (TH).

Overall, the present findings indicate that SP is present together with VIP, PHI, and CGRP in a population of presumably cholinergic paravertebral sympathetic ganglion cells of the cat that innervate exocrine sweat glands and blood vessels. Although the functional significance of acetylcholine coexisting with the vasodilatory peptides, SP, VIP, PHI, and CGRP, in a population of postganglionic sympathetic neurons is at present unclear, some conclusions may be drawn from earlier physiological studies. Sweat secretion seen upon sympathetic nerve stimulation is completely blocked by atropine, whereas the concomitant vasodilation is atropine-resistant.[6] This indicates that the four coexisting peptides do not each induce sweat secretion

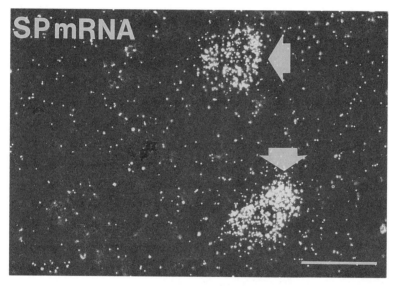

FIGURE 1. Emulsion autoradiograph of a section of a sympathetic S1 ganglion after hybridization with an oligonucleotide probe complementary to nucleotides 145–192 of rat β-PPT mRNA. The arrows point to two cells labeled with the β-PPT probe. The bar indicates 50 μm.

per se, but that they may participate in the noncholinergic control of vasodilation. It may be speculated that sweat secretion is regulated in a similar way as salivary secretion in the cat submandibular salivary gland (for review, see reference 7). Thus, the vasodilatory peptides may enhance the acetylcholine-induced sweat secretion by increasing blood flow or by directly affecting the secretory elements (or both). Finally, it should be emphasized that functions other than regulation of sweat secretion and blood flow must be considered for the four coexisting peptides. For instance, neuropeptides including SP, VIP, and CGRP have mitogenic effects (for review, see reference 8). This implies that they may be involved in physiological as well as pathophysiological processes, such as development and wound healing.

ACKNOWLEDGMENTS

For the generous supply of antisera, we thank A. C. Cuello, Department of Pharmacology and Therapeutics, McGill University, Montreal, Canada (SP); J. Fahrenkrug, Bispebjerg Hospital, Copenhagen, Denmark (VIP and PHI); J. Fischer, Department of Orthopedic Surgery and Medicine, University of Zürich, Switzerland (CGRP); and M. Goldstein, Department of Psychiatry, New York University Medical Center, New York (TH).

REFERENCES

1. LUNDBERG, J. M., T. HÖKFELT, M. SCHULTZBERG, K. UVNÄS-WALLENSTEN, K. KÖHLER & S. I. SAID. 1979. Occurrence of vasoactive intestinal polypeptide (VIP)–like immunoreactivity in certain cholinergic neurons of the cat: evidence from combined immunohistochemistry and acetylcholinesterase staining. Neuroscience 4: 1539–1559.
2. LINDH, B., J. M. LUNDBERG, T. HÖKFELT, L-G. ELFVIN, J. FAHRENKRUG & J. FISCHER. 1987. Coexistence of CGRP- and VIP-like immunoreactivities in a population of neurons in the cat stellate ganglia. Acta Physiol. Scand. 131: 475–476.
3. LINDH, B., J. M. LUNDBERG & T. HÖKFELT. 1989. NPY-, galanin-, VIP/PHI-, CGRP-, and substance P–immunoreactive neuronal subpopulations in cat autonomic and sensory ganglia and their projections. Cell Tissue Res. 256: 259–273.
4. KESSLER, J. A., J. ADLER, M. BOHN & I. B. BLACK. 1981. Substance P in sympathetic neurons: regulation by impulse activity. Science 214: 335–336.
5. KRAUSE, J. E., J. M. CHIRGWIN, M. S. CARTER, Z. S. XU & A. HERSHEY. 1987. Three rat preprotachykinin mRNAs encode the neuropeptides substance P and neurokinin A. Proc. Natl. Acad. Sci. U.S.A. 84: 881–885.
6. LANGLEY, J. N. 1922. The secretion of sweat. Part I. Supposed inhibitory nerve fibers on the posterior nerve roots: secretion after denervation. J. Physiol. (London) 56: 110–119.
7. LUNDBERG, J. M. & T. HÖKFELT. 1986. Multiple co-existence of peptides and classical transmitters in peripheral autonomic and sensory neurones—functional and pharmacological implications. In Progress in Brain Research, Vol. 68. T. Hökfelt, K. Fuxe & B. Pernow, Eds.: 241–262. Elsevier. Amsterdam/New York.
8. DALSGAARD, C-J., A. HULTGÅRDH-NILSSON, A. HÆGERSTRAND & J. NILSSON. 1989. Neuropeptides as growth factors: possible roles in human diseases. Regulat. Peptides 25: 1–9.

Neurokinin Innervation of the Rat Median Raphe Nucleus Does Not Originate in the Brain Stem

STANLEY A. LORENS,[a] JOSEPH M. PARIS,[b]
AND ERNST BRODIN[c]

[a] Department of Pharmacology
Loyola University Medical Center
Maywood, Illinois 60153

[b] Department of Pharmacology and Toxicology
University of Texas Medical Branch
Galveston, Texas 77550

[c] Department of Pharmacology
Karolinska Institute
Stockholm, Sweden

INTRODUCTION

Neurokinins, their molecular precursors, and their binding sites have been localized throughout the mammalian brain.[1-3] Numerous studies have examined the physiological effects of these peptides in the CNS. Our laboratory has demonstrated that infusions into the median raphe nucleus (MR) of senktide, DiMeC7, neurokinin A (NKA), and neurokinin B (NKB) produce locomotor hyperactivity. The increase in locomotor activity (LMA) appears to be mediated primarily by neurokinin-2 and -3 (NK-2 and NK-3) receptors[4] and depends upon intact MR serotonin (5-HT) neurons.[5,6] Neurokinin-like immunoreactivity (NKLI) and preprotachykinin mRNA have been discerned in the MR,[1,7] but the origin of this innervation is unknown. A number of brain stem nuclei that contain NKLI perikarya, including the interpeduncular nucleus (IPN), the laterodorsal tegmental nucleus (LDTG), the dorsal raphe nucleus (DR), and the rostral central gray (CG),[1,8-10] send efferent projections to the MR. The objective of the present study was to determine whether the neurokinin innervation of the MR originates in the brain stem.

METHODS

The fluorescent retrograde tracer Fluoro-Gold (FG) was microiontophoresed into the MR of adult male Sprague-Dawley rats ($n = 12$). Seven days later, the rats were stereotaxically injected with colchicine (100 μg) into the lateral ventricle. After 24 h, the rats were transcardially perfused in preparation for immunocytochemistry. Standard fluorescent immunocytochemical techniques were performed utilizing primary antisera directed against substance P (SP), NKA, and NKB.[1,8-10] In order to confirm the presence of the neurokinins in the midbrain raphe, adult male rats were sacrificed and tissue punches (1.5 mm in diameter and 1.0 mm thick; average weight = 3.4 mg/punch) were obtained from the MR, DR, IPN, and CG. The tissue

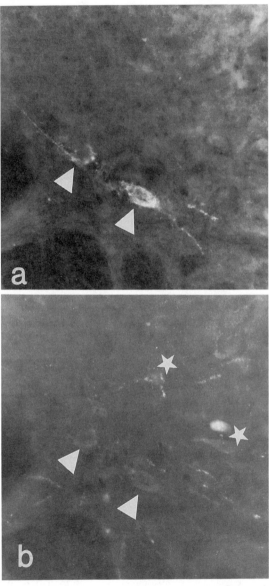

FIGURE 1. Photomicrographs of a coronal section through the DR showing distinct SP-immunoreactive and FG-filled neurons. The section was photographed (×250) to visualize (a) FITC- and (b) FG-labeled cells. Note that the FG-labeled cells (stars in b) are not visible in (a). Although some "bleed-through" of the fluorescence can be seen, the FITC-labeled cells (arrows in a) are not visible in (b).

was frozen on dry ice, pooled into three samples for each area, and then stored at −40 °C until analyzed by reverse-phase high performance liquid chromatography (HPLC) and radioimmunoassay (RIA).[9]

RESULTS

Retrogradely labeled cells were visualized in various brain stem nuclei including the IPN, LDTG, DR, and CG. These nuclei also contained NKLI perikarya. On the other hand, we did not observe any double-labeled cells in these nuclei (FIGURE 1). The biochemical analysis of midbrain tissue punches confirmed the presence of NKLI in these regions and indicated that NKB occurs in higher relative amounts in the IPN than in the other regions studied (TABLE 1).

TABLE 1. HPLC-RIA Analysis of Midbrain Tissue Punches[a]

	SPLI (SP2)	NKALI		NKA NKB	NKA NPK
		NKA5	E7		
MR	1971 ± 324	2679 ± 388	2337 ± 331	4.3	9.0
DR	1904 ± 418	2503 ± 567	2666 ± 413	4.4	8.2
CG	5630 ± 2430	3784 ± 572	4350 ± 922	5.4	6.4
IPN	2518 ± 1591	3626 ± 809	4343 ± 1044	1.9	5.0

[a]Data represent the mean ± SEM (fmol/sample) ($n = 3$) for each midbrain structure. Each sample consisted of punches obtained from 4–5 animals. The samples were assayed for SP-like immunoreactivity (SPLI) with antisera SP2 (rabbit anti-SP; cross-reactivities with NKA/NKB and with the related neuropeptide K were negligible) and for NKA/NKB-like immunoreactivity (NKALI) with antisera NKA5 (rabbit anti-NKA) and E7 (rabbit anti-eledoisin) (cross-react with NKB, 90% and 24%, respectively; with NPK, 54% and 93%, respectively).[9,10] Cross-reactivities of the antisera were accounted for in the calculation of the ratios.

DISCUSSION

The MR contains NKLI fibers, but not NKLI cell bodies. A number of brain stem nuclei that contain NKLI perikarya[1] send axons to the MR.[8] The results obtained in the present study, though, suggest that the NKLI fibers in the MR do not originate in the brain stem. Thus, the neurokinin innervation of the MR may arise in the forebrain. Additional anatomical and biochemical studies are needed to confirm this hypothesis.

REFERENCES

1. LJUNGDAHL, A., T. HÖKFELT & G. NILSSON. 1978. Neuroscience **3**: 861–943.
2. WARDEN, M. K. & W. S. YOUNG III. 1988. J. Comp. Neurol. **272**: 90–113.
3. SAFFROY, M., J. BEAUJOUAN, Y. TORRENS, J. BESSEYRE, L. BERGSTROM & J. GLOWINSKI. 1988. Peptides **9**: 227–241.
4. PARIS, J. M. & S. A. LORENS. 1989. J. Pharmacol. Exp. Ther. **251**: 388–393.
5. PARIS, J. M. & S. A. LORENS. 1987. Behav. Brain Res. **26**: 139–151.
6. PARIS, J. M., H. MITSUSHIO & S. A. LORENS. 1989. Brain Res. **476**: 183–188.

7. HARLAN, R. E., M. M. GARCIA & J. E. KRAUSE. 1987. J. Comp. Neurol. **287:** 179–212.
8. PARIS, J. M. & S. A. LORENS. 1988. Soc. Neurosci. Abstr. **14:** 1183.
9. BRODIN, E., N. LINDEFORS, C. J. DALSGAARD, E. THEODORSSON-NORHEIM & S. ROSELL. 1986. Regulat. Peptides **13:** 253–272.
10. LINDEFORS, N., E. BRODIN, E. THEODORSSON-NORHEIM & U. UNGERSTEDT. 1985. Regulat. Peptides **10:** 217–230.

Substance P and Somatostatin Levels in Rheumatoid Arthritis, Osteoarthritis, and Psoriatic Arthritis Synovial Fluid

S. MARABINI,[a] M. MATUCCI-CERINIC,[a] P. GEPPETTI,[a]
E. DEL BIANCO,[a] A. MARCHESONI,[b] S. TOSI,[b]
M. CAGNONI,[a] AND G. PARTSCH[c]

[a] Institute of Internal Medicine and Therapeutics IV
University of Florence
50139 Florence, Italy

[b] Institute of Rheumatology
University of Milan
Milan, Italy

[c] Ludwig Boltzmann Institute of Rheumatology
Wien, Austria

Substance P (SP) and somatostatin (SOM) have been identified in a distinct subpopulation of dorsal root sensory neurons and their peripheral endings.[1] Nerve fibers, stained for SP, have been observed in human joint synovia.[2] The role of peptidergic sensory neurons and of the "neurogenic inflammation" in rheumatoid arthritis (RA) and, particularly, in the involvement of SP in the articular destruction in experimental arthritis has been demonstrated.[3-5] High levels of SP have been detected in synovial fluid (SF) of rheumatoid arthritis patients.[6] We have assayed the SF levels of SP and SOM in patients affected with inflammatory joint diseases [RA and psoriatic arthritis (PA)] and degenerative joint disease [osteoarthritis (OA)].

PATIENTS AND METHODS

The SF samples were obtained by knee arthrocentesis from 18 patients with RA, 12 patients with OA, and 8 patients with PA. SF samples were collected in ice and were immediately frozen. SP and SOM immunoreactivities (SP-LI, SOM-LI) were assayed, in ethanol acid extracts, by radioimmunoassay (Amersham, United Kingdom; sensitivity of the assay was 1.1 fmol/tube for SP-LI and 0.8 fmol/tube for SOM-LI). Differences among groups were evaluated using Student's t test. Logarithmic regression analyses were used to compare the value of the erythrocyte sedimentation rate (ESR) and the SF neuropeptide levels.

RESULTS

The SP-LI (pmol/mL) mean level was significantly higher in RA (P) (43.1 ± 9.8) than in OA (12.0 ± 1.3) or PA (24.7 ± 1.8). Likewise, SOM-LI was higher in RA (P) (22.8 ± 1.4) than in OA (13.6 ± 4.7) or PA (14.7 ± 4.8). A significant correlation was found between the ESR and SP levels in RA SF ($r = 0.447P$).

DISCUSSION

The present data about higher SP levels in the SF of RA patients are in agreement with previous reports.[6] Various evidences indicate that SP is involved in the joint inflammatory process in rheumatic diseases.[3-5] It may be hypothesized that the higher SP-LI levels detected in RA SF could be related with the intense inflammation of the knee joint of RA patients. We have demonstrated that intra-articular SOM induces a clinical improvement in RA patients.[7] The observation that SOM inhibits SP release from sensory nerves[8] might have some relationship with the high SOM-LI levels that we have detected in the SF of RA patients. Furthermore, the correlation between the high level of SP and the increase in ESR, a specific index of inflammation, further suggests that this peptide represents an important agent in the development of rheumatic disease.

REFERENCES

1. HÖKFELT, T., R. ELDE et al. 1976. J. Neurosci. **1:** 131–136.
2. GRONBLAD, M., Y. T. KONTTINEN et al. 1988. J. Rheumatol. **15:** 1807–1810.
3. LEVINE, J. D., D. R. CLARK et al. 1984. Science **226:** 547–549.
4. LEVINE, J. D., D. H. COLLIER et al. 1985. J. Rheumatol. **12:** 406–411.
5. LEVINE, J. D., S. J. DARDICK et al. 1986. J. Neurosci. **6:** 3423–3429.
6. DEVILLIER, P., B. WEILL et al. 1987. N. Engl. J. Med. **314:** 1323.
7. MATUCCI-CERINIC, M. & S. MARABINI. 1988. Med. Sci. Res. **16:** 233–234.
8. LEMBECK, F., J. DONNERER et al. 1982. Eur. J. Pharmacol. **85:** 171–176.

The Glycine-extended SP Precursor, SP-G, Is Normally Expressed in SP-containing Neurons

JAMES E. MARCHAND AND RICHARD M. KREAM

Anesthesia Research
Tufts University School of Medicine
Boston, Massachusetts 02111

The glycine-extended precursor form of substance P (SP), substance P–glycine (SP-G), is probably the immediate precursor to SP, although we cannot rule out the possibility that large NH_2-terminal-extended forms are first amidated, followed by endoproteolytic cleavage and release of mature SP. We have used highly specific antisera to SP-G in combination with the radioimmunoassay (RIA) technique to quantify the levels of SP-G in brain tissue extracts from spinal cord, brain stem, hypothalamic, and forebrain regions. These data demonstrate that the relative content of immunoreactivities corresponding to SP-G, normalized against those of SP, varied from less than 0.5% in the substantia nigra to approximately 5% in the dorsal root ganglia. Combined HPLC/RIA analyses indicated that immunoreactivities corresponding to SP and SP-G were in fact authentic. After fractionation by gradient reverse-phase HPLC, the major immunoreactive peaks of SP and SP-G immunoreactivity were coeluted with authentic standards.

Immunohistochemical analyses performed with affinity-purified anti-SP-G sera demonstrated discrete localization of immunoreactive SP-G to a subset of SP-containing neural elements, most prominently in sensory terminals in the substantia gelatinosa and dorsolateral medulla. Additional areas of strong terminal-like labeling included the nucleus of the solitary tract, the interpeduncular nucleus, and the substantia nigra. In the normal animal, analyses performed with antisera to SP and SP-G also labeled cell bodies, although the SP-G labeling existed as a subset of the SP somal labeling. Specifically, SP-G-labeled cell bodies were located in the dorsal root ganglia, the nucleus of the solitary tract, and the lateral dorsal tegmental nucleus of the pons. SP-labeled cell bodies were localized in each of these regions and, in addition, significant somal labeling was localized in the superior colliculus, the periaqueductal gray, the interpeduncular nucleus, and the medial habenular nucleus.

In order to examine the total number of SP- and SP-G-containing cell bodies in the normal animal, a colchicine model was utilized. Colchicine was injected into the cisterna magnum and the relative distribution of SP and SP-G immunoreactive cell bodies was examined in caudal hypothalamic, brain stem, and cervical spinal cord regions. The colchicine treatment elicited differential patterns of labeling of immunoreactive SP-G-containing somata in selected brain areas. Most prominently, the paraolivary nucleus of the ventrolateral medulla exhibited dense staining of SP-G-positive somata after colchicine treatment, but not in saline-treated controls. Also, the periaqueductal gray and the nucleus of the solitary tract exhibited moderately dense somal staining using the antisera to SP-G. In contrast, the superior colliculus, the interpeduncular nucleus, and the ventral premammillary nucleus, all of which contained extensive SP immunoreactive somal labeling after colchicine treatment, were devoid of SP-G immunoreactive somal labeling.

These data demonstrate that the glycine-extended precursor to SP, SP-G, is present in the normal animal as a significant percentage of the SP levels. Both the RIA and the immunohistochemical data indicate regional differences in the relative percent of this precursor, suggesting regional differences in steady state processing. Finally, the response of these systems to the challenge of colchicine treatment suggests functional differences in dynamic processing of the preprotachykinin molecule in tachykinin-containing neurons.

Neurokinin Receptor–mediated Regulation of [Ca]$_i$ and Ca-sensitive Ion Channels in Mammalian Colonic Muscle

E. A. MAYER,[a,b] X. P. SUN,[a] S. SUPPLISSON,[b]
A. KODNER,[a] M. REGOLI,[c] AND G. SACHS[a,b]

[a]Department of Medicine
Veterans Administration Wadsworth Medical Center
Los Angeles, California 90073

[b]Department of Physiology
University of California at Los Angeles
Los Angeles, California 90024

[c]Department of Medicine
University of Sherbrooke
Sherbrooke, Quebec, Canada J1H 5N4

INTRODUCTION

The positive inotropic effect of substance P on the colonic longitudinal muscle layer is largely mediated by dihydropyridine-sensitive Ca^{2+} influx.[1] However, the membrane pathway by which neurokinin (NK) receptor activation results in depolarization required for the activation of voltage-sensitive Ca^{2+} channels is not known. Furthermore, it is not known if the effect of substance P is mediated by differential membrane effects mediated by the NK-1 and NK-2 receptors. To address these questions, we studied NK receptor–mediated changes (a) in intracellular Ca^{2+} concentration ($[Ca^{2+}]_i$) and (b) in membrane ion channels in single myocytes.

METHODS

Freshly dispersed myocytes from the longitudinal muscle layer of the rabbit colon were incubated for 30 min with Fura-2 AM (5 μM) at 37 °C and $[Ca^{2+}]_i$ was monitored using single cell imaging techniques.[2] Cells were also studied using the patch-clamp technique in the cell-attached configuration.[3]

RESULTS

[Ca^{2+}]$_i$ Imaging Studies

$[Ca^{2+}]_i$ in fully relaxed cells was homogeneously distributed within the cells and was found to be 150 ± 7 nM (mean ± SEM; $n = 30$). The NK-1 receptor agonist, [Sar^9,Met(O$_2$)^{11}]-SP, and the NK-2 receptor agonist, [bAla^8]NKA(4–10), both induced $[Ca^{2+}]_i$ oscillations confined to the subplasmalemmal space (FIGURE 1). The peptide effect on the amplitude of the oscillations was dose-dependent (10^{-12}–10^{-8}

M), reaching a maximal amplitude of 1 μM. Addition of nifedipine (3×10^{-7} M) to the bath ($n = 6$) or bathing the cells in 126 mM KCl Ringer's solution with a free $[Ca^{2+}]$ of 5×10^{-8} M ($n = 4$) reduced the $[Ca^{2+}]_i$ response to both NK agonists (10^{-8} M) by 40% and 60%, respectively.

Patch-Clamp Studies

Under control conditions with pipette and bath solutions as shown in FIGURE 2, no channel activity was seen at pipette potentials between 80 and -30 mV. The addition of both NK receptor agonists (10^{-10} M) transiently activated a chloride (Cl^-)–selective ion channel at a pipette holding potential of 60 mV. Under these conditions, the channel showed strong voltage dependence and was only seen at pipette potentials more positive than -20 mV (corresponding to membrane hyperpolarization). The slope conductance was 18 pS. The addition of the Ca^{2+} ionophore A23187 (10^{-5} M) to the bath (free $[Ca^{2+}] = 10^{-6}$ M) resulted in a transient activation of the Cl^- channel at the holding potential followed by inactivation.

SUMMARY AND CONCLUSIONS

In conclusion, these findings suggest the following:

(1) NK receptor activation results in $[Ca^{2+}]_i$ oscillations;
(2) the receptor-mediated $[Ca^{2+}]_i$ increase is partially due to influx of Ca^{2+} through L-type Ca^{2+} channels and partially to release from intracellular stores;

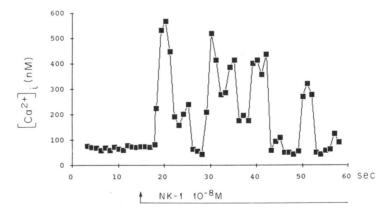

FIGURE 1. Neurokinin receptor activation stimulates $[Ca^{2+}]_i$ oscillations: a representative experiment showing $[Ca^{2+}]_i$ during control conditions (perfusion with Ringer's solution; $[Ca^{2+}] = 1$ mM) and repetitive $[Ca^{2+}]_i$ transients of a myocyte following continuous infusion with the bath solution containing the NK-1 receptor agonist (10^{-8} M). $[Ca^{2+}]_i$ was monitored within the subplasmalemmal space. $[Ca^{2+}]_i$ was estimated from the ratio of images in Fura-2-loaded myocytes[2] acquired at excitation wavelengths of 340 and 380 nm at a sampling rate of one image pair per second. The bath temperature was 22 °C.

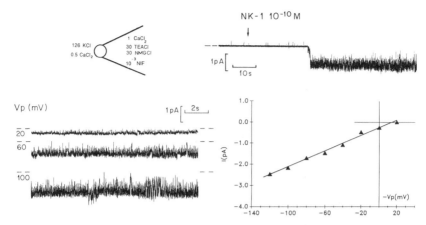

FIGURE 2. Neurokinin receptor activation results in activation of a Cl⁻ channel: a representative patch-clamp experiment in the cell-attached configuration. Recording conditions are illustrated in the cartoon (concentrations are shown in mM; left upper quadrant). At a holding pipette potential (V_p) of 60 mV, the addition of the NK-1 agonist (10^{-10} M) to the bath resulted in the activation of a channel-mediating inward current (right upper quadrant). At negative pipette potentials, the channel was primarily in the open state (left lower quadrant). The current-voltage (I-V) relationship of the channel is shown in the right lower quadrant. No channel activity was seen at V_p values more negative than -20 mV. The extrapolated reversal potential of the channel corresponds to the Cl⁻ reversal potential, assuming an intracellular Cl⁻ concentration of 30 mM. The bath solution was 126 mM Ringer's solution with 0.5 mM $CaCl_2$. The bath temperature was 22 °C. Records were filtered at 500 Hz. Abbreviations: NMGCl, *N*-methyl glucosamine hydrochloride; NIF, nifedipine.

(3) the receptor-mediated depolarization results from activation of a Cl⁻ channel at the cell resting potential;

(4) NK receptor–mediated release of $[Ca^{2+}]_i$ may play a role in Cl⁻ channel activation;

(5) there is no evidence for multiple NK receptor types involved in cell activation.

REFERENCES

1. KOELBEL, C. B. M., E. A. MAYER, J. R. REEVE, JR., W. J. SNAPE, JR., A. PATEL & F. J. HO. 1989. Involvement of substance P in noncholinergic excitation of rabbit colonic muscle. Am. J. Physiol. **256**(Gastrointest. Liver Physiol. 19): G246–G253.
2. JACOB, R., J. E. HALLAM & T. J. RINK. 1988. Repetitive spikes in cytoplasmic calcium evoked by histamine in human endothelial cells. Nature **335**: 40–45.
3. MAYER, E. A., D. D. F. LOO, A. KODNER & S. N. REDDY. 1990. Differential modulation of Ca^{2+}-activated K^+ channels by substance P. Am. J. Physiol. **257**(Gastrointest. Liver Physiol. 20): G887–G897.

Characteristics of Tachykinin Transport Vesicles in the Optic Nerve

PETER J. MORIN,[a] ROBIN J. JOHNSON,[a] IDIT SHACHAR,[a]
RICHARD E. FINE,[a] AND SUSAN E. LEEMAN[b]

[a]Department of Biochemistry
Boston University School of Medicine
Boston, Massachusetts 02118

[b]Department of Physiology
University of Massachusetts Medical Center
Worcester, Massachusetts 01655

Using kinetic and biochemical criteria, we have previously identified and characterized three classes of vesicles that are rapidly transported in the rabbit optic nerve.[1] Our data suggested that, whereas two classes of low density vesicles account for the majority of the rapidly transported protein, a third class of higher density vesicles carrying tachykinins and a smaller amount of membrane protein are also rapidly transported. Of particular interest here was the observation that the tachykinin vesicles, although rapidly transported, experienced a delay in their appearance in the axon, suggesting a delay in their export from their site of synthesis in the retinal ganglion cell body. Here, we provide additional documentation of this phenomenon.

Synaptophysin-containing vesicles were immunoadsorbed from retinal cell preparations at three time points after intraocular injection of tracer (FIGURE 1). At 1.5 h, labeled vesicles were adsorbed from gradient regions corresponding to both the low and high density rapid transport vesicles. By 3 h, the lighter vesicles were relatively depleted. At 24 h, the dense vesicles with the same density as the axonal tachykinin vesicles remained in the retina, consistent with their delayed export.

Synaptophysin was immunoprecipitated from the optic nerve (ON), the optic tract (OT), and the lateral geniculate nucleus (LGN) at the indicated times after intraocular injection (FIGURE 2). Synaptophysin appears to arrive at the LGN in two waves: the first is seen at 3 h and the second begins by 24 h. The first wave presumably moves through the ON by 3 h and the second is seen in the ON at 24 h and in the OT at 12 h and 24 h, again indicating a delayed export of newly synthesized material bound for the nerve terminal.

We conclude that the dense population of tachykinin-containing vesicles are rapidly transported into the optic nerve and tract and that they experience a significant (up to one day) delay in export from their site of synthesis in the retinal ganglion cell bodies. Nearly identical kinetics have been described for synapsin I, a synaptic vesicle phosphoprotein, and have been interpreted as arising from a prolonged maturational process prior to export.[2] However, because the maturation of peptidergic secretory granules is typically measured in hours and not days, we offer the alternative hypothesis that the delayed export results from temporary sequestration of newly produced, mature vesicles in a storage pool whose purpose is to facilitate a rapid and efficient response of the neuron during periods of increased activity without the necessity of new protein synthesis. We would therefore postulate further that the export of vesicles from the storage pool, that is, the initiation of rapid transport of this species, be coupled to the cell's electrical activity.

442

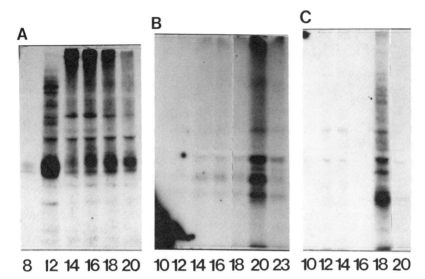

FIGURE 1. Rapid transport vesicles were immunoadsorbed from sucrose density gradient fractions of retinal preparations using monoclonal antisynaptophysin (Boehringer Mannheim, Chicago, Illinois) at (A) 1.5, (B) 3, and (C) 24 hours after intraocular injections of Trans [^{35}S]-label (containing 80% [^{35}S]-methionine and 20% [^{35}S]-cysteine and with a specific activity of 1000–1200 Ci/mmole; from ICN Biomedicals, Costa Mesa, California), as described in reference 1. Adsorbed radiolabeled vesicles were detected by SDS-gel electrophoresis and fluorography. They are seen here in gradient fractions corresponding to low and high density rapid transport vesicles. The lighter vesicles are progressively diminished with kinetics consistent with their immediate export from the retina, whereas the denser, presumed tachykinin-containing vesicles are retained for at least 24 h.

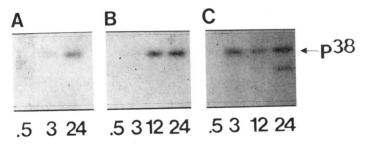

FIGURE 2. Synaptophysin was immunoprecipitated from (A) the optic nerve, (B) the optic tract, and (C) the lateral geniculate nucleus at the indicated times after intraocular injection of 0.5 mCi tracer, as described in reference 1. Precipitated protein was detected by SDS-gel electrophoresis and fluorography and consisted of the 38-kilodalton protein shown here (p38). See text for discussion.

REFERENCES

1. MORIN, P. J., N. LIU, R. J. J. BENSON, S. E. LEEMAN & R. E. FINE. 1991. J. Neurochem. **56:** 415–427.
2. BAITINGER, C. & M. WILLARD. 1987. J. Neurosci. **7**(11): 3723–3735.

The Effect of Substance P on Guanine Nucleotide–activated Striatal Adenylate Cyclase

ANDREAS MOSER

Department of Neurology
Medical University of Lübeck
D-2400 Lübeck 1, Federal Republic of Germany

High amounts of substance P are present in the perikarya and axons of neurons of the striatonigral pathway, where it may act as a neurotransmitter.[1] In the caudate putamen, substance P is localized in spiny I or II efferent neurons of the striatum.[2] However, the interaction at the molecular level of substance P–ergic neurons with dopaminergic afferents is unknown. In order to clarify a potential interaction between substance P and D-1 receptors in this brain area, we used a pellet preparation of rat caudate putamen to measure dopamine-sensitive adenylate cyclase activity and the effects of substance P thereupon. Female Wistar rats were decapitated and the caudate putamen areas were dissected on ice. The tissues were homogenized in an ice-cold calcium-free solution of 10 mM TRIS-HCl and 4 mM EDTA, pH 7.6, centrifuged at 1500g; this was then resuspended and recentrifuged three times at 0 °C. The incubation medium was composed according to previous studies.[3] The assay was linear with protein concentrations up to 100 μg. The formation of ^{32}P–cyclic AMP was measured according to Salomon.[4]

In the presence of substance P, no change in the basal adenylate cyclase was observed. Stimulation of adenylate cyclase produced by submaximal or maximal concentrations of dopamine and 2-chloro-adenosine, previously depressed by adenosine deaminase, was not influenced by substance P (FIGURE 1). The effects of calcium chloride over a range of concentrations and of magnesium chloride were not affected by addition of substance P (FIGURE 1). When the guanosine nucleotide Gpp(NH)p was present in the incubation medium, substance P (10 μM) stimulated the enzyme activity to approximately 140% when compared to control (FIGURE 2). Substance P was most effective in a concentration of 10 μM. In contrast to this, after employment of guanosine-triphosphate, substance P inhibited adenylate cyclase activity in a dose-dependent manner with an apparent V_{max} that was 58% of the GTP (10 μM)–induced response (FIGURE 2).

Thus, the guanine nucleotide analogues are essential cofactors for hormonal stimulation of adenylate cyclase,[5] acting on a guanine nucleotide–sensitive subunit that presents a multicomponent regulatory complex including inhibitory and excitatory binding sites.[6] Sunyer *et al.*[7] found that G_i is capable of hydrolyzing GTP, where the natural effector GTP presented the highest affinity of the GTP-ase system in comparison to other guanosine nucleotide analogues like Gpp(NH)p. In agreement with Macdonald and Boyd,[8] who have found that the effect of the binding of substance P to receptors in peripheral tissues is mediated by a G protein, which is required for high affinity binding, we suggest that substance P interacts with the guanine nucleotide regulatory subunit without directly affecting D-1 dopamine receptors in the caudate putamen of the rat. However, further studies are necessary.

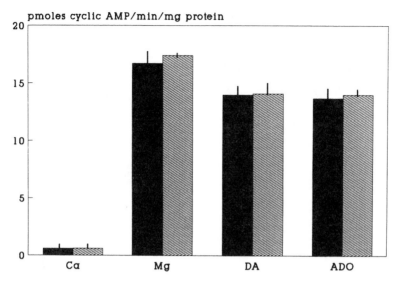

FIGURE 1. Effects of calcium chloride (Ca, 2 mM), magnesium chloride (Mg, 4 mM), dopamine (DA, 1 mM), and 2-chloro-adenosine (ADO, 1 mM) in the absence (■) and presence (▨) of substance P (1 μM) on the adenylate cyclase activity in pmoles cyclic AMP/min/mg protein ± SD.

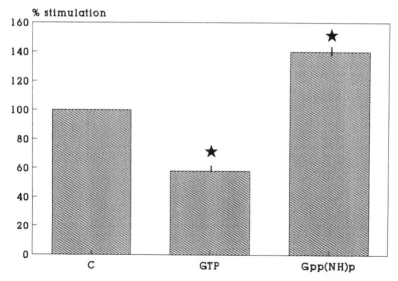

FIGURE 2. Effect of substance P (10 μM) in the presence of guanosine-triphosphate (GTP) or in the presence of guanylylimido-diphosphate [Gpp(NH)p] as a percent of the basal adenylate cyclase activity ± SD; (∗) $p < 0.01$, significant compared to control (C).

REFERENCES

1. MROZ, E. A., M. J. BROWNSTEIN & S. E. LEEMAN. 1977. Brain Res. **125:** 305–311.
2. GROVES, P. M. 1983. Brain Res. Rev. **5:** 109–132.
3. MOSER, A., C. REAVILL, P. JENNER, C. D. MARSDEN & H. CRAMER. 1986. Exp. Brain Res. **62:** 567–571.
4. SALOMON, Y. 1979. Adv. Cyclic Nucleotide Res. **10:** 35–55.
5. NORMURA, Y., T. ARIMA & T. SWGAWA. 1987. Int. J. Dev. Neurosci. **5:** 271–279.
6. CODINA, J., J. D. HILDEBRANDT, T. SUNYER, R. D. SEKURA, C. R. MANCLARK, R. IYENGAR & L. BIRNBAUMER. 1984. Adv. Cyclic Nucleotide Res. **17:** 111–125.
7. SUNYER, T., J. CODINA & L. BIRNBAUMER. 1984. J. Biol. Chem. **259:** 15447–15451.
8. MACDONALD, S. G. & N. D. BOYD. 1989. J. Neurochem. **53:** 264–272.

Multiple Tachykinin Receptors in Rat Submandibular Gland[a]

CHRISTIAN J. MUSSAP AND ELIZABETH BURCHER[b]

School of Physiology and Pharmacology
University of New South Wales
Kensington, New South Wales 2033, Australia

INTRODUCTION

Early *in vivo* studies showed substance P (SP) to be more potent than both neurokinin A (NKA) and neurokinin B (NKB) in stimulating salivation in the rat.[1,2] This rank order of potency (SP > NKA > NKB) is indicative of action via an NK1 receptor. These observations have been supported by radioligand binding studies in salivary glands.[3-5] However, Murray and co-workers[6] have suggested that all three tachykinin receptor types may be present in rat salivary glands. In their salivation study, the response to NKB was antagonized by atropine, indicating that NKB may mediate acetylcholine release via NK3 receptors localized presynaptically on postganglionic, parasympathetic neurons. Recently, Takeda and Krause have shown that the novel tachykinins, neuropeptide K and neuropeptide γ, both N-terminally extended forms of NKA, are potent sialogogues *in vivo*.[7,8]

We have recently developed a new radioligand, [^{125}I]-Bolton-Hunter scyliorhinin II (BHSCYII), which is selective for the NK3 receptor in rat brain[9] and, unlike the relatively unselective [^{125}I]-Bolton-Hunter eledoisin (BHELE), has low affinity for other tachykinin binding sites in peripheral tissues. The aim of this study was to recharacterize the tachykinin binding sites in the rat submandibular gland using selective analogues as competitors of our novel radioligand BHSCYII and BHELE.

METHODS

Radioligands were synthesized and purified by reverse-phase HPLC as previously described.[9] Crude membranes of submandibular gland from Sprague-Dawley rats of either sex were prepared as described before.[5] Aliquots (2% final concentration) of homogenates of submandibular gland were incubated at 25 °C with the respective radioligand in incubation buffer containing 50 mM Tris-HCl (pH 7.4, 25 °C), $MnCl_2$ (3 mM), bovine albumin (0.02%), and the peptidase inhibitors, chymostatin (4 μg/mL) and phosphoramidon (1 μM). At equilibrium, (120 min) incubations were terminated by rapid filtration through Whatman GF/B glass fiber filters. Filter-bound radioligand was quantified using a gamma counter. Nonspecific binding for BHSCYII and BHELE was defined with 1 μM SCYII and ELE, respectively. Estimates for K_D and B_{max} were determined using "cold" saturation experiments analyzed using the computer programs EBDA and LIGAND.[10] Standard solutions of most peptides (Auspep, Australia) were stored (-20 °C) in 0.01 M acetic acid

[a]This study was supported by the National Health and Medical Research Council of Australia.

[b]To whom all correspondence should be addressed.

containing 1% β-mercaptoethanol. SCYII was stored without β-mercaptoethanol (to maintain the disulfide bridge) and NKB was dissolved in dimethylsulfoxide.

RESULTS

Binding of both radioligands was saturable and reversible, reaching maximum specific binding at 120 min. Hill coefficients were close to unity. Scatchard analysis of "cold" saturation experiments revealed binding of BHELE to a single population of high affinity, noninteracting sites (K_D, 2.72 ± 0.18 nM; FIGURE 1). In contrast,

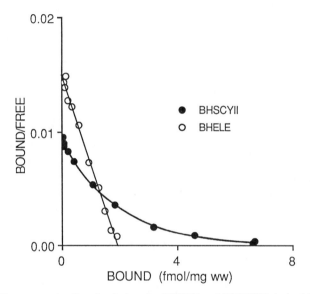

FIGURE 1. Representative Scatchard plots for BHELE and BHSCYII derived from "cold" saturation experiments in homogenates of submandibular gland. The Scatchard for BHELE is linear, indicating binding to a single class of high affinity, noninteracting sites (Hill coefficients ≈ 1 for both radioligands). The Scatchard for BHSCYII is distinctly curvilinear and could be resolved into two components. Bound radioligand is expressed as fmol/mg wet weight (ww) tissue.

Scatchard plots for BHSCYII were biphasic and were resolved into high affinity sites (K_D, 1.71 ± 0.57 nM) and low affinity sites (K_D, 69.9 ± 25.6 nM), representing 10% and 90% of total sites bound, respectively. The maximum number of binding sites was similar (BHELE: B_{max}, 1.85 ± 0.12 fmol/mg wet weight; BHSCYII: 2.24 ± 0.61 fmol/mg wet weight).

For both radioligands, the most potent competitors for the binding were the NK1-preferring compounds, namely, physalaemin (PHYS), SP, and the NK1 selective analogue, [$Sar^9,Met(O_2)^{11}$]-SP. NKA and NKB were approximately equipotent, whereas the NK3 selective analogues, [$MePhe^7$]-NKB and senktide, were very weak competitors. Against BHSCYII binding, the inhibition curves for PHYS and the NK3-preferring SCYII and NKB could be resolved into two components (refer to

TABLE 1. Binding Parameters for Tachykinins and Analogues as Competitors for BHSCYII and BHELE Binding in Homogenates of Rat Submandibular Gland[a]

Competitor	BHELE			BHSCYII		
	Slope Factor	K_D (nM)	RA	Slope Factor	K_D (nM)	RA
substance P	0.93 ± 0.03	0.04 ± 0.01	100	0.86 ± 0.06	0.79 ± 0.24	100
physalaemin	0.96 ± 0.04	0.04 ± 0.01	100	0.92 ± 0.04	0.22 ± 0.04 (90%)	359
neuropeptide γ	0.88 ± 0.01	0.01 ± 0.009 (72%)	400		22.6 ± 34.9 (10%)	3.49
		2.84 ± 3.09 (28%)	1.41	0.92 ± 0.05	1.57 ± 0.15	50.3
[Sar^9,Met(O$_2$)^{11}]-SP	0.94 ± 0.03	0.05 ± 0.15	80.0	0.81 ± 0.07	0.60 ± 0.17	131
kassinin	0.79 ± 0.06	1.56 ± 0.25	2.56	0.82 ± 0.02	1.68 ± 0.22	47.0
neuropeptide K	0.95 ± 0.02	1.86 ± 0.19	2.15	0.93 ± 0.04	3.34 ± 0.42	23.7
eledoisin	0.92 ± 0.06	2.19 ± 0.28	1.82	0.92 ± 0.02	4.99 ± 0.73	15.8
scyliorhinin II	0.91 ± 0.02	3.05 ± 0.58	1.31	0.66 ± 0.05	1.38 ± 1.03 (66%)	57.2
					108 ± 111 (34%)	0.73
neurokinin A	0.77 ± 0.05	7.80 ± 2.85	0.51	0.78 ± 0.18	10.4 ± 3.24	7.59
neurokinin B	0.85 ± 0.09	9.62 ± 3.08	0.41	0.81 ± 0.11	4.96 ± 3.40 (10%)	15.9
					682 ± 634 (90%)	0.11
[MePhe^7]-NKB	0.84 ± 0.02	602 ± 123	0.01	1.00 ± 0.01	757 ± 154	0.10
senktide	0.96 ± 0.20	4377 ± 56	<0.01	1.00 ± 0.30	4205 ± 1150	0.02

[a]Values are means ± SE (approximate) of 3–6 experiments and were derived from LIGAND analysis. Slope factors were derived using the program EBDA. Terms: K_D, equilibrium dissociation constant; RA, relative affinity when SP is set to 100.

TABLE 1). The ratio of high to low affinity sites was approximately 1:9 for NKB and 9:1 for PHYS. The novel tachykinin, neuropeptide γ, yielded a biphasic inhibition profile against BHELE binding, with high affinity (K_D, 0.01 nM) at 72% of the sites.

DISCUSSION

In this study, binding of both BHSCYII and BHELE to rat submandibular gland was characterized as being to an NK1 site, a finding in agreement with earlier data showing that this tissue contains predominantly NK1 receptors.[1,3-5] However, BHSCYII binding was to two distinct classes of sites, suggesting that a minor population of another tachykinin receptor type may also be present in this tissue. For BHSCYII, the majority (90%) of sites were labeled with low affinity (K_D, 70 nM), consistent with earlier findings that SCYII has moderate affinity at NK1 sites.[11] We have previously demonstrated that BHSCYII exhibits high affinity for NK3 receptors in rat brain (K_D, 1.3 nM).[9] The saturation K_D estimates for the high affinity component of BHSCYII binding to membranes of submandibular gland (K_D, 1.7 nM) correlate well with the K_D values obtained from binding to brain NK3 receptors. It is therefore suggested that these small numbers of high affinity sites in the submandibular gland may be of the NK3 type.

The resolution of the inhibition profiles of several competitors into high and low affinity components is further evidence for the existence of at least two tachykinin receptor classes in this gland. Although neuropeptide K is the most potent tachykinin in stimulating salivation,[7] it was not potent in displacing BHSCYII or BHELE binding in submandibular gland. However, this does not preclude it having a more specific secretory role in either the sublingual or parotid gland. The biphasic inhibition of BHELE by neuropeptide γ is also of interest because most of the binding (72%) was displaced with high affinity (K_D, 0.01 nM). Krause and Takeda have shown that neuropeptide γ is also a potent sialogogue *in vivo*[8] and they have recently described high affinity binding sites for iodinated neuropeptide γ in rat brain and duodenum.[12] These findings suggest that NK2 or NK2-like receptors may be present in the rat salivary glands.

Although the rat submandibular gland is enriched with NK1 receptors, a small number of other tachykinin receptor types are present for which the NK3-preferring BHSCYII has high affinity. Although these sites may represent NK3 receptors, the possibility exists that there may also be receptors for endogenous neuropeptide K and/or neuropeptide γ in this tissue. Clearly, further autoradiographic and functional studies utilizing selective analogues and antagonists will be needed to conclusively demonstrate the physiological roles that these (perhaps NK3) receptors and their endogenous ligands play in the salivation response in the rat.

REFERENCES

1. LEEMAN, S. E. & R. HAMMERSCHLAG. 1967. Stimulation of salivary gland secretion by a factor extracted from hypothalamic tissue. Endocrinology **81:** 803–810.
2. TAKANO, Y., Y. TAKEDA, M. DOTEUCHI, K. INOUYI & H. KAMIYA. 1985. Effect of a novel tachykinin, substance K, in salivation in rats. Eur. J. Pharmacol. **111:** 381–383.
3. LIANG, T. & M. A. CASCIERI. 1981. Substance P receptor on parotid cell membranes. J. Neurosci. **1:** 1133–1141.
4. LEE, C. M., J. A. JAVITCH & S. H. SNYDER. 1983. ³H–Substance P binding to salivary gland membranes. Mol. Pharmacol. **23:** 563–569.

5. BUCK, S. H. & E. BURCHER. 1985. The rat submaxillary gland contains predominantly P-type tachykinin binding sites. Peptides **6:** 1079–1084.

6. MURRAY, C. W., A. COWAN, D. L. WRIGHT, J. L. VAUGHT & H. I. JACOBY. 1987. Neurokinin-induced salivation in the anesthetized rat: a three receptor hypothesis. J. Pharmacol. Exp. Ther. **242:** 500–506.

7. TAKEDA, Y. & J. E. KRAUSE. 1989. Neuropeptide K potently stimulates salivary gland secretion and potentiates substance P–induced salivation. Proc. Natl. Acad. Sci. U.S.A. **86:** 392–396.

8. TAKEDA, Y. & J. E. KRAUSE. 1989. γ-Preprotachykinin-(72–92)-peptide amide potentiates substance P–induced salivation. Eur. J. Pharmacol. **161:** 267–271.

9. MUSSAP, C. J. & E. BURCHER. 1990. [^{125}I]-Bolton-Hunter scyliorhinin II: a novel, selective radioligand for the tachykinin NK3 receptor in rat brain. Peptides **11:** 827–836.

10. MCPHERSON, G. A. 1983. A practical computer-based approach to the analysis of radioligand binding systems. Comput. Programs Biomed. **17:** 107–114.

11. BUCK, S. H. & J. L. KRSTENANSKY. 1987. The dogfish peptides scyliorhinin I and scyliorhinin II bind with differential selectivity to mammalian tachykinin receptors. Eur. J. Pharmacol. **144:** 109–111.

12. DAM, T-V., Y. TAKEDA, J. E. KRAUSE, E. ESCHER & R. QUIRION. 1990. γ-Preprotachykinin-(72–92)-peptide amide: an endogenous preprotachykinin I gene–derived peptide that preferentially binds to neurokinin-2 receptors. Proc. Natl. Acad. Sci. U.S.A. **87:** 246–250.

SP Immunoreactivity in the Dental Pulp and Periodontium during Tooth Movement

O. NICOLAY,[a] J. SHANFELD,[b] Z. DAVIDOVITCH,[b]
AND K. ALLEY[b]

[a] School of Dental and Oral Surgery
Columbia University
New York, New York 10032

[b] College of Dentistry
Ohio State University
Columbus, Ohio 43210

Mechanical stress applied to a tooth for orthodontic treatment initiates an inflammatory reaction that induces remodeling of the periodontal tissues, leading to tooth movement. Because the periodontal ligament (PDL) and the dental pulp are well innervated and contain numerous receptors for noxious stimuli, it is conceivable that neurotransmitters, particularly SP, could mediate the biologic response to mechanical stress applied to teeth during orthodontic treatment.

This hypothesis was investigated immunohistochemically in cats that had one maxillary canine tipped distally for a period of time ranging from 1 h to 14 days. Horizontal histological sections, 5 μm thick, collected from frozen specimens were stained by an immunoglobulin-enzyme bridge method using rabbit anti-SP polyclonal antibodies. In the dental pulp of untreated canines, SP-containing varicosities and/or terminals were mainly apparent in the walls of small vessels. On the other hand, in the PDL of these teeth, nervous elements exhibiting positive staining were detected in a few localized areas, some in close vicinity to the alveolar bone. The application of an orthodontic force to the teeth resulted in an apparent higher density of SP immunoreactivity. This phenomenon occurred rapidly in the dental pulp, after 3 h (FIGURE 1), but later in the PDL. At tension sites, positive staining was scarce at each of the various time periods and was mostly localized near the osteoblastic zone after 24 h of treatment. In contrast, the areas of periodontal compression were more likely to exhibit SP-immunoreactive nervous elements, starting 24 h after force application. Positive staining could still be detected after 14 days, but the density of SP immunoreactivity appeared to peak after 7 days of treatment (FIGURE 2).

The results of this preliminary study demonstrate that the stimulation of periodontal nerve fibers by means of orthodontic forces may induce peripheral release of SP in the pulp and PDL. The temporal variations in the appearance of SP immunoreactivity suggest two different types of action: a role in pain perception in the pulp and an active participation by the nervous system in alveolar bone remodeling subsequent to mechanical stress. In compression sites, SP released by antidromic nerve stimulation may contribute to or enhance inflammation induced by mechanical deformation of the tissues. Vasodilatation and plasma extravasation occur, vascular elements (i.e., mast cells, macrophages, and lymphocytes) may consequently migrate

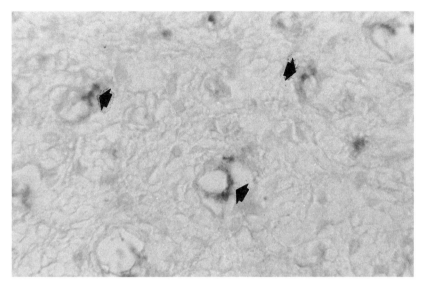

FIGURE 1. Dental pulp of a cat maxillary canine after 3 h of orthodontic treatment. Note the number of elements staining positively for SP (arrows). Magnification: ×200.

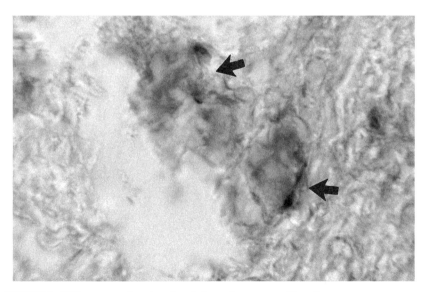

FIGURE 2. PDL compression site after 7 days of treatment. Note the numerous structures staining positively for SP (arrows). Magnification: ×200.

into the local environment, and their active products (e.g., histamine, interleukins, and interferons) may interact with target cells. It is important to note that the SP staining density started to increase at 24 hours, in unison with the peaks of intracellular cAMP and cGMP levels (12 to 24 h), suggesting that SP may be associated with the activation of periodontal cells by applied mechanical force *in vivo*.

In conclusion, the stimulation of periodontal nerve terminals by means of mechanical force applied to a tooth may induce the release of neurotransmitters, particularly SP. SP may be the initial trigger for a biochemical cascade leading to the activation of target cells in the periodontium. SP may either act directly on target cells as a "first messenger" or enhance the release of other "first messengers" such as prostaglandins and cytokines, leading to an increase in intracellular "second messengers". In either case, SP appears to play a key role in regulating the cellular responses to mechanical forces *in vivo*.

Alterations of Preprotachykinin (PPT) mRNA in Medullary Raphe Occur following Manipulation of Serotonin[a]

L. A. RILEY, P. D. WALKER, R. P. HART,
AND G. M. JONAKAIT

Department of Biological Sciences
Rutgers University
Newark, New Jersey 07102

Substance P (SP) is colocalized with serotonin (5-HT) in neurons of the medullary raphe, but its role and regulation there are not well understood. We have sought to determine whether manipulation of 5-HT affects the biosynthesis of SP. Recently, we showed that depletion of 5-HT by chronic inhibition of 5-HT biosynthesis increased levels of PPT mRNA in medullary raphe neurons.[1] The current study was undertaken to determine whether increases in extracellular 5-HT would cause the opposite response.

Rats were treated with the specific 5-HT uptake inhibitor, zimelidine (10 mg/kg twice daily), for 1, 5, or 14 days or with the monoamine oxidase inhibitor, clorgyline (1 mg/kg/day), for 1, 5, 14, or 21 days. RNA prepared from the medullary raphe of individual animals was subjected to Northern blot hybridization using a [^{32}P]-labeled probe for rat PPT mRNA. The SP content of thoracic ventral spinal cord sections was determined in the same animals using radioimmunoassay.

Animals treated with zimelidine for 1 or 5 days showed significant decreases in the levels of PPT mRNA (FIGURE 1). After 14 days of zimelidine treatment, however, PPT mRNA levels were not significantly different from control animals. In the same animals, the SP peptide content of the ventral spinal cord was not significantly decreased until 14 days of zimelidine treatment.

Clorgyline also decreased PPT mRNA, but only after 5 days of treatment (FIGURE 2). Like zimelidine, PPT mRNA levels recovered after 14 days of drug treatment. A decrease in spinal cord SP not accompanied by a change in PPT mRNA occurred after 1 day of clorgyline administration. This may represent an acute increase in SP release rather than a change in SP synthesis. Spinal cord SP levels were also significantly, but transiently decreased after 14 days of drug treatment.

In summary, both zimelidine and clorgyline decrease the level of PPT mRNA in medullary raphe neurons, but PPT mRNA levels recover with continued drug treatment. A decrease in spinal cord SP content follows the decrease in PPT mRNA, suggesting that the change in message levels leads to a change in peptide synthesis. These results suggest that increases in 5-HT neurotransmission caused by both 5-HT uptake inhibition and monoamine oxidase inhibition transiently decrease SP biosynthesis in medullary raphe cells.

[a]This work was supported by Grant No. MH43365 and the AHA-NJ.

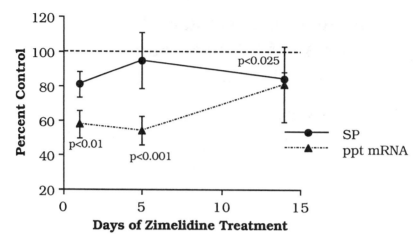

FIGURE 1. SP and PPT mRNA levels in animals treated with zimelidine. Data are expressed as the mean ± standard error ($n = 10$).

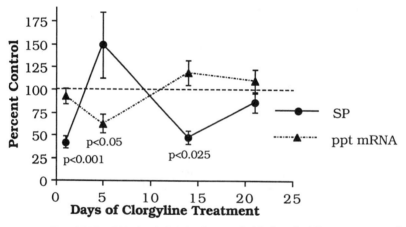

FIGURE 2. SP and PPT mRNA levels in animals treated with clorgyline. Data are expressed as the mean ± standard error ($n = 10$).

REFERENCE

1. WALKER, P. D., S. SCHOTLAND, R. P. HART & G. M. JONAKAIT. 1990. Tryptophan hydroxylase inhibition increases preprotachykinin mRNA in developing and adult medullary raphe nuclei. Mol. Brain Res. **8:** 113–119.

Pharmacological Properties of the Tachykinin Receptor Subtype in the Endothelial Cell and Vasodilation

RYO SAITO,[a] SHIGEYUKI NONAKA,[a] HIROKI KONISHI,[a]
YUKIO TAKANO,[a] YASUYUKI SHIMOHIGASHI,[b]
HIROSHI MATSUMOTO,[b] MOTONORI OHNO,[b]
AND HIRO-O KAMIYA[a]

[a]*Department of Pharmacology*
Faculty of Pharmaceutical Sciences
Fukuoka University
Fukuoka 814-01, Japan

[b]*Laboratory of Biochemistry*
Faculty of Science
Kyushu University
Fukuoka 812, Japan

Vascular endothelial cells are involved in the regulation of vascular tone through production of an endothelium-derived relaxing factor (EDRF).[1] Substance P (SP) and related peptides have been shown to cause endothelium-dependent relaxation of precontracted arteries of several mammalian species.[2] However, no direct evidence of SP receptor binding to endothelial cells has been studied. Here, we report that SP-induced relaxation is mediated by the NK-1 receptor subtype.

Fresh porcine coronary arteries mounted on hooks were placed in a 5-mL organ bath filled with Krebs solution. The preparations were precontracted with 10^{-5} M prostaglandin $F_{2\alpha}$ and the change in length was measured with an isometric transducer.

Agonist for the NK-1 tachykinin receptor subtype, SP, a dimeric analogue of SP (D-SP$_{3-11}$),[3] [Sar^9,Met(O$_2$)^{11}]SP, and physalaemin elicited the potent, transient, and endothelium-dependent relaxation. The SP-induced relaxation and the increase of cGMP content were inhibited by hemoglobin, methylene blue, and L-N^G-monomethyl-D-arginine (L-NMMA). These results suggest that the relaxation induced by SP is mediated by EDRF (NO). The relaxation was also reduced by ouabain, K$^+$-free, TMB-8, and Ca^{2+}-free pretreatment, but not by indomethacin or nicardipine.

In addition, we examined ^{125}I-Bolton-Hunter SP (^{125}I-BHSP) binding to the endothelial cell membranes of porcine aorta by the method of Higuchi *et al.*[3] The cells had a single high affinity binding site with a $K_d = 0.10 \pm 0.01$ nM and a $B_{max} = 52.2 \pm 2.7$ fmol/mg protein. The GTP analogue caused a marked reduction in the number of binding sites. TABLE 1 shows the constants for binding affinity and relaxing activity. NK-1 receptor agonists were most potent for the displacing of ^{125}I-BHSP binding. This result is in agreement with the results of the vasodilating responses.

In conclusion, as shown in the schematic model (FIGURE 1), SP and related peptides stimulate the release of at least two EDRFs in the presence of Ca^{2+} through

TABLE 1. Constants for Binding Affinity and Relaxing Activity

	Binding IC_{50} (nM)	Vasodilation EC_{50} (nM)
substance P	0.05	0.11
[Sar^9,Met(O$_2$)^{11}]SP	0.19	0.22
physalaemin	0.33	0.21
D-SP$_{3-11}$	0.48	0.11
D-SP$_{2-11}$	0.54	0.40
neurokinin A	2.59	1.77
neuropeptide γ	4.76	1.99
neurokinin B	9.03	4.47

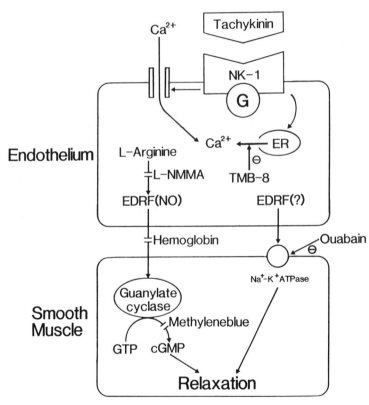

FIGURE 1. Proposal model of tachykinin-induced relaxation; G: a certain GTP-binding protein.

the NK-1 receptor subtype, which is coupled with a certain GTP-binding protein. Vascular relaxation induced by these EDRFs may be mediated by guanylate cyclase and the Na^+/K^+ pump, respectively.

REFERENCES

1. FURCHGOTT, R. F. & J. V. ZAWADSKI. 1980. The obligatory role of the endothelial cells in the relaxation of arterial smooth muscle by acetylcholine. Nature **288:** 373–376.
2. COCKS, T. M. & J. A. ANGUS. 1983. Endothelium-dependent relaxation of coronary arteries by noradrenaline and serotonin. Nature **305:** 627–629.
3. HIGUCHI, Y., Y. TAKANO, H. SHIMAZAKI, Y. SHIMOHIGASHI, H. KODAMA, H. MATSUMOTO, K. SAKAGUCHI, S. NONAKA, R. SAITO, M. WAKI & H. KAMIYA. 1989. Dimeric substance P analogue shows a highly potent activity of the *in vivo* salivary secretion in the rat. Eur. J. Pharmacol. **160:** 413–416.

Endogenous Opioids and Ruthenium Red Inhibit the Flare Reaction in the Pig Skin by Different Mechanisms

FR-K. PIERAU,[a] R. ERNST,[a] H. SANN,[a] AND L. BARTHÓ[b]

[a] Max-Planck-Institut für Physiologische und Klinische Forschung
W. G. Kerckhoff-Institut
D-6350 Bad Nauheim, Federal Republic of Germany

[b] Department of Pharmacology
University Medical School
H-7643 Pécs, Hungary

Mechanical or chemical irritation of the human skin is usually accompanied by a spreading erythema: the flare response. A similar vasodilation can be produced by antidromic electrical stimulation of peripheral nerves. Evidence has accumulated that both the antidromic vasodilation and the flare response result from the release of sensory neuropeptides, for example, tachykinins, calcitonin gene–related peptide (CGRP), etc., from the peripheral terminals of capsaicin-sensitive sensory nerve fibers, which directly or via a release of other mediators, for example, by mast cell degranulation, affect cutaneous blood vessels. To investigate pharmacological effects upon the flare response and the antidromic vasodilation, the pig's skin was used as a model because the flare reaction can be easily observed in the pig.[1]

Domestic pigs were anesthetized with a mixture of halothane and nitrous oxide. The intensity and the duration of the changes in cutaneous blood flux were measured with a laser Doppler flow meter (Perimed, PF2). The extension of the flare was documented on transparent foil. Two hypodermic needles (distance, 10 mm) served for electric stimulation (32 impulses, 40 V, 0.5 ms, 1 Hz). Flux probes between the needles indicated antidromic vasodilation, whereas the flare was determined by probes 20 mm apart from the stimulation site. Chemical stimulation was accomplished by intracutaneous injection (ic, 20 µL) of solutions of different concentrations. The opioid agonist [D-Met^2,Pro^5]enkephalinamide (enk, 0.015 or 0.15 µM/kg) and naloxone (nal, 0.1 mg/kg) were injected intravenously or intramuscularly. To study the effects of ruthenium red (RR), flare was induced by a 5-min perfusion of 30 µM capsaicin through a suction-induced skin blister. Thirty minutes prior to and during capsaicin application, RR (5 or 10 µM) or Ringer's solution (1 mL/min) was constantly perfused.

The most potent chemical irritant in regard to the induction of flare was capsaicin, which produced flare areas up to 15 cm^2 (3 mM) for about 15 minutes. Histamine and serotonin, which effectively produced flare in the human skin, induced only small flares in the pig's skin. Substance P (100 µM) and calcitonin gene–related peptide (10 µM) did not induce flare areas larger than those produced by injection of saline.

Opioid agonists have been demonstrated to inhibit plasma extravasation[2] and vasodilation[3] in the rat skin. A similar impairment of antidromic vasodilation (FIGURE 1A) and flare induced by electrical stimulation was observed after systemic application of enk, which was completely reversed by nal (FIGURE 1A). The inhibition by enk was much smaller at 10-Hz stimulation, but still significant. In

460

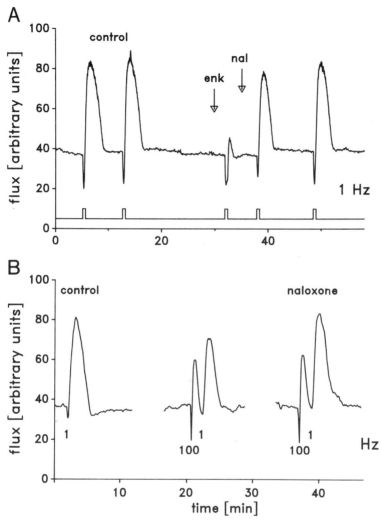

FIGURE 1. Effect of [D-Met^2,Pro^5]enkephalinamide (A) and high frequency stimulation (B) upon antidromic vasodilation. Vasoreactions are recorded by laser Doppler (flux); upward deflection: vasodilation. A: A train of 32 impulses (40 V, 0.5 ms) at 1 Hz produces a short vasoconstriction followed by a prolonged vasodilation. The inhibitory effect of enk is reversed by naloxone (nal). Arrows indicate iv injection of 0.15 μM/kg enk and 0.1 mg/kg nal. Squares in the horizontal line represent electrical stimulation. B: The control shows the vasodilation induced by 32 impulses and 1 Hz. A conditioning stimulus by a train of 32 impulses at 100 Hz reduces the vasodilation. This effect is completely reversed by 0.1 mg/kg naloxone.

contrast, flare reactions induced by capsaicin, pinpricks, or noxious heat (52 °C for 10 s) were not affected by enk or nal. This might indicate that different populations of peptidergic afferents are involved or that high frequency bursts, which are probably induced by capsaicin or heat stimulation, are not opioid-sensitive. Alternatively, different membrane mechanisms, for example, voltage-gated versus voltage-independent ionic channels, might be opioid-susceptible.

In the central nervous system, higher frequency stimulation is usually necessary to demonstrate an effect of endogenous opioids. We have therefore used a 100-Hz train of 32 impulses as a conditioning stimulus. After the vasoreaction returned to control flux levels, a usual 1-Hz train followed the high frequency conditioning stimulus. Under these conditions, the vasodilation produced by the 1-Hz train was reduced by about 30% (FIGURE 1B). Conditioning with trains of 1 or 5 Hz did not reduce the vasodilation produced by 1-Hz stimulation. Indeed, the fact that nal completely reversed the effect of the 100-Hz conditioning stimulation indicates that endogenous opioids are responsible for the reduction of antidromic vasodilation. This is in agreement with the observation that afferent neurons of pigs contain a

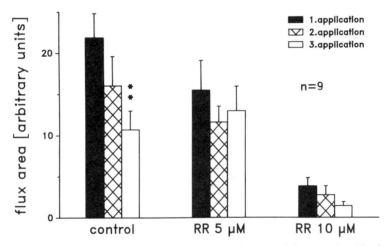

FIGURE 2. Effect of ruthenium red (RR) on the capsaicin-induced flare reaction. The flare is induced by perfusion of capsaicin through a blister. Bars represent the areas of the capsaicin-induced flare reaction measured 15 mm apart from the blister. Subsequent capsaicin perfusions cause desensitization. Five μM RR prevents the desensitization; 10 μM RR reduces flare reactions by about 80%; flags: standard error; ** = $p > 0.01$ compared with control perfusion.

reasonable amount of enkephalin and dynorphin (E. Weihe, personal communication).

A compound that appears to specifically interfere with the action of capsaicin on small afferent nerve fibers is RR.[4] As demonstrated in FIGURE 2, perfusion of a blister in the pig's skin with 5 μM RR prevents the desensitization produced by successive capsaicin application. Whereas the reduction of the capsaicin-induced flare at this low concentration is not significant, perfusion with 10 μM RR reduces the flare response by about 80% (FIGURE 2). The RR effect appears to be capsaicin-specific because flare produced by blister perfusion with mustard oil is not impaired by RR.

REFERENCES

1. PIERAU, FR-K. & J. SZOLCSANYI. 1989. Neurogenic inflammation: axon reflex in pigs. Agents Actions **26:** 231–232.
2. BARTHÓ, L. & J. SZOLCSANYI. 1981. Opiate agonists inhibit neurogenic plasma extravasation in the rat. Eur. J. Pharmacol. **73:** 101–104.
3. GAMSE, R. & A. SARIA. 1987. Antidromic vasodilatation in the hindpaw measured by laser Doppler flowmetry: pharmacological modulation. J. Auton. Nervous Syst. **19:** 105–111.
4. MAGGI, C. A., R. PATACCHINI, P. SANTICIOLI, S. GIULIANI, P. GEPPETTI & A. MELI. 1988. Protective action of ruthenium red toward capsaicin desensitization of sensory fibers. Neurosci. Lett. **88:** 201–205.

Endogenous 5-Hydroxytryptamine Modulates the Release of Tachykinins and Calcitonin Gene–related Peptide from the Rat Spinal Cord via 5-HT$_3$ Receptors

ALOIS SARIA,[a] FRIEDRICH JAVORSKY,[a]
CHRISTIAN HUMPEL,[a] AND RAINER GAMSE[b]

[a]Neurochemistry Unit
Department of Psychiatry
University of Innsbruck Medical School
A-6020 Innsbruck, Austria

[b]Preclinical Research Unit
Sandoz Limited
Basel, Switzerland

INTRODUCTION

Recent autoradiographic studies showed high densities of 5-HT$_3$ receptors in Rexed's laminae I and II of the rat dorsal spinal cord, presumably located on central terminals of capsaicin-sensitive primary afferent neurons.[1] Some of them contain tachykinins (TK) such as substance P (SP), neurokinin A (NKA), and calcitonin gene–related peptide (CGRP).[2] We investigated the release of SP-, NKA-, and CGRP-like immunoreactivities (LI) from superfused slices of rat dorsal spinal cord *in vitro* in the presence and absence of 5-HT (5-hydroxytryptamine) and 5-HT$_3$ receptor antagonists.

METHODS

Sprague-Dawley rats were decapitated and their whole spinal cords were removed. The dorsal half was separated from the ventral half, sliced into $300 \times 300 \ \mu$m cubes, and superfused in a polyacrylamide chamber as described.[3,4] Peptides were determined by radioimmunoassay.[4]

RESULTS AND DISCUSSION

Superfusion with 30 mM potassium chloride for 4 min (30 K) caused a significant release of all three peptides measured, that is, 140–190% of the spontaneous outflow. Release of peptides at 30 K was slightly enhanced in the presence of 3×10^{-5} M 5-HT. In contrast, a significant inhibition of potassium-evoked NKA-LI and CGRP-LI was observed when 10^{-7} M BRL 43694 (granisetron) and ICS 205-930, two specific 5-HT$_3$ receptor antagonists, were each superfused together with 5-HT (FIGURE 1). The latter effect was less pronounced on SP-LI release (FIGURE 1).

In contrast to NKA and CGRP, part of the SP in the spinal cord is of intrinsic origin (see reference 2). Hence, the lack of a significant effect of 5-HT$_3$ receptor antagonists on SP release may be explained by the absence of 5-HT$_3$ receptors on intrinsic spinal SP-containing neurons. Because 5-HT slightly enhanced release and the antagonists reduced the release below the release evoked by 30 K alone, it is suggested that part of the potassium-response is due to endogenously released 5-HT. Therefore, it is concluded that endogenous 5-HT may increase the release of peptides from central terminals of primary sensory neurons via 5-HT$_3$ receptors.

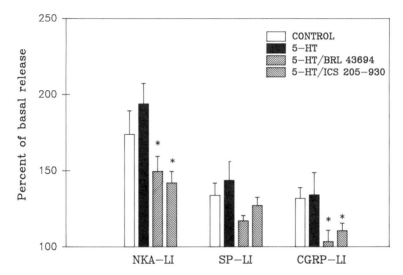

FIGURE 1. Release of SP-like immunoreactivity (LI), NKA-LI, and CGRP-LI from the superfused rat spinal cord evoked by 30 mM potassium (control), 30 mM potassium plus 3 × 10^{-5} M 5-HT (5-HT), potassium and 5-HT plus 10^{-7} M BRL 43694 (5-HT/BRL 43694), or potassium and 5-HT plus 10^{-7} M ICS 205-930 (5-HT/ICS 205-930). The total evoked release is expressed as the percent of the spontaneous peptide outflow during the same time period preceding the potassium pulse. The asterisks indicate significant differences from the respective 5-HT group, $p < 0.05$. Values represent mean values ± SEM, $n \geq 7$.

REFERENCES

1. HAMON, M., M. C. GALLISSOT, F. MENARD, H. GOZLAN, S. BOURGOIN & D. VERGE. 1989. Eur. J. Pharmacol. **164:** 315–322.
2. MAGGI, C. A. & A. MELI. 1988. Gen. Pharmacol. **19:** 1–43.
3. SARIA, A., R. GAMSE, J. PETERMANN, J. A. FISCHER, E. THEODORSSON-NORHEIM & J. M. LUNDBERG. 1986. Neurosci. Lett. **63:** 310–314.
4. HUMPEL, C., G. A. KNAUS, B. AUER, H. G. KNAUS, C. HARING, E. THEODORSSON & A. SARIA. 1990. Synapse **6:** 1–9.

Neurokinin-1 Receptors in the Human Eye

Characterization and Autoradiographic Distribution

GERHARD F. KIESELBACH,[a] ROBERT RAGAUT,[a]
HANS G. KNAUS,[a] PAUL KÖNIG,[b] ALOIS SARIA,[c]
AND CHRISTIAN J. WIEDERMANN[b]

[a] Department of Ophthalmology
[b] Department of Internal Medicine
[c] Department of Psychiatry
Neurochemistry Unit
University of Innsbruck
A-6020 Innsbruck, Austria

INTRODUCTION

Peptides of the tachykinin family, such as the undecapeptide substance P (SP), are known to have important effects on peripheral tissues including the eye. In pharmacological studies, involvement of specific tachykinin receptors in the action of SP has been suggested by the finding of typical structure-activity relationships and by inhibition by SP antagonists in the eye.[1] We therefore investigated the presence and distribution of SP receptors in the human eye using autoradiographic and direct ligand binding techniques utilizing ^{125}I-Bolton-Hunter SP (BH-SP).

RESULTS AND DISCUSSION

Ligand binding data were analyzed by double reciprocal plot analysis to provide the affinity and binding capacity of the binding site for BH-SP. At room temperature, binding reached a plateau within approximately 30 minutes, being half-maximal at 12 minutes. The incubation time of further experiments was 40 minutes. A double reciprocal plot of the data revealed that the mean observed binding was of high affinity ($K_d = 0.27 \pm 0.1$ nM) and that the mean B_{max} was 0.2 ± 0.03 fmol/mg protein. The ability of SP, SP(3–11), SP(1–9), NKA, and NKB to inhibit BH-SP binding was then investigated. The mean concentrations of SP and SP(3–11) ($n = 3$) displacing 50% of the specifically bound BH-SP were 0.66×10^{-9} M and 0.55×10^{-8} M, respectively. In contrast, similar concentrations of SP(1–9) failed to significantly inhibit the binding. Neurokinin A (NKA) and neurokinin B (NKB) also failed to inhibit the specific binding of BH-SP.

Furthermore, autoradiography has revealed that SP binding sites are concentrated in the choroidea and retina with comparable densities. Sclera does not show significant amounts of specific BH-SP binding. Unfortunately, radioligand binding studies to human eye tissues are scanty. However, the use of slide-mounted tissue preparations allows biochemical and morphological examination of receptors.[2] We have obtained significant specific binding in such preparations, thereby allowing calculation of the kinetic constants. The low ratio of specific binding to nonspecific binding may result from the low amount of SP receptors expressed. Because, in the human eye, SP and SP(3–11) exhibited highest potencies in displacing the radiolabel, whereas NKA and NKB were practically inactive, our data indicate expression of NK-1 receptors. Additional expression of NK-2 and/or NK-3 receptors, though, cannot be ruled out because the affinity of the ligand BH-SP to these subtypes of tachykinin receptors has not been established in monoreceptorial assays. In addition, pharmacological experiments are consistent with expression of NK-1 receptors in the eye, but they also suggest a role for NK-2 and possibly NK-3 receptors in mediating the ocular effects of tachykinins.[3]

Concerning the functional significance of NK receptors in the human eye, it is interesting to note that SP levels in the intraocular fluid are elevated in proliferative vitreoretinopathy (26.9 fmol/mL versus 2.2 fmol/mL in controls). Therefore, our results indicate that SP and NK-1 receptors are present in the human eye and may be involved in pathophysiological processes.

REFERENCES

1. HOLZER, P. 1988. Local effector functions of sensory nerve endings. Neuroscience **3:** 739–768.
2. QUIRION, R. & P. GAUDREAU. 1985. Strategies in neuropeptide receptor binding. Res. Neurosci. Biobehav. Rev. **9:** 413–420.
3. BEDING-BARNEKOW, B., E. BRODIN & R. HÅKANSON. 1988. Substance P, neurokinin A, and neurokinin B in the ocular response to injury in the rabbit. Br. J. Pharmacol. **95:** 259–267.

Substance P and Antagonists

Surface Activity, Conformations, and Lipid Binding

ANNA SEELIG[a] AND REINHARD DOELZ[b]

[a]Department of Biophysical Chemistry
[b]Department of Biocomputing
Biocenter
University of Basel
CH-4056 Basel, Switzerland

The molecular properties of substance P (SP) and three of its antagonists were derived by measuring the Gibbs adsorption isotherm, providing information on the surface activity, the cross-sectional area, and the pK values of the different molecules.[1] The following three antagonists were investigated: [D-Arg^1,D-Pro^2,D-Trp^{7,9},Leu^{11}]SP, ANT I; [D-Arg^1,D-Trp^{7,9},Leu^{11}]SP, ANT II; and [D-Pro^2,D-Trp^{7,9}]SP, ANT III. SP is only moderately surface-active. However, the amino acid substitutions lead to an increased surface activity of the antagonists (FIGURE 1). From the concentration-dependence of the surface activity, it was possible to quantify the packing characteristics of the individual neuropeptides. SP shows cross-sectional areas of 300 ± 5 Å^2 to 240 ± 5 Å^2 (pH 5 to 8, 154 mM NaCl) at concentrations below 10^{-5} M, that is, in the physiological concentration range, indicating a folded SP conformation. Upon increasing the packing density to concentrations larger than 10^{-5} M, the surface area was only half as large (148 ± 5 Å^2 to 124 ± 3 Å^2), suggesting a relatively extended conformation of the SP molecule with its long molecular axis perpendicular to the air/water interface. In contrast, the three antagonists were characterized by surface areas of 147 ± 3 Å^2 to 126 ± 3 Å^2, which were almost independent of concentration (FIGURE 2). The antagonists thus adopt a relatively extended conformation in the whole concentration range measured.

This is further supported by computer modeling. Molecular modeling studies provided evidence for conformational constraints introduced to the SP structure by replacing Phe^7 and Gly^9 by D-tryptophan. Whereas SP is capable of adopting a variety of theoretically possible conformations including a fully extended and an alpha-helical structure, the antagonists did not permit either of these two extremes upon rigid-body modeling. Additional molecular dynamics studies indicated that the antagonists might adopt a relatively extended conformation.

As observed by circular dichroism and monolayer measurements,[2,3] these peptides insert into lipid membranes; however, they do so to different extents. Taking into account the charge effects by means of the Gouy-Chapman theory, the insertion process can be described by a simple partition equilibrium for all four peptides investigated. SP has a low hydrophobic binding constant ($K_o = 1$–1.9 M^{-1}). Its lipid insertion is therefore mainly driven by electrostatic interactions. However, hydrophobic peptide-lipid interactions contribute to the insertion of the antagonists. The hydrophobic binding constants are on the order of 10^3 M^{-1} for ANT III and 10^4 M^{-1} for ANT I and ANT II.

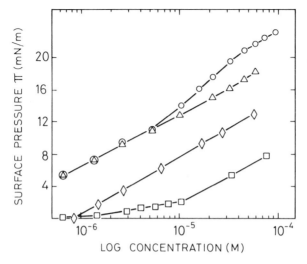

FIGURE 1. Surface pressure π as a function of the logarithm of the concentration of SP ($\square$), ANT III ($\diamond$), ANT II ($\triangle$), and ANT I ($\bigcirc$) at pH 7.4 (10 mM Tris/HCl, 154 mM NaCl).

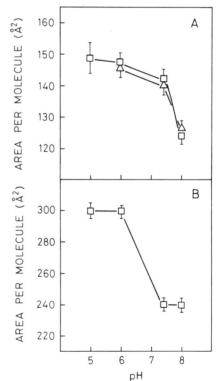

FIGURE 2. Area per molecule as a function of the pH of the solution. A: ANT II ($\triangle$) and SP ($\square$) at concentrations $> 10^{-5}$ M; B: SP ($\square$) at concentrations of 1.5×10^{-6} M to 10^{-5} M.

REFERENCES

1. SEELIG, A. 1990. Biochim. Biophys. Acta **1030:** 111–118.
2. SEELIG, A. & P. M. MACDONALD. 1989. Biochemistry **28:** 2490–2496.
3. SEELIG, A. 1990. Cell. Biol. Int. Rep. **14:** 369–380.

Immunochemical Characterization of SP Processing Intermediates in Sensory Ganglia[a]

HIROYUKI SHIMONAKA AND RICHARD M. KREAM[b]

Anesthesia Research
Tufts University School of Medicine
Boston, Massachusetts 02111

We have recently developed a high affinity antiserum that recognizes the epitope representing the midportion of SP, that is, SP_{4-10}. A47 is probably the first midportion anti-SP serum yet described that does not display strong preference for the free NH_2-terminus of the molecule. Originally generated against the SP precursor determinant SP-G-K-R found in the primary sequence of all PPT forms, competitive binding analyses performed on later bleedings confirmed the decided midportion character of the antiserum. The reagent reacts directly on an apparent equimolar basis with diverse molecular forms of short peptides containing the midportion of SP. These include SP, SP_{3-11}, SP_{4-11}, SP-free acid, SP-G, SP-G-K, and SP-G-K-R. In addition, the molar cross-reactivities of SP_{5-11} and SP_{1-9} versus SP were minimal. The potencies of a related series of tachykinin peptides including NKA, NKA-G, NKA-G-K, NKB, NKB-G, and NKB-G-K were compared to SP and all displayed $<0.001\%$ molar cross-reactivities. For quantification of the total peptide equivalents containing the SP_{4-10} epitope, a highly sensitive RIA was developed that utilizes A47, ^{125}I-labeled Bolton-Hunter-conjugated SP as the tracer, and SP as the peptide standard.

For the present study, rat dorsal root ganglia (DRG) were extracted in 20 vol of 2 N acetic acid, followed by an additional 20 vol of CH_3CN. After lyophilization, reconstituted extracts were fractionated by analytical reverse-phase HPLC performed with a Vydac C18 column (4.6 × 250 mm) using a linear gradient of 23–63% in 0.1% TFA at a flow rate of 1 mL/min. Then, 0.5-mL fractions were collected. Standard retention times were calculated by RIA analyses performed on aliquots of collected fractions after HPLC fractionation of 5 ng each of synthetic SP, SP-G, SP-G-K, and SP-G-K-R. Specific RIAs for SP, SP-G, and SP-G-K were performed on HPLC fractions. RIAs using A47 were performed on HPLC fractions before and after trypsin digestion (0.1 μg trypsin/100 μL HPLC fraction, 22 °C, 17 h). To evaluate the effects of capsaicin on SP turnover in DRG, separate groups of animals were treated with either capsaicin (50 mg/kg, sc) or vehicle (10% EtOH, 0.5% Tween) and were sacrificed after three days (see TABLE 1).

Levels of SP-LI quantified by RIA using A47 were consistently found to be 15–30% higher than those quantified by RIA using our COOH-terminal antisera. Combined HPLC/RIA analyses of DRG extracts indicated multiple areas of SP-LI as monitored by RIA using A47. Based on these analyses, we have initially established the intrinsic molar ratios of immunoreactivities corresponding to SP and its graded series of small unamidated precursors, that is, SP-G-K-R, SP-G-K, and SP-G,

[a] This work was supported by NIDA Grant No. DA 04128.
[b] To whom all correspondence should be addressed.

TABLE 1. The Effects of Capsaicin Treatment on DRG Peptide Content

Peptide	Control (fmol/mg tissue)	Capsaicin (fmol/mg tissue)
SP-LI	56.5	58.7
SP-G-LI	3.7	1.6
SP-G-K-LI	0.9	1.7
SP-G-K-R-LI	1.8	0.8
Total SP-LI (A47)	69.1	72.3
Recovery[a]	91.1%	86.8%

[a]As a function of the total SP-LI.

TABLE 2. Relative Immunoreactivities with Four Antisera (% Cross-reactivity)[a]

Peptide	Anti-SP (A7)	Anti-SP-G (A1)	Anti-SP-G-K (A4)	Anti-SP-G-K-R (A47)
SP-G-K-R	0.03	0.03	0.80	102.0
SP-G-K	0.03	0.09	100.0	92.0
SP-G	0.01	100.0	1.40	105.0
SP	100.0	0.03	0.01	100.0
SP-FA	0.03	0.03	0.04	108.0
SP(3–11)	33.3	0.03	0.01	101.0
SP(4–11)	17.5	0.02	0.01	76.0
SP(5–11)	45.5	0.001	<0.001	1.2
SP(1–9)	<0.01			2.0
SP(1–7)	<0.01			0.02
NKA	<0.01	<0.01	<0.002	<0.002
NKA-G	<0.01	0.16	<0.001	<0.002
NKA-G-K	<0.01	<0.001	<0.001	<0.002
NKB	<0.01	<0.001	<0.001	<0.002
NKB-G	<0.01	0.01	<0.001	<0.002
NKB-G-K	<0.01	0.001	0.2	<0.002

[a]Values are calculated on a % molar basis with 100% corresponding to the amount of homologous peptide needed to displace 50% of the bound ^{125}I-BH tracer.

in rat dorsal root ganglia. The respective RIA values for SP-G-K-R, SP-G-K, SP-G, and SP were 2.5%, 1.0%, 5.7%, and 86.6% of the total recovered immunoreactivity (TABLE 2). Thus, it is highly probable that these small peptide determinants are genuine intermediates in the normal pathway of the biosynthetic maturation of SP. The relatively high steady-state levels of SP-G, as compared to the other unamidated forms, suggest a rate-limiting role for terminal amidation in SP expression in DRG neurons. Other, presumably larger SP precursors have been initially identified as immunoreactivities contained in HPLC-fractionated DRG extracts. Finally, treatment of animals with capsaicin resulted primarily in decreased levels of SP-G-LI, suggesting decreased turnover of SP. Overall, changes in the steady-state levels of unamidated SP precursors versus the steady-state levels of mature SP may reflect meaningful alterations in the rates of biosynthesis coupled to utilization or turnover of SP.

Resiniferatoxin

An Ultrapotent Neurotoxin of Capsaicin-sensitive Primary Afferent Neurons

J. SZOLCSANYI,[a] A. SZALLASI,[b] Z. SZALLASI,[b] F. JOO,[c]
AND P. M. BLUMBERG[b]

[a]Department of Pharmacology
Medical University
H-7643 Pécs, Hungary

[b]National Cancer Institute
Bethesda, Maryland 20892

[c]National Institute of Neurological Disorders and Stroke
Bethesda, Maryland 20892

A major group of primary afferent neurons is characterized by being selectively susceptible for the excitatory, sensory-blocking, and neurotoxic effects of capsaicin.[1] Both the peripheral and spinal terminals of these neurons are sites of release of neuropeptides such as substance P (SP) and calcitonin gene–related peptide (CGRP), which mediate neurogenic inflammation and a variety of smooth muscle responses (efferent functions) and which modify the spinal nociceptive pathway (afferent

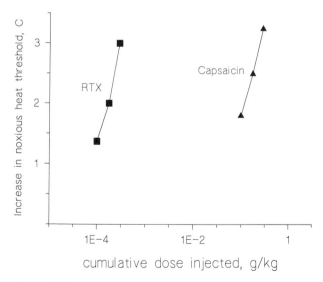

FIGURE 1. Effect of RTX and capsaicin pretreatment on the noxious heat threshold in the rat. Self control values of the noxious heat threshold were determined on the hindpaw of each rat before treatment. Then, 100, 200, and 300 μg/kg cumulative doses of RTX were injected subcutaneously in 100 μg/kg doses given daily. Capsaicin data are from reference 6.

function): these responses are thought to have an important role in various disease states.[2] Capsaicinoids are of interest as potential nonnarcotic analgesic and anti-inflammatory agents, but their systemic use is limited by their narrow therapeutic range.[1,2]

Resiniferatoxin (RTX), a naturally occurring diterpene containing a homovanillic acid ester, a key structural motif of capsaicin, functions as an ultrapotent capsaicin analogue.[3-5] Moreover, its therapeutic range is wider: RTX desensitized the neurogenic inflammatory pathway with an ED_{50} value that was two orders of magnitude below its lethal dose, whereas capsaicin caused respiratory distress at its ED_{50} for desensitization.[3]

We report here that RTX, like capsaicin, acts selectively on primary sensory neurons in the rat to produce ultrastructural alterations and depletion of CGRP-like

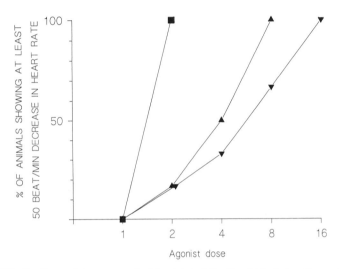

FIGURE 2. Cardiovascular component of the triad of the Bezold-Jarisch reflex evoked by iv injection of capsaicin before (■) and after RTX treatment (▲, 0.1 μg/kg; ▼, 1.0 μg/kg iv); percent of animals showing an at least 50 beats per minute decrease in heart rate. The threshold control dose of capsaicin (0.1–1.0 μg/kg) was determined in each of the rats; further agonist doses were administered based on the self control values.

immunoreactivity (not shown). RTX increased the noxious heat threshold in the rat with a 1000-fold higher potency than did capsaicin (FIGURE 1). Strikingly, RTX, unlike capsaicin, did not evoke the Bezold-Jarisch reflex in the rat (not shown); however, RTX did desensitize this reflex pathway to capsaicin (FIGURE 2) and phenyldiguanide (not shown). Thus, the failure of RTX to provoke the Bezold-Jarisch reflex, which is the main limiting factor (respiratory distress) in the use of capsaicin, furnishes RTX with a very wide therapeutic range.

REFERENCES

1. BUCK, S. H. & T. F. BURKS. 1986. The neuropharmacology of capsaicin: review of some recent observations. Pharmacol. Rev. **38:** 179–226.

2. MAGGI, C. A. & A. MELI. 1988. The sensory-efferent function of capsaicin-sensitive sensory neurons. Gen. Pharmacol. **19:** 1–43.
3. SZALLASI, A. & P. M. BLUMBERG. 1989. Resiniferatoxin, a phorbol-related diterpene, acts as an ultrapotent analog of capsaicin, the irritant constituent in red pepper. Neuroscience **30:** 515–520.
4. WINTER, J., A. DRAY, J. N. WOOD, J. C. YEATS & S. BEVAN. 1991. Cellular mechanism of action of resiniferatoxin: a potent sensory neuron excitotoxin. Brain Res. In press.
5. MAGGI, C. A., R. PATACCHINI, M. TRAMONTANA, R. AMANN, S. GIULIANI & P. SANTICIOLI. 1990. Similarities and differences in the action of resiniferatoxin and capsaicin on central and peripheral endings of primary sensory neurons. Neuroscience **37:** 531–539.
6. SZOLCSANYI, J. 1987. Acta Physiol. Hung. **69:** 323–332.

Tachykinin Receptor Subtype

Central Cardiovascular Regulation of Tachykinin Peptides

YUKIO TAKANO, AKIRA NAGASHIMA, TETSUYA HAGIO,
YASUHISA NAKAYAMA, AND HIRO-O KAMIYA

Department of Pharmacology
Faculty of Pharmaceutical Sciences
Fukuoka University
Fukuoka 814-01, Japan

Central neural circuits play important roles in cardiovascular control by regulating autonomic functions or vasopressin release from the hypothalamus. On the basis of cardiovascular and neurochemical evidence, substance P (SP) has become of interest as a neuropeptide regulating blood pressure (BP) in the ventral medulla, nucleus tractus solitarii (NTS), and spinal cord.[1-4] However, little is known about the mechanisms of central cardiovascular regulation induced by other tachykinin peptides.

Here, we report studies on the central mechanisms of action of tachykinin peptides thought to be involved in cardiovascular regulation. First, we studied the effects of sympathetic blockade and a vasopressin antagonist on tachykinin-induced central pressor responses. Then, we examined the effects of intracerebroventricular (i.c.v.) injection of tachykinin peptides on the plasma vasopressin level.

Experiments on cardiovascular responses were described previously.[4,5] Rats were anesthetized with urethane (1 g/kg, ip). Each rat was placed in a stereotaxic apparatus. A guide cannula was inserted into the lateral brain ventricle. Peptides were dissolved in artificial cerebrospinal fluid (ACSF) and 10-μL volumes of solutions were injected manually over a period of 1 min with a Hamilton microsyringe.

The central pressor responses to the tachykinin peptides were dose-dependent, reaching maxima at 4–6 min after injections of the peptides and then persisting for at least 40 min. The pressor responses due to SP, neurokinin A (NKA), and neuropeptide γ (NPγ) were blocked by sympathetic blocking agents (FIGURE 1, parts A and B). In contrast, the pressor response to a neurokinin B (NKB) analogue, senktide, was not blocked by the ganglionic blocking agent or adrenalectomy. The senktide-induced pressor response was inhibited by pretreatment with a vasopressin antagonist (FIGURE 1, part C) and senktide caused an increase in the plasma vasopressin level. However, the vasopressin antagonist did not influence the SP-, NKA-, and NPγ-induced pressor responses.

These results suggest that central SP, NKA, and NPγ, derived from the preprotachykinin A gene, increase the BP and heart rate (HR) via sympathetic nerve activity, whereas central NKB, derived from the preprotachykinin B gene, increases the BP via release of vasopressin from the hypothalamus (FIGURE 2).

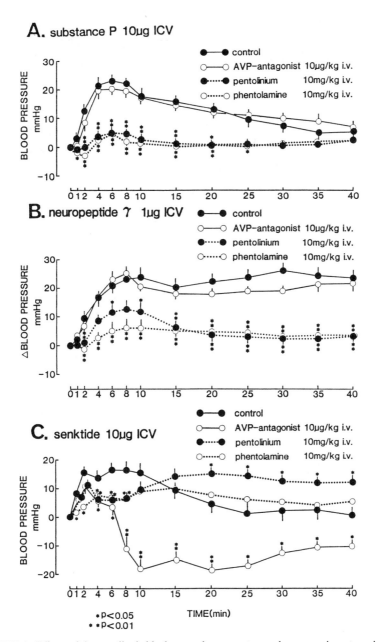

FIGURE 1. Effects of the ganglionic blocker, α-adenoreceptor, and vasopressin antagonist on the cardiovascular responses to tachykinin peptides (see text).

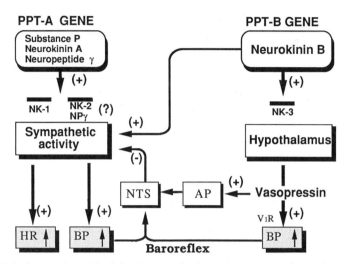

FIGURE 2. Proposed model of the dual mechanisms of central cardiovascular regulation induced by tachykinin peptides: NTS, nucleus tractus solitarii; AP, area postrema; PPT, preprotachykinin; BP, blood pressure; HR, heart rate.

REFERENCES

1. HELKE, C. J., T. L. O'DONOHUE & D. M. JACOBOWITZ. 1980. Substance P as a baro- and chemo-receptor afferent neurotransmitter: immunocytochemical and neurochemical evidence in the rat. Peptides **1:** 1–9.
2. TAKANO, Y., W. B. SAWYER & A. D. LOEWY. 1985. Substance P mechanisms of the spinal cord related to vasomotor tone in the spontaneously hypertensive rat. Brain Res. **334:** 106–116.
3. NAGASHIMA, A., Y. TAKANO, K. TATEISHI, Y. MATSUOKA, T. HAMAOKA & H. KAMIYA. 1989. Cardiovascular role of tachykinin peptides in the nucleus tractus solitarii of rats. Brain Res. **487:** 392–396.
4. NAGASHIMA, A., Y. TAKANO, K. TATEISHI, Y. MATSUOKA, T. HAMAOKA & H. KAMIYA. 1989. Central pressor actions of neurokinin B: increases in neurokinin B contents in discrete nuclei in spontaneously hypertensive rats. Brain Res. **499:** 198–203.
5. TAKANO, Y., A. NAGASHIMA, T. HAGIO, K. TATEISHI & H. KAMIYA. 1990. Role of central tachykinin peptides in cardiovascular regulation in rats. Brain Res. **528:** 231–237.

Pharmacological and Molecular Biological Studies on the Diversity of Rat Tachykinin NK-2 Receptor Subtypes in Rat CNS, Duodenum, Vas Deferens, and Urinary Bladder[a]

YASUO TAKEDA AND JAMES E. KRAUSE

Department of Anatomy and Neurobiology
Washington University School of Medicine
St. Louis, Missouri 63110

Over the past few years, the members of the mammalian tachykinin peptide family have grown to five, including substance P (SP), neurokinin A (NKA), neuropeptide K (NPK), and neuropeptide γ (NPγ).[1] Although it is established that there exist three different tachykinin receptors that preferentially interact with SP (NK-1 subtype), NKA (NK-2 subtype), and NKB (NK-3 subtype), it is unclear whether the multiple NKA-related peptides, including NKA, NKA(3–10), NPK, and NPγ, interact with a single class of binding sites (NK-2) or whether they differentially interact with other undiscovered tachykinin receptor subtypes. To understand the functional relevance of these multiple NKA-related peptides, we have examined the diversity of the NK-2 receptor subclass in rat using pharmacological and molecular biological approaches.

SMOOTH MUSCLE CONTRACTION BIOASSAYS

NPγ, NPK, and NKA strongly induced smooth muscle contraction in rat duodenum, vas deferens, and urinary bladder strips in *in vitro* assays. The pattern of the smooth muscle contraction induced by NPγ and NPK was similar to that stimulated by NKA, but not by SP. These contractile activities induced by NPγ and NPK were slightly more potent and more long-acting than those by NKA.

LIGAND BINDING ASSAYS USING ^{125}I-NPγ

For pharmacological binding studies, we used ^{125}I-NPγ as a radiolabeled ligand to examine the properties of the NK-2 receptor in rat duodenum, vas deferens, and urinary bladder. ^{125}I-NPγ was prepared by chloramine T iodination and HPLC purification. The tissue membrane preparations and the binding experimental procedure were similar to methods described in our previous report.[2] ^{125}I-NPγ specific binding to rat duodenum, vas deferens, and urinary bladder membranes was

[a] This work was supported by NIH Grant No. NS21937.

saturable, reversible, and temperature-dependent. A comparison of the binding parameters of ^{125}I-NPγ in these tissue membranes is shown in TABLE 1. By Scatchard analysis, the binding affinity (K_d) and the binding capacity (B_{max}) of ^{125}I-NPγ to these membrane preparations were calculated from the data obtained in saturation binding assays. The numbers described in the table indicate that ^{125}I-NPγ specifically binds to a single class of high affinity site in the three tissues. The differences in the rank-order potency of several tachykinin peptides in displacing ^{125}I-NPγ binding in duodenum, vas deferens, and urinary bladder suggested that there existed NK-2 receptor subtype heterogeneity in the rat. The rank-order potency of naturally occurring mammalian tachykinin peptides was NPγ = NPK > NKA > NKB > SP in duodenum and NPγ = NPK = NKA > NKB > SP in vas deferens and urinary bladder. Also, ELE-RP, that is, [Lys^6]eledoisin(6–10), had the same potency as ELE itself in displacing ^{125}I-NPγ binding in duodenum, but it was about 10-fold less potent than ELE, even lower than SP, in vas deferens and urinary bladder membrane preparations (TABLE 1).

ANALYSIS OF NK-2 RECEPTOR mRNA LEVELS BY NUCLEASE PROTECTION METHODS

We recently cloned one of the NK-2 receptor cDNAs from rat tissues and its sequence matched that recently reported by Sasai and Nakanishi.[3] To examine the distribution and the level of the NK-2 receptor mRNA in rat, we performed nuclease protection analysis using the NK-2 receptor cRNA fragment (FIGURE 1). The

TABLE 1. The Characteristics of Tachykinin NK-2 Receptor Subtypes in Rat Duodenum, Vas Deferens, and Urinary Bladder Membrane Preparations

	Characteristics of ^{125}I-NPγ Binding^a			Relative Amount of NK-2R mRNA^c
Tissue	K_d (nM)	B_{max} (fmol/mg protein)	Agonist Potency^b	
duodenum	0.23 ± 0.01	59.0 ± 3.4	NPγ = NPK > NKA > NKB = ELE = [βAla] > SP > PHY > ELE-RP	0.08
vas deferens	0.14 ± 0.01	16.5 ± 0.6	NPγ = NPK = NKA > NKB = ELE = ELE-RP = [βAla] > SP > PHY	0.33
urinary bladder	0.26 ± 0.03	50.8 ± 3.0	NPγ = NPK = NKA > NKB = ELE = ELE-RP = [βAla] > SP > PHY	1.0

^{a}The ^{125}I-NPγ was prepared by chloramine T iodination and HPLC purification. ^{125}I-NPγ at 0.05 nM was used for analysis of the potency of the tachykinin receptor agonists in displacing ^{125}I-NPγ specific binding. Binding affinity (K_d) and binding capacity (B_{max}) of ^{125}I-NPγ specific binding to these tissue membranes were calculated by Scatchard analysis using the nonlinear, least-squares curve-fitting LIGAND program.

^{b}Terms—NPγ: neuropeptide γ; NPK: neuropeptide K; NKA: neurokinin A; NKB: neurokinin B; ELE: eledoisin; ELE-RP: [Lys^6]eledoisin(6–10); [βAla]: [βAla^8]NKA(4–10); SP: substance P; PHY: physalaemin.

^{c}The relative amount of NK-2 receptor mRNA in rat duodenum, vas deferens, and urinary bladder RNA preparations was measured by nuclease protection analysis using the NK-2 receptor antisense cRNA fragment (see FIGURE 1).

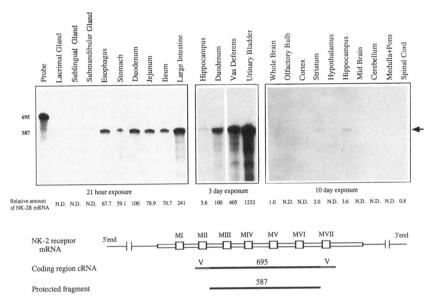

FIGURE 1. Distribution of the NK-2 receptor mRNA by nuclease protection analysis. The procedure for the nuclease protection analysis was described in detail in a previous report.[4] In this study, the NK-2 receptor antisense cRNA fragment was used for nuclease protection analysis. The length of the probe for the NK-2 receptor coding region including vector sequences was 695 bases and the protected NK-2 receptor mRNA was 587 bases (as depicted in the lower portion of the figure). The arrow depicts the NK-2 receptor mRNA protected species. The relative amount of NK-2 receptor mRNA per 25 μg of total RNA in various rat tissues is represented as a percentage of the amount of NK-2 receptor mRNA in rat duodenum.

highest level of NK-2 receptor mRNA expression was with urinary bladder RNA and relatively high expression was found with vas deferens and gastrointestinal tissue RNAs. Expression was also detected in hippocampus, striatum, and spinal cord RNA preparations, but the levels were about 500-fold lower than in urinary bladder. Interestingly, although the number of ^{125}I-NPγ binding sites in rat duodenum membrane was slightly higher than that in urinary bladder membrane, the NK-2 receptor mRNA expression with duodenum RNA was about 10-fold less as compared to that with urinary bladder RNA (TABLE 1). The distribution pattern and level of NK-2 receptor mRNA expression in rat was clearly distinct from that of NK-1 receptor mRNA expression.[4]

From these studies, we conclude that there apparently exist two distinct subtypes of the NK-2 receptor in rat tissues. One subtype of the rat NK-2 receptor may be expressed in duodenum and another subtype of the rat NK-2 receptor may be expressed in vas deferens and urinary bladder. To better analyze the diversity of the functional NK-2 receptor subtypes in rat, radiolabeled NPγ and NPK, two N-terminally extended forms of NKA, may be more useful than the radiolabeled NKA-related peptides used to date. We are currently trying to molecularly characterize the distinct NK-2 receptor subtypes using a variety of cloning strategies.

REFERENCES

1. HELKE, C. J., J. E. KRAUSE, P. W. MANTYH, R. COUTURE & M. J. BANNON. 1990. Diversity in mammalian tachykinin peptidergic neurons: multiple peptides, receptors, and regulatory mechanisms. FASEB J. **4**(6): 1606–1615.
2. TAKEDA, Y. & J. E. KRAUSE. 1989. Neuropeptide K potently stimulates salivary gland secretion and potentiates substance P–induced salivation. Proc. Natl. Acad. Sci. U.S.A. **86:** 392–396.
3. SASAI, Y. & S. NAKANISHI. 1989. Molecular characterization of rat substance K receptor and its mRNAs. Biochem. Biophys. Res. Commun. **165:** 695–702.
4. HERSHEY, A. D. & J. E. KRAUSE. 1990. Molecular characterization of a functional cDNA encoding the rat substance P receptor. Science **247:** 958–962.

Multiple NK$_2$ Receptor Subtypes Are Suggested by Physiological and Biochemical Studies with Neurokinin A (NKA) Analogues and Antagonists

P. L. M. VAN GIERSBERGEN,[a,b] S. A. SHATZER,[a]
S. L. HARBESON,[a] N. ROUISSI,[c] F. NANTEL,[c]
AND S. H. BUCK[a]

[a]Marion Merrell Dow Research Institute
Cincinnati, Ohio 45215

[b]Department of Pharmacology and Cell Biophysics
University of Cincinnati
Cincinnati, Ohio 45267

[c]Department of Pharmacology
University of Sherbrooke
Quebec J1H 5N4, Canada

INTRODUCTION

Pharmacological and biochemical evidence indicates the existence of three distinct tachykinin receptors—NK$_1$, NK$_2$, and NK$_3$—for which substance P, NKA, and NKB may be the preferred endogenous ligands, respectively.[1] In the present study, both the potency of a number of NK$_2$ receptor agonists and antagonists to inhibit iodinated NKA binding and the effect of a Leu$^9\Psi$(CH$_2$NH)Leu^{10} analogue of NKA, MDL 28,564, on smooth muscle contraction were determined in a variety of tissues. The results suggest NK$_2$ receptor heterogeneity.

METHODS

Receptor binding and *in vitro* smooth muscle assays were performed as previously described.[2,3] Phosphatidylinositol (PI) turnover was determined according to Bristow *et al.*[4] with some modifications. The assay was carried out at room temperature and the anion exchange columns were eluted with 10 mL of water, 5 mL of 5 mM disodium tetraborate/60 mM sodium formate, and 10 mL of 1 mM ammonium formate/0.1 M formic acid.

RESULTS AND DISCUSSION

In the tissues studied, the potency of agonists, NKA, Nle^{10}NKA(4–10), neuropeptides K and γ (NK$_2$), substance P (NK$_1$), and senktide (NK$_3$), to inhibit iodinated NKA binding was very similar. However, in hamster urinary bladder (HUB) and in rat urinary bladder and vas deferens (RVD), the affinity of a series of both linear and cyclic NK_2 antagonists was at least 20-fold higher than in bovine stomach and urinary bladder and in SKLKB82#3 cells (transfected with pSKR56S cDNA from bovine stomach). In TABLE 1, the K_I values of one agonist (NKA) and one antagonist [cyclo(Gln-Trp-Phe-Gly-Leu-Met), L-659,877[5]] are shown. These binding data indicate the existence of two NK_2 receptors that can be distinguished by NK_2 antagonists, but not by tachykinin agonists. In *in vitro* contraction assays, MDL 28,564 was a full contractile agonist in guinea pig trachea (GPT) and in rabbit pulmonary artery with an EC_{50} of 100 nM and with an efficacy of 100% of NKA in both tissues. In contrast, in HUB and RVD (NK_2 tissues), in dog carotid artery (NK_1 tissue), and in rat portal vein (NK_3 tissue), MDL 28,564 did not affect smooth muscle tone and was a competitive antagonist of NKA-induced contraction (HUB). Both MDL 28,564 and NKA stimulated PI turnover in GPT with similar efficacy, but NKA was approximately three orders of magnitude more potent than MDL 28,564. In HUB, MDL 28,564 competitively antagonized NKA-stimulated PI turnover and only had 10% of the activity of NKA to stimulate PI turnover. Thus, MDL 28,564, which has weak affinity for NK_1 ($K_I > 250$ μM) and NK_3 ($K_I > 500$ μM) receptors, can distinguish

TABLE 1. K_I Values (nM) for NKA and L-659,877 in Several Tissues and in SKLKB82#3 Cells[a]

| | Tissues and Cells | | | | | |
Peptide	Bovine Stomach	Bovine Bladder	SKLKB82#3 Cells	Hamster Bladder	Rat Vas Deferens	Rat Bladder
NKA	2.5 ± 0.5	0.43 ± 0.05	1.1 ± 0.1	1.33 ± 0.13	0.97 ± 0.12	0.68 ± 0.09
L-659,877	66.5 ± 33.6	65.3 ± 7.9	45 ± 0	1.6 ± 0.8	0.73 ± 0.38	0.07 ± 0.07

[a]Values represent the mean ± SEM of 2–3 experiments done in duplicate.

between the NK_2 receptors of GPT and rabbit pulmonary artery, where it displays full agonist activity, versus those in HUB and RVD, where it is an antagonist.

In conclusion, biochemical and physiological data have been presented suggesting NK_2 receptor heterogeneity among species, but, so far, not within one species.

REFERENCES

1. BUCK, S. H., R. M. PRUSS, J. L. KRSTENANSKY, P. J. ROBINSON & K. A. STAUDERMAN. 1988. Trends Pharmacol. Sci. **9:** 3–5.
2. BURCHER, E. & S. H. BUCK. 1986. Eur. J. Pharmacol. **128:** 165–177.
3. DION, S., P. D'ORLEANS-JUSTE, G. DRAPEAU, N-E. RHALEB, N. ROUISSI, C. TOUSIGNANT & D. REGOLI. 1987. Life Sci. **41:** 2269–2278.
4. BRISTOW, D. R., N. R. CURTIS, N. SUMAN-CHAUHAN, K. J. WATLING & B. J. WILLIAMS. 1987. Br. J. Pharmacol. **90:** 211–217.
5. MCKNIGHT, A. T., J. J. MAGUIRE, B. J. WILLIAMS, A. C. FOSTER, R. TRIDGETT & L. L. IVERSEN. 1988. Regulat. Peptides **22:** 127.

Serotonin Innervation Affects SP Biosynthesis in Rat Neostriatum[a]

PAUL D. WALKER, LI NI, LEIGH A. RILEY,
G. MILLER JONAKAIT, AND RONALD P. HART

Department of Biological Sciences
Rutgers University
Newark, New Jersey 07102

Substance P (SP) is synthesized and used by projection neurons of the neostriatum (NS) and is affected by neurological disorders such as Parkinson's disease.[1,2] Previous studies have shown that afferent nigrostriatal dopamine (DA) neurotransmission exerts a positive control on striatal SP biosynthesis.[3-5] Because the NS also receives a substantial serotonergic innervation from midbrain raphe cell groups, we sought to determine whether the manipulation of serotonin (5-HT) neurotransmission would also alter the biosynthesis of striatal SP.

In order to suppress 5-HT, adult rats received *p*-chlorophenylalanine [*p*CPA, an inhibitor of tryptophan hydroxylase (TPH)] for two weeks (100 mg/kg/day *p*CPA sc via an Alzet minipump) and were sacrificed at various times during and after drug treatment. During *p*CPA administration, steady-state levels of the mRNA coding for preprotachykinin (PPT, the prohormone precursor to SP) were decreased more than 80% (FIGURE 1) as determined by Northern blot analysis, but they recovered substantially (65% of control) one week after drug treatment ended (data not shown).

In another attempt to deplete 5-HT, neonatal rat pups received 5,7-dihydroxytryptamine (50 µg intracisternally) to destroy serotonergic neurons. Dopamine (DA) neurons in the substantia nigra were protected from the toxin by pretreatment of pups with desipramine. Cortical TPH activity (measured radioenzymatically) fell 82%, confirming a successful lesion. Ten days following the lesion, SP content had fallen to $56 \pm 3.1\%$ of control ($p < 0.02$) and remained depressed after four weeks (FIGURE 1). However, PPT mRNA was not similarly depressed. These data taken together suggest that depletion of 5-HT depresses steady-state levels of PPT mRNA or lowers striatal SP content (or both).

In contrast, raising extracellular 5-HT with zimelidine (5-HT uptake inhibitor; 10 mg/kg/twice daily ip for 5 days) increased both PPT mRNA ($171 \pm 16\%$ of control, $p < 0.025$) and SP peptide content ($123 \pm 2\%$ of control, $p < 0.05$ as measured by RIA) in the NS (FIGURE 1). Increased 5-HT due to inhibition of its oxidation with clorgyline (1 mg/kg/day) increased PPT mRNA to $171 \pm 25\%$ after three weeks of treatment ($p < 0.025$). Moreover, treatment with the 5-HT$_2$ receptor agonist DOI (7.5 mg/kg/day for 9 days sc via an Alzet minipump) also raised PPT mRNA ($208 \pm 26\%$ of control, $p < 0.0005$) and SP peptide content ($128 \pm 5\%$ of control, $p < 0.05$) in the NS (FIGURE 1).

Together, these data suggest that 5-HT exerts a positive influence on SP biosynthesis in the NS, an effect similar to that reported following manipulation of dopamine neurotransmission.[3-5] However, a straightforward anatomic substrate for such serotonergic regulation of SP remains unresolved because 5-HT cells can

[a] This work was supported by Grant No. MH43365 and the AHA-NJ.

485

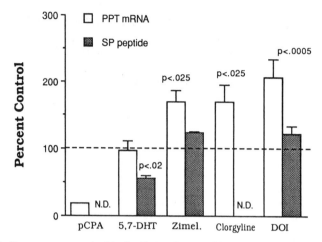

FIGURE 1. Rats were treated with the drugs shown. *p*CPA treatment was for one week; 5,7-DHT measurements were made 10 days after a neonatal lesion; zimelidine was given daily for 5 days; clorgyline was given daily for 21 days; DOI treatment was for 9 days. Total RNA was prepared from the NS of individual animals and Northern blots were performed using a ^{32}P-labeled cRNA probe for PPT.[6,7] Individual Northern blots were scanned densitometrically in order to perform statistical analyses. SP (pg/mg wet weight) was measured by RIA. Each bar represents the mean ± SEM for a minimum of five samples.

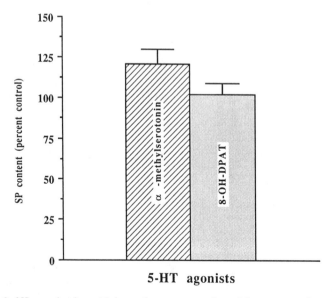

FIGURE 2. NS samples from 16-day embryos were explanted into organ culture and were grown in the presence or absence of 5-HT agonists for 10 days. At the end of that time, SP content was measured by RIA. Each bar represents the mean ± SEM for a minimum of seven cultures.

influence the NS via two separate neural pathways: a direct raphe-striatal pathway and an indirect route via projections to the substantia nigra. This latter pathway would involve DA as a mediator of 5-HT action. The latter possibility also requires intact dopaminergic innervation to the NS in order for 5-HT to affect SP biosynthesis.

In order to begin to address the possibility that 5-HT may require an intermediate to affect SP biosynthesis, embryonic NS tissue was grown for 10 days in organotypic cultures in the absence of afferent pathways and in the presence of drugs that mimic 5-HT neurotransmission (FIGURE 2). SP levels in culture were unaffected by the addition of either 8-OH-DPAT (5-HT$_{1A}$ agonist) or α-methyl-serotonin (mixed 5-HT$_1$/5-HT$_2$ agonist), suggesting that serotonergic regulation of SP biosynthesis requires an intermediary—perhaps the dopaminergic nigrostriatal pathway. Future studies will address this issue.

REFERENCES

1. MAUBORGNE, A., F. JAVOY-AGRID, J. C. LEGRAND, Y. AGID & F. CESSETIN. 1983. Decrease of substance P–like immunoreactivity in the substantia nigra and pallidum of parkinsonian brains. Brain Res. **263:** 167–170.
2. TENOVNO, O., V. K. RUNNE & M. K. VILJANEN. 1984. Substance P immunoreactivity in the post-mortem parkinsonian brain. Brain Res. **303:** 113–166.
3. BANNON, M. J., P. J. PETER & E. B. BUNNEY. 1987. Striatal tachykinin biosynthesis: regulation of mRNA and peptide levels by dopamine agonists and antagonists. Mol. Brain Res. **3:** 31–37.
4. HAVERSTICK, D. M., A. RUBENSTEIN & M. J. BANNON. 1989. Striatal tachykinin gene expression regulated by interaction of D-1 and D-2 dopamine receptors. J. Pharmacol. Exp. Ther. **248:** 858–862.
5. HAVERSTICK, D. M. & M. J. BANNON. 1989. Evidence for dual mechanisms involved in methamphetamine-induced increases in striatal preprotachykinin mRNA. J. Biol. Chem. **264:** 13140–13144.
6. KRAUSE, J. E., J. M. CHIRGWIN, M. S. CARTER, Z. S. XU & A. D. HERSHEY. 1987. Three rat preprotachykinin mRNAs encode the neuropeptides substance P and neurokinin A. Proc. Natl. Acad. Sci. U.S.A. **84:** 881–885.
7. WALKER, P. D., S. SCHOTLAND, R. P. HART & G. M. JONAKAIT. 1990. Tryptophan hydroxylase inhibition increases preprotachykinin mRNA in developing and adult medullary raphe nuclei. Mol. Brain Res. In press.

Effect of Acupuncture on Release of Substance P

LI-XIA ZHU,[a] FEI-YUE ZHAO,[a] AND REN-LIN CUI[b]

[a]Department of Physiology
[b]Department of Biochemistry
Institute of Acupuncture
China Academy of Traditional Chinese Medicine
Beijing 100700, China

In previous work, accompanying the analgesic effect, the content of substance P (SP) in the lumbar spinal cord was significantly elevated by acupuncture.[1] This might have resulted from the acupuncture-induced inhibition of the release of SP from nociceptive primary afferents. In this report, the effects of acupuncture on the release of SP from central terminals and from peripheral endings were further investigated.

The lumbar spinal cords of rats were push-pull perfused with artificial cerebrospinal fluid through two intrathecal polyethylene tubes (PE-10). SP released from the central terminals at the lumbar level in the perfusate (collected at 1 mL/20 min) was measured with radioimmunoassay methods. Release of SP from peripheral endings was indirectly determined by antidromic neurogenic plasma extravasation.[2]

Electroacupuncture (EA) at bilateral Huan-Tiao (GB 30) points for 30 minutes did not change the content of SP in the perfusate, but it did significantly reduce the common peroneal nerve stimulation–induced elevation of SP (FIGURE 1). Nerve stimulation alone increased the SP content to 15.50 ± 1.97 pmol/g. Compared with

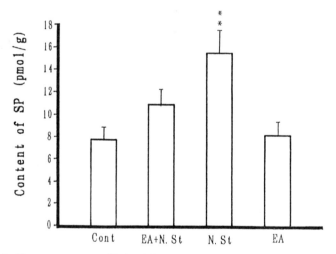

FIGURE 1. Electroacupuncture (EA) at bilateral Huan-Tiao points (GB 30) applied concurrently with the common peroneal nerve stimulation (N. St) reduced the nerve stimulation–induced elevation of SP release in the lumbar spinal cord perfusate. EA alone did not change the SP release. (∗∗) Compared with the control, $P < 0.01$.

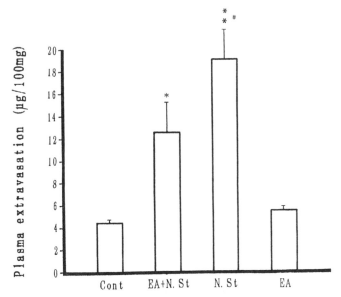

FIGURE 2. EA at San-Yin-Jiao (SP 6) and Xue-Hai (SP 10) points applied 20 minutes prior to ipsilateral saphenous nerve stimulation reduced the antidromic neurogenic plasma extravasation. Plasma extravasation in the ipsilateral ankle due to EA was 69.1 ± 10.1% ($n = 7$, $P < 0.01$) of that in the contralateral case. (*) Compared with the background, $P < 0.05$. (**) Compared with the background, $P < 0.01$. (#) Comparison between ipsilateral (EA + N. St) and contralateral (N. St) sides, $P < 0.01$.

the control (7.66 ± 1.17 pmol/g), the difference was significant ($P < 0.01$). When EA was applied concurrently with nerve stimulation, the SP content was slightly increased (10.90 ± 1.12 pmol/g, $P > 0.05$).

Similarly, with EA at San-Yin-Jiao (SP 6) and Xue-Hai (SP 10) points alone, plasma extravasation expressed by the quantity of Evan's Blue (5.50 ± 0.50 μg/100 mg) in the skin of the medial ankle was similar to the background (4.45 ± 0.13 μg) (FIGURE 2). When EA was applied 20 minutes prior to ipsilateral saphenous nerve stimulation, the antidromic nerve stimulation–induced neurogenic plasma extravasation was markedly attenuated. Plasma extravasation in the ipsilateral ankle (12.54 ± 2.67 μg) due to EA was 69.1 ± 10.1% ($n = 7$, $P < 0.01$) of that in the contralateral case (19.08 ± 2.73 μg).

We conclude that EA at certain points with parameters insufficient to promote the release of SP might reduce the noxious nerve stimulation–induced release of SP from both central terminals and peripheral endings of the primary sensory neurons. It may be an important event in acupuncture analgesia.

REFERENCES

1. CUI, R-L., *et al.* 1990. The influence of electro-acupuncture analgesia on substance P level in the central nervous system of rats. Acupuncture Res. **15:** 280–281.
2. LEMBECK, F. & P. HOLZER. 1979. Substance P as neurogenic mediator of antidromic vasodilation and neurogenic plasma extravasation. Naunyn-Schmiedeberg's Arch. Pharmacol. **310:** 175–183.

Concluding Remarks

FRED LEMBECK

Institute for Experimental and Clinical Pharmacology
University of Graz
A-8010 Graz, Austria

The Symposium in Worcester was the seventh symposium on substance P (SP) organized since 1975. The "morphological basis" of this symposium was, like a backbone, the presentations of 32 speakers; these then gave reliable support to "essential organs", as which the 150 posters might be regarded. Organized in a brilliant way by Susan E. Leeman, coordinated by Carolyn Rassias, and arranged in the lovely environment of Worcester, Massachusetts, the symposium gave a broad view about recent advances in this field and induced in the participants new ideas for coming projects.

The regulation of gene expression, the mechanism of precursor splicing, and the posttranslational processing of protachykinins were covered mainly in the first session. From a single preprotachykinin gene, six biologically active tachykinin peptides were produced, whereas neurokinin B, which did not exist in peripheral neurons, was produced from a different PPT gene. A pituitary cell line was seen to be most suitable for model studies in the production of tachykinins.

A considerable number of factors influencing the concentration of PPT mRNA were described in many communications; this parameter seems to be the most suitable way to obtain new information about the physiological functions of tachykinin-containing CNS neurons. Thyroid hormones and sex steroids exert influences on PPT mRNA in the pituitary. Removal of the presynaptic input to the superior cervical ganglion induces an increase in PPT mRNA. In cultures of superior cervical ganglion cells, IL-1 increases PPT mRNA. Other signals from nonneuronal cells also induce the expression of PPT mRNA in cultured sympathetic neurons.

Changes of PPT mRNA concentration were observed in seizure-induced pathological processes of some CNS regions. Manipulations of serotonin levels in the CNS had controversial effects on PPT mRNA. An increase of PPT mRNA in the nucleus tractus solitarius seems to be correlated to the onset of breathing after birth in the rabbit. These examples indicate the multiplicity of approaches in this field.

The terminal amidation in the expression of SP is regarded as the rate-limiting step of its production. Inhibition of the amidating enzyme by the copper chelating agent DDC causes a 26–44% decrease of SP in various brain regions of the rat. N-Terminal extended peptides have been found to occur in the CNS and their release has been demonstrated. In addition, certain SP fragments, especially SP(6–11), were shown to have defined functions.

Nerve growth factor (NGF) has been shown to play an important role not only in the embryological development of peripheral SP neurons, but also in the response of mature neurons to nerve injury. Lack of NGF to reach the dorsal root ganglion reduces the synthesis of SP and the expression of VIP. NGF acts by the induction of PPT mRNA expression as shown in vagal sensory neurons. The significance of NGF might be seen in the light of recent results published elsewhere: Thoenen et al.[1] described its influence on certain neuronal pathways within the CNS. Furthermore, Levy-Montalcini[2] described behavioral changes in rats after repeated injections of NGF and NGF-antibodies. She ascribed these effects to a regulatory function of

NGF in the maintenance of homeostasis. It might be assumed that these effects of NGF could finally be mediated by those peptides that act as transmitters of NGF-dependent neurons. The question comes up as to which disease could result from a deficiency of NGF or from formation of autoantibodies to NGF.

The second session dealt with receptors. Three different tachykinin receptors have been isolated in the last two years and the human NK-2 receptor can be expected soon. All three receptors are fairly homogeneous in their seven transmembrane regions and in their cytoplasmatic loops. They are G protein–coupled and they activate phosphatidylinositol- and Ca^{2+}-mediated second messenger systems. Their tissue distribution and their ligand peptide binding are different. The SP receptor gene has been isolated and extensively characterized. Expression of the SP receptor mRNA shows peak levels at birth. The SP receptor is photolabeled when linked to its G protein and this technique is currently applied to identify the specific G protein. A wide range of methods was used to analyze the effects resulting from the interactions of tachykinins with their receptors and to explore the ion channel mechanisms and the phosphatidylinositol- and Ca^{2+}-operated second messenger systems. Electrophysiology, *Xenopus leavis* oocytes, cultured cholinergic neurons from forebrain, smooth muscle preparations, and glandular tissues were used for this exploration.

The classification of neurokinin (or tachykinin) receptors was already a matter of considerable discussion at the two preceding symposia. Relative potency orders or absolute potencies of tachykinins were estimated on a great variety of isolated organ preparations. Selective and nonselective radioligand studies and immunohistochemical studies supplemented these investigations. Available antagonists are of a more or less limited specificity to one or another of the receptors. The present classification of receptor subtypes was regarded as oversimplistic. The general picture seemed to be confusing at present. In view of the growing number of new findings, the members of the symposium refrained from discussing the nomenclature and asked Elizabeth Burcher to coordinate such a discussion at the next symposium. It might be speculated that conformational changes of the receptor molecules during contact with agonists or antagonists might become visible by highly developed physical methods used in molecular biology.

The interaction of SP and SP-antagonists with lipid bilayers was an unconventional approach. Binding to lipid bilayers was related to their surface activity. The biological relevance of these findings needs further evaluation.

Neurokinin antagonists were the main topic in the third session. Two advantages concerning antagonists should be mentioned. Spantide II was found to be devoid of neurotoxic side effects and without histamine-releasing potency. The antagonist A(4–10) was rather resistant to metabolism by peptidases. This property could allow further *in vivo* studies by means of this antagonist. Up to now, *in vivo* studies of the antagonists have been fairly rare, presumably because most of them are split by the same enzymes that destroy tachykinins, that is, neutral endopeptidase and angiotensin converting enzyme. A metabolic stable tachykinin antagonist would possibly open a new "per exclusionem" approach to define the physiological role of coexisting nontachykinin peptides when released by nerve stimulation. Another requirement of a really potent tachykinin antagonist would be its ability to enter the CNS and then to interact with tachykinins released from CNS neurons.

Capsaicin, the tool so helpful in exploring the physiological function of peripheral afferent tachykinin-containing and related neurons, found a new highly powerful competitor, resiniferatoxin. Ruthenium red was shown to interact selectively with the action of capsaicin without influencing other modalities of afferent fibers. Although progress in the understanding of the mode of action of capsaicin was recently achieved, no explanation for its selective activity on peripheral neurons or for the almost complete absence of action on neurochemically identical peptidergic neurons within the CNS can be offered so far.

The SP-containing peripheral nerves are generally assumed to be processes of sensory neurons. SP, in coexistence with VIP and CGRP, was also found in cholinergic sympathetic neurons of sweat glands. Are there further "efferent" SP neurons? SP-containing cells exist in the carotid body. Amacrine cells of the retina contain SP. In addition, the "extraneuronal" presence of SP, such as in enterochromaffin cells, in the intestinal mucosa, and in vascular endothelium, deserves further attention.

Functional approaches were covered by the fourth and fifth sessions. The value of experimental research on afferent neurons can be seen in the elucidation of a neurogenic protective mechanism in the gastric mucosa against acid back-diffusion, which is mediated by mucosal vasodilatation induced by CGRP.

Capsaicin served to explain the neuroendocrine copulation response. Copulation is signaled via capsaicin-sensitive afferent fibers and initiates the endocrine mechanisms required for nidation of the blastocyte. Investigation of the sensory innervation of the rat uterus and vagina revealed a complex circuitry of chemically coded nerves.

Activation of the stress hormone cascade ACTH/corticosterone in response to different modes of somatosensory stimuli is signaled by SP afferents. Catecholamine release from the adrenal medulla is the end result induced by hypothalamic centers when these receive relevant stimuli from the periphery by SP afferents, for example, in hypoglycemia. Signals conveyed by SP afferents to the CNS are therefore essential for vital regulatory responses. In contrast, local effects of SP on the nicotinic response of chromaffin cells, as described *in vitro*, still lack physiological relevance.

The role of SP neurons in the CNS is, apart from changes in PPT mRNA, more difficult to investigate. The involvement of SP neurons in the hypoxic ventilatory drive might be essential for the onset of continuous breathing after birth. SP levels in the carotid body are changed by hypoxia. Victims of sudden infant death syndrome (SIDS) have higher levels of SP in the medulla and in blood, findings that seem to be of high clinical significance.

Electrophysiological investigations indicated influences of SP only on the slow synaptic input by nociceptive neurons in the spinal cord. Is SP a transmitter, promoter, or modulator in the pathway of nociceptive signals? A recent comment by MacMahon and Koltzenburg[3] put some doubt on Sherrington's old definition of specific nociceptors and selective pain fibers; it was assumed that pain is encoded by increased discharge frequencies of primary afferent fibers that also respond to nonnoxious events. SP afferents, though, have been shown to carry many more essential signals to the CNS besides those of "pain". They serve primarily as the afferent limb of autonomic reflexes and they link neurogenic information to endocrine mechanisms that do not come to our consciousness. However, when the amount of stimuli exceeds a certain level, these afferents attain a "nociceptive" quality.

When SP is released from the central terminals of afferent fibers in the spinal cord, releases of ACh, which is Ca^{2+}- and TTX-sensitive, and of GABA, which is Ca^{2+}- and TTX-insensitive, are evoked. This shows the complexity of the mechanism at this first afferent synapse. In addition, besides the known effects of opiates at this level, interactions with serotonin and its antagonists have been described. A relationship between tachykinins and nigral dopaminergic neurons was found. The possible influence of SP in pituitary functions allows speculations about direct regulatory mechanisms. Pituitaries of male rats contain more SP than those of females. Tachykinins were found to influence LH secretion, copulation, and feeding behavior. SP neurons in the hypothalamus seem to be under a regulatory influence of ovarian hormones. These recent findings indicate that SP and other neuropeptides are the keys to investigations of further neural and neuroendocrine central regulations.

The actions of endogenously released or exogenously applied substances on physiological functions have always been used as a guideline for research in pharmacology. It is known that substance P was discovered by U. S. von Euler and J. H. Gaddum, both belonging to the scientific subpopulation of pharmacologists. Research on substance P then expanded into almost all branches of life sciences. A word by J. H. Gaddum, dedicated originally to pharmacology, can now be applied to life sciences in general and to research on substance P especially: "Pharmacology is not only the handmaid of therapeutics; it is a science in its own right and has many other tasks to perform. The most important one is to find out how drugs act." Both parts of this statement refer to the achievements presented at this symposium. Essential new information about physiological functions was acquired by the experimental work performed; the aim to use this new knowledge for protection of health and for the search of new treatments will remain an essential and continuous guideline.

REFERENCES

1. THOENEN, H., C. BANDTLOW, R. HEUMANN, D. LINDHOLM, M. MEYER & M. SPRANGER. 1990. Role played by interleukin-I (IL-I) in the regulation of nerve growth factor (NGF) synthesis under physiological and pathophysiological conditions. Eur. J. Pharmacol. **183:** 36–37.
2. LEVY-MONTALCINI, R. 1990. A role for nerve growth factor in nervous, endocrine, and immune systems. Prog. Neuroendoimmunol. **3:** 1–10.
3. MACMAHON, S. & M. KOLTZENBURG. 1990. The changing role of primary afferent neurones in pain. Pain **43:** 269–272.

Index of Contributors